INTRODUCTION TO NUMERICAL ANALYSIS

INTRODUCTION TO
NUMERICAL ANALYSIS

F. B. HILDEBRAND

Associate Professor of Mathematics
Massachusetts Institute of Technology

New York   Toronto   London

McGRAW-HILL BOOK COMPANY, INC.

1956

INTRODUCTION TO NUMERICAL ANALYSIS

Library of Congress Catalog Card Number 55-8284

x

28760

THE MAPLE PRESS COMPANY, YORK, PA.

PREFACE

This volume is intended to provide an introductory treatment of the fundamental processes of numerical analysis which is compatible with the expansion of the field brought about by the development of the modern high-speed calculating devices, but which also takes into account the fact that very substantial amounts of computation will continue to be effected by desk calculators (and by hand or slide rule), and that familiarity with computation on a desk calculator is a desirable preliminary to large-scale computation in any case.

Whereas the availability of large-scale rapid calculators has made feasible the numerical solution of many problems of previously prohibitive complexity, the effective use of such devices depends strongly upon continued advancement of research in relevant fields of mathematical analysis. In addition, there is a continuing need for personnel sufficiently well grounded in both the principles and the existent techniques of numerical analysis to be capable, not only of adapting available methods to a given machine, but also of comprehending the inherent limitations of each method and of devising error controls and modified techniques which are particularly appropriate to that machine.

The urgency of the initial need for such personnel required a training which led as rapidly as possible to a fair working knowledge of techniques associated with some of the more sophisticated aspects of the field, and in which only a limited amount of time was available for the treatment of the fundamental elementary processes upon which those techniques are based. However, it would appear that the long-range needs will demand a somewhat more comprehensive college teaching program.

The present text is based on the premise that the introductory course should provide a fairly substantial grounding in the basic operations of computation, approximation, interpolation, numerical differentiation and integration, and the numerical solution of equations, as well as in applications to such processes as the smoothing of data, the numerical summation of series, and the numerical solution of ordinary differential equations. It is believed that this course not only should exhibit techniques available for each purpose, but also should attempt to derive the relevant formulas in such a way that the underlying hypotheses are in evidence and that methods of generalization and modification are reasonably apparent, and that the problems of error analysis, convergence, and stability should be treated as adequately as time and preparation permit. Furthermore, the course desirably should be accompanied by a problem laboratory, in which enough actual computation is effected (presumably by use of desk calculators) to establish the practical significance of the theoretical developments.

Such an introduction should afford preparation for an "advanced course," dealing with certain of the somewhat more sophisticated aspects of the solution of equations and with modern methods of matrix inversion and determination of characteristic values of matrices, together with the numerical solution of partial differential equations and of integral equations, and for a course dealing specifically with the principles of large-scale calculating devices and with the various processes of organizing computations (programming) for them.

This book is a revised version of a set of mimeographed notes originally prepared for classroom use in an introductory course offered at the Massachusetts Institute of Technology. It is hoped that sufficient detail is included to permit an instructor to provide a survey of a substantial portion of the text in a single semester, when this is desirable, by delegating liberal amounts of the material to home reading and restricting classroom treatments to the more important or more difficult points, or, preferably, to provide a more thorough coverage in two semesters. Some of the more involved error analyses, such as those of §§5.11, 5.12, 6.8, 6.11, and 6.12, can be omitted in a first course without materially interrupting the continuity of the presentation.

The chapter treating the numerical solution of equations is independent of the other chapters and is placed at the end of the text, so that relevant portions of its content can be inserted when they are needed in other developments, at the discretion of the instructor. Thus, for example, some information relative to the practical solution of sets of linear algebraic equations should precede the consideration of least-squares methods in Chapter 7. Alternatively, it may be desirable to introduce part or all of Chapter 10 immediately following the introductory Chapter 1.

In order to facilitate the use of the volume for reference purposes, a directory of techniques is included in Appendix C.

The presentations were influenced particularly by the earlier texts of Steffensen and of Whittaker and Robinson, and by the more recent texts of Milne. The author is indebted also to a number of colleagues and students for suggestions and criticisms; to the Office of Naval Research for the stimulus afforded by a sponsored project on machine methods of computation and numerical analysis at the Massachusetts Institute of Technology, under the direction of Professor P. M. Morse; and to Mrs. Mary Kuntavanish, Mrs. Dorothy Harvey, and Miss Ruth Goodwin for assistance in the preparation of the manuscript.

F. B. HILDEBRAND

CONTENTS

CHAPTER 1

INTRODUCTION

1.1. Numerical Analysis. The ultimate aim of the field of numerical analysis is to provide convenient methods for obtaining useful solutions to mathematical problems and for extracting useful information from available solutions which are not expressed in tractable forms. Such problems may each be formulated in terms of an algebraic or transcendental equation, an ordinary or partial differential equation, or an integral equation, or in terms of a set of such equations.

This formulation may correspond exactly to the situation which it is intended to describe; more often, it will not. Analytical solutions, when available, may be precise in themselves, but may be of unacceptable form because of the fact that they are not amenable to direct interpretation in numerical terms, in which case the numerical analyst may attempt to devise a method for effecting that interpretation in a satisfactory way, or he may prefer to base his analysis instead upon the original formulation.

More frequently, there is no known method of obtaining the solution in a precise form, convenient or otherwise. In such a case, it is necessary either to attempt to approximate the problem satisfactorily by one which *is* amenable to precise analysis, to obtain an approximate solution to the original problem by methods of numerical analysis, or to combine the two approaches.

On the other hand, the problem itself may not be clearly defined, and the analyst may be provided only with its partial solution, perhaps in the form of a table of approximate data, together with a certain amount of information with regard to its reliability, or perhaps in the form of an integral defining a function which cannot be expressed in terms of a finite number of tabulated functions. His purpose is then to obtain additional useful information concerning the function so described.

Generally the numerical analyst does not strive for exactness. Instead, he attempts to devise a method which will yield an approximation differing from exactness by less than a specified tolerance, or by an amount which has less than a specified probability of exceeding that tolerance. When the information supplied to him is inexact, he attempts both to obtain a dependable measure of the uncertainty which results from that inexactness and also to obtain an approximation which possesses a specified reliability compatible with that uncertainty.

He tries to devise a procedure which would be capable of affording an arbitrarily high degree of accuracy, in a wide class of situations, if the reliability of given information and of available calculating devices were correspondingly high. Even when successful in this attempt, he still seeks alternative procedures which may possess certain advantages in convenience, in certain situations, but which may be of less general applicability, or which may have the property that the degree of accuracy obtainable, even under ideal circumstances, cannot exceed a certain limit which depends upon the function to be analyzed. In this last case, which is of frequent occurrence, he attempts to ascertain that limit and to classify the situations in which it is not sufficiently high.

Needless to say, there are relatively few situations in which all these objectives have been, or can be, perfectly attained, as will be illustrated in the sequel. However, research with these aims in view continues to provide new procedures, as well as additional information with regard to the basic advantages and disadvantages of the older ones. Additional impetus has been afforded by the comparatively recent development of automatic desk calculators and of large-scale computing machines. For example, certain methods have long been known to possess important theoretical advantages, but have not been *convenient*, from the point of view of the labor and time involved, for use in hand calculation or in calculation based on the use of the slide rule or of tables of logarithms, and hence have been considered as little more than mathematical curiosities. However, technological developments have promoted several of them into a much more active status and have also created additional need for reexamination and modification of other existing methods and for a search for new ones.

Perhaps the most rapidly expanding phase of numerical analysis is that which deals with the approximate solution of partial differential equations. But a basic understanding of the more involved problems which arise in that phase of the analysis depends strongly upon familiarity with similar problems which arise, in a somewhat simpler way, in connection with the processes of interpolation, numerical differentiation and integration, and the approximate solution of *ordinary* differential equations, in which only one independent variable is involved. These are the topics which are to be treated, for the most part, in what follows.

1.2. Approximation. In many of the problems which arise in numerical analysis, we are given certain information about a certain function, say $f(x)$, and we are required to obtain additional or improved information, in a form which is appropriate for interpretation in terms of numbers. Usually $f(x)$ is known or required to be *continuous* over the range of interest.

A technique which is frequently used in such cases can be described, in general terms, as follows. A convenient set of $n + 1$ *coordinate functions*, say $\phi_0(x)$, $\phi_1(x)$, . . . , $\phi_n(x)$, is first selected. Then a procedure is invented which has the property that it would yield the desired additional information *simply* and *exactly* (barring inaccuracies in calculation) if $f(x)$ were a member of the set S_n of all functions which are expressible exactly as linear combinations of the coordinate functions. Next, use is made of an appropriate *selective process* which tends to choose from among all functions in S_n that one, say $y_n(x)$, whose properties are as nearly as possible identified with certain of the known properties of $f(x)$. In particular, it is desirable that the process be one which would select $f(x)$ if $f(x)$ were in S_n. The required property of $f(x)$ is then approximated by the corresponding property of $y_n(x)$. Finally, a method is devised for using additional known properties of $f(x)$, which were not employed in the selective process, for estimating the error in this approximation.

Clearly, it is desirable, first of all, to choose coordinate functions which are convenient for calculational purposes. The $n + 1$ functions 1, x, x^2, . . . , x^n, which generate the algebraic *polynomials* of degree n or less, are particularly appropriate, since polynomials are readily evaluated and since their integrals, derivatives, and products are *also* polynomials.

Of much greater importance, however, is the natural requirement that it be possible, by taking n sufficiently large, to be certain that the set S_n of generated functions will contain at least one member which approximates the function $f(x)$ within any preassigned tolerance, within the interval of interest. It is a most fortunate fact that the convenient set S_n, which consists of all polynomials of degree n or less, possesses this property if only $f(x)$ is continuous over that interval and the interval is of finite extent.†

Principally for these two reasons, *polynomial approximation* is of wide general use when the function to be approximated is continuous and the interval of approximation is finite, as well as in certain other cases, and accordingly is to form the basis of the major part of the work which follows. Other types of approximations are considered in Chap. 9.

Following the choice of the set S_n, an appropriate selective process must be chosen in accordance with the nature of the available information concerning the function $f(x)$. When the value of $f(x)$ is known for at least $n + 1$ values of x, say $x_0, x_1, . . . , x_n$, the simplest and most often

---

† This fact was established in 1885 by a famous theorem of Weierstrass, which states, in fact, that any function which is continuous in a closed interval can be *uniformly* approximated within any prescribed tolerance, over that interval, by **some** polynomial.

used process consists in selecting, from the members of S_n, a function $y_n(x)$ which takes on the same value as does $f(x)$ for each of those $n + 1$ values of x. Here again the choice of polynomials is convenient. For, whereas in the general case there may be no such function in S_n, or there may be several, it is a well-known fact that there exists one and only one polynomial of degree n or less which takes on prescribed values at each of $n + 1$ points. In particular, if $f(x)$ is indeed in S_n, this process will then select it. Another useful process is described in Chap. 7.

The final problem, that of devising an appropriate method of estimating the *error*, is a troublesome one and cannot be discussed here. Clearly, the precision of the estimate must depend upon the amount of available information relative to $f(x)$, and its usefulness will depend upon the form in which that information is supplied. In particular, if *all* available information is needed by the selective process, *no error estimate is possible*.

It is of some importance to notice that, if S_n is indeed taken as the set of all polynomials of degree n or less, then the Weierstrass theorem guarantees only the *existence* of a member of S_n which affords a satisfactory approximation to a continuous function $f(x)$, over any finite interval, when n is sufficiently large. This does *not* imply that the particular member chosen by a particular selective process will tend to afford such an approximation as n increases indefinitely. Only when a dependable method of estimating the error is available can this question be resolved with certainty. Furthermore, even though it were possible to devise a selective process which had this property, it would not necessarily follow (for example) that the *derivative* of the selected polynomial $y_n(x)$ would tend to approximate the derivative of $f(x)$, even though the latter were known to exist and to be continuous. Again, recourse must be had to an error estimate.

1.3. Errors. Most numerical calculations are inexact, either because of inaccuracies in given data, upon which the calculations are based, or because of inaccuracies introduced in the subsequent analysis of those data. In addition to *gross errors*, occasioned by unpredictable *mistakes* (human or mechanical) and hypothetically assumed to be absent in the remainder of this discussion, it is convenient to define first a *round-off error* as the consequence of using a number specified by n correct digits to approximate a number which requires more than n digits (generally infinitely many digits) for its exact specification.† Such errors are frequently present in given data, in which case they may be called *inherent* errors, due either to the fact that those data are empirical, and are known only to n digits, or to the fact that, whereas they are known exactly, they are "rounded" to n digits according to the dictates of convenience or of the capacity of a calculating device. They are introduced in sub-

† It is assumed here and elsewhere that the decimal notation is used.

sequent analysis either because of deliberate rounding or because of the fact that a calculating device is capable of supplying only a certain number of digits.

It is then convenient to define a *truncation error*, by exclusion, as any error which is neither a gross error nor a round-off error. Thus, a truncation error is one which would be present even in the hypothetical situation in which no "mistakes" were made, all given data were exact, and infinitely many digits were retained in all calculations. Frequently, a truncation error corresponds to the fact that, whereas an exact result would be afforded by an infinite sequence of steps, the process is "truncated" after a certain *finite* number of steps. However, it is rather conventional to apply the term in the more general sense defined here.

We define the error associated with an approximate value as the result of subtracting that approximation from the true value,

$$\text{True value} = \text{approximation} + \text{error}, \tag{1.3.1}$$

with a remark that both this definition and that in which the algebraic sign of the error is reversed are used elsewhere in the literature.

The preceding definitions can be illustrated, for example, by calculations based on the use of power series. Thus, if a function $f(x)$ possesses n continuous derivatives everywhere in the interval (a,x), it can be represented by a *finite* Taylor series of the form

$$f(x) = f(a) + \frac{f'(a)}{1!}(x - a) + \frac{f''(a)}{2!}(x - a)^2 + \cdots$$
$$+ \frac{f^{(n-1)}(a)}{(n-1)!}(x - a)^{n-1} + \frac{f^{(n)}(\xi)}{n!}(x - a)^n \tag{1.3.2}$$

where ξ is *some* number between a and x. If $f(x)$ satisfies more stringent conditions, it can be represented by an *infinite* Taylor series

$$f(x) = f(a) + \frac{f'(a)}{1!}(x - a) + \frac{f''(a)}{2!}(x - a)^2 + \cdots$$
$$+ \frac{f^{(n)}(a)}{n!}(x - a)^n + \cdots, \tag{1.3.3}$$

when $|x - a|$ is sufficiently small.

If $f(x)$ is *approximated* by the sum of the first n terms of (1.3.3), then the *error* committed is represented by the last term (*remainder*) in (1.3.2). Thus, for example, if $f(x) = e^{-x}$ and $a = 0$, we have the relation

$$e^{-x} = 1 - x + \tfrac{1}{2}x^2 - \tfrac{1}{6}x^3 + E_T(x), \tag{1.3.4}$$

where the truncation error is of the form

$$E_T = \tfrac{1}{24}e^{-\xi}x^4 \qquad (\xi \text{ between } 0 \text{ and } x). \tag{1.3.5}$$

If x is positive, the same is true of ξ, and, by making use of the fact that

$e^{-\xi}$ is then smaller than unity, we may deduce that the approximation

$$e^{-x} \approx 1 - x + \tfrac{1}{2}x^2 - \tfrac{1}{6}x^3 \qquad (1.3.6)$$

is in error by a positive amount smaller than $\tfrac{1}{24}x^4$. In particular, we have

$$e^{-\frac{1}{3}} \approx 1 - \tfrac{1}{3} + \tfrac{1}{18} - \tfrac{1}{162} = \tfrac{116}{162} \qquad (1.3.7)$$

with an error between zero and $\tfrac{1}{1944}$. Since $\tfrac{1}{1944} \doteq 0.00051$, where the symbol $\doteq$ is used to signify "rounds to," the truncation error is smaller than 5.2×10^{-4}. If $\tfrac{116}{162}$ is rounded to four places, to give $e^{-\frac{1}{3}} \approx 0.7160$, the additional error introduced by the round-off is less than (but here very nearly equal to) five units in the first neglected place and hence smaller than 0.5×10^{-4}. It follows finally that $e^{-\frac{1}{3}} \approx 0.7160$ with an error of magnitude smaller than 5.7×10^{-4}. However, whether $e^{-\frac{1}{3}} \doteq 0.716$ or 0.717 is not established. If *each* of the terms in (1.3.7) were rounded to four places before the terms were combined, a total round-off error as great as 1.5×10^{-4} would be possible. Finally, if the exponent $\tfrac{1}{3}$ represented only an approximation to a value of x, which was not known exactly but which was known to lie, say, between 0.333 and 0.334, the approximate maximum error due to this uncertainty could be determined by noticing that the change δe^{-x} corresponding to a small change δx is approximately $(de^{-x}/dx)\,\delta x = -e^{-x}\,\delta x$. Thus, if the number $\tfrac{1}{3}$ is in error by an amount between -3×10^{-4} and $+7 \times 10^{-4}$, the magnitude of the maximum corresponding error in the calculated value is about $(0.716)(7 \times 10^{-4}) \approx 5 \times 10^{-4}$.

The magnitude of the round-off errors could be reduced arbitrarily by retaining additional digits, and that of the truncation error could be reduced within any prescribed tolerance by retaining sufficiently many terms of the convergent Maclaurin expansion of e^{-x}. The inherent error could be reduced only if the uncertainty of the value of x were decreased.

It is useful to notice that, since the *sign* of the truncation error associated with (1.3.7) is known, the magnitude of the maximum possible error due to truncation can be halved by replacing the approximation $\tfrac{116}{162}$ by the approximation $\tfrac{116}{162} + \tfrac{1}{2}\tfrac{1}{1944} = \tfrac{2785}{3888} \doteq 0.7163$, with a corresponding truncation error accordingly known to lie between the limits $\pm 2.6 \times 10^{-4}$.

As an example of a somewhat different nature, we refer to the relation

$$\int_x^\infty \frac{e^{x-t}}{t}\,dt = \frac{1}{x} - \frac{1!}{x^2} + \frac{2!}{x^3} - \frac{3!}{x^4} + \cdots + (-1)^{n-1}\frac{(n-1)!}{x^n}$$
$$+ (-1)^n n! \int_x^\infty \frac{e^{x-t}}{t^{n+1}}\,dt \qquad (x > 0), \quad (1.3.8)$$

which is readily established by successive integration by parts. If we denote the left-hand member by $F(x)$, we can thus write

$$F(x) \approx \frac{1}{x} - \frac{1!}{x^2} + \frac{2!}{x^3} - \frac{3!}{x^4} + \cdots + (-1)^{n-1} \frac{(n-1)!}{x^n} \quad (1.3.9)$$

when $x > 0$, with a "truncation error"

$$E_T = (-1)^n n! \int_x^\infty \frac{e^{x-t}}{t^{n+1}} \, dt. \quad (1.3.10)$$

Since $x - t$ is nonpositive in the range of integration, so that $e^{x-t} \leq 1$, we may deduce that

$$|E_T(x,n)| \leq n! \int_x^\infty \frac{dt}{t^{n+1}}$$

or
$$|E_T(x,n)| \leq \frac{(n-1)!}{x^n}. \quad (1.3.11)$$

Hence the truncation error is smaller in absolute value than the last term retained in the approximation and also is evidently of opposite sign.

Further, since $1/t^{n+1} \leq 1/x^{n+1}$ in the integration range, we see that

$$|E_T(x,n)| \leq \frac{n!}{x^{n+1}} \int_x^\infty e^{x-t} \, dt = \frac{n!}{x^{n+1}}, \quad (1.3.12)$$

so that the truncation error here is also smaller in absolute value than the first term *neglected*, and is clearly of the *same* sign.

For a fixed number (n) of terms, the truncation error clearly is small when x is large and can be made *arbitrarily* small by taking x *sufficiently* large. However, for a given x, the error *cannot* be made arbitrarily small by retaining sufficiently many terms. In fact, we may notice that if the right-hand member of (1.3.9) were considered as the result of retaining the first n terms of an infinite series, then the ratio of the $(n + 1)$th term of that series to the nth would be $-n/x$. Hence, the successive terms decrease steadily in magnitude as long as $n < x$, but then *increase* unboundedly in magnitude as n increases beyond x. Thus the series does not converge for any value of x.

Nevertheless, it is useful for computation when x is fairly large. Thus, if $x = 10$, the smallest term occurs when $n = x = 10$ and is given by $-9!/10^{10} \doteq -3.6 \times 10^{-5}$. Thus, the approximation afforded by retention of 10 terms would be in error by a positive quantity smaller than 4×10^{-5}. This would be the best possible approximation obtainable from (1.3.9), when $x = 10$, since retention of additional terms would increase the possible magnitude of the error.

A divergent series of the type considered, for which the magnitude of the error associated with retention of only n terms can be made arbitrarily small by taking a parameter x sufficiently near a certain fixed value x_0 (or sufficiently large in magnitude), and for which the error first decreases as n increases but eventually increases unboundedly in magnitude with increasing n, when x is given a *fixed* value other than x_0, is often called an *asymptotic series*. An example of the former type, with $x_0 = 0$, is afforded by the relation

$$\int_0^\infty \frac{e^{-u}\,du}{1+xu} = 1 - 1!x + 2!x^2 - 3!x^3 + \cdots + (-1)^n n!x^n + E(x,n),$$

when $x > 0$, which can be obtained from (1.3.8) by replacing x by $1/x$ and making the change of variables $t = (1 + xu)/x$ in the integral, and for which it is true that $x^{-n}E(x,n) \to 0$ as x tends to zero from the positive direction, but $|E(x,n)| \to \infty$ as $n \to \infty$ for any fixed $x \neq 0$.

For a representation of the form

$$f(x) = a_0 + \frac{a_1}{x} + \frac{a_2}{x^2} + \cdots + \frac{a_n}{x^n} + E(x,n),$$

it is usually stipulated also that $x^n E(x,n)$ is to tend to zero as $|x| \to \infty$; for an expansion of the form

$$f(x) = a_0 + a_1(x - x_0) + a_2(x - x_0)^2 + \cdots + a_n(x - x_0)^n + E(x,n),$$

the additional requirement that $E(x,n)/(x - x_0)^n$ is to tend to zero as $x \to x_0$ is usually imposed. Equation (1.3.12) shows that (1.3.9) is thus asymptotic in the strict sense. However, the term is often applied somewhat more loosely to expansions of more general type, which are not necessarily power series.

When x is fixed, the error frequently decreases rapidly, as additional terms are taken into account, until a point of diminishing return is reached, after which the error begins to increase in magnitude. In such cases, if the error is reduced within the prescribed tolerance before that point is attained, then the approximate calculation can be successfully effected.

A great many of the expansions which are of frequent use in numerical analysis are essentially of this type. For them, the term "truncation error" generally applies only in the general sense of the definition given earlier in this section, and generally does *not* correspond to the result of truncating a convergent infinite process after a finite number of steps, but to the result of truncating a process which first tends to converge, but would ultimately diverge, at a stage before the tendency to diverge manifests itself.

1.4. Significant Figures. The conventional process of *rounding* or "forcing" a number to n digits consists in replacing that number by an n-digit approximation with minimum error.† When this requirement

---

† This type of abridgment is to be distinguished from the process of *chopping*, which consists in merely discarding all digits following the nth digit without modifying the nth digit and which must be used when capacity limitations of a calculating device do not permit the determination of more than n digits.

leads to two admissible roundings, that one for which the nth digit of the rounded number is *even* is generally selected. Thus $4.05149 \doteq 4.0515$, 4.051, 4.05, 4.1, and 4; but $4.0515 \doteq 4.052$ and $4.05 \doteq 4.0$. With this rule, the error is never larger in magnitude than one-half unit of the place of the nth digit in the rounded number.† The errors introduced in the rounding of a large set of numbers, which are to be combined in a certain way, also tend to be equally often positive and negative, so that their effects often tend to cancel. The slight favoring of even numbers is prompted by the fact that any subsequent operations on the rounded numbers are then somewhat less likely to necessitate additional round-offs.

Each correct digit of this approximation, except a zero which serves only to fix the position of the decimal point, is called a *significant* digit or figure. Thus, the numbers 2.159, 0.04072, and 10.00 each contain four significant figures. Whether or not the last digit of 14620 is significant depends upon the context. If "a number known to be between 14615 and 14625" is intended, then that zero is not significant and the number would preferably be written as 1.462×10^4. Otherwise the form 1.4620×10^4 would be appropriate.

More generally, if any approximation $\bar{N}$ to a number N has the property that both $\bar{N}$ and N round to the same set of n significant figures, then $\bar{N}$ may be said to *approximate N to n significant figures*. Thus, if $N = 34.655000 \cdots$ and $\bar{N} = 34.665000 \cdots$, then $n = 4$. Clearly, the error $N - \bar{N}$ cannot exceed one unit of the place of the nth digit, but, as this example illustrates, the error may take on that maximum value. On the other hand, if $N \doteq 38.501$ and $\bar{N} \doteq 38.499$, then $n = 4$ but $n \neq 2$, in spite of the fact that the error is less than three units in the place of the *fifth* digit. This point is of practical importance only in that it illustrates the fact that, no matter how accurately a calculation is to be effected, the result of rounding the calculated value to n digits cannot be guaranteed in advance to possess n *correct* digits, but may differ from the rounded true value by one unit in the last digit.

It may be seen that the concept of significant figures is related more intimately to the *relative* error,

$$\text{Relative error} = \frac{\text{true value} - \text{approximation}}{\text{true value}}, \qquad (1.4.1)$$

than to the error itself. In order to exhibit the relationship more specifically, it is useful to define N^* and r such that

$$N = N^* \times 10^r \qquad \text{where } 1 < N^* < 10, \qquad (1.4.2)$$

---

† It should be noticed that, when 9.95 is rounded to 10.0, the result still contains *three* correct digits; the error amounts to one-half unit in the third figure of the rounded number, but to five units in the third figure of the original number.

where r is an integer and hence is that integer for which $10^r < N < 10^{r+1}$, when N is positive and not an integral multiple of 10, as will be assumed here. Thus $N^* = N$ when $1 < N < 10$, $= N/10$ when $10 < N < 100$, $= 10N$ when $0.1 < N < 1$, and so forth. If we write $E = N - \bar{N}$ and $R = E/N$, for the error and relative error, respectively, and suppose that $\bar{N}$ approximates N to n significant figures, so that

$$|E| \leq 10^{r-n+1}, \tag{1.4.3}$$

it then follows that

$$|R| \equiv \frac{|E|}{N} \leq \frac{10^{r-n+1}}{N^* \times 10^r} = \frac{10^{-n+1}}{N^*}. \tag{1.4.4}$$

In particular, we have $|R| < 10^{-n+1}$.

Further, if $\bar{N}$ is the result of rounding N to n significant figures, (1.4.3) is then replaced by the stronger estimate

$$|E| \leq 5 \times 10^{r-n}, \tag{1.4.5}$$

and there then follows

$$|R| \leq \frac{5}{N^*} \times 10^{-n}. \tag{1.4.6}$$

In particular, $|R| < 5 \times 10^{-n}$.

If we also write

$$E = \omega \times 10^{r-n+1}, \tag{1.4.7}$$

it follows that ω is the error expressed in units of the place of the nth digit of N, and we have also

$$\omega = \frac{E}{10^{r-n+1}} = \frac{NR}{10^{r-n+1}} = N^*R \times 10^{n-1}. \tag{1.4.8}$$

Suppose next that two numbers N_1 and N_2 are each rounded to n significant figures, and that the corresponding maximum error in the *product* $P = N_1N_2$ is required. We notice first that, if $R(P)$ refers to P and R_1, R_2 to N_1, N_2, there follows

$$R(P) = \frac{N_1N_2 - \bar{N}_1\bar{N}_2}{N_1N_2} = 1 - (1 - R_1)(1 - R_2) = R_1 + R_2 - R_1R_2.$$

Thus we see that $|R(P)|$ is largest when R_1 and R_2 are *negative*, and, from (1.4.6), there follows

$$|R(P)| \leq 5\left(\frac{1}{N_1^*} + \frac{1}{N_2^*}\right) \times 10^{-n} + \frac{25}{N_1^*N_2^*} \times 10^{-2n},$$

and hence, by using (1.4.8), we obtain

$$|\omega(P)| \leq \frac{(N_1N_2)^*}{2}\left(\frac{1}{N_1^*} + \frac{1}{N_2^*}\right) + \frac{5}{2}\frac{(N_1N_2)^*}{N_1^*N_2^*} \times 10^{-n}. \tag{1.4.9}$$

Since $(N_1 N_2)^* = N_1^* N_2^* \times 10^{-\rho}$, where ρ is either 0 or 1, the right-hand member of (1.4.9) is of the form

$$\frac{10^{-\rho}}{2} (N_1^* + N_2^* + 5 \times 10^{-n}),$$

and the most unfavorable cases are those for which $\rho = 0$. Under this constraint, the function $\phi(N_1^*, N_2^*) \equiv \frac{1}{2}(N_1^* + N_2^* + 5 \times 10^{-n})$ is to be considered only for $1 < N_1^* < 10$, $1 < N_2^* < 10$, and $1 < N_1^* N_2^* < 10$, and clearly cannot take on a maximum value in this open region. The maximum value of ϕ on the boundary of the region is easily seen to occur when either $N_1^* = 1$ and $N_2^* = 10$ or $N_1^* = 10$ and $N_2^* = 1$. Thus the right-hand member of (1.4.9) cannot exceed the limiting value corresponding to $(N_1 N_2)^* = 10-$ and either $N_1^* = 1+$, $N_2^* = 10-$ or $N_1^* = 10-$, $N_2^* = 1+$, and there follows

$$|\omega_n(N_1 N_2)| < \tfrac{11}{2} + \tfrac{5}{2} \times 10^{-n} < 6, \tag{1.4.10}$$

where ω_n is the error expressed in units of the place of the nth digit of the true value.

This means that *if two numbers are rounded to n significant figures, the product of the rounded numbers differs from the true product by less than six units in the place of its nth significant digit.* In illustration, when $N_1 = 1.05+$ and $N_2 = 9.45+$ there follows $N_1 N_2 = 9.9225+$, whereas, if N_1 and N_2 are rounded to two significant figures to give $\bar{N}_1 = 1.1$ and $\bar{N}_2 = 9.5$, there follows $\bar{N}_1 \bar{N}_2 = 10.45$. Thus, in this extreme case, $\omega_2 = -(5.275-)$.

When $N_1 = N_2 \equiv N$, the worst (limiting) situation is that in which $(N^*)^2 = (N^2)^* = 10-$. Thus there follows

$$|\omega_n(N^2)| < 10^{\frac{1}{2}} + \tfrac{5}{2} \times 10^{-n} < 4, \tag{1.4.11}$$

so that *the square of a number rounded to n digits differs from the square of the unrounded number by less than four units in the place of its nth digit.*

More generally, if we consider $P = N_1 N_2 \cdots N_m$, we find that

$$R(P) = 1 - [(1 - R_1)(1 - R_2) \cdots (1 - R_m)]$$

and hence

$$|\omega_n(P)| \leqq \frac{(N_1 \cdots N_m)^*}{2\alpha_n} [(1 + |R_1|)(1 + |R_2|) \cdots (1 + |R_m|) - 1]$$

$$\leqq \frac{(N_1 \cdots N_m)^*}{2\alpha_n} \left[\left(1 + \frac{\alpha_n}{N_1^*}\right) \left(1 + \frac{\alpha_n}{N_2^*}\right) \cdots \left(1 + \frac{\alpha_n}{N_m^*}\right) - 1 \right], \tag{1.4.12}$$

where

$$\alpha_n \equiv 5 \times 10^{-n}. \tag{1.4.13}$$

Here the worst situation is that in which $m - 1$ of the m numbers N_k^*

are $1+$ and the remaining one is $10-$, such that also

$$N_1^* \cdots N_m^* = (N_1 \cdots N_m)^* = 10-.$$

Thus there follows, from (1.4.12),

$$|\omega_n(N_1 \cdots N_m)| < \frac{5}{\alpha_n}\left[(1+\alpha_n)^{m-1}\left(1+\frac{\alpha_n}{10}\right) - 1\right]. \quad (1.4.14)$$

Corresponding numerical bounds on the quantity $|\omega_n(N_1 \cdots N_m)|$ are given in Table 1.1.

TABLE 1.1

$\diagdown$ m n $\diagdown$	1	2	3	4	6	8	10
2	0.5	6	11	17	29	42	56
$\geqq 3$	0.5	6	11	16	26	36	46

In the special case when $N_1 = N_2 = \cdots = N_m \equiv N$, there follows

$$|\omega_n(N^m)| \leqq \frac{(N^m)^*}{2\alpha_n}\left[\left(1+\frac{\alpha_n}{N^*}\right)^m - 1\right], \quad (1.4.15)$$

and the worst situation is that in which $(N^*)^m = (N^m)^* = 10-$, when m is a positive integer, so that

$$|\omega_n(N^m)| < \frac{5}{\alpha_n}\,[(1+10^{-1/m}\alpha_n)^m - 1] \quad (m-1, 2, \ldots). \quad (1.4.16)$$

Numerical bounds on $|\omega_n(N^m)|$ are given in Table 1.2.

TABLE 1.2

$\diagdown$ m n $\diagdown$	1	2	3	4	6	8	10
2	0.5	4	8	12	23	35	48
$\geqq 3$	0.5	4	7	12	21	31	41

When $P = N^m$, with $m \equiv 1/p$ the *reciprocal* of a positive integer, so that the operation involved is that of root extraction, the relation (1.4.15) again holds, but here the worst case is that in which $N = 10^{(k-m)/m}+$, where k is any integer, so that $(N^m)^* = 10^{1-m}+$ and $N^* = 1+$, in accordance with which there follows

$$|\omega_n(N^m)| < \frac{5}{\alpha_n} \times 10^{-m}[(1+\alpha_n)^m - 1] \quad (m - \tfrac{1}{2}, \tfrac{1}{3}, \ldots). \quad (1.4.17)$$

Numerical bounds on $|\omega_n(N^{1/p})|$, where p is a positive integer, are given in Table 1.3.

TABLE 1.3

p / n	1	2	3	4	8	16	32
$\geqq 2$	0.50	0.79	0.78	0.71	0.47	0.28	0.15

The given bounds apply for all N, but may be quite conservative in any specific case. Thus, if it is known only that $|N - 9.61| \leqq 0.005$, then it can be verified that $|\sqrt{N} - 3.100| \leqq 0.0009$, whereas Table 1.3 gives a bound of 0.0078. (Here the guaranteed accuracy of the calculated result is greater than that of the basic data.) Still, none of the bounds can be appreciably lowered, since each is nearly attained in some case.

In illustration, we may note that, if $N = 1.445$ and if N^6 is approximated by $(1.44)^6 \doteq 8.916 \doteq 8.92$, the result differs from the true value $N^6 \doteq 9.103 \doteq 9.10$ by about 19 in units of the third digit. Table 1.2 gives an upper limit of 21. The number $(106.4)^{\frac{1}{3}}$ should be reliable to three significant figures, according to Table 1.3, with the fourth digit in error by no more than 1. The calculated value rounds to 4.7385, whereas $(106.35)^{\frac{1}{3}} \doteq 4.7378$ and $(106.45)^{\frac{1}{3}} \doteq 4.7393$. The maximum error is thus about 0.8 units of the place of the fourth digit, as is just admitted by Table 1.3, and the *last digit* of the rounded four-place value, 4.738, is in error by not more than 1. However, whereas the value actually calculated is in error by an amount not exceeding 0.8×10^{-3}, as predicted, the rounded value may be in error by 1.3×10^{-3}.

The calculated value of the product

$$(3.658)(24.765)(1.4345)(72.43)$$

certainly will be in error by less than 16 units of the place of its fourth significant digit, in virtue of Table 1.1, under the assumptions that each factor is correctly rounded to the digits written and that sufficiently many digits are retained in the calculation itself. However, since the second and third factors each involve five significant figures, their product alone will be correct within 6 units of its fifth digit, so that actually the maximum error is the same as that associated with the product of *three* four-digit numbers and hence will be less than 11 units in the place of the fourth digit. Clearly (contrary to advice sometimes given) the procedure of deliberately rounding each of the factors to four digits before the multiplication would be a wasteful one, since it thus would increase the maximum possible error. Multiplication actually yields the calculated value 9.412×10^3 (to four digits), while the largest and smallest possible values of the true product are found to round to 9.415×10^3 and 9.410×10^3. Thus the maximum error here is only 3 in the fourth digit. The result of rounding each factor to four digits before multiplying rounds to

9.407 $\times$ 10^3, which hence *certainly* is in error by at least 3 in the fourth digit, and which *may* be in error by as much as 8.

1.5. Error Bounds. When *any* function $f(N)$, with a continuous derivative, is evaluated with N replaced by an approximation $\bar{N}$, the relation

$$f(N) - f(\bar{N}) = (N - \bar{N})f'(\eta) \qquad (\eta \text{ between } N \text{ and } \bar{N}) \quad (1.5.1)$$

permits us to deduce that

$$|E(f(N))| \leqq |f'(\eta)|_{\max}|E(N)| \tag{1.5.2}$$

and
$$|R(f(N))| \leqq \frac{|f'(\eta)|_{\max}}{|f(N)|} |E(N)|. \tag{1.5.3}$$

Analogous results are readily obtained in cases when several independent variables are involved.

In illustration, if $f(N) = \log_{10} N$, there follows

$$|E(\log_{10} N)| \leqq \frac{\log_{10} e}{|\eta|} |E(N)| \qquad [\eta \text{ between } N - E(N) \text{ and } N + E(N)]$$

and hence, if $N \geqq 1$ and $|E(N)| < \frac{1}{2}$,

$$|E(\log_{10} N)| \leqq \frac{0.44}{1 - |E|} |E(N)| < |E(N)|, \tag{1.5.4}$$

so that the error in the common logarithm is smaller than the error in its argument, when that argument exceeds unity. On the other hand,

$$|E(10^N)| = \frac{10^\eta}{\log_{10} e} |E(N)|,$$

and hence, if $|E(N)| < \frac{1}{2}$,

$$|R(10^N)| \leqq 2.31 \times 10^{|E(N)|}|E(N)| < 8|E(N)|. \tag{1.5.5}$$

Thus, the error in 10^N, expressed in units of the place of its nth significant figure, is less than $8|E(N)| \times 10^n$. Hence, if the error in the common logarithm is smaller in magnitude than 1 in units of the nth decimal place, then the antilogarithm is in error by less than 8 in units of its nth *significant figure* and hence is correct to at least $n - 1$ significant figures.

As a further illustration of the use of (1.5.1), we next investigate the degree of indeterminacy of the quantity†

$$\log \sin 1.412762,$$

---

† The notation log u, with no base specified, is to be used consistently to denote $\log_e u$; the arguments of trigonometric functions are always to be expressed in radians unless degrees are explicitly specified.

under the assumption that the argument is a rounded number. The use of (1.5.1) gives the bound

$$|E| \leq (5 \times 10^{-7})|\cot \eta|_{max} \qquad (1.4127615 \leq \eta < 1.4127625)$$

on the inherent error E, and, since $0.17 > \cot x > 0.15$ for $1.41 < x < 1.42$, there follows $|E| < 0.85 \times 10^{-7}$, so that the desired quantity is determinate to within less than one unit in the seventh decimal place.

In the linear processes of *addition* and *subtraction*, the error in the result is merely the algebraic sum of the errors in the separate terms, and the magnitude of the maximum error is the sum of the magnitudes of the component errors. Thus, whereas in multiplication and division we are concerned principally with *ratios* of errors to true quantities, and with the number of significant figures, and the absolute position of the decimal point is of importance only in fixing the magnitude of the end result, in addition and subtraction the errors themselves are the important quantities, significant figures are involved only incidentally, and the orientation of a digit sequence relative to the decimal point is of importance throughout the calculation.

Thus, if k numbers (positive or negative) are each rounded to n *decimal places*, so that each is in error by an amount less than $5 \times 10^{-n-1}$ in magnitude, the magnitude of the maximum error of the sum is clearly $5k \times 10^{-n-1}$, corresponding to the situation in which the signs of the errors are such that they combine without cancellation. Accordingly, the result can be in error by as much as $k/2$ units in the nth decimal place.

Formal addition assigns to the sum

$$56.434 + 251.37 - 2.6056 + 84.674 - 396.06 + 7.0228$$

the value 0.8352. However, if each number is correct only to the five significant figures given, the error in the result can have any value between the limits ± 0.0111, so that the result would be recorded as 0.84, with the last digit in doubt by two units,† and only one truly significant digit remains. Rounding all of the numbers to the two decimal places which are in common, before addition, would lead to the result 0.82, but would increase the error limits to ± 0.03. Rounding each of the more accurate numbers to *one* place beyond the last place of the least-accurate one gives 0.835 with error limits ± 0.012, so that the recorded entry is again 0.84 (or 0.8_4), with the last digit in doubt by two units, and is a procedure which is generally to be recommended in such cases.

A somewhat similar situation, in which the outcome is, however, reversed, is of some importance. Tables of functions often provide a

---

† The notation 0.8_4 is often used to indicate that, whereas the 4 is not significant, the maximum error associated with 0.84 is less than (or probably less than) that associated with 0.8.

column of differences between successive entries, to facilitate linear interpolation, according to the formula

$$f(x_0 + \theta h) \approx f(x_0) + \theta[f(x_1) - f(x_0)] \qquad (0 < \theta < 1), \qquad (1.5.6)$$

where x_0 and x_1 are successive tabular arguments and $h = x_1 - x_0$. In constructing such a table, in which (say) all entries are to be rounded to a certain number of decimal places, the question arises as to whether the number tabulated for the difference $f(x_1) - f(x_0)$ should represent the rounded value of the difference or the difference between the rounded values, in those cases where these values differ. Intuition perhaps would recommend the former procedure, since it appears to make use of additional information. However, if ϵ represents the maximum round-off, the maximum error in that case is clearly $(1 + \theta)\epsilon$, whereas, since in the second case the right-hand member is properly to be considered in the form $(1 - \theta)f(x_0) + \theta f(x_1)$, and since $0 < \theta < 1$, the maximum error in that case is seen to be $(1 - \theta)\epsilon + \theta\epsilon = \epsilon$. Thus the maximum error is less if the difference of the rounded values is used (for a more detailed discussion of this question, see Ostrowski [175]†). In particular, the *user* of tables which do not explicitly list differences need not regret the fact that he is *forced* to employ that procedure when using (1.5.6). The *truncation* error associated with that formula is considered in the following chapter.

The loss of significant figures in subtraction is one of the principal sources of error in numerical analysis, and it is highly desirable to arrange the sequence of calculations so that such subtractions are avoided, if possible, or so that their effects are brought into specific evidence. As a simple example, in calculating $ab - ac \equiv a(b - c)$, where b and c are very nearly equal, the products ab and ac may have many of their leading digits in common, and the number of significant figures which must be retained in each product, in order that sufficiently many significant figures will remain in the difference, can be determined only after both products have been evaluated. This dilemma is avoided if $b - c$ is calculated first. Naturally, if a, b, and c are specified only to a certain number of significant figures, and if no round-offs are introduced, the order of the calculations is irrelevant from this point of view, and the corresponding degree of uncertainty in the result merely must be accepted.

Frequently it is possible to exploit special properties of functions involved in the analysis. Thus, if a and b are nearly equal, it is convenient to replace $\log b - \log a$ by $\log (b/a)$, $\sin b - \sin a$ by the product $2 \sin \frac{1}{2}(b - a) \cos \frac{1}{2}(a + b)$, and $\sqrt{b} - \sqrt{a}$ by $(b - a)/(\sqrt{a} + \sqrt{b})$.

For example, if $4AC \ll B^2$, the *quadratic formula* is inconvenient for

† Numbers in brackets refer to items of the bibliography, Appendix B.

the determination of the smaller root of the equation $Ax^2 + Bx + C = 0$. In this case, when $B > 0$, it is desirable to replace the usual formula $x_1 = (-B + \sqrt{B^2 - 4AC})/2A$ by the equivalent form

$$x_1 = \frac{-2C}{B + \sqrt{B^2 - 4AC}},$$

for a specific calculation, or to write

$$-B + \sqrt{B^2 - 4AC} = -B\left(1 - \sqrt{1 - \frac{4AC}{B^2}}\right)$$

in the original form and to expand the result by the binomial theorem to give

$$x_1 = -\frac{C}{B}\left(1 + \frac{AC}{B^2} + \cdots\right),$$

when the dependence of x_1 on the literal parameters is to be studied.

1.6. Random Errors. If 1000 positive numbers, each rounded to n decimal places, were added, the total error due to round-off could amount to 500 units in the last place of the sum. Whereas this maximum error could be attained only in the case when all numbers were rounded in the same direction, by exactly one-half unit, the *possibility* of its occurrence forces us to accept its value as *the* least upper bound on the possible error.

However, the price of *certainty* in such a case is a high one, and in most situations it cannot be tolerated. Furthermore, in a great number of practical cases certainty cannot be attained. Thus each member of a set of 1000 numbers, to be added, may itself represent the mean of a set of empirical values of a physical quantity, in which case one generally cannot *guarantee* that the error associated with it is less than, say, $5 \times 10^{-n-1}$, but can only estimate the *probability* that this is the case.

In most such cases it is assumed that the errors are symmetrically distributed about a zero mean and that, in a sufficiently large set of measurements, the probability of the occurrence of an error between x and $x + dx$ is, to a first approximation, of the form

$$\phi(x)\, dx = \frac{1}{\sqrt{2\pi}\, \sigma}\, e^{-x^2/2\sigma^2}\, dx, \tag{1.6.1}$$

where σ is a constant parameter, to be adjusted to the observations. The function ϕ is called the *frequency function* of the distribution. The probability that an error not exceed x algebraically is then given by the *normal distribution function*

$$\Phi(x) = \int_{-\infty}^{x} \phi(t)\, dt = \frac{1}{\sqrt{2\pi}\, \sigma} \int_{-\infty}^{x} e^{-t^2/2\sigma^2}\, dt, \tag{1.6.2}$$

the numerical coefficient in (1.6.1) having been determined so that $\Phi(\infty) = 1$,

$$\int_{-\infty}^{\infty} \phi(t) \, dt = \frac{1}{\sqrt{2\pi}\,\sigma} \int_{-\infty}^{\infty} e^{-t^2/2\sigma^2} \, dt = 1, \qquad (1.6.3)$$

in accordance with the requirement of unit probability that any error lie *somewhere* in $(-\infty, \infty)$.

Further, the probability $P(x)$ that an error chosen at random lie between $-|x|$ and $+|x|$, that is, that its *magnitude* not exceed $|x|$, is clearly given by

$$P(x) = \Phi(|x|) - \Phi(-|x|) = \int_{-|x|}^{|x|} \phi(t) \, dt = 2\int_0^{|x|} \phi(t) \, dt$$

or
$$P(x) = \frac{\sqrt{2}}{\sqrt{\pi}\,\sigma} \int_0^{|x|} e^{-t^2/2\sigma^2} \, dt, \qquad (1.6.4)$$

whereas the probability that it *exceed* $|x|$ in magnitude is $Q(x) \equiv 1 - P(x)$. Equation (1.6.4) can also be written in the form

$$P(x) = \frac{2}{\sqrt{\pi}} \int_0^{|x|/\sqrt{2}\,\sigma} e^{-s^2} \, ds \equiv \operatorname{erf}\left(\frac{|x|}{\sqrt{2}\,\sigma}\right), \qquad (1.6.5)$$

in terms of the "error function."

Details must be omitted here with respect to the wide class of situations in which the use of this so-called *normal-distribution* law is justifiable, but the literature on this subject is extensive (for example, see Feller [76]). In particular, even though the "frequency distribution" of the errors in a single quantity may not be capable of good approximation by a *normal* frequency distribution, of the form specified by (1.6.1), it generally is true that, when many such independent component errors are compounded, the resultant distribution *can* be so approximated.

The parameter σ is called the *standard deviation* of the distribution. It is easily seen that the points of inflection of the curve representing $\phi(\epsilon)$ lie at distance σ on each side of the maximum at $\epsilon = 0$. The parameter $h = 1/(\sqrt{2\pi}\,\sigma)$ is called the *modulus of precision* and is a measure of the steepness of the frequency curve near its peak at the origin.

If ϵ is a random variable, the *mean value* of any function $g(\epsilon)$, relative to the assumed distribution, is given by

$$(g(\epsilon))_{\text{mean}} = \int_{-\infty}^{\infty} \phi(\epsilon)g(\epsilon) \, d\epsilon = \frac{1}{\sqrt{2\pi}\,\sigma} \int_{-\infty}^{\infty} e^{-\epsilon^2/2\sigma^2} g(\epsilon) \, d\epsilon, \quad (1.6.6)$$

under the assumption that this integral exists. In particular, since $\phi(\epsilon)$ is an even function of ϵ, we verify directly that the mean value of ϵ itself then is indeed zero, and we find also, for example, that

$$|\epsilon|_{\text{mean}} = 2 \int_0^\infty \epsilon \phi(\epsilon) \, d\epsilon = \sqrt{\frac{2}{\pi}} \, \sigma \qquad (1.6.7)$$

and
$$(\epsilon^2)_{\text{mean}} = 2 \int_0^\infty \epsilon^2 \phi(\epsilon) \, d\epsilon = \sigma^2. \qquad (1.6.8)$$

Mean values of higher powers of $|\epsilon|$ can be expressed similarly, in terms of the parameter σ.

Thus, this parameter could be determined in such a way that any one of these "moments," thus calculated for an assumed normal distribution, is made to equal the corresponding moment of the distribution actually under consideration, if that moment could be calculated or approximated. It happens that the choice of the *second* moment leads to the most convenient analysis and also is recommended by certain theoretical considerations.   Thus we specify the parameter σ of the approximating normal distribution (1.6.1) in such a way that it is equal to the square root of the mean of the squared errors in the true distribution,

$$\sigma = \epsilon_{\text{RMS}}. \qquad (1.6.9)$$

In general, ϵ_{RMS} for the entire distribution can be estimated only from a sample of, say, the deviations of k measurements from their mean value, and an appropriate estimate is then afforded by the formula†

$$\epsilon_{\text{RMS}} \approx \sqrt{\frac{1}{k} (\epsilon_1^2 + \epsilon_2^2 + \cdots + \epsilon_k^2)}. \qquad (1.6.10)$$

Having obtained such an approximation to σ, one can make use of Eq. (1.6.4) to estimate the probability that the magnitude of a random error exceed (or not exceed) a certain specified amount.   A few useful values of $1 - P$ are listed in Table 1.4.   Thus, the probability of an error

TABLE 1.4

$\dfrac{\epsilon}{\epsilon_{\text{RMS}}}$	$1 - P(\epsilon)$
0.674	0.500
0.842	0.400
1.000	0.317
1.036	0.300
1.282	0.200
1.645	0.100
2.576	0.010

† A theoretically better estimate, which tends to take into account the probable deviation of the mean of the observations from the unknown true mean, is obtained by replacing $1/k$ by $1/(k - 1)$ in (1.6.10).   This modification is of practical significance only when k is relatively small, in which cases the validity of the statistical analysis itself may be open to question.

of magnitude greater than ϵ_{RMS} is 0.317.   Only 20 per cent of the errors should exceed $1.282\epsilon_{RMS}$, 10 per cent should exceed $1.645\epsilon_{RMS}$, and 1 per cent should exceed $2.576\epsilon_{RMS}$, *if* the distribution is sufficiently nearly normal.

The number 0.67449σ is often called the *probable error* of the distribution.   It should be noticed that this is merely that number which should be exceeded by the magnitude of half the errors; it is in no sense the *most probable error*, as the name tends to suggest.   The quantity σ^2 is often called the *variance*.

If the approximation (1.6.10) were calculated for a large number of sets of samples, each containing k errors chosen at random from the same distribution, and if the mean of the estimates were selected as the best approximation to the true ϵ_{RMS}, the deviations of the various estimates from this best one would also be normally distributed, to a first approximation, with an RMS value of $\epsilon_{RMS}/\sqrt{2k}$, when k is sufficiently large. This fact is often useful in estimating the reliability of the estimated value of ϵ_{RMS}.

Now suppose that ϵ is the sum of two independent errors u and v, each of which varies about a zero mean.   Then the mean value of ϵ^2 is the sum of the mean values of u^2, $2uv$, and v^2.   But, since u and v are independent, the mean of uv is the product of the means of u and v and hence is zero. Thus there follows

$$\epsilon_{RMS} = \sqrt{u_{RMS}^2 + v_{RMS}^2}. \tag{1.6.11}$$

This argument generalizes to show that *the RMS value of the sum of n independent errors* (each having a zero mean) *is the square root of the sum of the squares of the RMS values of the component errors*.

It can be shown (see Prob. 24) that the normal-distribution law has the property that, if u and v are independent and normally distributed, with standard deviations σ_u and σ_v, then $\epsilon = u + v$ is also normally distributed, with standard deviation $\sigma = \sqrt{\sigma_u^2 + \sigma_v^2}$.   Thus if, in accordance with (1.6.9), we identify σ_u with u_{RMS} and σ_v with v_{RMS}, it will follow also that $\sigma_{u+v} = (u + v)_{RMS}$.

In illustration, if each of the numbers in the sum

$$426.44 - 43.26 + 2.72 + 9.61 - 104.26 - 218.72$$

represents the mean of a set of observations, and if the (approximate) RMS error associated with each is, say, 0.05, then the formal sum 72.53 would possess an RMS error of $\sqrt{6}\,(0.05) \doteq 0.12$.   Such a result is often recorded as 72.53 ± 0.12, although some writers use the *probable error* $(0.674)(0.12) \doteq 0.07$, and write 72.53 ± 0.07, while still others use the notation $N \pm d$ to indicate that d is the *maximum* error in N (which would be undefined in the present case).

If we consider the error ϵ which arises from *rounding* a number to n decimal places, it is clear that the distribution of values of ϵ will *not* be well approximated by any normal distribution, since here the frequency function has the constant value $1/(2|\epsilon|_{max})$ when $|\epsilon| < |\epsilon|_{max} = 5 \times 10^{-n-1}$ and the value zero otherwise. However, the distribution function corresponding to errors which are (exactly or approximately) linear combinations of many such errors generally will be appropriate for approximation by a normal distribution function. Thus, in such cases, the error analysis may be based with some confidence upon the result of treating the individual errors as though they were normally distributed. (See Prob. 25.)

For this purpose, we may notice that if x takes on all values between $-\frac{1}{2}$ and $\frac{1}{2}$, and if all those values are equally likely, the RMS value of x is

$$\left(\frac{1}{1} \int_{-\frac{1}{2}}^{\frac{1}{2}} x^2 \, dx\right)^{\frac{1}{2}} = \frac{1}{6}\sqrt{3} \doteq 0.2887.$$

Hence, *if ϵ is round-off error due to rounding to the nth decimal place, there follows*

$$\epsilon_{RMS} = 0.2887 \times 10^{-n}. \tag{1.6.12}$$

Thus, if k numbers are each rounded to n decimal places, the error in the sum of the results can be considered to be normally distributed, with an RMS value of $0.2887 \sqrt{k} \times 10^{-n}$, if k is not too small.

In particular, when 1000 such numbers are added, the RMS error in the sum is less than 10 units in the nth place. According to Table 1.3, the probability of an error of 17 units is less than 0.1, and the odds are 99 to 1 that the error will not exceed 26 units. Nevertheless, an error of 500 units in the nth place is indeed *possible*.

In order that such analyses be reliable, it is essential that the round-offs be effected without bias. Methods are available in the literature for the purpose of minimizing the possibility of its occurrence (see Forsythe [79]).

1.7. Mathematical Preliminaries. In this section, we list certain analytical results to which reference occasionally will be made in the sequel. Proofs of most are omitted.

First, it may be stated that, in most of the following chapters, it is supposed that all functions dealt with are real and continuous in the range considered and, in addition, that they possess as many continuous derivatives as the analysis may require.

The basic fact that *a function $f(x)$ which is continuous for $a \leqq x \leqq b$ takes on each value between $f(a)$ and $f(b)$* is intuitively "obvious," but is capable of rigorous proof. Two immediate consequences of this result are the following:

THEOREM 1. If $f(x)$ is continuous for $a \leq x \leq b$, and if $f(a)$ and $f(b)$ are of opposite sign, then $f(\xi) = 0$ for at least one number ξ such that $a < \xi < b$.

THEOREM 2. If $f(x)$ is continuous for $a \leq x \leq b$, and if λ_1 and λ_2 are positive constants, then $\lambda_1 f(a) + \lambda_2 f(b) = (\lambda_1 + \lambda_2)f(\xi)$ for at least one ξ such that $a \leq \xi \leq b$.

If also $f'(x)$ exists and is continuous for $a < x < b$, two additional results can be established:

THEOREM 3. If $f(x)$ is continuous for $a \leq x \leq b$ and $f'(x)$ is continuous for $a < x < b$, and if $f(a) = f(b) = 0$, then $f'(\xi) = 0$ for at least one ξ such that $a < \xi < b$. (This is *Rolle's theorem*.)

THEOREM 4. If $f(x)$ is continuous for $a \leq x \leq b$ and $f'(x)$ is continuous for $a < x < b$, then $f(b) - f(a) = (b - a)f'(\xi)$ for at least one ξ such that $a < \xi < b$. (This is the *mean-value theorem* for the derivative.)

In the following statements, it is assumed that the integrals involved exist and that $b > a$.

THEOREM 5. If $|f(x)| \leq M$ in (a,b), where M is a constant, then

$$\left| \int_a^b f(x)\, dx \right| \leq \int_a^b |f(x)|\, dx \leq M(b - a).$$

THEOREM 6. If $f(x)$ is continuous for $a \leq x \leq b$, then

$$\int_a^b f(x)\, dx = (b - a)f(\xi)$$

for at least one ξ such that $a < \xi < b$. (This is the *first law of the mean*.)

THEOREM 7. If $m \leq f(x) \leq M$ and $g(x)$ is nonnegative, for $a \leq x \leq b$, then

$$m \int_a^b g(x)\, dx \leq \int_a^b f(x)g(x)\, dx \leq M \int_a^b g(x)\, dx.$$

THEOREM 8. If $f(x)$ is continuous for $a \leq x \leq b$ and $g(x)$ does not change sign inside (a,b), then

$$\int_a^b f(x)g(x)\, dx = f(\xi) \int_a^b g(x)\, dx$$

for at least one ξ such that $a < \xi < b$. (This is the *second law of the mean*.)

The three following theorems with relation to integrals involving a parameter are of frequent use:

THEOREM 9. If a and b are finite constants and $F(x,s)$ is continuous in x and s, then

$$\lim_{x \to c} \int_a^b F(x,s)\, ds = \int_a^b F(c,s)\, ds.$$

THEOREM 10.   If a and b are finite constants and if $\partial F/\partial x$ is continuous, then

$$\frac{d}{dx}\int_a^b F(x,s)\,ds = \int_a^b \frac{\partial F(x,s)}{\partial x}\,ds.$$

THEOREM 11.   If a is a finite constant, u is a differentiable function of x, and $\partial F/\partial x$ is continuous, then

$$\frac{d}{dx}\int_a^u F(x,s)\,ds = \int_a^u \frac{\partial F(x,s)}{\partial x}\,ds + F(x,u)\frac{du}{dx}.$$

Finally, a useful result relevant to repeated integration may be stated as follows:

THEOREM 12.   If $F_n(x)$ denotes the result of integrating $F(x)$ successively n times over (a,x), then

$$F_n(x) = \frac{1}{(n-1)!}\int_a^x (x-s)^{n-1}F(s)\,ds.$$

The truth of each of these assertions, except perhaps for the last two, is nearly self-evident, and the details of their proofs are rather easily supplied once the preliminary basic properties of continuous functions are established.

The validity of Theorem 11 follows from the fact that, if we write $I(x) = \int_a^u F(x,s)\,ds$, there follows

$$I(x + \Delta x) - I(x) = \int_a^u [F(x + \Delta x,\, s) - F(x,s)]\,ds$$
$$+ \int_u^{u+\Delta u} F(x + \Delta x,\, s)\,ds$$
$$= \left(\int_a^u F_x(\xi,s)\,ds\right)\Delta x + F(x + \Delta x,\, \eta)\,\Delta u,$$

where ξ is between x and $x + \Delta x$ and η is between u and $u + \Delta u$, in virtue of Theorems 4 and 6, and hence

$$I'(x) = \lim_{\Delta x \to 0}\int_a^u F_x(\xi,s)\,ds + \lim_{\Delta x \to 0} F(x + \Delta x,\, \eta)\frac{\Delta u}{\Delta x}$$
$$= \int_a^u F_x(x,s)\,ds + F(x,u)\frac{du}{dx},$$

in virtue of the content of Theorem 9.

Theorem 12 can be established by successive integration by parts, or verified by the use of Theorem 11, making use of the facts that, from the definition, there follows $F_k'(x) = F_{k-1}(x)$ and $F_k(a) = 0$ for $k = 1, 2, \ldots,$ n, and $F_1'(x) = F_0(x) \equiv F(x)$.

This result is useful in deriving the finite Taylor series, with an error term expressed in a form which is often more useful than that given in (1.3.2), and also for deriving the form given there. For if we write

$$F(x) = f^{(n)}(x) \equiv \frac{d^n f(x)}{dx^n}, \tag{1.7.1}$$

and use the notation of Theorem 12, the results of integrating the equal members successively over (a,x) are seen to be

$$F_1(x) = f^{(n-1)}(x) - f^{(n-1)}(a),$$
$$F_2(x) = f^{(n-2)}(x) - f^{(n-2)}(a) - (x - a)f^{(n-1)}(a),$$
$$F_3(x) = f^{(n-3)}(x) - f^{(n-3)}(a) - (x - a)f^{(n-2)}(a) - \frac{(x - c)^2}{2!} f^{(n-1)}(a),$$

and finally, after n integrations,

$$F_n(x) = f(x) - f(a) - (x - a)f'(a) - \frac{(x - a)^2}{2!} f''(a) - \cdots$$
$$- \frac{(x - a)^{n-1}}{(n - 1)!} f^{(n-1)}(a). \tag{1.7.2}$$

Thus, after a transposition and a reference to Theorem 12, we deduce that *if the nth derivative of $f(x)$ exists and is integrable throughout an interval including $x = a$, then in that interval there follows*

$$f(x) = f(a) + f'(a)(x - a) + \frac{f''(a)}{2!} (x - a)^2 + \cdots$$
$$+ \frac{f^{(n-1)}(a)}{(n - 1)!} (x - a)^{n-1} + E(x) \tag{1.7.3}$$

where

$$E(x) = \frac{1}{(n - 1)!} \int_a^x (x - s)^{n-1} f^{(n)}(s) \, ds. \tag{1.7.4}$$

Further, since $(x - s)^{n-1}$ does not change sign as s varies from a to x, we can invoke the second law of the mean (Theorem 8) to rewrite (1.7.4) in the form

$$E(x) = \frac{f^{(n)}(\xi)}{(n - 1)!} \int_a^x (x - s)^{n-1} \, ds$$
$$= \frac{f^{(n)}(\xi)}{n!} (x - a)^n \qquad (\xi \text{ between } a \text{ and } x), \tag{1.7.5}$$

under the additional assumption that $f^{(n)}(x)$ is continuous. Whereas the form (1.7.5) has the advantage of simplicity, the form (1.7.4) is often preferable because of the fact that it is *explicit,* while (1.7.5) involves a parameter which is known only to lie between a and x.

A useful generalization of the Taylor-series expansion (1.7.3) can be obtained by starting with the representation

$$F(t) = F(0) + \sum_{k=1}^{n-1} c_k t^k + E, \tag{1.7.6}$$

where
$$c_k = \frac{1}{k!}\left[\frac{d^k F(t)}{dt^k}\right]_{t=0}, \qquad E = \frac{t^n}{n!}\left[\frac{d^n F(t)}{dt^n}\right]_{t=\tau}, \qquad (1.7.7)$$

with τ between 0 and t, and writing
$$t = g(x) - g(a), \qquad F(t) = f(x), \qquad (1.7.8)$$

under the assumption that
$$g'(x) \neq 0 \qquad (1.7.9)$$

over some interval I including $x = a$, so that $g(x) - g(a)$ increases or decreases steadily as x increases over I. The result of this substitution takes the form
$$f(x) = f(a) + \sum_{k=1}^{n-1} c_k[g(x) - g(a)]^k + E, \qquad (1.7.10)$$

where
$$c_k = \frac{1}{k!}\left[\left\{\frac{1}{g'(x)}\frac{d}{dx}\right\}^k f(x)\right]_{x=a}, \qquad E = \frac{[g(x)-g(a)]^n}{n!}\left[\left\{\frac{1}{g'(x)}\frac{d}{dx}\right\}^n f(x)\right]_{x=\xi}, \qquad (1.7.11)$$

and where ξ lies between a and x, when x is in I, under the assumption that $f^{(n)}(x)$ and $g^{(n)}(x)$ are continuous and $g'(x) \neq 0$ in I.

If we define a sequence of auxiliary functions $\alpha_0(x)$, $\alpha_1(x)$, . . . by the recurrence formula
$$\alpha_k(x) = \frac{\alpha'_{k-1}(x)}{g'(x)} \qquad (k = 1, 2, \ldots), \qquad (1.7.12)$$
$$\alpha_0(x) = f(x), \qquad (1.7.13)$$
with
it follows that
$$c_k = \frac{1}{k!}\alpha_k(a), \qquad E = \frac{1}{n!}\alpha_n(\xi)[g(x)-g(a)]^n. \qquad (1.7.14)$$

The expansion (1.7.10) is often known as a *Bürmann series* and is useful when a certain value of a function $g(x)$ is known and the corresponding value of a second function $f(x)$ is required. The special case when $f(x)$ is identified with x itself is of most frequent occurrence.

It can be shown (see Whittaker and Watson [235]) that the coefficient c_k can also be expressed by the formula
$$c_k = \frac{1}{k!}\left[\frac{d^{k-1}}{dx^{k-1}}\left\{f'(x)\left[\frac{x-a}{g(x)-g(a)}\right]^k\right\}\right]_{x=a}. \qquad (1.7.15)$$

While this is the form usually given, the use of the form given in (1.7.11) or (1.7.14) often leads to a somewhat less involved calculation, particularly when $(x - a)$ cannot be explicitly factored from $g(x) - g(a)$.

Lastly, mention should be made of the so-called *fundamental theorem* of elementary algebra, namely, that *any polynomial*† *other than a constant possesses at least one zero*, the usual proofs of which depend upon results established in the theory of analytic functions of a complex variable. Elementary treatments *assume* the truth of this theorem and deduce easily that *any polynomial of degree n possesses exactly n zeros*, with the convention that repeated zeros are to be counted a number of times equal to their multiplicities. This last result will be of basic importance in the sequel.

1.8. Supplementary References. The bibliography (Appendix B) lists many of the existing general texts on numerical analysis, together with a selection of collateral text and journal references and of certain sources of relevant mathematical tables and formulas. Nörlund [13] and Whittaker and Robinson [20] are good sources of references to the classical works. Graphical methods, which are not treated here, are included in Lipka [8], Von Sanden [16], and Willers [21]. References [60], [73], [104], and [187] provide information concerning modern, large-scale calculating machines. For comprehensive treatments of the general theory of approximation, see Jackson [123], de la Vallée Poussin [229], and Walsh [232]. An illustration of the precise analysis of round-off errors in machine calculation is presented by Householder [3] (chap. 1). The general mathematical bases of probability and statistical analysis may be found in texts such as Cramér [63] and Feller [76]; associated techniques and applications are dealt with by Fisher [78], Hoel [113], Mood [162], and others.

PROBLEMS

Section 1.2

1. Determine A_0, A_1, and A_2 such that the function $y(x) = A_0 + A_1x + A_2x^2$ and the function $f(x) = 1/(1 + x)$ have each of the following sets of properties in common:

(a) $f(0), f(\frac{1}{2}), f(1)$.

(b) $f(0), f'(0), f''(0)$.

(c) $f(\frac{1}{2}), f'(\frac{1}{2}), f''(\frac{1}{2})$.

(d) $f'(0), f(\frac{1}{2}), f'(1)$.

(e) $\int_0^1 f(x)\, dx, \int_0^1 x f(x)\, dx, \int_0^1 x^2 f(x)\, dx$.

2. Calculate three-place values of the function $f(x) = 1/(1 + x)$ and of each of the parabolic approximations obtained in Prob. 1 at an interval of 0.1 over $(0,1)$, and plot curves representing the errors in each approximation on a common graph.

3. Determine that member $y(x)$ of the set of all linear functions which best approximates the function $f(x) = x^2$ over $(0,1)$ in the sense that each of the following quantities is minimized:

† The term *polynomial* is to be used in its common restricted sense, to denote an expression of the form $a_0x^n + a_1x^{n-1} + \cdots + a_n$, where n is a nonnegative integer and the a's are constants.

(a) $\int_0^1 [f(x) - y(x)]^2 \, dx.$

(b) $[f(0) - y(0)]^2 + [f(\tfrac{1}{2}) - y(\tfrac{1}{2})]^2 + [f(1) - y(1)]^2.$

(c) $\max_{0 \le x \le 1} |f(x) - y(x)|.$

(d) $\int_0^1 x(1 - x)[f(x) - y(x)]^2 \, dx.$

4. Determine c_1, c_2, and c_3 in such a way that the formula

$$\int_{-1}^1 w(x)f(x) \, dx = c_1 f(-1) + c_2 f(0) + c_3 f(1)$$

yields an exact result when $f(x)$ is 1, x, x^2, and x^3, and hence also when $f(x)$ is any linear combination of those functions, for each of the following weighting functions:

(a) $w(x) = 1$; (b) $w(x) = \sqrt{1 - x^2}$; (c) $w(x) = \dfrac{1}{\sqrt{1 - x^2}}.$

Section 1.3

5. Let $S = u_0 + u_1 + \cdots + u_k + R_k$ for $k = 0, 1, \ldots$. By noticing that

$$u_n + R_n = R_{n-1}, \qquad u_{n+1} + R_{n+1} = R_n,$$

deduce that *if R_n and R_{n-1} have opposite signs, then R_n is smaller than u_n in magnitude, and is of opposite sign, whereas if also R_n and R_{n+1} have opposite signs, then R_n is also smaller than u_{n+1} in magnitude, and is of the same sign.* (This is often known as *Steffensen's error test.*)

6. Let $S_k = v_0 - v_1 + v_2 - \cdots + (-1)^{k-1}v_{k-1}$ for $k = 1, \ldots$, where all v's are positive. Assume also that $v_{k+1} < v_k$ for all k, and that $v_k \to 0$ as $k \to \infty$. Show that S_{2k} is positive and increasing with k, but that S_{2k} cannot exceed v_0. Hence deduce that S_{2k} tends to a limit as $k \to \infty$. Show also that S_{2k+1} tends to the same limit, and hence that the series

$$\sum_{k=0}^{\infty} (-1)^k v_k$$

then converges to a limit S. Finally, show that the truncation error R_k is of the same sign as the first neglected term and is smaller than that term in magnitude. (Notice that any finite number of terms not satisfying the stated requirements may be added to the series initially, without impairing its convergence.)

7. Suppose that the alternating series

$$S = v_0 - v_1 + v_2 - \cdots \equiv \sum_{k=0}^{\infty} (-1)^k v_k$$

converges. Show that the series

$$\tfrac{1}{2}v_0 + \tfrac{1}{2}(v_0 - v_1) - \tfrac{1}{2}(v_1 - v_2) + \cdots = \tfrac{1}{2}v_0 + \tfrac{1}{2}\sum_{k=0}^{\infty} (-1)^k (v_k - v_{k+1})$$

converges to the same sum.

8. Use the transformation of Prob. 7 repeatedly to show that

$$S \equiv 1 - \tfrac{1}{2} + \tfrac{1}{3} - \tfrac{1}{4} + \cdots = \sum_{k=0}^{\infty} \frac{(-1)^k}{k+1}$$

$$= \tfrac{1}{2} + \tfrac{1}{2} \sum_{k=0}^{\infty} \frac{(-1)^k}{(k+1)(k+2)} = \tfrac{5}{8} + \tfrac{1}{2} \sum_{k=0}^{\infty} \frac{(-1)^k}{(k+1)(k+2)(k+3)}$$

$$= \tfrac{2}{3} + \tfrac{3}{4} \sum_{k=0}^{\infty} \frac{(-1)^k}{(k+1)(k+2)(k+3)(k+4)} = \cdots.$$

Show that the retention of five terms in the last sum given ensures that $0.69306 < S < 0.69330$ or that $S \approx 0.69318$ with a maximum error of ± 12 units in the place of the fifth digit. About how many terms of the original series would be needed to ensure this accuracy? (The true value is $S = \log 2 \doteq 0.69315$.)

9. If $f(x)$ is a positive decreasing function of x, and if $\int_K^\infty f(x)\,dx$ exists for some K, show that $\sum_1^\infty f(k)$ converges. Show also that

$$\int_K^\infty f(x)\,dx < \sum_{k=K}^\infty f(k) < \int_{K-1}^\infty f(x)\,dx.$$

How many terms of the series

$$\sum_{k=1}^\infty \frac{1}{k^2+1}$$

would be required to determine the sum to four digits?

10. By making appropriate use of the known results

$$\sum_{k=1}^\infty \frac{1}{k^2} = \frac{\pi^2}{6}, \qquad \sum_{k=1}^\infty \frac{1}{k^4} = \frac{\pi^4}{90}, \qquad \sum_{k=1}^\infty \frac{1}{k^6} = \frac{\pi^6}{945},$$

evaluate the sum

$$\sum_{k=1}^\infty \frac{1}{k^2+1} \equiv \sum_{k=1}^\infty \left[\frac{1}{k^2} - \frac{1}{k^2(k^2+1)} \right] \equiv \cdots$$

correctly to four digits.

11. The error function is defined by the relation

$$\operatorname{erf} x = \frac{2}{\sqrt{\pi}} \int_0^x e^{-t^2}\,dt.$$

It is known that $\operatorname{erf} x \to 1$ as $x \to \infty$. With the definitions

$$F_1(x) = \int_0^x e^{-t^2}\,dt, \qquad F_2(x) = \int_x^\infty e^{-t^2}\,dt,$$

there follows

$$\operatorname{erf} x = \frac{2}{\sqrt{\pi}} F_1(x) = 1 - \frac{2}{\sqrt{\pi}} F_2(x).$$

Show that

$$F_1(x) = \sum_{k=0}^{\infty} \frac{(-1)^k x^{2k+1}}{(2k+1)k!},$$

where the series converges for all x. About how many terms would be required for five-digit accuracy when $x = 0.2$, 1, and 2?

12. With the notation of Prob. 11, make use of repeated integration by parts to show that

$$e^{x^2}F_1(x) = x + \frac{2}{3}x^3 + \frac{2}{3}\cdot\frac{2}{5}x^5 + \cdots + \left(\frac{2}{3}\cdot\frac{2}{5}\cdots\frac{2}{2n-1}\right)x^{2n-1}$$
$$+ \left(\frac{2}{3}\cdot\frac{2}{5}\cdots\frac{2}{2n-1}\right)\cdot 2\int_0^x e^{x^2-t^2}t^{2n}\,dt,$$

and hence that

$$F_1(x) = e^{-x^2}\left[x + \frac{2}{3}x^3 + \frac{2}{3}\cdot\frac{2}{5}x^5 + \cdots + \left(\frac{2}{3}\cdot\frac{2}{5}\cdots\frac{2}{2n-1}\right)x^{2x-1}\right] + E_n(x),$$

where
$$E_n(x) = \left(\frac{2}{1}\cdot\frac{2}{3}\cdot\frac{2}{5}\cdots\frac{2}{2n-1}\right)\int_0^x e^{-t^2}t^{2n}\,dt.$$

Show also that $E_n(x)$ is smaller in magnitude than the term following the last one retained in the coefficient of e^{-x^2}, and is of the same sign, that the *relative* error cannot exceed $(2x)^{2n}n!/(2n)!$, and that the infinite series obtained when $n \to \infty$ converges for all x.

13. With the notation of Prob. 11, show that

$$e^{x^2}F_2(x) = \int_x^{\infty} (te^{x^2-t^2})\frac{dt}{t}$$

and, after successive integrations by parts (each followed by multiplication and division by t in the integrand), deduce that

$$e^{x^2}F_2(x) = \frac{1}{2}\left[\frac{1}{x} - \frac{1}{2}\frac{1}{x^3} + \frac{1}{2}\cdot\frac{3}{2}\frac{1}{x^5} - \cdots + (-1)^n\left(\frac{1}{2}\cdot\frac{3}{2}\cdots\frac{2n-1}{2}\right)\frac{1}{x^{2n+1}}\right.$$
$$\left.+ (-1)^{n+1}\left(\frac{1}{2}\cdot\frac{3}{2}\cdots\frac{2n+1}{2}\right)\cdot 2\int_x^{\infty} e^{x^2-t^2}\frac{dt}{t^{2n+2}}\right]$$

and hence that

$$\operatorname{erf} x = 1 - \frac{e^{-x^2}}{\sqrt{\pi}}\left[\frac{1}{x} - \frac{1}{2}\frac{1}{x^3} + \frac{1}{2}\cdot\frac{3}{2}\frac{1}{x^5} - \cdots + (-1)^n\left(\frac{1}{2}\cdot\frac{3}{2}\cdots\frac{2n-1}{2}\right)\frac{1}{x^{2n+1}}\right]$$
$$+ E_n(x),$$

where
$$E_n(x) = (-1)^n\frac{2}{\sqrt{\pi}}\left(\frac{1}{2}\cdot\frac{3}{2}\cdots\frac{2n+1}{2}\right)\int_x^{\infty} e^{-t^2}\frac{dt}{t^{2n+2}}.$$

Show also that the series is divergent but asymptotic (in the strict sense) and that the truncation error due to neglect of $E_n(x)$ is smaller than the last term retained and of opposite sign. Obtain the best possible approximation when $x = 2$, and give numerical bounds on the error.

14. By making use of the known expansions of e^x, $\cos x$, $\sin x$, and $(1 - x)^{\frac{1}{2}}$ in powers of x, obtain the coefficients of powers of x through the fourth in the corresponding expansions of the following functions:

(a) $e^x \cos x$; (b) $\dfrac{e^x}{\cos x}$; (c) $(\cos x)^{\frac{1}{2}}$; (d) $e^{\sin x}$.

15. Under the assumption that a given series

$$y = a_0 + a_1 x + a_2 x^2 + \cdots \qquad (a_1 \neq 0)$$

converges for sufficiently small values of x, and that x can be expanded in a series of powers of $(y - a_0)/a_1$ which converges for y sufficiently near to a_0, in the form

$$x = u + A_2 u^2 + A_3 u^3 + \cdots \qquad \left(u = \frac{y - a_0}{a_1} \right),$$

show that the leading coefficients in the inverted series can be determined from the relations

$$a_1 A_2 = -a_2,$$
$$a_1 A_3 = -2a_2 A_2 - a_3,$$
$$a_1 A_4 = -a_2(A_2^2 + 2A_3) - 3a_3 A_2 - a_4,$$
$$\cdots \cdots \cdots \cdots \cdots \cdots \cdots \cdots \cdots$$

Show also that the first n terms of the inverted series can be obtained by a sequence of $n - 1$ substitutions in the right-hand member of the relation

$$x = u - \frac{a_2}{a_1} x^2 - \frac{a_3}{a_1} x^3 - \cdots,$$

starting with $x^{(1)} = u$, and retaining only powers of u not exceeding the $(r + 1)$th in the rth substitution. Illustrate both methods in obtaining the first four terms in the result of inverting the series $e^x = 1 + x + \frac{1}{2}x^2 + \cdots$.

16. It is required to determine the symmetrically placed pair of nonzero roots of the equation

$$\sinh x = cx,$$

where c is a real constant such that $c > 1$. Show that, with the abbreviations $s = 6(c - 1)$, $t = x^2$, the problem can be considered as that of inverting the series

$$s = t + \frac{3!}{5!} t^2 + \frac{3!}{7!} t^3 + \frac{3!}{9!} t^4 + \cdots,$$

and deduce the expansion

$$x^2 = s - \frac{1}{20}s^2 + \frac{2}{525}s^3 - \frac{13}{37800}s^4 + \cdots.$$

Sections 1.4, 1.5

17. Show that the number $(2.46)^{.4}$ is known within less than one unit in the place of its *fifth* significant digit if 2.46 is known only to be correctly rounded to three digits.

18. Using only five-place tables of $\sin x$ and $\cos x$, determine $\cos 0.10 - \cos 0.12$ and $\tan 0.12 - \tan 0.10$ to four significant figures.

19. Values of $\cos x$ are calculated from a five-place table of $\sin x$, by use of the formula $\cos x = (1 - \sin^2 x)^{\frac{1}{2}}$. What can be said about the accuracy of the calculated values?

20. If all coefficients in the definition

$$f(x) = \frac{5.03241x + 0.11095}{0.75995x + 0.014915}$$

are rounded numbers, to how many significant figures is $f(x)$ determinate when x is known only to round to 3.26?

21. If $f(x) = (\sinh x - \sin x)/(\cosh x - \cos x)$, determine $f(0.1)$ to 10 significant figures.

22. Determine bounds on the degree of indeterminancy of each of the quantities $\tan^{-1} 4.017216$, $\sin^{-1} 0.986423$, $\cos 18.4178$, and $\cos 18417.8$, under the assumption that the arguments are rounded values. To how many *significant figures* are the last two quantities determinate?

Section 1.6

23. If $f_1(x)$ and $f_2(x)$ are the frequency functions of ϵ_1 and ϵ_2, respectively, where ϵ_1 and ϵ_2 are independent random variables, show that the distribution function of $\epsilon_1 + \epsilon_2$ is

$$\int \int_{s+t<x} f_1(s)f_2(t) \, ds \, dt = \int_{-\infty}^{x} \left[\int_{-\infty}^{\infty} f_1(u - t)f_2(t) \, dt \right] du,$$

and hence that the frequency function of $\epsilon_1 + \epsilon_2$ is

$$\int_{-\infty}^{\infty} f_1(x - t)f_2(t) \, dt.$$

24. Use the result of Prob. 23 to show that, if ϵ_1 and ϵ_2 are independent and are normally distributed about zero means, with standard deviations σ_1 and σ_2, then $\epsilon_1 + \epsilon_2$ is also normally distributed about a zero mean, with standard deviation $\sigma = (\sigma_1^2 + \sigma_2^2)^{\frac{1}{2}}$. [Determine constants λ_1, λ_2, and α such that

$$\frac{(x - t)^2}{\sigma_1^2} + \frac{t^2}{\sigma_2^2} \equiv \frac{x^2}{\lambda_1^2} + \frac{(t - \alpha x)^2}{\lambda_2^2}$$

and set $t - \alpha x = \sqrt{2}\, \lambda_2 v$, making use of the fact that

$$\int_{-\infty}^{\infty} e^{-v^2} \, dv = \sqrt{\pi},$$

in evaluating the integral defining the required frequency function.]

25. Suppose that $\epsilon_1, \epsilon_2, \ldots$ are independent random variables with a common *uniform* frequency function

$$f(x) = \begin{cases} 1 & (-\tfrac{1}{2} \leq x \leq \tfrac{1}{2}), \\ 0 & (\text{otherwise}), \end{cases}$$

and denote the frequency function of $\epsilon_1 + \epsilon_2 + \cdots + \epsilon_n$ by $f_n(x)$. Use the result of Prob. 23 to show that

$$f_{n+1}(x) = \int_{-\infty}^{\infty} f_1(x - t)f_n(t) \, dt = \int_{x-\frac{1}{2}}^{x+\frac{1}{2}} f_n(t) \, dt.$$

In particular, deduce that $f_2(x)$ is a triangular function,

$$f_2(x) = \begin{cases} 1 + x & (-1 \leq x \leq 0), \\ 1 - x & (0 \leq x \leq 1), \\ 0 & (\text{otherwise}), \end{cases}$$

and that $f_3(x)$ is defined by the relations

$$f_3(x) = \begin{cases} \tfrac{1}{2}(\tfrac{3}{2} + x)^2 & (-\tfrac{3}{2} \leq x \leq -\tfrac{1}{2}), \\ \tfrac{3}{4} - x^2 & (-\tfrac{1}{2} \leq x \leq \tfrac{1}{2}), \\ \tfrac{1}{2}(\tfrac{3}{2} - x)^2 & (\tfrac{1}{2} \leq x \leq \tfrac{3}{2}), \\ 0 & (\text{otherwise}). \end{cases}$$

Finally, plot each of the functions f_1, f_2, and f_3, and compare it graphically with the frequency function corresponding to the *normal* distribution which has the same standard deviation $\sigma_n = \sqrt{n/12}$ ($n = 1, 2, 3$).

26. If the coefficients of the polynomial

$$f(x) = \sum_{k=0}^{n} a_k x^k$$

are independently subject to random error distributions with mean value zero and with a common RMS value σ_{RMS}, whereas x is subject to an error distribution with RMS value η_{RMS}, show that the corresponding RMS error ϵ_{RMS} in $f(x)$ is given approximately by

$$\epsilon_{\text{RMS}}^2 = \frac{x^{2n+2} - 1}{x^2 - 1} \sigma_{\text{RMS}}^2 + [f'(x)]^2 \eta_{\text{RMS}}^2.$$

27. Use the result of Prob. 26 to estimate the RMS error in the calculated value of

$$f(x) = 1.47x^3 - 2.48x^2 + 2.21x - 1.65$$

when $x = 2.03$, under the assumption that the values of x and the coefficients are known only to be rounded correctly to the three digits given. Within what limits is $f(x)$ actually determinate in this case? Within what limits does its value lie with probability of about 0.9?

28. If $x_1, x_2, \ldots, x_r$ are each rounded to n decimal places, show that the corresponding RMS error in $f(x_1, x_2, \ldots, x_r)$ is approximated by

$$\epsilon_{\text{RMS}} \approx (0.29 \times 10^{-n}) \left[\sum_{k=1}^{r} \left(\frac{\partial f}{\partial x_k} \right)^2 \right]^{\frac{1}{2}}.$$

Show also that if

$$\left[\sum_{k=1}^{r} \left(\frac{\partial f}{\partial x_k} \right)^2 \right]^{\frac{1}{2}} < 2K,$$

and if r is not too small (say $r > 3$), then the odds are about 10 to 1 that the error in f does not exceed K units in the nth decimal place.

Section 1.7†

29. If $(a,b) = (-1,1)$, show that the conclusions of Theorems 1 and 2 do not hold for $f(x) = 1/x$, that those of Theorems 3 and 4 do not hold for $f(x) = 1 - x^{\frac{2}{3}}$, and that those of Theorems 7 and 8 do not hold for $f(x) = x$ and $g(x) = x^3$. Account for each of these situations.

30. Assuming the fact that

$$\int_0^{\infty} \frac{\sin t}{t} \, dt = \frac{\pi}{2},$$

show that

$$\int_0^{\infty} \frac{\sin xs}{s} \, ds = \begin{cases} -\dfrac{\pi}{2} & (x < 0), \\ 0 & (x = 0), \\ \dfrac{\pi}{2} & (x > 0). \end{cases}$$

† The truth of the theorems stated in §1.7 may be assumed in the following problems.

Thus show that the conclusions of Theorems 9 and 10 do not hold for

$$F(x,s) = \frac{\sin xs}{s}$$

with $(a,b) = (0, \infty)$.

31. If $f(x)$ vanishes at $n + 1$ distinct points in the interval $a \leqq x \leqq b$, and if $f^{(n)}(x)$ is continuous for $a \leqq x \leqq b$, show that $f^{(n)}(x)$ vanishes at least once inside (a,b).

32. If $a_r > 0$ for $r = 1, 2, \ldots, n$, show that

$$a_0 \sin t + a_1 \sin 2t + \cdots + a_n \sin nt = \sin \theta t \sum_{r=1}^{n} a_r$$

for some θ such that $1 < \theta < n$.

33. Show that

$$\int_x^{\infty} \frac{dt}{t^4 + 1} < \frac{1}{3x^3} \qquad (x > 0)$$

and that

$$\int_0^x t^2 e^{-t^2} \frac{dt}{t^3 + 1} < \frac{1}{3} \log (1 + x^3) < \frac{1}{3} x^3 \qquad (x > 0).$$

34. Show that

$$\int_{-1}^{1} (1 - x^2)f(x) \, dx = \tfrac{4}{3} f(\xi)$$

for some ξ in $(-1,1)$, if $f(x)$ is continuous in that interval. Also determine ξ when $f(x) = x^2$.

35. If $F(k)$ is defined by the integral

$$F(k) = \int_0^1 \frac{x(x - 1)(x - 2) \cdots (x - k + 1)}{k!} \, dx \qquad (k \geqq 2),$$

use the second law of the mean to show that

$$F(k) = (-1)^{k+1} \frac{(k - 1 - \xi)(k - 2 - \xi) \cdots (2 - \xi)}{6k!} \qquad (0 < \xi < 1),$$

and deduce that

$$\frac{1}{6k(k - 1)} < (-1)^{k+1}F(k) < \frac{1}{6k}.$$

36. If $g(x)$ is continuous and $f(x)$ possesses a continuous derivative, and if

$$\phi(x) = \int_0^x f(x - t)g(t) \, dt,$$

obtain an expression for $d\phi/dx$. By making an appropriate change of variables in the definition of $\phi(x)$, obtain an alternative expression for $d\phi/dx$ when the hypotheses regarding f and g are interchanged.

37. If $y'' = 2 \sin y + 12x^2$ and $y(0) = y'(0) = 0$, show that

$$y(x) = x^4 + 2 \int_0^x (x - s) \sin y(s) \, ds,$$

and deduce that $y(x)$ lies between $x^4 - x^2$ and $x^4 + x^2$.

38. Determine the first three coefficients in the Bürmann series :

$$\sin x = c_1(e^x - 1) + c_2(e^x - 1)^2 + c_3(e^x - 1)^3 + \cdots$$

and use the result to determine approximately the value of $\sin x$ when $e^x = 1.012$.

39. If $y = a_0 + a_1 x + a_2 x^2 + \cdots$ and if x can be expanded in a series of powers of $y - a_0$ for y near a_0, use the Bürmann expansion to show that the leading coefficients in the expansion

$$x = c_1(y - a_0) + c_2(y - a_0)^2 + c_3(y - a_0)^3 + \cdots$$

are given by

$$c_1 = \frac{1}{a_1}, \qquad c_2 = -\frac{a_2}{a_1^3}, \qquad c_3 = \frac{2a_2^2 - a_1 a_3}{a_1^5},$$

and verify that the results agree with those of Prob. 15.

CHAPTER 2

INTERPOLATION WITH DIVIDED DIFFERENCES

2.1. Introduction. Any one who has had occasion to consult tables of mathematical functions is familiar with the method of *linear interpolation* and probably has encountered situations in which this method of "reading between the lines of the table" has appeared to be unreliable. If more reliable interpolates are desired, it is clearly necessary to make use of more information than that consisting merely of tabulated values (*ordinates*) of a function, corresponding to two successive abscissas. Whereas that additional information could consist, for example, of known values of certain *derivatives* of the function at those two points, it is supposed in most of what follows (an exception is found in §8.2) that the interpolation process is to be based only on tabulated values of the function itself, with any further available information reserved for use in estimating the error involved.

There exist a number of interpolation formulas which have this property, most of which possess certain advantages in certain situations, but no one of which is preferable to all others in all respects. Whereas certain of these formulas are expressed explicitly in terms of all the ordinates on which they depend (Chap. 3), most of them involve only one or two of the ordinates explicitly and express their dependence upon other ordinates only in terms of differences of ordinates and successive differences of differences.

In the general case, when the abscissas are not necessarily equally spaced, the use of so-called *divided differences* is convenient. The principal purpose of this chapter is to define such differences and investigate certain of their properties, to obtain a basic interpolation formula due to Newton (§2.5), from which most of the other formulas of the type described can be deduced, and to obtain expressions for the error term (§2.6). Related methods of iterated linear interpolation (§2.7) and inverse interpolation (§2.8) are also treated.

2.2. Linear Interpolation. The assumption that a function $f(x)$ is approximately *linear*, in a certain range, is equivalent to the assumption that the ratio

$$\frac{f(x_1) - f(x_0)}{x_1 - x_0} \qquad (2.2.1)$$

is approximately independent of x_0 and x_1 in that range. This ratio is called the *first divided difference* of $f(x)$, relative to x_0 and x_1, and may be designated by $f[x_0,x_1]$:†

$$f[x_0,x_1] \equiv \frac{f(x_1) - f(x_0)}{x_1 - x_0}. \qquad (2.2.2)$$

It is clear that $f[x_1,x_0] = f[x_0,x_1]$.

Thus the linear approximation may be expressed in the form

$$f[x_0,x] \approx f[x_0,x_1], \qquad (2.2.3)$$

which leads to the interpolation formula

$$f(x) \approx f(x_0) + (x - x_0)f[x_0,x_1] \qquad (2.2.4)$$

or

$$f(x) \approx f(x_0) + \frac{x - x_0}{x_1 - x_0} [f(x_1) - f(x_0)] \qquad (2.2.4')$$

or, equivalently, to the formula

$$f(x) \approx \frac{1}{x_1 - x_0} [(x_1 - x)f(x_0) - (x_0 - x)f(x_1)], \qquad (2.2.4'')$$

which can also be expressed in the convenient *determinantal* form

$$f(x) \approx \frac{1}{x_1 - x_0} \begin{vmatrix} f(x_0) & x_0 - x \\ f(x_1) & x_1 - x \end{vmatrix}. \qquad (2.2.5)$$

It may be noticed that (2.2.4) involves one ordinate and a divided difference, (2.2.4′) one ordinate and an ordinary difference, and (2.2.4″) involves the two ordinates directly. The last form (2.2.5) is particularly well adapted to machine computation, since its evaluation involves the continuous operation of the formation of a *cross product* followed by a division.

It is convenient to designate the linear function defined by the right-hand member of (2.2.4) by $y_{0,1}(x)$, the subscripts corresponding to the ordinates used in its formation. For symmetry of notation, it is desirable to write also

$$y_0(x) \equiv f[x_0] \equiv f(x_0), \qquad (2.2.6)$$

so that $f[x_0]$ is defined as the *zeroth* divided difference relative to x_0 and is merely the value of $f(x)$ at $x = x_0$, and $y_0(x)$ is the approximating polynomial of degree *zero* which agrees with $f(x)$ at $x = x_0$. With this notation, Eqs. (2.2.4) and (2.2.5) become

$$f(x) \approx y_{0,1}(x) \equiv f[x_0] + (x - x_0)f[x_0,x_1] \qquad (2.2.7)$$

and

$$y_{0,1}(x) = \frac{1}{x_1 - x_0} \begin{vmatrix} y_0(x) & x_0 - x \\ y_1(x) & x_1 - x \end{vmatrix}. \qquad (2.2.8)$$

† Various other notations are used, such as $[x_0,x_1]$, $f(x_0,x_1)$, and (x_0,x_1).

These forms are given here principally to correspond to more general forms to be obtained in following sections.

We see that the approximation $f(x) \approx y_{0,1}(x)$ is exact for *all* values of x if $f(x)$ is indeed a linear function, of the form $f(x) = A_0 + A_1 x$, and, further, that the approximation is exact at the points $x = x_0$ and x_1 for any function $f(x)$.

As a numerical example, the linear interpolation of sinh x for $\bar{x} = 0.23$, from tabulated five-place values for $x_0 = 0.20$ and $x_1 = 0.30$, may be arranged as follows:

x_i	$f(x_i)$	$x_i - \bar{x}$
0.20	0.20134	−0.03
0.30	0.30452	0.07

$$f(0.23) \approx \frac{(0.07)(0.20134) - (-0.03)(0.30452)}{0.10} = 0.23229.$$

Since the true five-place value is 0.23203, it is seen that linear interpolation here affords only three-place accuracy.

It is useful to notice that, since a linear interpolation merely effects a certain *weighted average* of the two ordinates involved, the result of an interpolation involving two ordinates such as 13.6340 and 13.6393 can be considered as the sum of 13.6300 and the result of effecting the same interpolation on 40 and 93, with this result added to 13.6300 in units of its last place.

Further, since the numerator and denominator of the ratio (2.2.5) are homogeneous in the abscissas, the entries x_i and $x_i - \bar{x}$ in the computational array may be multiplied by any convenient common factor. In particular, the x's in the preceding table could be replaced by 20 and 30, and the entries in the last column correspondingly by −3 and 7. This will be done in subsequent examples involving linear interpolation.

Unless $f(x)$ is linear, the secant slope $f[x_0,x_1]$ will depend upon the abscissas x_0 and x_1. However, if $f(x)$ were a second-degree polynomial, the secant-slope function $f[x_1,x]$ would itself be a linear function of x, for fixed x_1. That is, the ratio

$$\frac{f[x_1,x_2] - f[x_0,x_1]}{x_2 - x_0}$$

would be independent of x_0, x_1, and x_2. This ratio is called the *second divided difference*, relative to those three abscissas, and is designated here by $f[x_0,x_1,x_2]$:

$$f[x_0,x_1,x_2] \equiv \frac{f[x_1,x_2] - f[x_0,x_1]}{x_2 - x_0}. \qquad (2.2.9)$$

In particular, since $f[x_1,x_0,x] = f[x_0,x_1,x]$ (see §2.3), the difference between the two members of (2.2.3) can be expressed as

$$f[x_0,x] - f[x_0,x_1] = f[x_0,x] - f[x_1,x_0] = (x - x_1)f[x_0,x_1,x],$$

so that the *approximation* (2.2.4) can be replaced by the *identity*

$$f(x) = f[x_0] + (x - x_0)f[x_0,x_1] + (x - x_0)(x - x_1)f[x_0,x_1,x]. \qquad (2.2.10)$$

Thus the *error* committed in (2.2.7), by replacing $f(x)$ by $y_{0,1}(x)$, is given by

$$E(x) \equiv f(x) - y_{0,1}(x) = (x - x_0)(x - x_1)f[x_0,x_1,x]. \qquad (2.2.11)$$

Whereas knowledge of $f[x_0,x_1,x]$ is tantamount to knowledge of the exact interpolant $f(x)$, the form (2.2.11) of the error is a special case of a more general form to be obtained, which (as will be shown) is frequently useful in obtaining an *estimate* of the error in an actual calculation. For any *linear* function $f(x)$, the error term will indeed vanish identically, as may be verified directly.

Before generalizing the result just obtained, it is desirable to define divided differences of all orders, and to investigate certain of their properties.

2.3. Divided Differences. Divided differences of orders $0, 1, 2, \ldots ,$ k are defined iteratively by the relations

$$f[x_0] = f(x_0), \qquad f[x_0,x_1] = \frac{f[x_1] - f[x_0]}{x_1 - x_0}, \qquad \ldots ,$$

$$f[x_0, \ldots , x_k] = \frac{f[x_1, \ldots ,x_k] - f[x_0, \ldots ,x_{k-1}]}{x_k - x_0}. \qquad (2.3.1)$$

We notice that the first $k - 1$ arguments in the first term of the numerator are the same as the last $k - 1$ arguments in the second term and that the denominator is the difference between those arguments which are not in common to the two terms. It is clear from the definition that $f[x_0, \ldots ,x_k]$ is a linear combination of the $k + 1$ ordinates $f(x_0), \ldots ,$ $f(x_k)$, with the coefficients depending upon the corresponding $k + 1$ abscissas.

When $k = 1$, the divided difference obviously is a symmetric function of its arguments, that is, $f[x_1,x_0] = f[x_0,x_1]$. It is shown next that the same statement applies to divided differences of all orders. In order to establish this fact directly in the case of $k = 2$, we may write

$$f[x_0,x_1,x_2] = \frac{f[x_1,x_2] - f[x_0,x_1]}{x_2 - x_0} = \frac{1}{x_2 - x_0}\left[\frac{f(x_2) - f(x_1)}{x_2 - x_1} - \frac{f(x_1) - f(x_0)}{x_1 - x_0}\right]$$

and the result can be put in the symmetric form

$$f[x_0,x_1,x_2] = \frac{f(x_0)}{(x_0 - x_1)(x_0 - x_2)}$$
$$+ \frac{f(x_1)}{(x_1 - x_0)(x_1 - x_2)} + \frac{f(x_2)}{(x_2 - x_0)(x_2 - x_1)}.$$

This result suggests the truth of the more general relation

$$f[x_0, \ldots ,x_k] = \frac{f(x_0)}{(x_0 - x_1) \cdots (x_0 - x_k)} + \frac{f(x_1)}{(x_1 - x_0) \cdots (x_1 - x_k)}$$
$$+ \cdots + \frac{f(x_k)}{(x_k - x_0) \cdots (x_k - x_{k-1})} \quad (2.3.2)$$

for any positive integer k, so that the coefficient of $f(x_i)$ is

$$\alpha_i^{(k)} = \frac{1}{(x_i - x_0) \cdots (x_i - x_k)} \quad (i = 0, 1, \ldots , k), \quad (2.3.3)$$

where the zero factor $(x_i - x_i)$ is to be omitted in the denominator.

In order to establish this conjecture by induction, suppose that it has been proved for $k = r$. If we recall the definition

$$f[x_0, \ldots ,x_{r+1}] = \frac{1}{x_{r+1} - x_0} \{f[x_1, \ldots ,x_{r+1}] - f[x_0, \ldots ,x_r]\} \quad (2.3.4)$$

it then follows that, for $i = 1, 2, \ldots , r$, the coefficient of $f(x_i)$ in the right-hand member is given by

$$\frac{1}{x_{r+1} - x_0} \left[\frac{1}{(x_i - x_1) \cdots (x_i - x_{r+1})} - \frac{1}{(x_i - x_0) \cdots (x_i - x_r)} \right]$$
$$= \frac{1}{(x_i - x_0) \cdots (x_i - x_{r+1})} = \alpha_i^{(r+1)}, \quad (2.3.5)$$

in accordance with (2.3.3) with $k = r + 1$. When $i = 0$ or $r + 1$, only one of the terms in the right-hand member of (2.3.4) involves the ordinate $f(x_i)$, and the respective coefficient also is easily seen to be in accordance with (2.3.3) with $k = r + 1$. Thus, if (2.3.2) is valid for $k = r$, it is valid also for $k = r + 1$. Since it has been established for $k = 1$ (and $k = 2$), it is therefore valid for any positive integer k, as was to be shown.

It follows, from the symmetry of (2.3.2), that the order of the arguments is irrelevant. Hence $f[x_0, \ldots ,x_k]$ can be expressed as the difference between two divided differences of order $k - 1$, having any $k - 1$ of their k arguments in common, divided by the difference between those arguments which are *not* in common. For example, there follows

$$f[x_0,x_1,x_2,x_3] = \frac{f[x_1,x_2,x_3] - f[x_0,x_1,x_2]}{x_3 - x_0}$$
$$= \frac{f[x_0,x_2,x_3] - f[x_1,x_2,x_3]}{x_0 - x_1} = \cdots .$$

In those cases when two or more arguments in a divided difference become coincident, recourse must be had to appropriate limiting processes. Thus, for example, if we set $x_1 = x + \epsilon$, there follows

$$f[x_1,x] \equiv f[x + \epsilon, x] = \frac{f(x + \epsilon) - f(x)}{\epsilon}$$

and, in the limit when $\epsilon \to 0$, we have

$$f[x,x] = f'(x), \qquad (2.3.6)$$

if $f(x)$ is differentiable. A similar argument shows that

$$\frac{d}{dx} f[x_0, \ \ldots \ ,x_k,x] = f[x_0, \ \ldots \ ,x_k,x,x], \qquad (2.3.7)$$

if $x_0, \ \ldots \ , x_k$ are constants. If $u_1, u_2, \ \ldots \ , u_n$ are differentiable functions of x, there follows also

$$\frac{d}{dx} f[x_0, \ \ldots \ ,x_k,u_1, \ \ldots \ ,u_n] = \sum_{\nu = 1}^{n} f[x_0, \ \ldots \ ,x_k,u_1, \ \ldots \ ,u_n,u_\nu] \frac{du_\nu}{dx}$$

and hence, by taking $u_1 = \cdots = u_n = x$, we may deduce that

$$\frac{d}{dx} f[x_0, \ \ldots \ ,x_k,\overset{n\ times}{x, \ \ldots \ ,x}] = nf[x_0, \ \ldots \ ,x_k,\overset{n+1\ times}{x, \ \ldots \ ,x}]. \quad (2.3.8)$$

Finally, by successive differentiation of (2.3.7) combined with the use of (2.3.8) at each step, we may establish the additional useful formula

$$\frac{d^r}{dx^r} f[x_0, \ \ldots \ ,x_k,x] = r!f[x_0, \ \ldots \ ,x_k,\overset{r+1\ times}{x, \ \ldots \ ,x}]. \qquad (2.3.9)$$

In particular, we may deduce that *the result of allowing $r + 1$ arguments of a divided difference to become coincident is finite if the rth derivative of $f(x)$ is finite at the point of confluence.*

It is seen that $f[x_0, \ \ldots \ ,x_k,x]$ is continuous at $x = \bar{x}$ if $\bar{x}$ is not identified with $x_0, x_1, \ \ldots \ $, or x_k, and if $f(x)$ is continuous at $\bar{x}$. If $f'(x)$ does not exist at x_0, the function $f[x_0, \ \ldots \ ,x_k,x]$ generally will not tend to a finite limit as $x \to x_0$. Thus, for example, if $f(x) = \sqrt{x}$, there follows $f[0,x] = 1/\sqrt{x}$, and this function naturally becomes infinite as $x \to 0$. However, the product $(x - x_0)f[x_0, \ \ldots \ ,x_k,x]$ is identical with

$$f[x,x_1, \ \ldots \ ,x_k] - f[x_0,x_1, \ \ldots \ ,x_k]$$

and, since the function $f[x,x_1, \ \ldots \ ,x_k]$ is continuous at x_0 if $f(x)$ is continuous there, it follows that the product will tend to zero at x_0 if $f(x)$ is continuous at x_0. Thus we may deduce that *the product $(x - x_0) \cdots (x - x_k)f[x_0, \ \ldots \ ,x_k,x]$ tends to zero as x approaches any one of the $k + 1$ distinct points $x_0, \ \ldots \ , x_k$ if $f(x)$ is continuous at that point.*

It may be expected that *the kth divided difference of a polynomial of degree n is a polynomial of degree $n - k$ if $k \leqq n$, and is identically zero if $k > n$.* The proof follows easily from the fact that the first divided difference of x^m,

$$\frac{x^m - x_0^m}{x - x_0} = x^{m-1} + x_0 x^{m-2} + \cdots,$$

is a polynomial of degree $m - 1$ in x, when m is a positive integer.

2.4. Second-order Interpolation. If the accuracy afforded by a linear interpolation is inadequate, a generally more accurate result may be based upon the supposition that $f(x)$ may be approximated by a polynomial of *second* degree near the abscissa of the interpolate. This is equivalent to assuming that, within a certain prescribed tolerance, the first divided difference $f[x,x_0]$ is a linear function of x for fixed x_0 or, equivalently, that the second divided difference $f[x,x_0,x_1]$ is constant. The hypothesis

$$f[x,x_0,x_1] \approx f[x_2,x_0,x_1] \equiv f[x_0,x_1,x_2] \tag{2.4.1}$$

then takes the form

$$\frac{f[x,x_0] - f[x_0,x_1]}{x - x_1} \approx f[x_0,x_1,x_2]$$

or, after another reduction,

$$f(x) \approx y_{0,1,2}(x) \equiv f[x_0] + (x - x_0)f[x_0,x_1] + (x - x_0)(x - x_1)f[x_0,x_1,x_2]. \tag{2.4.2}$$

Since the difference between the two members of (2.4.1) is

$$(x - x_2)f[x_0,x_1,x_2,x],$$

the error in the approximation (2.4.2) is given by

$$E(x) = (x - x_0)(x - x_1)(x - x_2)f[x_0,x_1,x_2,x]. \tag{2.4.3}$$

From this result, we may deduce that $E(x) \equiv 0$ if $f(x)$ is a polynomial of degree two or less, and that $E = 0$ when $x = x_0$, x_1, or x_2 for *any* continuous function $f(x)$. Thus $y_{0,1,2}(x)$ is a polynomial of degree two which agrees with $f(x)$ when $x = x_0$, x_1, and x_2.

In order to make use of (2.4.2), one may first form a *difference table* as follows:

$$
\begin{array}{ll}
a_0 & f(a_0) \\
 & \qquad\quad f[a_0,a_1] \\
a_1 & f(a_1) \qquad\qquad\qquad f[a_0,a_1,a_2] \\
 & \qquad\quad f[a_1,a_2] \\
a_2 & f(a_2)
\end{array}
$$

Here each entry is given by the difference between diagonally adjacent entries to its left, *divided by the difference between the abscissas corresponding to the ordinates intercepted by the diagonals passing through the calculated entry.*

Thus, for $f(x) = \sinh x$, the following table may be formed, in illustration, with the abscissas 0.0, 0.2, and 0.3:

$$
\begin{array}{lll}
a_0 = 0.00 & 0.00000 & \\
& & 1.0067 \\
a_1 = 0.20 & 0.20134 & \qquad 0.08367 \\
& & 1.0318 \\
a_2 = 0.30 & 0.30452 &
\end{array}
$$

Suppose that only the given data are available and that the value of $f(0.23)$ is to be interpolated. If we take $x_i = a_i$, the calculation from (2.4.2) is of the form

$$f(0.23) \approx 0.00000 + (0.23)(1.0067) + (0.23)(0.03)(0.08367)$$
$$\doteq 0.00000 + 0.231541 + 0.000577 \doteq 0.23212,$$

with an associated error of -0.00009. (One extra place was carried through the intermediate calculation, with the final result rounded to five places.)

By renumbering the x's, the calculation can be rearranged in various ways. For example, since the argument of the interpolant is nearest a_1, it may be suggested that we take $x_0 = a_1$ and, say, $x_1 = a_2$ and $x_2 = a_0$. In this case, there follows

$$f(0.23) \approx 0.20134 + (0.03)(1.0318) + (0.03)(-0.07)(0.08367)$$
$$\doteq 0.20134 + 0.030954 - 0.000176 \doteq 0.23212,$$

with the same end result.

The first calculation uses differences on the indicated *forward diagonal* starting from $f(a_0)$, the second uses differences on the indicated *zigzag* path starting from $f(a_1)$. By further renumbering, other paths also terminating with $f[a_0,a_1,a_2]$ could be selected, *all of which would give exactly the same value of the interpolant if no intermediate round-off errors were present.*

The second path is the one which departs least from an imaginary horizontal line through the argument of the interpolant. Accordingly, the new information introduced at each stage of the calculation is that which may be expected to be most relevant to that interpolant, so that the *rate of approach* to the final value may be expected to be maximized at each step of the path. In addition, since the coefficients by which the successive divided differences are multiplied are smaller in magnitude along the preferred path, the effects of round-offs introduced in the calculation of those divided differences will be somewhat reduced.†

† In this connection, it should be mentioned that, if divided differences of rounded values (not divided rounded differences of true values) are used, if the results of the

If the value of $f(0.10)$ were required, from the given data alone, the first path would be the preferred one from the preceding point of view and would lead to the calculation

$$f(0.10) \approx 0.00000 + (0.10)(1.0067) + (0.10)(-0.10)(0.08367)$$
$$\doteq 0.00000 + 0.10067 - 0.000837 \doteq 0.09983,$$

whereas the true five-place value is 0.10017.   Finally, to interpolate for $f(0.27)$, a path along the *backward diagonal* starting with $f(a_2)$ is preferable.   Hence we would set $x_0 = a_2$, $x_1 = a_1$, and $x_2 = a_0$, and would obtain

$$f(0.27) \approx 0.30452 + (-0.03)(1.0318) + (-0.03)(0.07)(0.08367)$$
$$\doteq 0.30452 - 0.030954 - 0.000176 \doteq 0.27339,$$

as compared with the true five-place value 0.27329.

In the preceding calculations, and in similar ones, when the number of differences to be retained has been decided in advance, and when the end point of the path is also predetermined, the reduction in loss of accuracy afforded by the "preferred path" is usually of no great consequence and the rate of approach to the final value at intermediate stages is irrelevant to the final result.   Thus, the choice of paths is then relatively unimportant.   However, in the more involved cases when differences of higher order are available, and when the point at which the path is to be terminated is not preassigned, it is desirable to choose that path which, when terminated after any number of steps, may be expected to afford the best result obtainable with that number of steps.   The preceding examples were intended to illustrate such paths in simple cases.

2.5. Newton's Fundamental Formula. The identities (2.2.10) and (2.4.2) are special cases of a general formula, due to Newton, which may be derived as follows.

From the basic definition (2.3.1), there follows

$$f(x) = f[x_0] + (x - x_0)f[x_0,x],$$
$$f[x_0,x] = f[x_0,x_1] + (x - x_1)f[x_0,x_1,x], \tag{2.5.1}$$
$$\dots \dots \dots \dots \dots \dots \dots \dots \dots$$
$$f[x_0, \dots ,x_{n-1},x] = f[x_0, \dots ,x_n] + (x - x_n)f[x_0, \dots ,x_n,x].$$

By substituting the second relation in the first, one obtains (2.2.10),

$$f(x) = f[x_0] + (x - x_0)f[x_0,x_1] + (x - x_0)(x - x_1)f[x_0,x_1,x],$$

---

divisions do not require additional round-offs, and if all following calculations are effected without round-off, all paths which incorporate the same given data will lead to *exactly* the same end results.   Thus the preferred path does *not* minimize the effects of *inherent* errors in the given data (as is sometimes argued).   Those effects depend only upon the *end point* of the path and are considered in §3.2.

and, by successively substituting from subsequent relations in (2.5.1), there follows finally

$$f(x) = f[x_0] + (x - x_0)f[x_0,x_1] + (x - x_0)(x - x_1)f[x_0,x_1,x_2] + \cdots$$
$$+ (x - x_0) \cdots (x - x_{n-1})f[x_0, \ldots ,x_n] + E(x), \quad (2.5.2)$$

where
$$E(x) = (x - x_0) \cdots (x - x_n)f[x_0, \ldots ,x_n,x]. \quad (2.5.3)$$

The obvious details of the induction are omitted.

The approximate relation obtained by suppressing the error term in (2.5.2) is known as *Newton's interpolation formula with divided differences.* The resultant right-hand member, which is clearly a polynomial of degree n, may be denoted by $y_{0,\ldots,n}(x)$. An inspection of the error term then shows that $y_{0,\ldots,n}(x)$ is identical with $f(x)$ if $f(x)$ is a polynomial of degree n or less, and that it agrees with $f(x)$ at the $n + 1$ points $x = x_0, \ldots ,x_n$, regardless of the form of f. Further, there exists no *other* polynomial $Y(x)$ of degree n or less having this property, since, if this were the case, $Y - y$ would be a polynomial of maximum degree n with $n + 1$ zeros. This situation is impossible unless $Y - y$ vanishes identically.

Thus, if $f(x)$ is known at $n + 1$ distinct points $a_0, a_1, \ldots , a_n$, where $a_0 < a_1 < \cdots < a_n$, a variety of equivalent forms of the interpolation polynomial $y_{0,\ldots,n}(x)$ of degree n (or less) which agrees with $f(x)$ at these points can be obtained by identifying each of the x's in (2.5.2) with one of the a's. The various possible forms are not considered here in explicit detail. However, in Chap. 4 a more detailed consideration is given to the situation in which the abscissas $a_0, \ldots , a_n$ are *equally spaced*, so that certain simplifications are possible, and convenient use can be made of available tables of certain coefficient functions.

In illustration, we suppose that values of sinh x are given to five places for $x = 0.0, 0.20, 0.30,$ and 0.50, and that sinh 0.23 is required by use of third-order interpolation. The calculation may be arranged as follows:

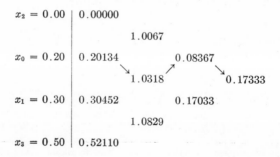

$$f(0.23) \approx 0.20134 + (0.03)(1.0318) + (0.03)(-0.07)(0.08367)$$
$$+ (0.03)(-0.07)(0.23)(0.17333)$$
$$\doteq 0.20134 + 0.030954 - 0.000176 - 0.000084 \doteq 0.23203.$$

The initial point x_0 was taken to be as near as possible to the argument of the interpolant, and the remaining abscissas were numbered in accordance with the indicated zigzag path of differences. The same end result, which is correct to the five places given, could also have been obtained by any one of a number of other orderings of the abscissas.

Once an appropriate continuous path of differences (made up of diagonal segments, each sloping upward or downward to the right) has been selected, reference to (2.5.2) shows that *the coefficient of the kth difference encountered is the product of k factors, each of which represents the difference between the abscissa of the interpolant and the abscissa of an ordinate used in the formation of a difference previously encountered.*†

It is convenient to speak of the data lying inside and on the boundary of the triangular region, limited by the column of ordinates (zeroth differences) in a difference table and the two diagonals passing through a specific difference in that table, as comprising the *region of determination* for that difference. It is then easily seen that *the ordinates involved in the formation of any difference are exactly those ordinates which lie in its region of determination.* Further, for a difference path of the sort considered here, the region of determination of the kth difference encountered includes the regions relevant to all differences previously encountered.

These facts permit us to write down, by inspection, the coefficient of any difference encountered in a chosen path. For example, in order to obtain the coefficient of 0.08367 in the preceding calculation, we notice that the region of determination for the *preceding* difference in the path (1.0318) includes the ordinates corresponding to the abscissas 0.20 and 0.30. Hence the desired coefficient is

$$(0.23 - 0.20)(0.23 - 0.30) = -0.0021.$$

2.6. Error Formulas. It was shown in the preceding section that, if $f(x)$ is approximated by a polynomial $y(x) \equiv y_{0,\ldots,n}(x)$ of maximum degree n, which coincides with it at the $n + 1$ distinct points $x_0, \ldots, x_n$, then the error $E(x) = f(x) - y(x)$ is given by

$$E(x) = \pi(x)f[x_0, \ldots, x_n, x], \qquad (2.6.1)$$

where $\pi(x)$ is the polynomial of degree $n + 1$ defined as the product

$$\pi(x) = (x - x_0)(x - x_1) \cdots (x - x_n). \qquad (2.6.2)$$

This form of the error term will be particularly useful in considering the accuracy of formulas for *numerical differentiation* and *integration* in subsequent chapters.

† The instructions comprised in this statement are frequently referred to as *Sheppard's rules*. Actually, the path of differences need not be continuous, but discontinuous paths are inconvenient and can be avoided, in any case, by reordering the array of given data.

However, if $f(x)$ possesses $n + 1$ continuous derivatives in the relevant interval, there exists another form of the remainder which is often more useful in certain other considerations. In order to obtain it, we notice first that both $f(x) - y(x)$ and $\pi(x)$ vanish at the $n + 1$ points $x = x_0$, $x_1, \ldots, x_n$. We then consider a linear combination of these functions,

$$F(x) \equiv f(x) - y(x) - K\pi(x), \tag{2.6.3}$$

and determine the constant K in such a way that $F(x)$ vanishes, not only at these $n + 1$ points, but also at an arbitrarily chosen point $\bar{x}$ which differs from all these points. Since $\pi(x)$ vanishes *only* at the $n + 1$ points considered previously, K certainly can be so chosen.

Let $\bar{I}$ designate the closed interval limited by the smallest and largest of the $n + 2$ values $x_0, \ldots, x_n, \bar{x}$. Then $F(x)$ vanishes at least $n + 2$ times in the closed interval $\bar{I}$. By Rolle's theorem (§1.7), $F'(x)$ vanishes at least $n + 1$ times inside $\bar{I}$, $F''(x)$ at least n times, $\ldots$, and hence, finally, $F^{(n+1)}(x)$ vanishes at least once inside $\bar{I}$. Let one such point be denoted by $\bar{\xi}$. There then follows, from (2.6.3),

$$0 = f^{(n+1)}(\bar{\xi}) - y^{(n+1)}(\bar{\xi}) - K\pi^{(n+1)}(\bar{\xi}). \tag{2.6.4}$$

But since $y(x)$ is a polynomial of maximum degree n, its $(n + 1)$th derivative vanishes identically. Also, from the definition (2.6.2), there follows $\pi^{(n+1)}(x) \equiv (n + 1)!$. Hence (2.6.4) yields the determination

$$K = \frac{1}{(n + 1)!} f^{(n+1)}(\bar{\xi}),$$

and the relation $F(\bar{x}) = 0$ becomes

$$f(\bar{x}) - y(\bar{x}) = \frac{1}{(n + 1)!} f^{(n+1)}(\bar{\xi})\pi(\bar{x}),$$

for some $\bar{\xi}$ in $\bar{I}$. If $\bar{x}$ is identified with any one of the abscissas $x_0, \ldots, x_n$, both sides of this relation vanish, so that it is valid even in that previously excluded case. Since $\bar{x}$ is thus arbitrary, the bars may be suppressed, and there follows finally

$$E(x) = \frac{1}{(n + 1)!} f^{(n+1)}(\xi)\pi(x), \tag{2.6.5}$$

for some ξ in the interval I, where I is the interval limited by the largest and smallest of the numbers $x_0, x_1, \ldots, x_n, x$.

This result guarantees merely that, for any given x, there *exists* at least one corresponding number ξ in I such that the error is expressible in the given form.

Since (2.6.1) and (2.6.5) must be equivalent, we thus obtain also the useful result

$$f[x_0, \ldots ,x_n,x] = \frac{1}{(n+1)!} f^{(n+1)}(\xi), \qquad (2.6.6)$$

for some argument ξ in the interval I. This fact will be needed in later developments.

In order to illustrate the application of the error formula (2.6.5), we consider the second-order interpolation ($n = 2$) for $f(0.23)$ effected in §2.4. Under the assumption that the analytic expression for the interpolated function is *known* to be $f(x) = \sinh x$, there follows also $f'''(x) = \cosh x$. Thus the error committed is given by

$$E(0.23) = \frac{1}{3!}(0.23 - 0.00)(0.23 - 0.20)(0.23 - 0.30) \cosh \xi$$

$$= -0.0000805 \cosh \xi,$$

for some ξ such that $0 < \xi < 0.30$. It happens in this case that $\cosh x$ may be computed at the tabular points from the *given data*, by use of the formula $\cosh x = (1 + \sinh^2 x)^{\frac{1}{2}}$, and the range in $\cosh x$ over the given interval is thus found (without the need for additional data, but with use of the fact that $\cosh x$ *increases* throughout the interval) to be between 1 and 1.04534. Thus there follows

$$-0.0000842 < E(0.23) < -0.0000805,$$

so that the error in the last place retained in the calculation should be -8. Actually, the error was found to be -9 in the fifth place. The discrepancy is due, not to round-offs in calculation (which were sufficiently controlled by retention of a sixth digit, as may be verified), but to the fact that each of the *original data* possesses a round-off error which may be as large as 5×10^{-6}.

In other applications of interpolation, the analytic expression for $f(x)$ may not be known, and hence it may be impossible to determine the range of possible values of $f^{(n+1)}(\xi)$ in order to estimate the error E. In such cases, the relation (2.6.1) may be more useful. For, if sufficient data are available to permit the evaluation of one or more sample values of the $(n + 1)$th *divided difference*, these values may be taken as estimates of the value of the divided difference which is actually relevant to (2.6.1). Thus, from the data obtained in §2.5, the divided difference

$$f[0.00, 0.20, 0.30, 0.50] \doteq 0.17333$$

may serve as an estimate of the *required* value $f[0.00, 0.20, 0.30, 0.23]$, leading to the error estimate

$$E(0.23) \approx 0.17\pi(0.23) \doteq (-0.00048)(0.17) \doteq -0.00008.$$

The fact that this estimate is indeed good in this case is a consequence of the fact that the third derivative, and hence also the third divided difference, does not vary greatly in the range considered. It may be noticed that this error estimate is precisely the *correction term* which was involved in the calculation of §2.5 as a result of incorporating the contribution of the third difference. More generally, a consideration of (2.5.2) and (2.5.3) shows that if an interpolation for $f(\bar{x})$ is made, terminating with an nth difference, the error committed is given exactly by the product of the calculable number $\pi(\bar{x})$ and the $(n + 1)$th difference $f[x_0, \ldots, x_n, \bar{x}]$, which is *not* calculable unless $f(\bar{x})$ is known. On the other hand, the *first term omitted* in a calculation based on (2.5.2) is the product of $\pi(\bar{x})$ and the $(n + 1)$th difference $f[x_0, \ldots, x_n, x_{n+1}]$. If $f[x_0, \ldots, x_n, x]$ does not vary markedly over an interval including $x = \bar{x}$ and $x = x_{n+1}$, this *first term omitted* will indeed supply a good estimate of the error. This situation will exist, in particular, in consequence of (2.6.5), if $f^{(n+1)}(x)$ does not vary markedly over an interval $\bar{I}$ including $x = x_0, \ldots, x_{n+1}, \bar{x}$.

It may be noticed that, as n increases without limit, the length of the interval $\bar{I}$, as well as that of the interval limited by $\bar{x}$ and x_{n+1}, generally will also increase without limit, since the later abscissas introduced are generally more remote from $\bar{x}$, so that the uncertainty of this particular error estimate may be expected to increase. In fact, in many cases the result of omitting the error term in (2.5.2), and allowing n to become infinite, leads to an infinite *interpolation series* which is itself *not convergent.* That is, the error $E(x)$ associated with retention of differences of order not greater than n very often does not tend to zero as n increases without limit.† However, if the abscissas $x_0, x_1, x_2, \ldots$ are appropriately ordered, it is usually true that the magnitude of the error E first decreases fairly rapidly with increasing n, but then increases in magnitude as n continues to increase. In most practical cases, the minimal error is extremely small, and the minimal stage occurs for a value of n so large that it is not actually encountered.

In view of this situation, the error $E(x)$ is not generally one which can be reduced in magnitude within an arbitrarily prescribed tolerance by increasing the number of differences retained. Thus, although this error is commonly known as the "truncation error," it should be noticed again that this terminology often is somewhat misleading in that it would seem to imply an error committed by truncating a *convergent* infinite sequence of calculations after a finite number of steps.

As in §1.3, we continue to define a truncation error as any error which would be present even in the ideal case when the given data are exact and infinitely many decimal places are retained in the calculations, and we

---

† The series obviously terminates if $f(x)$ is a polynomial, and is a convergent infinite series in certain other cases. Some information with regard to this question is given in §4.11.

shall refer to $E(x)$ as a truncation error in this general sense.   The super-imposed effects of round-off errors may be of equal or greater importance. In fact, the most efficient procedure is frequently that one in which the maximum (or RMS) errors due to truncation and to round-off are of the *same* magnitude.

2.7. Iterated Interpolation.   In §2.2, it was shown that *linear* inter-polation can be conveniently effected by use of the formula

$$y_{0,1}(x) = \frac{1}{x_1 - x_0} \begin{vmatrix} y_0(x) & x_0 - x \\ y_1(x) & x_1 - x \end{vmatrix}, \qquad (2.7.1)$$

where $y_0(x)$ and $y_1(x)$ are two independent *interpolation polynomials of degree zero*,

$$y_0(x) = f(x_0), \qquad y_1(x) = f(x_1). \qquad (2.7.2)$$

In the same way, *quadratic* interpolation can be effected by linear interpolation over two independent linear interpolation polynomials, so that, for example,

$$y_{0,1,2}(x) = \frac{1}{x_2 - x_0} \begin{vmatrix} y_{0,1}(x) & x_0 - x \\ y_{1,2}(x) & x_2 - x \end{vmatrix} = \frac{1}{x_2 - x_1} \begin{vmatrix} y_{0,1}(x) & x_1 - x \\ y_{0,2}(x) & x_2 - x \end{vmatrix}. \qquad (2.7.3)$$

In order to verify this fact directly, we may notice, for example, that the first right-hand member of (2.7.3) is a polynomial of second degree, that it obviously takes on the values $f(x_0)$ and $f(x_2)$ when $x = x_0$ and $x = x_2$, respectively, and that when $x = x_1$ it correctly takes on the value

$$\frac{1}{x_2 - x_0} \begin{vmatrix} f(x_1) & x_0 - x_1 \\ f(x_1) & x_2 - x_1 \end{vmatrix} = f(x_1).$$

In a similar way, we may effect cubic interpolation by linear interpolation over two independent quadratic interpolation polynomials, and so forth (see Prob. 35).   This procedure is particularly useful for machine calculation.   Also, it has the advantage that it yields a *sequence* of inter-polates, from which the rate of effective convergence† can be estimated.

In *Aitken's method*, the first four stages of the calculation would be tabulated as follows:

x_0	y_0					$x_0 - \bar{x}$
x_1	y_1	$y_{0,1}$				$x_1 - \bar{x}$
x_2	y_2	$y_{0,2}$	$y_{0,1,2}$			$x_2 - \bar{x}$
x_3	y_3	$y_{0,3}$	$y_{0,1,3}$	$y_{0,1,2,3}$		$x_3 - \bar{x}$
x_4	y_4	$y_{0,4}$	$y_{0,1,4}$	$y_{0,1,2,4}$	$y_{0,1,2,3,4}$	$x_4 - \bar{x}$

Here, for example, the entry $y_{0,1,3}$ would be obtained by evaluating the determinant

$$\begin{vmatrix} y_{0,1} & x_1 - \bar{x} \\ y_{0,3} & x_3 - \bar{x} \end{vmatrix},$$

† The phrase *effective convergence* will be used in accordance with the generally asymptotic nature of the sequence.

the elements of which are seen to be conveniently located in the above array, and dividing the result by $x_3 - x_1$. Here an additional convenience is afforded by the fact that this divisor can be obtained as the difference $(x_3 - \bar{x}) - (x_1 - \bar{x})$ between the entries in the right-hand column.

The abscissas labeled as $x_0, \ldots, x_n$ may be arranged in any algebraic order; the final value $y_{0,\ldots,n}$ is independent of that arrangement (barring the effects of intermediate round-offs). However, it is often desirable to designate the abscissa nearest the argument of the interpolant $\bar{x}$ by x_0, the second nearest by x_1, and so forth. For then the entries $y_0, y_{0,1}, y_{0,1,2}$, and so forth, may be expected to represent the best possible estimates, based on the given data, which can be afforded by polynomial interpolation of orders zero, one, two, and so forth. Also, each such estimate makes use of all the information used in the preceding estimate, together with one additional datum. Thus the rate of effective convergence can be fairly confidently estimated by considering the sequence of entries in the *diagonal* of the table.

For the interpolation problem considered in §2.5, the work could be arranged as follows, through the third-order calculation:

20	0.20134				−3
30	0.30452	0.232294			7
0	0.00000	1541	0.232118		−23
50	0.52110	3316	1936	0.232034	27

In the absence of further information, the correctness of the fourth place probably would be presumed, whereas the fifth place would be considerably in doubt. In order to decrease the uncertainty, further information would be needed. If, for example, $f(0.60)$ were also available, an additional row of entries would then be calculated, as follows:

60	0.63665	0.233988	0.231899	0.232034	0.232034	37

Thus the value 0.23203 appears to be stabilized as the five-digit interpolate corresponding to the given data.

2.8. Inverse Interpolation. It frequently happens that a variable y is given in tabular form (or analytically) as a single-valued function of x, say $y = f(x)$, and that a value of the independent variable x is required for which the dependent variable y takes on a prescribed value (frequently zero). This is the problem of *inverse interpolation*.

If $\bar{y} = f(\bar{x})$, then over any x interval including $\bar{x}$, in which $dy/dx = f'(x)$ exists and does not vanish, a unique inverse function, say $x = F(y)$, exists, such that $\bar{x} = F(\bar{y})$. Thus, if dy/dx does not vanish near the point where the inverse interpolation is to be effected (so that y increases or decreases steadily in the neighborhood of that point), it may be that $F(y)$ can be satisfactorily approximated in that neighborhood by a polynomial of moderately low degree, so that the inverse interpolation may be effected by merely tabulating x as a function of y in that neighborhood, and using the preceding methods (or any other appropriate methods) of *direct* interpolation.

In illustration, suppose that the following data are available and that the zero of $y(x)$ between $x = 1.3$ and $x = 1.4$ is required.

x	1.1	1.2	1.3	1.4	1.5
y	0.769	0.472	0.103	−0.344	−0.875

If Aitken's method is used, with the entries ordered with respect to the nearness of an ordinate to zero, the calculations may be arranged as follows:

y	x					$y - \bar{y}$
103	1.3					103
−344	1.4	1.32304				−344
472	1.2	2791	1.32509			472
769	1.1	3093	548	1.32447		769
−875	1.5	2106	432	82	1.32463	−875

Thus, a fourth-order interpolation yields $x \approx 1.3246$, with its last place in doubt, although the uncertainty corresponding to the presence of round-off in the given data would also remain. Actually, the given data are exact values corresponding to the algebraic relation $y = -x^3 + x + 1$, and the problem can be considered as that of determining the real zero of the equation $x^3 - x - 1 = 0$, the true value of which is 1.32472, to five places.

Evidently, if this problem were stated in its analytic form, recourse to a semianalytic method such as that of successive substitutions or the Newton-Raphson iteration (see §10.8) would also be appropriate. Even when the correspondence is given only in tabular form, it would also be possible to approximate the relation $y = f(x)$ by the relation $y = y_{0,\dots,n}(x)$, where the equation of the approximation is expressed in explicit polynomial form, with the help of Newton's interpolation formula or of one of the other formulas to be obtained, and to solve the resultant approximating algebraic equation by such iterative methods. However, in order to estimate the accuracy obtained, it would be desirable to repeat the calculation for several values of n, each of which would lead to a distinct algebraic equation.

If dy/dx vanishes near the point $(\bar{x}, \bar{y})$ where the inverse interpolation is to be effected, then the derivative of the inverse function becomes infinite near that point, and a satisfactory approximation to the inverse function cannot be obtained by using a polynomial of low degree.   In such a case, a simple iterative procedure is useful. For this purpose, suppose first that two abscissas x_a and x_b are available with the property that $\bar{y}$ lies between $y_a = f(x_a)$ and $y_b = f(x_b)$ (see Fig. 2.1). If y_a and y_b are sufficiently nearly equal, and if $dy/dx \neq 0$ in the interval between x_a and x_b, *linear* inverse interpolation may then be used to obtain a first approximation to $\bar{x}$, say $\bar{x}^{(1)}$. Then, by direct interpolation, using the ordinates y_a, y_b, and an appropriate number of *other* known ordinates, the true value $f(\bar{x}^{(1)})$ may be approximated. Then, if that result is designated as $\bar{y}^{(1)}$, linear *inverse* interpolation based on $\bar{y}^{(1)}$ and either y_a or y_b (whichever one is separated from $\bar{y}^{(1)}$ by $\bar{y}$) is used to determine a second approximation to $\bar{x}$, say $\bar{x}^{(2)}$, and the cycle of operations is repeated as often as necessary.

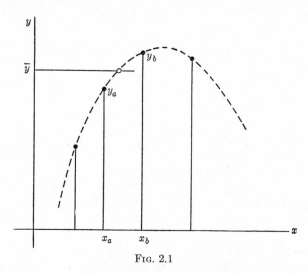

Fig. 2.1

Methods of this sort, in which the only *inverse* interpolation involved is *linear*, and in which high-order interpolation is effected only on the direct function $f(x)$, are particularly to be recommended in those cases when it is known that $f(x)$ can be satisfactorily approximated by a polynomial of reasonably low degree over an interval including $\bar{x}$, but when it is difficult to be certain that the inverse function $F(y)$, such that $\bar{x} = F(\bar{y})$, also can be fairly approximated by a polynomial in y, of comparable degree, over the corresponding interval in y. Whereas situations of this sort obviously are to be anticipated when $f'(x)$ vanishes for a real value of x near $\bar{x}$, they may also occur in the absence of such a warning.

In critical cases, in particular in the case when $dy/dx = 0$ *at* the desired point, it is usually desirable to use one of the semianalytic methods mentioned earlier, in which $f(x)$ is approximated by a polynomial $p(x)$ and the algebraic equation $p(x) = \bar{y}$ is solved by an appropriate iterative method.

2.9. Supplementary References. Most of the texts on numerical analysis listed in the bibliography deal with divided differences and with the basic Newtonian interpolation formula. Blanch [45] discusses the desirability of working with *modified* divided differences, of the form $h^n n! f[x_0,x_1, \ldots ,x_n]$, where h is a suitably chosen constant. A method of iterated interpolation similar to that of Aitken [25] is due to Neville [167]. For references to additional methods of inverse interpolation, see §§3.9 and 4.13.

PROBLEMS

Section 2.2

1. Use (2.2.5) to calculate approximate values of $f(x)$ when $x = 1.1416, 1.1600$, and 1.2000 from the following rounded data:

x	1.1275	1.1503	1.1735	1.1972
$f(x)$	0.11971	0.13954	0.15932	0.17903

2. Calculate the three first divided differences relevant to successive pairs of data in Prob. 1, and use (2.2.4) to determine approximate values of $f(x)$ for

$$x = 1.1600(0.0020)1.1700. \dagger$$

3. Prove that $f[x_0,x_1]$ is independent of x_0 and x_1 if and only if $f(x)$ is a linear function of x.

4. If $f(x) = u(x)v(x)$, show that

$$f[x_0,x_1] = u[x_0]v[x_0,x_1] + u[x_0,x_1]v[x_1].$$

5. If $f'(x)$ is continuous for $x_0 \leq x \leq x_1$, show that

$$f[x_0,x_1] = f'(\xi)$$

for some ξ between x_0 and x_1, and hence also that

$$f[x_0,x_0] \equiv \lim_{x_1 \to x_0} f[x_0,x_1] = f'(x_0).$$

Section 2.3

6. If the abscissas in Prob. 1 are numbered in increasing algebraic order, verify numerically that $f[x_0,x_1,x_2] = f[x_2,x_0,x_1]$.

7. Suppose that $x_r = x_0 + rh$ $(r = 1, 2, \ldots)$, so that the abscissas are at a uniform spacing h. Show that (2.3.3) then becomes

$$\alpha_i^{(k)} = \frac{(-1)^{k-i}}{i!(k-i)!}\frac{1}{h^k} = \frac{(-1)^{k-i}}{h^k k!}\binom{k}{i},$$

where $\binom{k}{i}$ is the binomial coefficient. Thus deduce that

$$f[x_0, \cdots ,x_k] = \frac{1}{h^k k!}\sum_{i=0}^{k}(-1)^{k-i}\binom{k}{i}f(x_i)$$

in this case.

† The notation $x = m(h)n$ denotes that x is to take on values between $x = m$ and $x = n$, inclusive, at intervals of h units.

8. Assuming that $x_r = x_0 + rh$, verify directly (from the definition) the truth of the following special cases of the relation established in Prob. 7:

$$f[x_0,x_1] = \frac{1}{h} [f(x_1) - f(x_0)],$$

$$f[x_0,x_1,x_2] = \frac{1}{2!h^2} [f(x_2) - 2f(x_1) + f(x_0)],$$

$$f[x_0,x_1,x_2,x_3] = \frac{1}{3!h^3} [f(x_3) - 3f(x_2) + 3f(x_1) - f(x_0)].$$

9. If $f'(x) \equiv df(x)/dx$, show that

$$\frac{d}{dx} f[x_0,x] \neq f'[x_0,x]$$

unless $f(x)$ is linear.

10. If $f(x) = u(x)v(x)$, show that the relation established in Prob. 4 generalizes to the form

$$f[x_0, \ldots ,x_n] = \sum_{k=0}^{n} u[x_0, \ldots ,x_k]v[x_k, \ldots ,x_n].$$

Use induction, assuming the truth of the relation for $n = N$, showing that then

$$f[x_1, \ldots ,x_{N+1}] - f[x_0, \ldots ,x_N] = \sum_{k=0}^{N} \{ (x_{N+1} - x_k)u[x_0, \ldots ,x_k]v[x_k, \ldots ,x_{N+1}]$$

$$+ (x_{k+1} - x_0)u[x_0, \ldots ,x_{k+1}]v[x_{k+1}, \ldots ,x_{N+1}] \},$$

and that this expression properly reduces to

$$(x_{N+1} - x_0) \left\{ u[x_0]v[x_0, \ldots ,x_{N+1}] + \sum_{k=1}^{N} u[x_0, \ldots ,x_k]v[x_k, \ldots ,x_{N+1}] \right. $$

$$\left. + u[x_0, \ldots ,x_{N+1}]v[x_{N+1}] \right\}.$$

Section 2.4

11. Repeat the calculations of Prob. 2, making use of the second difference $f[a_0,a_1,a_2]$.

12. Compare the results of Prob. 11 with those obtained by using the second difference $f[a_1,a_2,a_3]$ instead.

13. Obtain the formula

$$\int_{x_0}^{x_1} f(x)\ dx = (x_1 - x_0)f(x_0) + \tfrac{1}{2}(x_1 - x_0)^2 f[x_0,x_1] - \tfrac{1}{6}(x_1 - x_0)^3 f[x_0,x_1,x_2] + E,$$

where

$$E = \int_{x_0}^{x_1} (x - x_0)(x - x_1)(x - x_2)f[x_0,x_1,x_2,x]\ dx.$$

14. Apply the formula of Prob. 13, neglecting the error term, to the data of Prob. 1, obtaining approximate values of the integral of $f(x)$ over each subinterval, and hence obtaining also approximate values of the integral from the smallest abscissa to each of the others. Then use interpolation to obtain an approximate value of the integral over the range (1.14, 1.18).

Section 2.5

15. The following table lists the rounded value of the probability Q that the magnitude of a normally distributed error, with mean value zero and standard deviation unity, exceed ϵ, for certain values of ϵ and Q. Calculate from it approximate values of Q for $\epsilon = 0.7$, 0.9, 1.1, and 1.2.

ϵ	0.4	0.5	0.6	0.8	1.0	1.25
Q	0.68916	0.61708	0.54851	0.42371	0.31731	0.21130

16. Use the data of Prob. 15 to calculate approximate values of ϵ for $Q = 0.4$, 0.5, and 0.6.

17. Suppose that values of $f(x)$, $f'(x)$, and $f''(x)$ are known for $x = x_0$, values of $f(x)$ and $f'(x)$ for $x = x_1$, and the value of $f(x)$ for $x = x_2$. Show that the corresponding divided-difference table appears as follows, through third differences, where each *difference* is formed from diagonally adjacent entries to its left by the usual rule, the values of the *derivatives* being entered in advance:

$$
\begin{array}{llll}
x_0 & f(x_0) & & \\
 & & f'(x_0) & \\
x_0 & f(x_0) & & \tfrac{1}{2}f''(x_0) & & f[x_0,x_0,x_0,x_1] \\
 & & f'(x_0) & & f[x_0,x_0,x_1] & \\
x_0 & f(x_0) & & f[x_0,x_0,x_1] & & f[x_0,x_0,x_1,x_1] \\
 & & f[x_0,x_1] & & f[x_0,x_1,x_1] & \\
x_1 & f(x_1) & & f[x_0,x_1,x_1] & & f[x_0,x_1,x_1,x_2] \\
 & & f'(x_1) & & f[x_1,x_1,x_2] & \\
x_1 & f(x_1) & & f[x_1,x_1,x_2] & & \\
 & & f[x_1,x_2] & & \\
x_2 & f(x_2) & & \\
\end{array}
$$

Show also that Sheppard's rule remains applicable to any "difference path" made up of contiguous diagonal segments, and write down the formula which introduces successively the values of $f(x_0)$, $f'(x_0)$, $f''(x_0)$, $f(x_1)$, $f'(x_1)$, and $f(x_2)$.

18. The following rounded values of $Q(\epsilon)$ and its derivative $Q'(\epsilon)$ are known. By appropriately modifying the procedure illustrated in Prob. 17, construct a suitable difference table and calculate approximate values of Q for $\epsilon = 0.2(0.2)0.8$.

ϵ	Q	Q'
0.0	1.0000	−0.7979
0.5	0.6171	−0.7041
1.0	0.3173	−0.4839

19. Assuming that the third divided difference of $f(x)$ is constant for all x, fill in the spaces in the following divided-difference table (from right to left), and hence evaluate

56 INTRODUCTION TO NUMERICAL ANALYSIS

$f'(8)$ and $f''(8)$:

x	$f(x)$			
0	3			
		1		
1	4		4	
		13		1
3	30		10	
		63		1
6	219		17	
		148		—
8	515		—	
		—	—	
8	515		—	
		—		
8	515			

Also use a similar procedure to obtain $f'(3)$. Determine an analytic expression for $f(x)$, and check the results.

20. If $f(x_1), f(x_2)$, and $f(x_3)$ are values of $f(x)$ near a maximum or minimum point at $x = \bar{x}$, obtain the approximation

$$\bar{x} \approx \frac{x_1 + x_2}{2} - \frac{f[x_1,x_2]}{2f[x_1,x_2,x_3]}$$

and show that it can also be written in the more symmetrical form

$$\bar{x} \approx \frac{x_1 + 2x_2 + x_3}{4} - \frac{f[x_1,x_2] + f[x_2,x_3]}{4f[x_1,x_2,x_3]}.$$

Show also that, when the abscissas are equally spaced, it becomes

$$\bar{x} \approx x_2 - \frac{h}{2}\frac{f_3 - f_1}{f_1 - 2f_2 + f_3},$$

where h is the common interval.

Section 2.6

21. Show that the truncation error associated with linear interpolation of $f(x)$, using ordinates at x_0 and x_1 with $x_0 \leqq x \leqq x_1$, is not larger in magnitude than

$$\tfrac{1}{8}M_2(x_1 - x_0)^2,$$

where M_2 is the maximum value of $|f''(x)|$ in the interval (x_0,x_1). Does this result hold also for extrapolation?

22. Under the assumption that the data in Prob. 1 correspond to the function $f(x) = \sin(\log x)$, show that the truncation error corresponding to linear interpolation between successive ordinates is smaller than one unit in the fourth decimal place.

23. Show that the magnitude of the truncation error corresponding to linear interpolation of the error function

$$\operatorname{erf} x = \frac{2}{\sqrt{\pi}} \int_0^x e^{-t^2}\, dt,$$

between x_0 and x_1, cannot exceed

$$\frac{(x_1 - x_0)^2}{2\sqrt{2\pi e}},$$

and hence is smaller than $(x_1 - x_0)^2/8$.

24. In the special case when the abscissas are equally spaced, with separation h, show that the magnitude of the truncation error corresponding to second-order interpolation based on ordinates at x_0, x_1, and x_2 does not exceed $(M_3 h^3)/(9\sqrt{3})$, where M_3 is the maximum value of $|f'''(x)|$ over the interval (x_0, x_2). Show also that, on the average, the largest errors may be expected to occur at distances of about $h/\sqrt{3} \approx 0.58h$ from the central abscissa. (Translate the origin to the point $x = x_1$.)

25. Show that the magnitude of the truncation error associated with third-order interpolation based on ordinates at the equally spaced points x_0, x_1, x_2, and x_3 does not exceed $(3M_4 h^4)/128$ for interpolation between x_1 and x_2 and is, on the average, largest at the center of that interval. Show also that it does not exceed $(M_4 h^4)/24$ for interpolation between x_0 and x_1 or between x_2 and x_3, with a maximum to be expected, on the average, at a distance of about $(3 - \sqrt{5})h/2 \approx 0.38h$ from x_0 or x_3, where M_4 is the maximum value of $|f^{\mathrm{iv}}(x)|$ in (x_0, x_4) in all cases. [Translate the origin to the midpoint $(x_1 + x_2)/2$.]

26. Obtain the formula

$$f(x) = f(x_0) + (x - x_0)f'(x_0) + (x - x_0)^2 f[x_0, x_0, x_1]$$
$$+ (x - x_0)^2 (x - x_1)f[x_0, x_0, x_1, x_1] + E(x)$$

where $\qquad E(x) = \frac{1}{24}(x - x_0)^2 (x - x_1)^2 f^{\mathrm{iv}}(\xi) \qquad (x_0 < x, \xi < x_1)$,

and show that $\qquad |E(x)| \leqq \dfrac{h^4}{384} \max_{x_0 \leqq x \leqq x_1} |f^{\mathrm{iv}}(x)|$.

27. If $f(x) = 1/(x + 1)$ and $y(x)$ is the polynomial approximation of degree n which agrees with $f(x)$ when $x = 0, 1, 2, \ldots, n$, show that the use of (2.6.5) leads to the error bound

$$|E(x)| < |x(x - 1) \cdots (x - n)|$$

whereas (2.6.1) permits the less conservative bound

$$|E(x)| < \frac{1}{(n + 1)!} |x(x - 1) \cdots (x - n)|$$

when $x \geqq 0$.

28. Suppose that a table presents values of $f(x)$ rounded to r decimal places at a uniform interval h in x, and that linear interpolation is employed for the calculation of $f(\bar{x})$. Suppose also that the tabular abscissas are exact, that the abscissa $\bar{x}$ is rounded to s decimal places, and that the calculated approximate value of $f(\bar{x})$ is rounded to t decimal places. If $f''(x)$ is continuous over the tabular range, and if δ is the total error in the resultant interpolate, show that

$$|\delta| \leqq \tfrac{1}{8}M_2 h^2 + 5M_1 \times 10^{-s-1} + 5 \times 10^{-r-1} + 5 \times 10^{-t-1},$$

where M_1 and M_2 are the maximum values of $|f'(x)|$ and $|f''(x)|$, respectively, in the tabular range.

29. The function $f(x) = \log_{10} \sin x$ is tabulated for $x = 0.01(0.01)2.00$ to five decimal places. If linear interpolation is employed, with the abscissa of the interpolant rounded to five decimal places, and if the calculated result is also rounded to five places, determine the portions of the table for which the results certainly will be correct within five units, and within fifty units, in the fifth place. What accuracy could be guaranteed over those ranges if the abscissa of the interpolant were rounded to four places? To three places?

30. A table of values of the function $f(x) = (x^4 - x)/12$ is to be constructed for $0 \leqq x \leqq a$, in such a way that the error in linear interpolation would not exceed ϵ

if the effects of round-off were negligible. Show first that, if the spacing h is to be uniform, then h should be smaller than $2\sqrt{2\epsilon}/a$ and at least $a^2/(2\sqrt{2\epsilon})$ entries will be required. Show also that, if the range $(0,a)$ were divided into the ranges $(0,\alpha)$ and (α,a), and if uniform spacings h_1 and h_2 were used in those respective ranges, then the most efficient division would be such that the conditions $\alpha = a/2$, $h_2 = 2\sqrt{2\epsilon}/a$, and $h_1 = 2h_2$ were approximately satisfied, corresponding to a reduction of about 25 per cent in the number of entries.

31. From the following table of rounded values of $f(x) = (x/10)^{\frac{1}{2}}$, construct a divided-difference table and determine successive approximations to $f(0.5) = (0.05)^{\frac{1}{2}}$ corresponding to the use of one, two, three, four, and five successive ordinates, including that at $x = 0$. Compare these results with the true value. How could the existent situation have been predicted (without direct calculation) assuming knowledge of the analytical form of $f(x)$? What preliminary warning is afforded by reference to the difference table alone?

x	0	1	2	3	4
$f(x)$	0.00000	0.31623	0.44721	0.54772	0.63246

32. Form a divided-difference table based only on the ordinates of the function $f(x) = x^5 - 5x^3 + x^2 + 4x - 2$ at the points $x = -2$, -1, 0, 1, and 2. Then interpolate from this table approximate values of $f(x)$ at $x = -1.5$, -0.5, 0.5, and 1.5, and compare them with the true values. How could the possibility of the existent situation be predicted (without direct calculation) assuming knowledge of the analytical form of $f(x)$?

Section 2.7

33. Use the Aitken procedure to determine $Q(0.7)$ and $\epsilon(0.5)$ as accurately as possible from the data of Prob. 15.

34. Use the Aitken procedure to determine $f(0.20000)$ as accurately as possible from the following rounded values of $f(x) = \sin[\sinh^{-1}(x+1)]$:

x	0.17520	0.25386	0.33565	0.42078	0.50946
$f(x)$	0.84147	0.86742	0.89121	0.91276	0.93204

35. Deduce the validity of Aitken's method by establishing the relations

$$y_{0,1,\ldots,m,n}(x) = y_{0,1,\ldots,m-1,m}(x)$$
$$+ [(x - x_0)\cdots(x - x_{m-1})(x - x_m)]f[x_0,\ldots,x_m,x_n],$$
$$y_{0,1,\ldots,m,n}(x) = y_{0,1,\ldots,m-1,n}(x)$$
$$+ [(x - x_0)\cdots(x - x_{m-1})(x - x_n)]f[x_0,\ldots,x_m,x_n],$$

and eliminating $f[x_0,\ldots,x_m,x_n]$ between them.

Section 2.8

36. If $y = f(x)$ and if $f'(x) \neq 0$ for $x_0 < x < x_1$, show that the truncation error of linear inverse interpolation based on corresponding values (x_0,y_0) and (x_1,y_1) is given by

$$-(y - y_0)(y - y_1)\frac{f''(\xi)}{2[f'(\xi)]^3},$$

where $x_0 < \xi < x_1$, if $f''(x)/[f'(x)]^2$ exists and is continuous in that interval. Show also that the magnitude of this error is limited by each of the bounds

$$\frac{(y_1 - y_0)^2}{8} K, \qquad \frac{h^2}{8} M_1^2 K, \qquad \frac{h^2}{8} \left(\frac{M_1}{m_1}\right)^2 \frac{M_2}{m_1}$$

if $h = x_1 - x_0$, $|f''(x)/[f'(x)]^3| \leqq K$, $m_1 \leqq |f'(x)| \leqq M_1$, and $|f''(x)| \leqq M_2$ for $x_0 \leqq x \leqq x_1$.

37. Suppose that $f(x) = x^2$ is tabulated for $0 \leqq x \leqq 1$ with a uniform spacing of h in x. Assuming that sufficiently many significant figures are supplied and retained in the calculation to permit the neglect of the effects of round-off errors, determine α (as a function of h and ϵ) so that the error of linear inverse interpolation will not exceed a specified quantity ϵ over the range $(\alpha, 1)$. What spacing would be required to assure an accuracy within 0.005 for $0.1 \leqq x \leqq 1.0$?

38. Repeat the calculations of Prob. 37 when

$$f(x) = \int_0^x \sin t^2 \, dt.$$

[Use the inequality $\sin u > 2u/\pi$ $(0 < u < \pi/2)$ in bounding the error.]

39. Given the following data, use the iterative process of inverse and direct interpolation to determine, to four decimal places, the value of x between 1.50 and 1.60 for which $f(x) = 0.99800$:

x	1.40	1.50	1.60	1.70	1.80
$f(x)$	0.98545	0.99749	0.99957	0.99166	0.97385

40. Calculate an approximation to the value of x required in Prob. 39 by approximating $f(x)$ by the parabola $y(x)$ which agrees with $f(x)$ at the points for which $x = 1.50$, 1.60, and 1.70, and solving the quadratic equation $y(x) = 0.99800$. Then use the iterative method of Prob. 39 to obtain an improved approximation which may be expected to be correct to four decimal places.

41. The following *critical table* for the function $f(x) = x(x - 1)(2x - 1)/12$ has the property that, for any x between successive tabular abscissas, the corresponding value of $f(x)$ rounds to the entry given for that range:

x	$f(x)$
0.05667	
	0.0040
0.05844	
	0.0041
0.06025	
	0.0042
0.06208	
	0.0043
0.06394	

Construct the table, by first tabulating $f(x)$ for appropriate convenient values of x and then using inverse interpolation to obtain x when $f(x) = 0.00395(0.00010)0.00435$, or otherwise.

CHAPTER 3

LAGRANGIAN METHODS

3.1. Introduction. For many purposes, it is desirable that a formula for interpolation, numerical differentiation, or numerical integration be expressed explicitly in terms of the ordinates involved, rather than in terms of their differences or divided differences. Such formulas permit a more direct consideration of the effect on the end result of a change or error in one or more of the ordinates, and their use does not require the calculation or tabulation of differences. However, it is found that these advantages are attained only at the sacrifice of others.

The basic formula, apparently due to Waring, but associated with the name of Lagrange, is derived in §3.2, and its general use in interpolation, differentiation, and integration is illustrated in §§3.3 and 3.4. Certain specific formulas for numerical integration and differentiation are derived from it, in the cases when the abscissas are equally spaced, in the remaining sections of the chapter.

3.2. Lagrange's Interpolation Formula. Lagrange's form of the polynomial $y(x) \equiv y_{0,\dots,n}(x)$ of degree n, which takes on the same values as a given function $f(x)$ for the $n + 1$ distinct abscissas $x_0, x_1, \ldots, x_n$, differs from the Newtonian form derived in §2.5 in that the ordinates involved are displayed explicitly in the Lagrangian form, while the Newtonian form explicitly involves divided differences of those ordinates. Whereas it clearly must be possible to derive Lagrange's form from (2.5.2), its importance justifies the indication of three alternative methods of approach, which are typical of methods also useful in other considerations.

As a first approach, we could write $y(x)$ in the form

$$y(x) = A_0 + A_1 x + \cdots + A_n x^n \equiv \sum_{k=0}^{n} A_k x^k, \qquad (3.2.1)$$

where the A's are to be determined in such a way that $y(x_i) = f(x_i)$ for $i = 0, 1, \ldots, n$. These requirements are represented by the $n + 1$ linear equations

$$A_0 + A_1 x_0 + A_2 x_0^2 + \cdots + A_n x_0^n = f(x_0),$$
$$\cdots\cdots\cdots\cdots\cdots\cdots\cdots\cdots\cdots\cdots\cdots\cdots \qquad (3.2.2)$$
$$A_0 + A_1 x_n + A_2 x_n^2 + \cdots + A_n x_n^n = f(x_n).$$

If these equations are solved by use of determinants, the use of special properties of the determinants involved leads to rather simple expressions for the A's in terms of the ordinates, and the introduction of these results into (3.2.1) leads to the desired result (see Prob. 5). The requirement that the A's satisfy (3.2.1) *and* (3.2.2) can be expressed by the condition

$$\begin{vmatrix} y & 1 & x & x^2 & \cdots & x^n \\ f(x_0) & 1 & x_0 & x_0^2 & \cdots & x_0^n \\ \cdots\cdots\cdots\cdots\cdots\cdots \\ f(x_n) & 1 & x_n & x_n^2 & \cdots & x_n^n \end{vmatrix} = 0, \qquad (3.2.3)$$

the expanded form of which would also give the equation of the required interpolation polynomial $y = y_{0,\ldots,n}(x)$.

Alternatively, we could write $y(x)$ directly in the required form

$$y(x) = l_0(x)f(x_0) + l_1(x)f(x_1) + \cdots + l_n(x)f(x_n) \equiv \sum_{k=0}^{n} l_k(x)f(x_k),$$
$$(3.2.4)$$

where $l_0(x), \ldots, l_n(x)$ are polynomials of degree n or less, to be determined by the requirement that the result of replacing $y(x)$ by $f(x)$ be an *identity* when $f(x)$ is an arbitrary polynomial of degree n or less. It is clear that this situation will prevail if and only if the result of replacing $y(x)$ by $f(x)$ is an identity when $f(x) = 1, x, x^2, \ldots,$ and x^n. These requirements are represented by the $n + 1$ equations

$$l_0(x) + l_1(x) + \cdots + l_n(x) = 1,$$
$$x_0 l_0(x) + x_1 l_1(x) + \cdots + x_n l_n(x) = x,$$
$$\cdots\cdots\cdots\cdots\cdots\cdots\cdots\cdots\cdots \qquad (3.2.5)$$
$$x_0^n l_0(x) + x_1^n l_1(x) + \cdots + x_n^n l_n(x) = x^n,$$

from which the coefficient functions can be determined directly as ratios of determinants which can be expanded in simple forms. The eliminant of the Eqs. (3.2.4) and (3.2.5) is merely the result of interchanging rows and columns in the array whose determinant appears in (3.2.3), so that the equivalence of the final forms is indeed confirmed.

Rather than pursue either of these lines, we may avoid somewhat lengthy calculation by noticing that the expression (3.2.4) will indeed take on the value $f(x_i)$ when $x = x_i$ if $l_i(x_i) = 1$ and if $l_i(x_j) = 0$ when $j \neq i$. With the convenient notation of the so-called *Kronecker delta*,

$$\delta_{ij} = \begin{cases} 0 & \text{if } i \neq j, \\ 1 & \text{if } i = j, \end{cases} \qquad (3.2.6)$$

this requirement becomes merely

$$l_i(x_j) = \delta_{ij} \qquad (i = 0, \ldots, n; j = 0, \ldots, n). \qquad (3.2.7)$$

Since $l_i(x)$ is thus to be a polynomial of degree n which vanishes when $x = x_0, x_1, \ldots, x_{i-1}, x_{i+1}, \ldots, x_n$, there must follow

$$l_i(x) = C_i[(x - x_0) \cdots (x - x_{i-1})(x - x_{i+1}) \cdots (x - x_n)], \quad (3.2.8)$$

where C_i is a constant. The final requirement $l_i(x_i) = 1$ then determines C_i in the form

$$C_i = \frac{1}{(x_i - x_0) \cdots (x_i - x_{i-1})(x_i - x_{i+1}) \cdots (x_i - x_n)} \quad (3.2.9)$$

and the desired *Lagrangian coefficient functions* $l_i(x)$ are obtained by introducing (3.2.9) into (3.2.8).

In order to put this result in a somewhat more compact form, we first review the notation of (2.6.2):

$$\pi(x) = (x - x_0)(x - x_1) \cdots (x - x_n). \quad (3.2.10)$$

Now the *derivative* of $\pi(x)$ is clearly expressible as the sum of $n + 1$ terms, in each of which one of the factors of $\pi(x)$ is deleted. Thus, if we set $x = x_i$ in this expression, we obtain the useful result

$$\pi'(x_i) = (x_i - x_0) \cdots (x_i - x_n) = \frac{1}{C_i}, \quad (3.2.11)$$

where the factor $(x_i - x_i)$ is to be omitted in the product. Thus, after introducing (3.2.8) and (3.2.9) into (3.2.4), we obtain the *Lagrangian interpolation polynomial of degree* n in the form

$$y(x) = \sum_{k=0}^{n} \frac{\pi(x)}{(x - x_k)\pi'(x_k)} f(x_k) \equiv \sum_{k=0}^{n} l_k(x)f(x_k), \quad (3.2.12)$$

where

$$l_i(x) = \frac{\pi(x)}{(x - x_i)\pi'(x_i)}$$

$$= \frac{(x - x_0) \cdots (x - x_{i-1})(x - x_{i+1}) \cdots (x - x_n)}{(x_i - x_0) \cdots (x_i - x_{i-1})(x_i - x_{i+1}) \cdots (x_i - x_n)}. \quad (3.2.13)$$

The first expression for $l_i(x)$ is useful in theoretical considerations, the second in the actual calculation of the function.

It should be noticed that the definitions of the functions $\pi(x)$ and $l_i(x)$ involve the degree n of the interpolation polynomial. Generally, in the sequel, the value of n will be clear from the context. When a more explicit notation is necessary, we may replace $l_i(x)$ by $l_{i,n}(x)$ and $\pi(x)$ by $\pi_n(x)$.

The *direct* derivation of this result from the Newtonian form (2.5.2) is of some academic interest and may be effected by making use of (2.3.2) and comparing (2.3.3) with (3.2.11).

In view of the equivalence of (3.2.12) and (2.5.2), the error committed by replacing $f(x)$ by $y(x)$ is again given by either (2.6.1) or (2.6.5), so that we may write

$$f(x) = \sum_{k=0}^{n} l_k(x)f(x_k) + E(x), \qquad (3.2.14)$$

where

$$E(x) = \pi(x)f[x_0, \ldots, x_n, x] = \pi(x)\frac{f^{n+1}(\xi)}{(n+1)!} \qquad (3.2.15)$$

and where, as before, ξ is some number in the interval I limited by the largest and smallest of the numbers $x_0, x_1, \ldots, x_n$, and x.

To illustrate the use of the Lagrangian formula, we may write down the interpolation polynomial of degree three relevant to the data

x	-1	0	1	2
$f(x)$	1	1	1	-5

in the form

$$y = 1 \cdot \frac{(x-0)(x-1)(x-2)}{(-1-0)(-1-1)(-1-2)} + 1 \cdot \frac{(x+1)(x-1)(x-2)}{(0+1)(0-1)(0-2)}$$
$$+ 1 \cdot \frac{(x+1)(x-0)(x-2)}{(1+1)(1-0)(1-2)} - 5 \cdot \frac{(x+1)(x-0)(x-1)}{(2+1)(2-0)(2-1)}$$
$$= -\tfrac{1}{6}x(x-1)(x-2) + \tfrac{1}{2}(x+1)(x-1)(x-2)$$
$$- \tfrac{1}{2}(x+1)x(x-2) - \tfrac{5}{6}(x+1)x(x-1)$$

which may be reduced to

$$y = -x^3 + x + 1.$$

For the purpose of actual numerical interpolation, the reduction to this final form would not be necessary.

On the other hand, whereas the Newtonian method would require the formation of the divided-difference table

$$
\begin{array}{r|r}
-1 & 1 \\
 & \quad 0 \\
0 & 1 \quad\quad 0 \\
 & \quad 0 \quad\quad -1, \\
1 & 1 \quad -3 \\
 & \quad -6 \\
2 & -5
\end{array}
$$

the use of the indicated difference path would involve only the following calculation:

$$y = 1 + x(0) + x(x-1)(0) + x(x-1)(x+1)(-1)$$
$$= 1 - x(x-1)(x+1) = -x^3 + x + 1.$$

The Lagrange form of the interpolation formula $f(x) \approx y(x)$ possesses the advantage that its use does not involve preliminary differencing of data. However, it has the disadvantage that, unless $f(x)$ is given analytically, so that use may be made of the second form of (3.2.15), it is difficult to estimate the *truncation error* relevant to the result afforded by interpolation based on a given number of ordinates, or to estimate the number of ordinates needed to reduce the truncation error below prescribed limits. If the Newtonian formula is used, a more or less dependable estimate of accuracy, based essentially on the *first* form of (3.2.15), may be obtained by sampling the first neglected higher-order difference.

Furthermore, in order to improve a certain result by taking into account one or more additional ordinates, the coefficient functions $l_i(x)$ would have to be completely redetermined in the Lagrangian procedure, whereas the Newtonian procedure would require merely the formation of a higher-order difference, and the addition of a multiple of that difference to the previously calculated result.

On the other hand, the Lagrangian form is much better adapted to the analysis of the effects of *inherent errors* in the data. Thus, if the original data were all correctly rounded to r decimal places, so that the maximum error in each given ordinate is $5 \times 10^{-r-1}$, it is seen that the largest possible corresponding error in the interpolation for $f(x)$ would be

$$|R(x)|_{\max} = (5 \times 10^{-r-1}) \sum_{k=0}^{n} |l_k(x)|. \qquad (3.2.16)$$

The corresponding calculation based on the Newtonian form would be more complicated but would, of course, lead to the same result. In addition to this error, the errors due to truncation and to intermediate round-offs must be taken into account in either case.

3.3. Numerical Differentiation and Integration. Once an interpolation polynomial $y(x)$ has been determined so that it satisfactorily approximates a given function $f(x)$ over a certain interval I, it may be hoped that the result of differentiating $y(x)$, or of integrating it over an interval, will also satisfactorily approximate the corresponding derivative or integral of $f(x)$. However, if we visualize a curve, representing an approximating function and oscillating about the curve representing the function approximated, we may anticipate the fact that, even though the deviation between $y(x)$ and $f(x)$ be small throughout an interval, still the *slopes* of the two curves representing them may differ quite appreciably. Further, it is seen that round-off errors (or errors of observation) of alternating sign in consecutive ordinates could affect the calculation of the derivative quite strongly if those ordinates were fairly closely spaced.

On the other hand, since *integration* is essentially a smoothing process, it would be anticipated that the error associated with integration may be small even though the interpolation polynomial itself provides only a moderately good approximation to $f(x)$.

These expectations are borne out in practice. In particular, numerical differentiation should be avoided wherever possible, particularly when the data are empirical and subject to appreciable errors of observation. When such a calculation must be made, it is desirable first to *smooth* the data to a certain extent. Certain methods of effecting such a smoothing are considered in §7.13.

From the Lagrangian approximation

$$f(x) \approx \sum_{k=0}^{n} l_k(x)f(x_k), \qquad (3.3.1)$$

with associated error

$$E(x) = \pi(x) \frac{f^{(n+1)}(\xi)}{(n+1)!}, \qquad (3.3.2)$$

we obtain the corresponding integral formula

$$\int_a^b f(x)\, dx \approx \sum_{k=0}^{n} C_k f(x_k), \qquad (3.3.3)$$

where the *weighting coefficients* C_k are given by

$$C_k = \int_a^b l_k(x)\, dx \qquad (3.3.4)$$

and where the associated error can be expressed in the form

$$E = \frac{1}{(n+1)!} \int_a^b \pi(x) f^{(n+1)}(\xi)\, dx. \qquad (3.3.5)$$

With regard to (3.3.5), it should be remembered that ξ is a specific, but generally *unknown, function of x,* so that even though the $(n+1)$th derivative of f were known analytically it generally would be impossible to evaluate the integral defining E exactly. However, if it is known that, say, $|f^{(n+1)}(x)| \leq M$ in I, where I is limited by the largest and smallest of $x_0, x_1, \ldots, x_n, a,$ and b, and where M is a constant, it may be deduced that

$$E \leq \frac{M}{(n+1)!} \int_a^b |\pi(x)|\, dx. \qquad (3.3.6)$$

Further, in those cases where no one of the abscissas x_i lies in (a,b), the function $\pi(x)$ does not change sign in (a,b) and the second law of the mean (§1.7) may be invoked to show that

$$E = \frac{f^{(n+1)}(\eta)}{(n+1)!} \int_a^b \pi(x)\, dx, \qquad (3.3.7)$$

where η is some number in I. This last situation exists, in particular, in the frequently occurring cases when the integration is carried out over the interval *between two adjacent tabular points.*

Similarly, by differentiating (3.3.1) r times, one obtains the approximation

$$f^{(r)}(x) \approx \sum_{k=0}^{n} l_k^{(r)}(x)f(x_k) \tag{3.3.8}$$

with the associated error

$$E^{(r)}(x) = \frac{1}{(n+1)!}\frac{d^r}{dx^r}\left[\pi(x)f^{(n+1)}(\zeta)\right]. \tag{3.3.9}$$

However, since the dependence of ξ upon x is again unknown, the differentiation in (3.3.9) cannot be explicitly effected.

In order to obtain a somewhat more tractable form of the remainder, we replace (3.3.2) by the equivalent first form of (3.2.15), which involves the current variable x itself. The error (3.3.9) can then be expressed in the form

$$E^{(r)}(x) = \frac{d^r}{dx^r}\{\pi(x)f[x_0, \ldots, x_n, x]\}. \tag{3.3.10}$$

If use is made of *Leibnitz' formula* for the rth derivative of a product,

$$\frac{d^r}{dx^r}(uv) = u\,D^rv + r\,Du\,D^{r-1}v + \frac{r(r-1)}{2!}D^2u\,D^{r-2}v + \cdots + D^ru\,v$$

$$= \sum_{i=0}^{r}\binom{r}{i}D^iu\,D^{r-i}v, \tag{3.3.11}$$

where $D \equiv d/dx$ and where $\binom{r}{i}$ represents the binomial coefficient

$$\binom{r}{i} = \frac{r(r-1)\cdots(r-i+1)}{i!} = \frac{r!}{(r-i)!i!}, \tag{3.3.12}$$

Eq. (3.3.10) takes the form

$$E^{(r)}(x) = \sum_{i=0}^{r}\binom{r}{i}\pi^{(i)}(x)\frac{d^{r-i}}{dx^{r-i}}f[x_0, \ldots, x_n, x]$$

or, making use of (2.3.9),

$$E^{(r)}(x) = \sum_{i=0}^{r}\frac{r!}{i!}\pi^{(i)}(x)f[x_0, \ldots, x_n, \overbrace{x, \ldots, x}^{r-i+1 \text{ times}}]. \tag{3.3.13}$$

A generalization of the relation (2.6.6) leads to the fact that

$$f[x_0, \ldots, x_n, \overbrace{x, \ldots, x}^{m \text{ times}}] = \frac{1}{(n+m)!}f^{(n+m)}(\xi_m) \tag{3.3.14}$$

where, for given n, ξ_m lies somewhere in the interval I limited by the largest and smallest of $x_0, \ldots, x_n$ and x. Hence, finally, (3.3.13) can be expressed in the form

$$E^{(r)}(x) = \sum_{i=0}^{r} \frac{r!}{(n+r-i+1)! i!} \pi^{(i)}(x) f^{(n+r-i+1)}(\xi_i), \qquad (3.3.15)$$

where each of the $r + 1$ numbers $\xi_0, \ldots, \xi_r$ lies in I.

The expression for the error is thus rather complicated in the general case, and when the rth derivative is calculated by differentiating an interpolation polynomial of nth degree, the estimation of the error may involve the estimation of derivatives of $f(x)$ of orders $n + 1, n + 2, \ldots, n + r$, and $n + r + 1$ in the interval I.

It may be noticed that when $r > n$ the right-hand member of (3.3.8) vanishes identically, since $l_k(x)$ is a polynomial of degree n. Generally, at best only derivatives of order r for which r is small relative to n are given with any significant accuracy by this formula.

In the case $r = 1$, the formula (3.3.8) becomes

$$f'(x) \approx \sum_{k=0}^{n} l_k'(x) f(x_k), \qquad (3.3.16)$$

and the associated error, as given by (3.3.15), is of the form

$$E'(x) = \pi'(x) \frac{f^{(n+1)}(\xi_1)}{(n+1)!} + \pi(x) \frac{f^{(n+2)}(\xi_0)}{(n+2)!}, \qquad (3.3.17)$$

where both ξ_1 and ξ_0 lie in the interval I. In particular, for numerical differentiation *at a tabular point*, there follows

$$f'(x_i) = \sum_{k=0}^{n} l_k'(x_i) f(x_k) + \pi'(x_i) \frac{f^{(n+1)}(\xi_1)}{(n+1)!}, \qquad (3.3.18)$$

since $\pi(x)$ vanishes when $x = x_i$, where the factor $\pi'(x_i)$ has the simple form

$$\pi'(x_i) = (x_i - x_0) \cdots (x_i - x_n), \qquad (3.3.19)$$

in accordance with (3.2.11).

It is seen that this relation is the result which would be obtained by differentiating the formula

$$f(x) = \sum_{k=0}^{n} l_k(x) f(x_k) + \pi(x) \frac{f^{(n+1)}(\xi)}{(n+1)!}$$

with respect to x, overlooking the fact that ξ is a function of x, setting $x = x_i$ in the result, and changing ξ to a new parameter ξ_1. Except for the calculation of the *first* derivative *at a tabular point*, (3.3.15) shows that this procedure would not generally yield the correct expression for the error term.

It can be shown, however, that the error $E^{(r)}(x)$ *can* indeed be expressed in the analogous form

$$E^{(r)}(x) = \pi^{(r)}(x) \frac{f^{(n+1)}(\eta_r)}{(n + 1)!} \qquad (3.3.20)$$

for *any* positive integer r, where η_r is somewhere in I, *when x is outside or at one end of the range of the tabular values* $x_0, \ldots, x_n$ (see Prob. 8).

3.4. Calculation. Since the coefficient function $l_i(x)$ can be expressed in the form

$$l_i(x) = \frac{(x - x_0)(x - x_1) \cdots (x - x_{i-1})(x - x_{i+1}) \cdots (x - x_n)}{(x_i - x_0)(x_i - x_1) \cdots (x_i - x_{i-1})(x_i - x_{i+1}) \cdots (x_i - x_n)}, \qquad (3.4.1)$$

it is seen that the *form* of $l_i(x)$ is invariant under any linear change in variables

$$x = a + hs, \qquad x_i = a + hs_i, \qquad (3.4.2)$$

where a and h are constants:

$$l_i(x) = \frac{(s - s_0)(s - s_1) \cdots (s - s_{i-1})(s - s_{i+1}) \cdots (s - s_n)}{(s_i - s_0)(s_i - s_1) \cdots (s_i - s_{i-1})(s_i - s_{i+1}) \cdots (s_i - s_n)}. \qquad (3.4.3)$$

It is often desirable to choose a and h in such a way that the dimensionless variable s, which measures distance from a in units of h, takes on convenient values at the tabular points used in any specific interpolation. For equally spaced abscissas, h is conveniently identified with the spacing.

Thus, as a simple illustration, suppose that the following data are given, and that approximate values of $f(x)$ at intervals of 0.01 are to be obtained by Lagrange three-point interpolation:

x	1.10	1.20	1.35	1.50
$f(x)$	0.8912	0.9320	0.9757	0.9975

For interpolation between $x = 1.10$ and 1.35, the transformation

$$x = 1.20 + 0.1s$$

is useful, the variable s then taking on the values -1.0, 0, and 1.5 at the tabular points, and the values -0.9, -0.8, $\ldots$, 1.3, 1.4 at the points of interpolation.

With the abbreviation

$$y(x) = y(1.20 + 0.1s) \equiv y_s,$$

the interpolation formula $f(x) \approx y(x)$ then becomes

$$f(1.20 + 0.1s) \approx y_s = \frac{s(s - 1.5)}{(-1.0)(-2.5)} (0.8912)$$
$$+ \frac{(s + 1.0)(s - 1.5)}{(1.0)(-1.5)} (0.9320) + \frac{(s + 1.0)s}{(2.5)(1.5)} (0.9757)$$
$$= \tfrac{1}{75}[26.736s(s - 1.5) - 46.600(s + 1.0)(s - 1.5)$$
$$+ 19.514s(s + 1.0)],$$

a common denominator being extracted for final division, in order to avoid all intermediate round-off. In the range between 1.35 and 1.50, a new polynomial may be obtained, based on the ordinates at 1.20, 1.35, and 1.50, with, say, $x = 1.35 + 0.1s$. A comparison of a few values calculated between 1.20 and 1.35 by use of the new formula with those calculated by the preceding formula would give an estimate of the accuracy obtained.

If approximate values of $f'(x)$ are required at the same points, the formula

$$f'(1.20 + 0.1s) \approx y_s' = \tfrac{10}{75}(-0.7s + 2.71) = \tfrac{2}{15}(2.71 - 0.7s)$$

can be obtained by differentiating y_s with respect to s and multiplying by the factor $ds/dx = 10$. Finally, if approximate values of the function

$$F(x) = \int_{1.10}^{x} f(x) \, dx$$

are required, say, at intervals of 0.01 in x, use can be made of the formula

$$\int_{1.10}^{1.20+0.1s} f(x) \, dx \approx Y_s \equiv 0.1 \int_{-1.0}^{s} y_s \, ds$$
$$= \tfrac{1}{4500}(-0.7s^3 + 8.13s^2 + 419.4s + 410.57).$$

In the derivation of each of these formulas, the work was so arranged that no round-offs were committed.

The approximate values at $x = 1.30$ may be obtained, for example, in correspondence with $s = 1.0$, as

$$f(1.30) \approx y_1 = \tfrac{1}{75}(72.26) \doteq 0.96347,$$
$$f'(1.30) \approx y_1' = \tfrac{2}{15}(2.01) \doteq 0.26800,$$

and $\qquad \int_{1.10}^{1.30} f(x) \, dx \approx Y_1 = \tfrac{1}{4500}(837.4) \doteq 0.18609,$

to five places (not more than four of which would be expected to be significant).

It happens that the given data are four-place values of $f(x) = \sin x$. The approximations obtained may thus be considered as corresponding to $\sin 1.30 \doteq 0.96356$, $\cos 1.30 \doteq 0.26750$, and

$$\cos 1.10 - \cos 1.30 \doteq 0.18610.$$

In the cases when the abscissas are uniformly spaced, the Lagrangian coefficient functions have been tabulated rather extensively for various values of n. Formulas involving an *odd* number of ordinates are most often used, and, if that number is $n + 1 = 2m + 1$, the abscissas are then conventionally renumbered as $x_{-m}, \ldots, x_{-1}, x_0, x_1, \ldots, x_m$.

If the uniform spacing $x_{k+1} - x_k$ is denoted by h, and if s is measured from the *central* point, so that

$$x = x_0 + hs, \qquad x_i = x_0 + hs_i, \tag{3.4.4}$$

Eq. (3.4.3) then reduces to

$$l_i(x) =$$
$$\frac{(s + m)(s + m - 1) \cdots (s - i + 1)(s - i - 1) \cdots (s - m + 1)(s - m)}{(i + m)(i + m - 1) \cdots (2)(1)(-1)(-2) \cdots (i - m + 1)(i - m)}$$
$$\equiv L_i(s).$$

Thus
$$L_0(s) = \frac{(1 - s^2)(4 - s^2) \cdots (m^2 - s^2)}{(m!)^2} \tag{3.4.5}$$

and

$$L_i(s) = \frac{(-1)^{i+1}s(s + i)}{(m + i)!(m - i)!}$$
$$\cdot [(1 - s^2)(4 - s^2) \cdots (\overline{i - 1}^2 - s^2)(\overline{i + 1}^2 - s^2) \cdots (m^2 - s^2)] \tag{3.4.6}$$

for $i = \pm 1, \pm 2, \ldots, \pm m$.

In illustration, Table 3.1 presents exact values of the Lagrange coefficients for three-point (quadratic) interpolation to tenths, corresponding to $m = 1$ (a corresponding five-point table is included in §4.12):

TABLE 3.1

s	$L_{-1}(s)$	$L_0(s)$	$L_1(s)$	
0.0	0	1	0	0.0
0.1	−0.045	0.99	0.055	−0.1
0.2	−0.08	0.96	0.12	−0.2
0.3	−0.105	0.91	0.195	−0.3
0.4	−0.12	0.84	0.28	−0.4
0.5	−0.125	0.75	0.375	−0.5
0.6	−0.12	0.64	0.48	−0.6
0.7	−0.105	0.51	0.595	−0.7
0.8	−0.08	0.36	0.72	−0.8
0.9	−0.045	0.19	0.855	−0.9
1.0	0	0	1	−1.0
	$L_1(s)$	$L_0(s)$	$L_{-1}(s)$	s

From (3.4.6) it follows that $L_i(-s) = L_{-i}(s)$. This explains the fact that, for *negative* values of s, to be read from the right-hand margin, the column labels at the *foot* of the table are to be used.

Thus, for example, to interpolate the data

x	1.00	1.10	1.20	1.30
$f(x)$	0.8415	0.8912	0.9320	0.9636

or $f(1.24)$ by use of a three-point formula, the work would be centered at the nearest tabular point, $x = 1.20$. With $s = 0.04/0.10 = 0.4$, and with coefficients read from the preceding table, there would follow

$$f(1.24) \approx (-0.12)(0.8912) + (0.84)(0.9320) + (0.28)(0.9636)$$
$$= 0.945744 \doteq 0.9457.$$

To interpolate for $x = 1.02$, the work would be centered at $x = 1.10$. With $s = -0.8$, there would follow

$$f(1.02) \approx (0.72)(0.8415) + (0.36)(0.8912) + (-0.08)(0.9320)$$
$$= 0.852152 \doteq 0.8522.$$

The given data correspond to rounded values of $f(x) = \sin x$, and the results correspond to the tabulated five-place values $\sin 1.24 \doteq 0.94578$ and $\sin 1.02 \doteq 0.85211$.

Extensive tables of Lagrange coefficient functions, and of certain of their derivatives, may be found in the literature (see Appendix B).

3.5. Newton-Cotes Integration Formulas. In order to obtain formulas for the approximate evaluation of an integral of the form $\int_a^b f(x)\,dx$, where a and b are finite, we may first introduce the change of variables

$$x = a + \frac{b-a}{n}\,s, \tag{3.5.1}$$

where n is an integer, to obtain the relation

$$\int_a^b f(x)\,dx = \frac{b-a}{n}\int_0^n F(s)\,ds, \tag{3.5.2}$$

where

$$F(s) = f\left(a + \frac{b-a}{n}\,s\right). \tag{3.5.3}$$

If now it is assumed that $f(x)$ can be approximated over (a,b) by the polynomial which agrees with it at, say, $n+1$ equally spaced points in (a,b) we may obtain the approximate formula

$$\int_0^n F(s)\,ds \approx \sum_{k=0}^n C_k^{(n)} F(k), \tag{3.5.4}$$

where

$$C_k^{(n)} = \int_0^n \frac{s(s-1)\cdots(s-k+1)(s-k-1)\cdots(s-n)}{k(k-1)\cdots(k-k+1)(k-k-1)\cdots(k-n)}\,ds. \tag{3.5.5}$$

In accordance with (3.3.5), the error term omitted on the right in (3.5.4) can be expressed in the form

$$\bar{E}_n = \frac{1}{(n+1)!} \int_0^n s(s-1) \cdots (s-n)F^{(n+1)}(\xi_1)\, ds, \quad (3.5.6)$$

where $0 < \xi_1 < n$. Since the coefficient of $F^{(n+1)}$ is not of constant sign in $(0,n)$, the second law of the mean cannot be applied directly. However, it is possible to prove (see Steffensen [18]) that, when n is *odd*, the error can be expressed in the form which would be obtained if this procedure were valid,

$$\bar{E}_n = \frac{F^{(n+1)}(\xi_2)}{(n+1)!} \int_0^n s(s-1) \cdots (s-n)\, ds \quad (n \text{ odd}) \quad (3.5.7a)$$

whereas, when n is *even*, the error can be expressed in the form

$$\bar{E}_n = \frac{F^{(n+2)}(\xi_2)}{(n+2)!} \int_0^n \left(s - \frac{n}{2}\right) s(s-1) \cdots (s-n)\, ds \quad (n \text{ even}), \quad (3.5.7b)$$

where $0 < \xi_2 < n$ in each case.

If, as before, we write $h = (b-a)/n$ and $x_i = a + hi$, the result established can be put in the more explicit form

$$\int_{x_0}^{x_n} f(x)\, dx \approx h \sum_{k=0}^n C_k^{(n)} f(x_k), \quad (3.5.8)$$

where $C_k^{(n)}$ is defined by (3.5.5). By noticing that

$$\frac{d^r}{ds^r} F(s) = h^r \frac{d^r}{dx^r} f(x),$$

and that, from (3.5.2), the error in (3.5.8) is $h\bar{E}_n$, we obtain also the expressions

$$E_n = \frac{h^{n+2} f^{(n+1)}(\xi)}{(n+1)!} \int_0^n s(s-1) \cdots (s-n)\, ds \quad (n \text{ odd}) \quad (3.5.9a)$$

and

$$E_n = \frac{h^{n+3} f^{(n+2)}(\xi)}{(n+2)!} \int_0^n \left(s - \frac{n}{2}\right) s(s-1) \cdots (s-n)\, ds \quad (n \text{ even}),$$

$$(3.5.9b)$$

where $x_0 < \xi < x_n$ in each case.

In illustration, we consider the case $n = 2$. Here there follows, from (3.5.5),

$$C_0 = \int_0^2 \frac{(s-1)(s-2)}{(-1)(-2)}\, ds = \frac{1}{3}, \qquad C_1 = \int_0^2 \frac{s(s-2)}{(1)(-1)}\, ds = \frac{4}{3},$$

$$C_2 = \int_0^2 \frac{s(s-1)}{(2)(1)}\, ds = \frac{1}{3},$$

SHARE 709 SYMBOLIC CARD

LABEL

REMARKS

OPERATION | ADDRESS, TAG, DECREMENT / COUNT

SYMBOL

IBM C50859

nd (3.5.9*b*) gives

$$E_2 = \frac{h^5 f^{iv}(\xi)}{24} \int_0^2 s(s-1)^2(s-2) \, ds = -\frac{h^5 f^{iv}(\xi)}{90}.$$

The corresponding formula (3.5.8), with the error term, then takes the orm

$$\int_{x_0}^{x_2} f(x) \, dx = \frac{h}{3} (f_0 + 4f_1 + f_2) - \frac{h^5}{90} f^{iv}(\xi) \qquad (x_0 < \xi < x_2).$$

This is the celebrated formula of *Simpson's rule*.

In a similar way, the following formulas may be obtained:

$$\int_{x_0}^{x_1} f(x) \, dx = \frac{h}{2} (f_0 + f_1) - \frac{h^3}{12} f''(\xi), \tag{3.5.10}$$

$$\int_{x_0}^{x_2} f(x) \, dx = \frac{h}{3} (f_0 + 4f_1 + f_2) - \frac{h^5}{90} f^{iv}(\xi), \tag{3.5.11}$$

$$\int_{x_0}^{x_3} f(x) \, dx = \frac{3h}{8} (f_0 + 3f_1 + 3f_2 + f_3) - \frac{3h^5}{80} f^{iv}(\xi), \tag{3.5.12}$$

$$\int_{x_0}^{x_4} f(x) \, dx = \frac{2h}{45} (7f_0 + 32f_1 + 12f_2 + 32f_3 + 7f_4) - \frac{8h^7}{945} f^{vi}(\xi), \tag{3.5.13}$$

$$\int_{x_0}^{x_5} f(x) \, dx = \frac{5h}{288} (19f_0 + 75f_1 + 50f_2 + 50f_3 + 75f_4 + 19f_5)$$
$$- \frac{275h^7}{12096} f^{vi}(\xi), \tag{3.5.14}$$

$$\int_{x_0}^{x_6} f(x) \, dx = \frac{h}{140} (41f_0 + 216f_1 + 27f_2 + 272f_3 + 27f_4 + 216f_5 + 41f_6)$$
$$- \frac{9h^9}{1400} f^{viii}(\xi), \tag{3.5.15}$$

$$\int_{x_0}^{x_7} f(x) \, dx = \frac{7h}{17280} (751f_0 + 3577f_1 + 1323f_2 + 2989f_3 + 2989f_4$$
$$+ 1323f_5 + 3577f_6 + 751f_7) - \frac{8183h^9}{518400} f^{viii}(\xi), \tag{3.5.16}$$

$$\int_{x_0}^{x_8} f(x) \, dx = \frac{4h}{14175} (989f_0 + 5888f_1 - 928f_2 + 10496f_3 - 4540f_4$$
$$+ 10496f_5 - 928f_6 + 5888f_7 + 989f_8) - \frac{2368h^{11}}{467775} f^x(\xi). \tag{3.5.17}$$

An inspection of the error terms reveals that a formula involving an *odd* number $n + 1 = 2m + 1$ of points would yield *exact* results if $f(x)$ were a polynomial of degree $n + 1$ or less, whereas one involving an *even* number $n + 1 = 2m$ of points would be exact only if $f(x)$ were a polynomial of degree n or less. Thus the two formulas involving $2m$ and $2m - 1$

ordinates have the same order of accuracy, so that generally no great advantage is gained by advancing from a formula involving an odd number of ordinates to one involving one more ordinate. In particular, the error in *Simpson's rule* (3.5.11) is given by $-h^5 f^{iv}(\xi_1)/90$, and that in *Newton's rule* (3.5.12) is given by $-3h^5 f^{iv}(\xi_2)/80$, where both ξ_1 and ξ_2 are in (a,b). In comparing these errors, when both formulas are applied to the evaluation of *the same integral*, we must notice that $h = (b - a)/2$ in the former case, whereas $h = (b - a)/3$ in the latter. Hence the coefficient of $-(b - a)^5 f^{iv}$ is $\frac{1}{2880}$ in Simpson's rule and $\frac{1}{6480}$ in Newton's rule. Thus the latter (which involves one extra ordinate) may be expected to be only slightly more accurate than the former, on the average. Clearly, the advantage may be shifted in either direction if $f^{iv}(x)$ varies strongly over (a,b), so that $f^{iv}(\xi_1)$ and $f^{iv}(\xi_2)$ may differ appreciably, or if $f^{iv}(x)$ fails to exist or is discontinuous somewhere in (a,b), so that the error formulas are invalid.

Another useful set of integration formulas is obtained by dividing the interval (a,b), as before, into n equal parts by inserting $n - 1$ equally spaced interior abscissas, then approximating $f(x)$ by the polynomial of degree $n - 2$ which coincides with $f(x)$ *at the $n - 1$ interior points*, and approximating the relevant integral by integrating the resultant polynomial over (a,b). These formulas thus do not involve the ordinates at the *ends* of the interval and are said to be of *open* type, whereas those previously considered are said to be of *closed* type. The first few such formulas ($n = 3, \ldots, 6$) may be expressed as follows:

$$\int_{x_0}^{x_3} f(x)\, dx = \frac{3h}{2}(f_1 + f_2) + \frac{3h^3}{4} f''(\xi), \tag{3.5.18}$$

$$\int_{x_0}^{x_4} f(x)\, dx = \frac{4h}{3}(2f_1 - f_2 + 2f_3) + \frac{14h^5}{45} f^{iv}(\xi), \tag{3.5.19}$$

$$\int_{x_0}^{x_5} f(x)\, dx = \frac{5h}{24}(11f_1 + f_2 + f_3 + 11f_4) + \frac{95h^5}{144} f^{iv}(\xi), \tag{3.5.20}$$

$$\int_{x_0}^{x_6} f(x)\, dx = \frac{3h}{10}(11f_1 - 14f_2 + 26f_3 - 14f_4 + 11f_5) + \frac{41h^7}{140} f^{vi}(\xi). \tag{3.5.21}$$

The formulas of the type considered in this section are generally known as the *Newton-Cotes formulas*. Those of open type are principally of use in the numerical integration of differential equations.

Since all the integral formulas of the type considered in this chapter must, in particular, be *exact* if $f(x)$ is a *constant*, it follows that *the sum of the weighting coefficients in any formula must equal the length of the interval.* Thus, for example, that sum in (3.5.13) is $\frac{2}{45}h \cdot 90 = 4h = b - a$.

In place of using a single polynomial to approximate $f(x)$ over the complete range (a,b), it is clearly possible to divide (a,b) into subranges and tó approximate $f(x)$ by a different polynomial over each subrange. Thus, for example, by applying the two-point formula (3.5.10) to n successive subranges of length h, one obtains the so-called *trapezoidal rule:*

$$\int_a^b f(x)\, dx = h(\tfrac{1}{2}f_0 + f_1 + f_2 + \cdots + f_{n-2} + f_{n-1} + \tfrac{1}{2}f_n) - \frac{nh^3}{12} f''(\xi),$$
$$(3.5.22)$$

where $f_0 = f(a)$, $f_k = f(a + kh)$, and $f_n = f(b)$, and where now ξ is somewhere in (a,b). This formula corresponds to replacing the graph of $f(x)$ by the result of joining the ends of adjacent ordinates by line segments and is of remarkable simplicity. Whereas it is not of high accuracy, we may notice that, since $h = (b - a)/n$, the magnitude of the error can be written in the form

$$|E_n| = \frac{(b - a)^3}{12n^2} |f''(\xi)|.$$

Hence, if only $f''(x)$ is continuous (and hence bounded) in (a,b), the error will indeed *tend to zero* like $1/n^2$ as $n \to \infty$.

As will be seen, the accuracy afforded by a k-point Newton-Cotes formula does not *necessarily* increase as k increases, and, in fact, the accuracy may become worse and worse after a certain stage, even though $f(x)$ possess continuous derivatives of all orders for all real values of x, and even though no round-off errors be introduced. In such cases, unless the desired accuracy is attained before this stage is attained, the use of a *composite* rule such as the trapezoidal rule (or the parabolic rule, next to be considered) is essential, as well as convenient.

Another advantage of the trapezoidal rule consists in the fact that the weighting coefficients are nearly equal to each other. For it is easily seen that, if $n + 1$ ordinates are each liable to random errors of observation (or round-off), the RMS error in a linear combination of these ordinates, for which the sum of the constants of combination is fixed (here equal to $b - a$), is *least* when the constants of combination are equal. Newton-Cotes formulas of the open type are particularly objectionable from this point of view, since, for $n = 4$ and $n \geq 6$, their coefficients actually fluctuate in sign. Similar sign fluctuations also occur in formulas of closed type for $n \geq 8$.

By dividing the interval (a,b) into $n/2$ subranges of length $2h$, where n is an *even* integer, and applying Simpson's rule to each subrange [that is, by approximating the graph of $f(x)$ by a parabola in each subrange], the so-called *parabolic rule* is obtained in the form

$$\int_a^b f(x)\, dx = \frac{h}{3} (f_0 + 4f_1 + 2f_2 + 4f_3 + \cdots + 4f_{n-3} + 2f_{n-2}$$
$$+ 4f_{n-1} + f_n) - \frac{nh^5}{180} f^{\mathrm{iv}}(\xi), \quad (3.5.23)$$

where again $f_0 = f(a)$, $f_k = f(a + kh)$, and $f_n = f(b)$. Here, if $f^{iv}(x)$ is continuous in (a,b), the error associated with the use of $n + 1$ ordinates tends to zero like $1/n^4$ as $n \to \infty$. Thus the parabolic rule is usually more accurate than the trapezoidal rule, when n is sufficiently large, unless the function f displays an unusual behavior in (a,b). Since also its weighting coefficients are simple and do not fluctuate unduly in magnitude, it is perhaps the most widely used of all formulas for numerical integration. However, it can be used only when (a,b) is divided into an *even* number of intervals of length h, and its use may require a prohibitively large number of ordinates if a high degree of accuracy is required.

Other integration formulas are considered in Chaps. 5 and 8.

3.6. Use of Integration Formulas. In order to illustrate the preceding formulas in a simple case, we consider first the numerical evaluation of the integral

$$\int_0^1 \frac{dx}{1 + x} = \log 2 = 0.69314718 \cdots.$$

With $f(x) = 1/(1 + x)$, there follows also

$$f^{(k)}(x) = \frac{(-1)^k k!}{(1 + x)^{k+1}},$$

and hence $\quad 2^{-k-1} k! < (-1)^k f^{(k)}(x) < k! \qquad (0 < x < 1).$

Thus, for example, if use were to be made of the five-point formula (3.5.13), with $h = 0.25$, the upper and lower bounds

$$0.000002 < -E_5 < 0.0004$$

would be available with regard to the truncation error. Since $f^{(k)}(x)$ is positive in $(0,1)$ when k is even, it follows that each error term will be negative.

The following table of upper bounds on the magnitude of the *possible* error relevant to the Newton-Cotes (N-C), trapezoidal (T), and parabolic (P) rules, in the present case, is easily determined:

Ordinates	N-C	T	P
2	2×10^{-1}	2×10^{-1}	—
3	9×10^{-3}	5×10^{-2}	9×10^{-3}
4	4×10^{-3}	2×10^{-2}	—
5	4×10^{-4}	2×10^{-2}	6×10^{-4}
6	2×10^{-4}	7×10^{-3}	—
7	3×10^{-5}	5×10^{-3}	2×10^{-4}
8	2×10^{-5}	4×10^{-3}	—
9	2×10^{-6}	3×10^{-3}	4×10^{-5}

In particular, it can be predicted that the error involved in the use of the parabolic rule with $n + 1$ ordinates (where n is even) will be between

$1/(240n^4)$ and $2/(15n^4)$ in magnitude, and that involved in the use of the trapezoidal rule will be between $1/(48n^2)$ and $1/(6n^2)$.

The preliminary upper bounds may be quite conservative, but it is difficult to obtain more precise ones.

In addition to the truncation errors, one must consider the effect of round-off in the values of the ordinates used in the calculation. If each ordinate is rounded correctly to r decimal places, so that the maximum error in each ordinate is not greater than $5 \times 10^{-r-1}$, the maximum corresponding error in the final calculation is therefore not greater than $5 \times 10^{-r-1}$ times the sum of the *absolute values* of the relevant weighting coefficients. If those coefficients are all *positive*, this last sum must equal the length of the range of integration (here unity). Thus, in the present case, if all weighting coefficients are positive, the error in the final result, due to inaccuracies in the original data, cannot exceed the maximum of those inaccuracies. This situation prevails in all the formulas considered in the preceding tabulation except the Newton-Cotes nine-point formula, in which a magnification factor of $\frac{41142}{28350} \approx 1.5$ would be involved. Whereas a considerable amount of cancellation in the errors of round-offs would be expected (particularly if the weighting coefficients are nearly equal), it cannot be *guaranteed* in any particular case.

Suppose that the ordinates used in the present calculation are to be rounded to r decimal places, and that the final result is to be in error by less than one unit in the rth decimal place. If the parabolic rule is to be used, with $n + 1$ ordinates, an even integer n must then be determined such that

$$\frac{2}{15n^4} < 5 \times 10^{-r-1} \qquad \text{or} \qquad n > 0.72 \times 10^{r/4}.$$

The total error, due to truncation and initial round-off, then could not exceed 10^{-r}, under the assumption that no *intermediate* round-offs are effected. For $r = 4$, this condition gives $n > 7.2$, so that nine ordinates would be required; for $r = 5$, thirteen ordinates would suffice. If the trapezoidal rule were used, the need for about 58 ordinates would be predicted for four-place accuracy. Reference to the preceding table shows that a Newton-Cotes formula using nine ordinates would lead to a result in error by less than 2×10^{-6} due to truncation. If the ordinates were rounded to five places, the effect of that round-off here could be as large as 8×10^{-6}. Thus the final error could not exceed 10^{-5}.

Actual calculation, with the ordinates rounded to five places, shows that the error associated with Simpson's rule (three ordinates) is smaller than 2×10^{-3}, with the five-ordinate Newton-Cotes formula less than 3×10^{-5}, with the five-ordinate trapezoidal rule less than 4×10^{-3}, and with the five-ordinate parabolic rule less than 10^{-4}. The fact that some of the error predictions were quite conservative is a consequence of the variation of the higher derivatives of $f(x)$ over $(0,1)$. Thus, for example the error estimate for the five-ordinate Newton-Cotes formula assigned the maximum value 720 to $f^{vi}(x)$ in $(0,1)$, whereas all values from $\frac{45}{8}$ to 720 are admissible. A value of about 56 would have given the proper estimate.

In those cases where $f(x)$ is given empirically or, more generally, in such a form that information with regard to bounds on higher derivatives of $f(x)$ is not readily accessible, less dependable error estimates may be based on the calculation of one or more *divided differences* of order equal to that of the derivative involved in the error estimate.

Another method of estimating the error is of frequent usefulness, and it may be illustrated in the case of the parabolic rule. Suppose that *two* calculations are made, the first with $n_1 + 1$ ordinates and the second with $n_2 + 1$ ordinates, where n_1 and n_2 are even integers. Let the resultant approximations be designated by I_1 and I_2, and suppose that the true value is I. Then, if only truncation errors are considered, there follows from (3.5.23)

$$I = I_1 - \frac{(b-a)^5}{180 n_1^4} f^{iv}(\xi_1),$$

$$I = I_2 - \frac{(b-a)^5}{180 n_2^4} f^{iv}(\xi_2),$$

where ξ_1 and ξ_2 are in (a,b). If it is *assumed* that $f^{iv}(\xi_1) \approx f^{iv}(\xi_2)$, the unknown fourth derivative can be eliminated to give the approximate *extrapolation formula*†

$$I \approx \frac{n_2^4 I_2 - n_1^4 I_1}{n_2^4 - n_1^4} = I_2 + \frac{n_1^4}{n_2^4 - n_1^4}(I_2 - I_1). \tag{3.6.1}$$

In particular, if $n_2 = 2n_1$, there follows

$$I \approx I_2 + \tfrac{1}{15}(I_2 - I_1) \qquad (n_2 = 2n_1). \tag{3.6.2}$$

This approximation will certainly be valid if $f^{iv}(x)$ does not vary rapidly, and does not change sign, over (a,b), and generally may be used with some confidence in any case, if the correction to be added to I_2 is small relative to I_2 itself and if successive approximations appear to be approaching a limit from one side, without oscillating about it.

In the case of the preceding example, the approximation $I \approx 0.694444$ was obtained with $n = 2$ and the approximation $I \approx 0.693254$ was

---

† A procedure of this general type, in which two calculations are made, with errors of the respective forms $\phi(n_1)/n_1^r$ and $\phi(n_2)/n_2^r$, where $\phi(n)$ is an incompletely known function of n, and in which an extrapolation to $n = \infty$ is made under the assumption that $\phi(n)$ is nearly independent of n, is often known as *Richardson's deferred approach to the limit.* See Richardson and Gaunt [195].

btained with $n = 4$.   Use of the extrapolation formula (3.6.2) gives

$$I \approx 0.693254 - 0.000079 = 0.693175.$$

Thus the error in I_2 would be estimated as about -0.00008, and the value
.69317 would be expected to be correct within perhaps one or two units
n the last place, as is indeed the case.   When oscillation of the sequence
of successive approximations is present, this procedure may be completely
independable, as will be illustrated in the next section.

3.7. Asymptotic Behavior of Newton-Cotes Formulas.   This section
presents some results which relate to the choice between the use of a
single Newton-Cotes formula, over an entire range of $n + 1$ points, and
the use of lower-order formulas over successive subdivisions, when n is
large.

The problem consists in examining the behavior of the error term,

$$E_n = \begin{cases} h^{n+2}f^{(n+1)}(\xi) \int_0^n \dfrac{s(s-1) \cdots (s-n)}{(n+1)!}\, ds & (n\ \text{odd}), \qquad (3.7.1) \\[2em] h^{n+3}f^{(n+2)}(\xi) \int_0^n \left(s - \dfrac{n}{2}\right)\dfrac{s(s-1) \cdots (s-n)}{(n+2)!}\, ds & (n\ \text{even}), \\ & \qquad\qquad (3.7.2) \end{cases}$$

where $n + 1$ is the number of ordinates and ξ is somewhere in the relevant
range of integration, say (a,b).   As may be seen by an examination of
the error terms given explicitly in §3.5, the numerical factor represented
by the integral in (3.7.1) or (3.7.2) decreases slowly as n increases.
Indeed, it can be shown (see Prob. 37) that, *when n is sufficiently large*,
the integral in (3.7.1) is approximated by $-2/[n(\log n)^2]$, and that in
(3.7.2) by one-half that quantity.   Thus, in either case, the numerical
factor ultimately tends to zero somewhat more rapidly than $1/n$, but less
rapidly than $1/n^2$.

On the other hand, if $f(x)$ can be represented by a Taylor series in the
neighborhood of a point $x = \alpha$, and if the radius of convergence of that
series is R, then $|f^{(k)}(\alpha)|$ generally is of the order of magnitude of $k!/R^k$
when k is large.   Thus, if $f(x)$ can be so represented at each point of
(a,b), it follows that†

$$|E_n| = 0\left[\frac{n!}{(\log n)^2}\left(\frac{h}{R}\right)^{n+2} \right] \qquad (n\ \text{odd}), \qquad (3.7.3)$$

and
$$|E_n| = 0\left[\frac{(n+1)!}{(\log n)^2}\left(\frac{h}{R}\right)^{n+3} \right] \qquad (n\ \text{even}), \qquad (3.7.4)$$

where R is the radius of convergence of the Taylor-series expansion of
$f(x)$ about *some* point ξ in (a,b).

† The notation $f(n) = 0[g(n)]$ is used to indicate that the ratio $f(n)/g(n)$ tends to a
finite limit as $n \to \infty$.   If that ratio tends to *unity*, the notation $f(n) \sim g(n)$ is
conventional.

If the spacing h were held fixed and n were increased, the expressions in brackets would increase without limit, so long as R remained finite, and hence the error associated with the numerical integration would also ultimately tend to increase unboundedly in magnitude. This limiting process, however, corresponds to allowing the interval (a,b) to increase in proportion to n.

More usually, the interval (a,b) is fixed and is divided into n equal parts, so that $h = (b - a)/n$. The result of substituting this relation into (3.7.3) and (3.7.4) can be simplified if use is made of the *Stirling approximation to the factorial*,

$$n! \sim \sqrt{2\pi n}\; n^n e^{-n} \qquad (n \to \infty), \tag{3.7.5}$$

and a simple calculation leads to the desired result in the form

$$|E_n| = 0 \left[\frac{1}{n^{\frac{3}{2}}(\log n)^2} \left(\frac{b - a}{eR} \right)^n \right]. \tag{3.7.6}$$

Whereas the factor $n^{\frac{3}{2}}(\log n)^2$ in the denominator acts in favor of convergence, nevertheless, if it happens that

$$R < \frac{b - a}{e} \approx \frac{1}{3}(b - a), \tag{3.7.7}$$

the factor $[(b - a)/(eR)]^n$ will dominate the denominator and the error again will ultimately tend to increase unboundedly as n increases, although it may *decrease* with increasing n when n is sufficiently small.

It may be recalled that, when $f(x)$ is an analytic function of a *complex* variable x, the radius of convergence of the Taylor series centered at $x = \alpha$ is the distance, in the complex plane, between the point $x = \alpha$ and the nearest singularity of $f(x)$.

In the example of the preceding section, the only singularity of the function $f(x) = 1/(1 + x)$ is at $x = -1$, and the smallest value of R in the interval $(0,1)$ is accordingly *unity*, corresponding to the end point $x = 0$. Thus the ratio $(b - a)/(eR)$ here cannot exceed $e^{-1} \doteq 0.37$, and hence the difficulty does not arise. The fact that relatively large values of n are needed, in that case, to supply a specified degree of accuracy, is, however, a consequence of the relative nearness of the singularity.

Nearby singularities at *complex* points are, of course, just as troublesome as those which occur for *real* values of x. In order to illustrate this fact, we consider the integral

$$\int_{-4}^{4} \frac{dx}{1 + x^2} = 2 \tan^{-1} 4 \doteq 2.6516. \tag{3.7.8}$$

Here, although $f(x) = 1/(1 + x^2)$ is perfectly well behaved when x is real, it possesses singularities at the complex points $x = \pm i$. Thus

ere the minimum value of R is unity, corresponding to the central point
$= 0$, and $(b - a)/(eR)$ can be as large as $8/e \doteq 2.94$, so that an ulti-
nate increase in error with increasing n is to be expected if the successive
values of ξ involved in (3.7.1) and (3.7.2) are near the center of the interval, as might be anticipated from the symmetry of the integrand.

Direct calculation indicates that this undesirable situation does indeed
exist. The results of computations involving $n + 1 = 3, 5, 7, 9$, and 11
ordinates, and using Newton-Cotes formulas over the entire range in each
case, are compared in the following table with the results afforded by the
same ordinates with the use of the parabolic rule and of the trapezoidal
rule:

$n + 1$	N-C	P	T
3	5.490	5.490	4.235
5	2.278	2.478	2.918
7	3.329	2.908	2.701
9	1.941	2.573	2.659
11	3.596	2.695	2.6511

It is seen that the best of the Newton-Cotes approximations corresponds to the use of only five ordinates, and that the errors associated
with successive formulas of higher order oscillate with increasing amplitude about the true value.

The sequence of approximations afforded by the parabolic rule displays *damped* oscillations but is, of course, convergent. On the other
hand, the trapezoidal-rule sequence is converging toward the true value
at a rate which has not yet been exceeded by that of the parabolic-rule
sequence, although the incorporation of additional ordinates would
eventually reverse the advantage.

It is of importance to notice that the use of the *extrapolation formula*
(3.6.1) is undependable here, because of the oscillation. Thus, whereas
it gives a good prediction with $n_1 = 4$ and $n_2 = 8$, the prediction based
on $n_1 = 6$ and $n_2 = 8$ is worse than either of the approximations upon
which it is based.

The preceding example is not intended to generally discredit the
Newton-Cotes formulas which use many ordinates, but to serve as a
warning that there exist many *nonpathological* situations in which their
use is not appropriate. Such situations generally can be predicted in
advance when $f(x)$ is given analytically. In particular, if the Taylor-
series expansions of $f(x)$ converge everywhere [as for e^{-x^2}, $J_0(x)$, and so
forth], the difficulty noted does not arise. However, if only tabular
values of $f(x)$ are available, such a prediction cannot be made, and the
use of a more dependable formula, such as the parabolic rule (which
yields quartic convergence, if sufficient data are available, if only f^{iv} is
continuous) or the trapezoidal rule (which requires only continuity of

f'' for quadratic convergence), may be desirable. Also, if the data ar empirical, and of doubtful reliability, the trapezoidal rule is often to b preferred, although here it is generally still better to *smooth* the dat before integration (see §7.13).

Finally, it should be noticed that relations such as (3.7.3), (3.7.4), an (3.7.6) give only orders of magnitude when n is *sufficiently large* and ar not generally of quantitative significance in actual calculation.

3.8. Differentiation Formulas. To conclude this chapter, we list few formulas which may be used for numerical differentiation of tabulate functions at tabular points, when the need for such a calculation canno be avoided.

By differentiating three- and five-point Lagrangian interpolation for mulas and evaluating the results at tabular points (see §3.4), the followin; derivative formulas may be obtained, with a convenient renumbering c the ordinates.

Three-point Formulas:

$$f'_{-1} = \frac{1}{2h}(-3f_{-1} + 4f_0 - f_1) + \frac{h^2}{3}f'''(\xi), \qquad (3.8.1$$

$$f'_0 = \frac{1}{2h}(-f_{-1} + f_1) - \frac{h^2}{6}f'''(\xi), \qquad (3.8.2$$

$$f'_1 = \frac{1}{2h}(f_{-1} - 4f_0 + 3f_1) + \frac{h^2}{3}f'''(\xi). \qquad (3.8.3$$

Five-point Formulas:

$$f'_{-2} = \frac{1}{12h}(-25f_{-2} + 48f_{-1} - 36f_0 + 16f_1 - 3f_2) + \frac{h^4}{5}f^v(\xi), \qquad (3.8.4$$

$$f'_{-1} = \frac{1}{12h}(-3f_{-2} - 10f_{-1} + 18f_0 - 6f_1 + f_2) - \frac{h^4}{20}f^v(\xi), \qquad (3.8.5$$

$$f'_0 = \frac{1}{12h}(f_{-2} - 8f_{-1} + 8f_1 - f_2) + \frac{h^4}{30}f^v(\xi), \qquad (3.8.6$$

$$f'_1 = \frac{1}{12h}(-f_{-2} + 6f_{-1} - 18f_0 + 10f_1 + 3f_2) - \frac{h^4}{20}f^v(\xi), \qquad (3.8.7$$

$$f'_2 = \frac{1}{12h}(3f_{-2} - 16f_{-1} + 36f_0 - 48f_1 + 25f_2) + \frac{h^4}{5}f^v(\xi). \qquad (3.8.8$$

In each set of formulas, each ξ lies between the extreme values of the abscissas involved in that formula. It should be noticed that the truncation error is least when the derivative is calculated at the *central* point, and that the ordinate at that point is then not involved in the calculation.

An inspection of these formulas reveals the existence of a new problem in error control. For example, consider (3.8.2), and suppose that it is known that $|f'''(x)| < M_3$ in the interval $(x_0 - h, x_0 + h)$. Then, if all

.ven data were exact, the maximum possible error in the calculation of
(x₀) would be

$$|E_3|_{max} = \frac{M_3 h^2}{6}.$$

·n the other hand, suppose that each of the ordinates involved could be
ı error by $\pm \epsilon$. Then the magnitude of the corresponding error in the
ılculation of $f'(x_0)$ could be as large as

$$|R_3|_{max} = \frac{\epsilon}{h}.$$

Vhereas a reduction of the truncation error E_3 would generally require a
ecrease in h, a small value of h would lead to a large possible *round-off*
ːror R_3 and, conversely, a reduction in $|R_3|_{max}$ would generally correspond
o an increase in $|E_3|_{max}$.

A reasonable procedure consists in determining the interval h such that
ɦe predictable upper bounds on the two errors are about equal, if this is
ːasible. The optimum value of h and the corresponding maximum total
ːror T_3 are then found to be

$$h_{3,opt} \approx 1.8\epsilon^{\frac{1}{3}}M_3^{-\frac{1}{3}}, \qquad |T_3|_{max} \approx 1.1\epsilon^{\frac{2}{3}}M_3^{\frac{1}{3}}.$$

Corresponding results relevant to (3.8.6), and to similar seven-point
ɩnd nine-point formulas, can be obtained as follows:

$$h_{5,opt} \approx 2.1\epsilon^{\frac{1}{5}}M_5^{-\frac{1}{5}}, \qquad |T_5|_{max} \approx 1.4\epsilon^{\frac{4}{5}}M_5^{\frac{1}{5}},$$
$$h_{7,opt} \approx 2.2\epsilon^{\frac{1}{7}}M_7^{-\frac{1}{7}}, \qquad |T_7|_{max} \approx 1.7\epsilon^{\frac{6}{7}}M_7^{\frac{1}{7}},$$
$$h_{9,opt} \approx 2.2\epsilon^{\frac{1}{9}}M_9^{-\frac{1}{9}}, \qquad |T_9|_{max} \approx 1.9\epsilon^{\frac{8}{9}}M_9^{\frac{1}{9}}.$$

In illustration, suppose that empirical values were to be obtained for
ı function which is truly of the form $f(x) = \sin \omega x$, and that one of these
ʹormulas were to be used to approximate $f'(0) = \omega$. In this case, the
ːelevant quantities $M_k^{1/k}$ are each equal to ω. Thus, if, say, the maximum
ɔbservational error ϵ is 0.01, the optimum spacings for the three-, five-,
ɕeven-, and nine-point formulas are found to be about $0.39/\omega$, $0.84/\omega$,
ɭ.14/ω, and 1.32/ω, respectively, and the corresponding maximum total
ːrrors in the calculation of $f'(0) = \omega$ are found to be about 0.051ω,
ɔ.035ω, 0.033ω, and 0.032ω, respectively. The increase of h_{opt} with
increasing n, and the fact that an increase in n affords only slight improve-
ɱent in accuracy, are both worthy of note.

The results of this example are typical of most practical situations in
which the function $f(x)$ is representable by a Taylor series which converges for all values of x. When the series representations have finite

radii of convergence, the quantities $M_k^{1/k}$ tend to increase with increasing k, and the incorporation of additional ordinates may lead to a *decrease* in accuracy, at an early stage, when the inaccuracies in the given data are appreciable.

In practice, unless $f(x)$ is given analytically, the truncation error relevant to any Lagrangian formula can be estimated only roughly by making two or more independent calculations, based on different sets of ordinates, or by determining sample values of the divided difference of order equal to the number of ordinates used. It is apparent that recourse to the latter alternative would tend to nullify the computational advantages which are inherent to the Lagrangian methods. However, when *equally spaced* abscissas are used, divided differences of a given order can be calculated conveniently by use of simple formulas (see Probs. 7 and 8 of Chap. 2), without resort to the formation of a divided-difference table or to the calculation of intermediate differences of lower order. Equation (2.3.2) is available for the same purpose in the general case.

3.9. Supplementary References. References to tables relevant to Lagrangian interpolation, differentiation, and integration, corresponding to equally spaced abscissas, are listed in Appendix B. Salzer [262, 263] presents tables for inverse Lagrangian interpolation. Luke [256] tabulates coefficients relevant to Lagrange interpolation using the coordinate functions $e^{kx}(k = 0, 1, 2, \ldots)$. For derivations of the remainder terms in the Newton-Cotes formulas, see §5.12 and Steffensen [18]. Integration formulas expressing $\int_a^b w(x)f(x)\,dx$ approximately as linear combinations of values of $f(x)$ at equally spaced points are given by Kaplan [127] for several choices of $w(x)$ which correspond to the presence of singularities of various types in the integrand. Salzer [270] gives tables relevant to the case $(a,b) = (0, \infty)$, $w = e^{-px}$. See also Chap. 8 for other methods of dealing with such integrals. A useful formula for trigonometric integrals is given by Filon [77]. Lagrangian interpolation by trigonometric functions is outlined in Prob. 7; tables of the coefficients are given by Salzer [269].

PROBLEMS

Section 3.2

1. By noticing that the zeroth Lagrangian coefficient function of degree n takes on the value unity when $x = x_0$ and the value zero when $x = x_1, \ldots, x_n$, and by considering the associated divided-difference table (or otherwise), show that

$$l_0(x) = 1 + \frac{x - x_0}{x_0 - x_1} + \frac{(x - x_0)(x - x_1)}{(x_0 - x_1)(x_0 - x_2)} + \cdots + \frac{(x - x_0) \cdots (x - x_{n-1})}{(x_0 - x_1) \cdots (x_0 - x_n)}$$

and that similar expansions can be written down by symmetry for the other coefficient functions.

2. Derive the Lagrangian interpolation formula directly from Newton's divided-difference formula.

3. If $y(x)$ is the polynomial of degree n which agrees with $f(x)$ at the distinct points $x = x_0, x_1, \ldots, x_n$, and if $\pi(x) \equiv (x - x_0)(x - x_1) \cdots (x - x_n)$, obtain the Lagrangian form of $y(x)$ by determining the coefficients in the partial-fraction expansion of the ratio

$$\frac{y(x)}{\pi(x)} = \sum_{k=0}^{n} \frac{a_k}{x - x_k}.$$

(Multiply both members by $x - x_r$ and let $x \to x_r$.)

4. Show that

$$\begin{vmatrix} 1 & a_1 & a_1^2 \\ 1 & a_2 & a_2^2 \\ 1 & a_3 & a_3^2 \end{vmatrix} = (a_2 - a_1)(a_3 - a_1)(a_3 - a_2),$$

and use this fact to express the result of expanding the left-hand member of (3.2.3) with respect to the elements of the first column, and equating the result to zero, in Lagrangian form when $n = 2$.

5. Generalize the result of Prob. 4 to show that

$$\begin{vmatrix} 1 & a_1 & a_1^2 & \cdots & a_1^{n-1} \\ 1 & a_2 & a_2^2 & \cdots & a_2^{n-1} \\ 1 & a_3 & a_3^2 & \cdots & a_3^{n-1} \\ \cdots & \cdots & \cdots & \cdots & \cdots \\ 1 & a_n & a_n^2 & \cdots & a_n^{n-1} \end{vmatrix} = \begin{aligned} (a_2 - a_1)(a_3 - a_1)(a_3 - a_2)(a_4 - a_1)(a_4 - a_2)(a_4 - a_3) \\ \cdots (a_n - a_{n-1}) \end{aligned}$$

and to derive the Lagrangian form of the interpolation polynomial from (3.2.3) in the general case. (The determinant involved here is often called *Vandermonde's determinant*.)

6. By considering the limit of the three-point Lagrangian interpolation formula relative to x_0, $x_0 + \epsilon$, and x_1, as $\epsilon \to 0$, obtain the formula

$$f(x) = \frac{(x_1 - x)(x + x_1 - 2x_0)}{(x_1 - x_0)^2} f(x_0) + \frac{(x - x_0)(x_1 - x)}{x_1 - x_0} f'(x_0)$$
$$+ \frac{(x - x_0)^2}{(x_1 - x_0)^2} f(x_1) + E(x),$$

where
$$E(x) = \tfrac{1}{6}(x - x_0)^2(x - x_1)f'''(\xi).$$

7. Write down a determinantal equation analogous to (3.2.3), but corresponding to the requirement that $y(x) = A_0 + A_1 \cos x + A_2 \sin x$ agree with $f(x)$ when $x = x_0$, x_1, and x_2. Then establish the identity

$$\begin{vmatrix} 1 & \cos a_1 & \sin a_1 \\ 1 & \cos a_2 & \sin a_2 \\ 1 & \cos a_3 & \sin a_3 \end{vmatrix} = 4 \sin \tfrac{1}{2}(a_2 - a_1) \sin \tfrac{1}{2}(a_3 - a_1) \sin \tfrac{1}{2}(a_3 - a_2),$$

and use this result to express $y(x)$ in the following form (due to Gauss):

$$y(x) = \frac{\sin \tfrac{1}{2}(x - x_1) \sin \tfrac{1}{2}(x - x_2)}{\sin \tfrac{1}{2}(x_0 - x_1) \sin \tfrac{1}{2}(x_0 - x_2)} f(x_0) + \frac{\sin \tfrac{1}{2}(x - x_0) \sin \tfrac{1}{2}(x - x_2)}{\sin \tfrac{1}{2}(x_1 - x_0) \sin \tfrac{1}{2}(x_1 - x_2)} f(x_1)$$
$$+ \frac{\sin \tfrac{1}{2}(x - x_0) \sin \tfrac{1}{2}(x - x_1)}{\sin \tfrac{1}{2}(x_2 - x_0) \sin \tfrac{1}{2}(x_2 - x_1)} f(x_2).$$

Show also that the formula resulting from deleting the $\tfrac{1}{2}$'s in the arguments of the sines (and due to Hermite) defines the approximation $y = A_0 + A_1 \cos 2x + A_2 \sin 2x$

which agrees with $f(x)$ at the same three points. Also predict the form of the generalization of the Gauss formula to the case when an approximation of the form

$$y = A_0 + A_1 \cos x + A_2 \sin x + \cdots + A_{2n-1} \cos nx + A_{2n} \sin nx$$

is to agree with $f(x)$ at the $2n + 1$ points $x_0, x_1, \ldots, x_{2n}$, and verify the correctness of this conjecture.

Section 3.3

8. Prove that (3.3.20) is valid when x is outside the range R of the values $x_0, \ldots, x_n$, by writing $F(x) \equiv f(x) - y(x) - K\pi(x)$, showing that the function

$$F^{(r)}(x) = f^{(r)}(x) - y^{(r)}(x) - K\pi^{(r)}(x)$$

vanishes at least $n - r + 1$ times inside R, showing that all zeros of $\pi^{(r)}(x)$ lie inside R and hence that K can be so chosen that $F^{(r)}(x)$ also vanishes when $x = \bar{x}$ if $\bar{x}$ is not inside R, so that

$$E^{(r)}(\bar{x}) = K\pi^{(r)}(\bar{x}),$$

and proving that, with this K, there follows $0 = f^{(n+1)}(\bar{\eta}) - (n + 1)!K$ for some $\bar{\eta}$ between the smallest and the largest of $x_0, \ldots, x_n$, and $\bar{x}$.

9. Obtain the Lagrangian three-point first-derivative formula, in the case when the abscissas are equally spaced, at spacing h, and the origin is taken at the central point, in the form

$$f'(x) = \frac{2x - h}{2h^2} f(-h) - \frac{2x}{h^2} f(0) + \frac{2x + h}{2h^2} f(h) + E(x),$$

with $\quad E(x) = \frac{1}{6}(3x^2 - h^2)f'''(\xi_1) + \frac{1}{24}x(x^2 - h^2)f^{iv}(\xi_2),$

where ξ_1 and ξ_2 are in $(-h,h)$ if x is in that interval. Show also that, unless hf^{iv} is large in magnitude relative to f''', the error is least, on the average, at distances of about $0.6h$ from the central point.

10. By integrating the Lagrangian three-point formula, when the abscissas are at equal spacing h, with the origin taken at the central point, obtain the formula

$$\int_{-h}^{x} f(x)\, dx = \frac{5h^3 - 3hx^2 + 2x^3}{12h^2} f(-h) + \frac{2h^3 + 3h^2x - x^3}{3h^2} f(0)$$
$$- \frac{h^3 - 3hx^2 - 2x^3}{12h^2} f(h) + E(x)$$

and show that the truncation error is expressible in the form

$$E(x) = \int_{-h}^{x} x(x^2 - h^2) f[-h,0,h,x]\, dx.$$

11. If the upper limit of the integration in Prob. 10 does not lie outside the interval $(-h,0)$, show that

$$E(x) = \frac{1}{24}(x^2 - h^2)^2 f'''(\xi),$$

where $-h < \xi < h$. In particular, deduce the formula

$$\int_{x_0}^{x_0+h} f(x)\, dx = \frac{h}{12}[5f(x_0) + 8f(x_0 + h) - f(x_0 + 2h)] + \frac{h^4}{24} f'''(\xi),$$

where $x_0 < \xi < x_0 + 2h$, after a change in notation.

12. By integrating the expression for $E(x)$ in Prob. 10 by parts, and noticing that

$x(x^2 - h^2) = \frac{1}{4}[(x^2 - h^2)^2]'$, show that

$$E(x) = \frac{1}{4}(x^2 - h^2)^2 f[-h,0,h,x] - \frac{1}{4}\int_{-h}^{x}(x^2 - h^2)^2 f[-h,0,h,x,x]\,dx$$

and deduce that

$$E(x) = \frac{1}{24}(x^2 - h^2)^2 f'''(\xi_1) - \frac{1}{1440}(3x^5 - 10h^2 x^3 + 15h^4 x + 8h^5)f^{iv}(\xi_2),$$

where ξ_1 and ξ_2 lie between the smallest and largest of $-h$, h, and x. In particular, deduce the formula of *Simpson's rule* (see §3.5):

$$\int_{x_0}^{x_0+2h} f(x)\,dx = \frac{h}{3}[f(x_0) + 4f(x_0 + h) + f(x_0 + 2h)] - \frac{h^5}{90}f^{iv}(\xi),$$

where $x_0 < \xi < x_0 + 2h$.

Section 3.4

13. Determine the Lagrangian coefficient functions, in explicit polynomial form, relative to the ordinates of $f(x)$ at the four points $x = -2$, -1, 1, and 2. Use the results to obtain approximate expressions for $f(0)$, $f'(0)$, and $\int_{-2}^{2} f(x)\,dx$ in terms of those ordinates.

14. Use the results of Prob. 13 to determine the equation of the third-degree polynomial passing through the points $(-2,-5)$, $(-1,-1)$, $(1,1)$, and $(2,11)$.

15. Use the Lagrange interpolation formula to calculate approximate values of $f(x)$ when $x = 1.1300$, 1.1500, 1.1700, and 1.1900 from the following rounded data:

x	1.1275	1.1503	1.1735	1.1972
$f(x)$	0.11971	0.13954	0.15932	0.17903

16. Use the results of Prob. 15 and the coefficients of Table 3.1 to determine approximate values of $f(x)$ for $x = 1.1600(0.0010)1.1700$.

17. Under the assumption that the data in Prob. 15 correspond to the function $f(x) = \sin(\log x)$, obtain bounds on the truncation errors associated with the values calculated in Probs. 15 and 16.

18. Obtain bounds on the round-off errors associated with the values calculated in Probs. 15 and 16.

19. Use the table of five-point Lagrangian coefficients given in §4.12 to interpolate in that table itself for the coefficients relative to $s = 0.38, 0.05$, and 1.93, rounding the results to six places. If no round-offs were effected, what errors would be present in the calculated coefficients?

20. Show that, if $h^3|f'''(x)|$ does not exceed 16 units in the last place to be retained in a three-point Lagrange interpolation based on equally spaced abscissas with spacing h, then the truncation error cannot exceed one unit in that place.

21. Show that, if $h^5|f^v(x)|$ does not exceed 32 units in the last place to be retained in a five-point Lagrange interpolation based on equally spaced abscissas with spacing h, then the truncation error cannot exceed one unit in that place, and also that $h^5|f^v(x)|$ may be as large as 84 units if the interpolation is effected only between the second and fourth of the five successive abscissas.

Section 3.5

22. Prove directly, from Eq. (3.5.6), that a Newton-Cotes formula of closed type, employing $n + 1$ ordinates, is exact when applied to any polynomial of degree $n + 1$

when $n + 1$ is *odd*. [Notice that $F^{(n+1)}(\xi_1)$ is then constant, write $s = t + (n/2)$, and show that the resultant integrand is an odd function of t.]

23. Show that the factor $s - (n/2)$ can be replaced by $s - c$ in (3.5.9b), where c is any constant (see Prob. 22).

24. Derive the formulas resulting from neglect of the error terms in (3.5.18) and (3.5.19).

25. Show that the truncation error associated with a Newton-Cotes formula of closed type employing $n + 1$ ordinates can be expressed in the form

$$E = h^{n+2} \int_0^n s(s - 1) \cdots (s - n) f[x_0, \ldots, x_n, x_0 + hs] \, ds,$$

whereas that associated with a formula of open type employing $n - 1$ ordinates is given by

$$E = h^n \int_0^n (s - 1) \cdots (s - n + 1) f[x_1, \ldots, x_{n-1}, x_0 + hs] \, ds.$$

26. If $f_{(2k+1)/2}$ denotes the value of $f(x)$ at an abscissa midway between x_k and $x_{k+1} \equiv x_k + h$, derive the formulas

$$\int_{x_0}^{x_2} f(x) \, dx = h(f_{\frac{1}{2}} + f_{\frac{3}{2}}) + E_1,$$

$$\int_{x_0}^{x_3} f(x) \, dx = \frac{3h}{8} (3f_{\frac{1}{2}} + 2f_{\frac{3}{2}} + 3f_{\frac{5}{2}}) + E_2.$$

[These formulas are the first two of a set due to *Maclaurin*. It can be shown that $E_1 = h^3 f''(\xi)/12$ $(x_0 < \xi < x_2)$ and that $E_2 = 21 h^5 f^{iv}(\xi)/640$ $(x_0 < \xi < x_3)$.]

Section 3.6

27. Given the following rounded values of the function

$$f(x) = \sqrt{\frac{2}{\pi}} \, e^{-x^2/2},$$

calculate approximate values of the integral

$$P(1) = \sqrt{\frac{2}{\pi}} \int_0^1 e^{-t^2/2} \, dt$$

by use of the trapezoidal rule with $h = \frac{1}{2}, \frac{1}{4},$ and $\frac{1}{8},$ and compare the results with the rounded true value 0.68269:

x	$f(x)$	x	$f(x)$
0.000	0.79788	0.625	0.65632
0.125	0.79168	0.750	0.60227
0.250	0.77334	0.875	0.54411
0.375	0.74371	1.000	0.48394
0.500	0.70413		

28. Repeat the calculations of Prob. 27, using instead the parabolic rule, and compare the results with those of Prob. 27.

29 Repeat the calculations of Prob. 27, using instead the Newton-Cotes three-, five-, and nine-point formulas of closed type, and compare the results with those of Probs. 27 and 28.

30. Calculate approximate values of the integral

$$\int_0^1 e^{\cos 2\pi x}\, dx = I_0(1) \doteq 1.266066$$

by use of the trapezoidal rule with $h = \frac{1}{2}, \frac{1}{4}$, and $\frac{1}{8}$, retaining five decimal places, and compare the results with the true value.

31. Repeat the calculation of Prob. 30, using instead the parabolic rule, and compare the results with those of Prob. 30.

32. Repeat the calculations of Prob. 30, using instead the Newton-Cotes three-, five-, and nine-point formulas of closed type, and compare the results with those of Probs. 30 and 31.

33. Obtain an approximate evaluation of the integral

$$\int_0^1 \frac{\cos x}{\sqrt{x}}\, dx$$

(*a*) by writing it in the form

$$\int_0^1 \frac{dx}{\sqrt{x}} - \int_0^1 \frac{1 - \cos x}{\sqrt{x}}\, dx,$$

evaluating the first integral analytically, and applying the parabolic rule with $h = \frac{1}{8}$ to the second one, and (*b*) by making the change of variables $x = t^2$ in the original form and applying the parabolic rule with $h = \frac{1}{8}$ directly to the result.

Also compare the approximations with a more accurate value obtained by expanding the integrand of one of the forms in a power series and integrating term by term.

Section 3.7

34. Show that

$$\int_0^{2m+1} s(s - 1)\ \cdots\ (s - 2m - 1)\, ds = -\frac{2}{2m + 3} \int_0^1 s(s - 1)\ \cdots\ (s - 2m - 2)\, ds,$$

when m is a nonnegative integer. (Express the left-hand integral as a sum of integrals between successive integers, translate all lower limits to zero, and show that the $2m + 1$ terms in the resultant integrand can be telescoped into the sum of two terms. Then replace s by $1 - s$ in the integrand of one of those terms.)

35. Show that the numerical factor in (3.7.1) and (3.7.2) can be expressed in the form

$$I_{2m} = \int_0^{2m} \frac{s(s - 1)\ \cdots\ (s - 2m)(s - 2m - 1)}{(2m + 2)!}\, ds,$$

when $n = 2m$, and in the form

$$I_{2m+1} = \int_0^{2m+1} \frac{s(s - 1)\ \cdots\ (s - 2m)(s - 2m - 1)}{(2m + 2)!}\, ds$$

when $n = 2m + 1$, and show also that

$$I_{2m+1} - I_{2m} = \int_0^1 \frac{s(s - 1)\ \cdots\ (s - 2m - 1)}{(2m + 2)!}\, ds.$$

36. With the abbreviation

$$\alpha_k = \int_0^1 \frac{s(s-1) \cdots (s-k+1)}{k!} \, ds,$$

show that the results of Probs. 34 and 35 lead to the relations

$$I_{2m} = -2\alpha_{2m+3} - \alpha_{2m+2},$$
$$I_{2m+1} = -2\alpha_{2m+3},$$

and deduce that the error associated with a Newton-Cotes formula of closed type, employing $n + 1$ ordinates, can be expressed in the form

$$E_n = \begin{cases} -2\alpha_{n+2}h^{n+2}f^{(n+1)}(\xi) & (n \text{ odd}), \\ -(2\alpha_{n+3} + \alpha_{n+2})h^{n+3}f^{(n+2)}(\xi) & (n \text{ even}). \end{cases}$$

37. The constant α_k defined in Prob. 36 is expressible as a *generalized Bernoulli number* and is often denoted by $B_k^{(k)}(1)/k!$ or by $B_k^{(k)}/k! + B_{k-1}^{(k-1)}/(k-1)!$. It is known (see Steffensen [18]) that

$$\alpha_k \sim \frac{(-1)^{k+1}}{k(\log k)^2} \qquad (k \to \infty).$$

Assuming this fact, show that the numerical factor in the expression for E_n is approximated by $-2/[n(\log n)^2]$ when n is a large odd integer, and by $-1/[n(\log n)^2]$ when n is a large even integer.

Section 3.8

38. From the following rounded values of $f(x) = (1 + x)^{-2}$, determine approximate values of $f'(x)$ for $x = 1.0$, 1.1, and 1.2 by use of appropriate three- and five-point formulas, estimate the errors, and check the validity of the estimations:

x	1.0	1.1	1.2	1.3	1.4
$f(x)$	0.2500	0.2268	0.2066	0.1890	0.1736

39. Values of a function $f(x)$ are to be determined for $x = 0$ and for four additional positive values of x, and are to be used for the approximate determination of $f'(0)$. Assuming that the five abscissas are to be equally spaced and that the accuracy of the calculated values can be guaranteed only within 1 per cent, and supposing that the true function is $f(x) = 1/(1 + x)$, determine the spacing for which the sum of the squares of predictable upper bounds on the truncation and round-off errors is least, and calculate the corresponding upper bound on the total error. Also compare this situation with that in which only three ordinates are to be calculated.

CHAPTER 4

FINITE-DIFFERENCE INTERPOLATION

4.1. Introduction. This chapter returns to the consideration of formulas expressed in terms of differences, rather than of the ordinates themselves, but deals only with the cases in which the abscissas are equally spaced. Here the rather cumbersome notation of *divided* differences is not needed and is replaced by other notations which are explained in §4.2.

The most important of the interpolation formulas which involve differences, together with error terms, are derived in §§4.3 to 4.7, and their respective uses are discussed and illustrated in §4.8. In this connection, it is of some historical interest to note that the formulas bearing the names of Gauss, Stirling, and Bessel were apparently first known to Newton, while the formulas attributed to Newton (§4.3) are due to Gregory. Further, Everett's first formula is due to Laplace, and Everett's second formula was apparently first given by Steffensen.

The propagation and detection of errors in given data are considered in §4.9, whereas a useful method of taking certain higher differences into approximate account, by modifying certain earlier differences, is illustrated in §4.10.

The concluding section of the chapter provides some information concerning the behavior of the error term in certain interpolation formulas, as more and more differences are retained, and indicates the practical significance of that information.

4.2. Difference Notations. When data are tabulated for uniformly spaced abscissas, with spacing h, it is convenient to express formulations for interpolation and related processes in terms of the differences themselves, rather than the *divided* differences used in Chap. 2.

For calculation near a tabular point x_0 at the beginning of the tabulated range, it is conventional to define the *forward difference* $\Delta f(x_0)$ as

$$\Delta f(x_0) = f(x_0 + h) - f(x_0). \qquad (4.2.1)$$

If also $\Delta f(x_0 + h) = f(x_0 + 2h) - f(x_0 + h)$ is known, then the second forward difference associated with x_0 is defined as

$$\Delta^2 f(x_0) = \Delta f(x_0 + h) - \Delta f(x_0) = f(x_0 + 2h) - 2f(x_0 + h) + f(x_0),$$
$$(4.2.2)$$

91

and succeeding forward differences are defined by iteration. More generally, we introduce the definitions

$$\Delta f(x) = f(x + h) - f(x), \qquad \Delta^{r+1}f(x) = \Delta^r f(x + h) - \Delta^r f(x), \quad (4.2.3)$$

the spacing h being implied in Δ. If a more specific notation is needed, Δ_h may be used in place of Δ.

When forward differences are used, it is convenient to number the abscissas $x_0, x_1, \ldots$ in increasing algebraic order, so that

$$x_{k+1} = x_k + h. \qquad (4.2.4)$$

Then, with the notation of §2.3, there follows

$$\Delta f(x_k) = f(x_{k+1}) - f(x_k) = (x_{k+1} - x_k)f[x_k,x_{k+1}] = hf[x_k,x_{k+1}],$$
$$\Delta^2 f(x_k) = hf[x_{k+1},x_{k+2}] - hf[x_k,x_{k+1}] = h(x_{k+2} - x_k)f[x_k,x_{k+1},x_{k+2}]$$
$$= 2h^2 f[x_k,x_{k+1},x_{k+2}],$$

and, in general, induction shows that

$$\Delta^r f(x_k) = (r - 1)!h^{r-1}f[x_{k+1}, \ldots ,x_{k+r}] - (r - 1)!h^{r-1}f[x_k, \ldots ,x_{k+r-1}]$$
$$= (r - 1)!h^{r-1}(x_{k+r} - x_k)f[x_k, \ldots ,x_{k+r}]$$
$$= r!h^r f[x_k, \ldots ,x_{k+r}]. \qquad (4.2.5)$$

The beginning of the corresponding difference table is indicated in Fig. 4.1, where f_k is written for $f(x_k)$. We notice that the subscript remains constant along each *forward* diagonal of the table, and that the region of determination of $\Delta^r f_k$ is bounded by the kth forward diagonal and the $(r + k)$th backward diagonal. Hence the difference $\Delta^r f_k$ depends upon the ordinates $f_k, f_{k+1}, \ldots , f_{k+r}$, as is also indicated by (4.2.5).

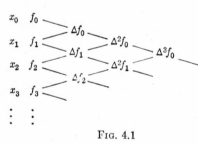

Fig. 4.1

For calculation near the *end* of a tabulated range, the notation of *backward differences* is often more convenient. Here we write

$$\nabla f(x) = f(x) - f(x - h), \qquad \nabla^{r+1}f(x) = \nabla^r f(x) - \nabla^r f(x - h). \quad (4.2.6)$$

If the abscissas are again numbered in accordance with (4.2.4), there follows

$$\nabla f(x_k) = f(x_k) - f(x_{k-1}) = (x_k - x_{k-1})f[x_k,x_{k-1}]$$
$$= hf[x_k,x_{k-1}]$$

and, in general,

$$\nabla^r f(x_k) = r!h^r f[x_k,x_{k-1}, \ldots ,x_{k-r}], \qquad (4.2.7)$$

in analogy with (4.2.5).

The end of the corresponding difference table is indicated in Fig. 4.2. Here the subscript remains constant along each *backward* diagonal. Also, it is seen that the difference $\nabla^r f_k$ depends upon the ordinates f_{k-r}, f_{k-r+1}, . . . , f_k, as is also indicated by (4.2.7).

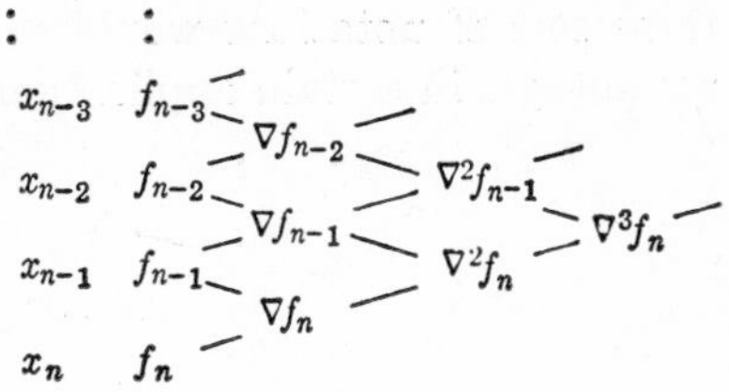

For the remaining calculation, the notation of so-called *central differences* is usually most convenient. If the calculation is to be effected near a certain interior tabular point, it is

FIG. 4.2

convenient to number that abscissa as x_0, and to number forward abscissas as x_1, x_2, . . . and backward abscissas as x_{-1}, x_{-2}, . . . , so that (4.2.4) again holds. In the central-difference notation, one writes

$$\delta f(x) = f(x + \tfrac{1}{2}h) - f(x - \tfrac{1}{2}h), \qquad \delta^{r+1}f(x) = \delta^r f(x + \tfrac{1}{2}h) - \delta^r f(x - \tfrac{1}{2}h).$$
$$(4.2.8)$$

It is seen that $\delta f_k \equiv \delta f(x_k)$ generally *does not involve tabulated ordinates.* However, the *second* central difference

$$\begin{aligned}
\delta^2 f_k &= \delta f(x_k + \tfrac{1}{2}h) - \delta f(x_k - \tfrac{1}{2}h) \\
&= [f(x_k + h) - f(x_k)] - [f(x_k) - f(x_k - h)] \\
&= f_{k+1} - 2f_k + f_{k-1}
\end{aligned}$$

does involve tabular entries, and the same is seen to be true of all central differences $\delta^{2m}f_k$ of *even* order. Furthermore, we may notice that

$$\delta f_{k+\frac{1}{2}} = f_{k+1} - f_k$$

and, more generally, that $\delta^{2m+1}f_{k+\frac{1}{2}}$ involves only tabulated arguments.

With the notation of §2.3, we may write, for example,

$$\delta f_{\frac{1}{2}} = f_1 - f_0 = hf[x_0,x_1], \qquad \delta f_{-\frac{1}{2}} = f_0 - f_{-1} = hf[x_0,x_{-1}],$$
$$\delta^2 f_1 = \delta f_{\frac{3}{2}} - \delta f_{\frac{1}{2}} = hf[x_1,x_2] - hf[x_0,x_1] = 2\,!\,h^2 f[x_0,x_1,x_2]$$

and, in general,

$$\delta^{2m+1}f_{k+\frac{1}{2}} = h^{2m+1}(2m + 1)\,!\,f[x_{k-m}, \ . \ . \ . \ ,x_k, \ . \ . \ . \ ,x_{k+m},x_{k+m+1}],$$
$$(4.2.9)$$

$$\delta^{2m+1}f_{k-\frac{1}{2}} = h^{2m+1}(2m + 1)\,!\,f[x_{k-m-1},x_{k-m}, \ . \ . \ . \ ,x_k, \ . \ . \ . \ ,x_{k+m}],$$
$$(4.2.10)$$

and $\quad \delta^{2m}f_k = h^{2m}(2m)\,!\,f[x_{k-m}, \ . \ . \ . \ ,x_k, \ . \ . \ . \ ,x_{k+m}].$ $\qquad (4.2.11)$

The portion of the corresponding difference table in the neighborhood of an interior tabular point x_0, near which calculations are to be made, is indicated in Fig. 4.3. Here the subscript remains constant along *horizontal* lines of the table, which pass through differences of only even or only odd orders.

Thus, once a set of adjacent entries in a difference table has been numbered, three different sets of notations are available for the differences themselves, as may be seen from the composite Fig. 4.4. Any one of these sets of notations would suffice. However, each possesses certain advantages in certain applications, as will be seen.

$\vdots$	$\vdots$				
x_{-2}	f_{-2}				
		$\delta f_{-3/2}$			
x_{-1}	f_{-1}		$\delta^2 f_{-1}$		
		$\delta f_{-1/2}$		$\delta^3 f_{-1/2}$	
x_0	f_0		$\delta^2 f_0$		$\delta^4 f_0$
		$\delta f_{1/2}$		$\delta^3 f_{1/2}$	
x_1	f_1		$\delta^2 f_1$		
		$\delta f_{3/2}$			
x_2	f_2				
$\vdots$	$\vdots$				

FIG. 4.3

$\vdots$	$\vdots$		
x_0	f_0		
		$\Delta f_0 = \delta f_{1/2} = \nabla f_1$	
x_1	f_1		$\Delta^2 f_0 = \delta^2 f_1 = \nabla^2 f_2$
		$\Delta f_1 = \delta f_{3/2} = \nabla f_2$	
x_2	f_2		
$\vdots$	$\vdots$		

FIG. 4.4

4.3. Newton Forward- and Backward-difference Formulas. In order to obtain an interpolation formula such that the retention of $n + 1$ terms leads to the polynomial of degree n taking on the values of $f(x)$ at $x_0, x_1 = x_0 + h, \cdots, x_n = x_0 + nh$, we may refer to Newton's divided-difference formula (2.5.2), making use of the relation

$$f[x_0, \ldots, x_r] = \frac{1}{r!h^r} \Delta^r f_0, \tag{4.3.1}$$

which follows from (4.2.5), to obtain the result

$$\begin{aligned} f(x) = f_0 + (x - x_0) \frac{\Delta f_0}{1!h} + (x - x_0)(x - x_1) \frac{\Delta^2 f_0}{2!h^2} + \cdots \\ + (x - x_0)(x - x_1) \cdots (x - x_{n-1}) \frac{\Delta^n f_0}{n!h^n} + E(x), \end{aligned} \tag{4.3.2}$$

where
$$E(x) = (x - x_0) \cdots (x - x_n) \frac{f^{(n+1)}(\xi)}{(n + 1)!}, \tag{4.3.3}$$

and where ξ is in the interval occupied by $x_0, \ldots, x_n$, and x, in accordance with (2.5.3) and (2.6.6).

The formula takes on a simpler form if we introduce a **dimensionless** variable s defined as distance from x_0 in units of h,

$$s = \frac{x - x_0}{h}, \qquad x = x_0 + hs. \qquad (4.3.4)$$

Since then there follows also $x - x_k = h(s - k)$, the preceding formula takes the form

$$f_s = f_0 + s\,\Delta f_0 + \frac{s(s-1)}{2!}\,\Delta^2 f_0 + \cdots$$

$$+ \frac{s(s-1)\cdots(s-n+1)}{n!}\,\Delta^n f_0 + E_s \qquad (4.3.5)$$

where $\quad E_s = \dfrac{h^{n+1}}{(n+1)!}\,s(s-1)(s-2)\cdots(s-n)f^{(n+1)}(\xi),\qquad (4.3.6)$

and where we have written

$$f_s \equiv f(x_0 + hs) = f(x), \qquad E_s \equiv E(x_0 + hs) = E(x).$$

The result of neglecting the error term E_s is known as *Newton's forward-difference formula* for interpolation. It makes use of the difference path indicated in Fig. 4.5.

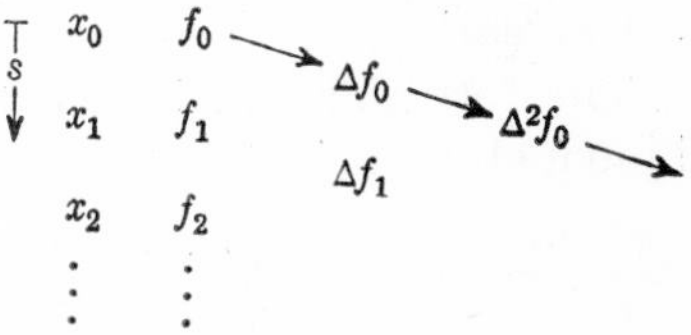

In a similar way, if we require a formula successively introducing the ordinates at x_n, x_{n-1}, x_{n-2}, and so forth, we may replace x_0 by x_n, x_1 by x_{n-1},

FIG. 4.5

$\ldots$, x_k by x_{n-k} in (2.5.2):

$$f(x) = f(x_n) + (x - x_n)f[x_n,x_{n-1}] + (x - x_n)(x - x_{n-1})f[x_n,x_{n-1},x_{n-2}]$$
$$+ (x - x_n)(x - x_{n-1})\cdots(x - x_1)f[x_n,x_{n-1},\ldots,x_0] + E(x)$$

and, writing here

$$s = \frac{x - x_n}{h}, \qquad x = x_n + hs, \qquad (4.3.7)$$

we may use (4.2.7) to reduce this result to the form

$$f_{n+s} = f_n + s\,\nabla f_n + \frac{s(s+1)}{2!}\,\nabla^2 f_n + \cdots$$

$$+ \frac{s(s+1)\cdots(s+n-1)}{n!}\,\nabla^n f_n + E_s, \qquad (4.3.8)$$

where $\quad E_s = \dfrac{h^{n+1}}{(n+1)!}\,s(s+1)\cdots(s+n)f^{(n+1)}(\xi). \qquad (4.3.9)$

This formula is known as *Newton's backward-difference formula*, when E_s is neglected, and it utilizes the difference path indicated in Fig. 4.6.

If $r + 1$ terms are retained in (4.3.5), the polynomial agreeing with $f(x)$ at $x_0, x_1, \ldots, x_r$ is obtained; the retention of $r + 1$ terms in (4.3.8) yields the polynomial agreeing with $f(x)$ at $x_n, x_{n-1}, \ldots, x_{n-r}$. If $n + 1$ terms were retained in each formula, the two formulas would involve the same ordinates and would yield the same polynomial approximation.

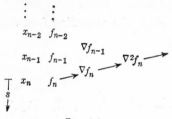

FIG. 4.6

More generally, the former would be used near the beginning of a tabulation (at which *only* forward differences are available) and the latter would be used near the end (where only backward differences are available. In particular, the backward-difference formula is especially useful in *extending* a tabulation, and for generating other formulas useful for advancing numerical solutions of differential equations. For this reason, s was measured *forward* in the table in both formulas, so that it is positive for *extrapolation* in (4.3.8), whereas it is positive for *interpolation* in (4.3.5). Either formula can, of course, be used for either interpolation or extrapolation.

The formulas can be written in more concise form in terms of the binomial coefficients

$$\binom{r}{k} = \frac{r(r-1) \cdots (r - k + 1)}{k!}. \tag{4.3.10}$$

With this notation, the *forward-difference* formula becomes merely

$$f_s \equiv f(x_0 + hs) \approx \sum_{k=0}^{n} \binom{s}{k} \Delta^k f_0. \tag{4.3.11}$$

Further, the coefficient of $\nabla^k f_n$ in (4.3.8) is seen to be

$$\binom{s + k - 1}{k} = \frac{s(s+1) \cdots (s + k - 1)}{k!}$$

$$= (-1)^k \frac{(-s)(-s-1) \cdots (-s - k + 1)}{k!}$$

$$= (-1)^k \binom{-s}{k}, \tag{4.3.12}$$

so that the *backward-difference* formula takes the form

$$f_{n+s} \equiv f(x_n + hs) \approx \sum_{k=0}^{n} (-1)^k \binom{-s}{k} \nabla^k f_n \tag{4.3.13}$$

or, alternatively,

$$f_{n-s} \equiv f(x_n - hs) \approx \sum_{k=0}^{n} (-1)^k \binom{s}{k} \nabla^k f_n. \qquad (4.3.14)$$

Extensive tables of the coefficient functions may be found in the literature (see references in Appendix B). A brief table, for interpolation or extrapolation by tenths, through fifth differences, is included in §4.12.

4.4. Gaussian Formulas. For interpolation at a point $\bar{x}$, it is desirable to have available a formula in which the successively introduced ordinates correspond to abscissas which are as near as possible to $\bar{x}$. If $\bar{x}$ is near one end of the tabulation, the Newtonian formulas of the preceding section serve this purpose as well as is possible. Otherwise, it is convenient to start with the abscissa x_0 nearest $\bar{x}$, then to introduce x_1 and x_{-1}, then x_2 and x_{-2}, and so forth.

If the ordinates are introduced in the order $f_0, f_1, f_{-1}, f_2, f_{-2}, \dots$, the result of replacing $x_0, x_1, x_2, x_3, x_4, \dots$ by $x_0, x_1, x_{-1}, x_2, x_{-2}, \dots$ in (2.5.2), and the subsequent use of (4.2.9) and (4.2.11), with $k = 0$, leads to the form

$$f(x) = f_0 + (x - x_0) \frac{\delta f_{\frac{1}{2}}}{1!h} + (x - x_0)(x - x_1) \frac{\delta^2 f_0}{2!h^2}$$

$$+ (x - x_0)(x - x_1)(x - x_{-1}) \frac{\delta^3 f_{\frac{1}{2}}}{3!h^3}$$

$$+ (x - x_0)(x - x_1)(x - x_{-1})(x - x_2) \frac{\delta^4 f_0}{4!h^4} + \cdots.$$

If we write

$$s = \frac{x - x_0}{h}, \qquad x = x_0 + hs, \qquad (4.4.1)$$

this result takes the form

$$f_s = f_0 + s\, \delta f_{\frac{1}{2}} + \frac{s(s-1)}{2!}\, \delta^2 f_0 + \frac{s(s^2 - 1^2)}{3!}\, \delta^3 f_{\frac{1}{2}}$$

$$+ \frac{s(s^2 - 1^2)(s - 2)}{4!}\, \delta^4 f_0 + \cdots$$

$$+ \frac{s(s^2 - 1^2) \cdots (s^2 - \overline{m - 1}^2)(s - m)}{(2m)!}\, \delta^{2m} f_0$$

$$or \qquad + \frac{s(s^2 - 1^2) \cdots (s^2 - m^2)}{(2m + 1)!}\, \delta^{2m+1} f_{\frac{1}{2}}$$

$$+ E_s, \qquad (4.4.2)$$

where, if nth differences are retained, $n = 2m$ when n is even and $n = 2m + 1$ when n is odd. The error term takes the form

$$E_s = h^{2m+1} \frac{s(s^2 - 1^2) \cdots (s^2 - m^2)}{(2m + 1)!}\, f^{(2m+1)}(\xi) \qquad (4.4.3)$$

when $n = 2m$, and the form

$$E_s = h^{2m+2} \frac{s(s^2 - 1^2) \cdots (s^2 - m^2)(s - m - 1)}{(2m + 2)!} f^{(2m+2)}(\xi) \quad (4.4.4)$$

when $n = 2m + 1$.

This formula employs the *forward* zigzag difference path indicated in Fig. 4.7 and is known as *Gauss's forward formula*.

In a completely similar way, by introducing the ordinates in the sequence $f_0, f_{-1}, f_1, f_{-2}, f_2, \ldots$, using (4.2.10) and (4.2.11) with $k = 0$, and again introducing the abbreviation (4.4.1), we obtain the form

$$f_s = f_0 + s\, \delta f_{-\frac{1}{2}} + \frac{s(s + 1)}{2!}\, \delta^2 f_0 + \frac{s(s^2 - 1^2)}{3!}\, \delta^3 f_{-\frac{1}{2}}$$

$$+ \frac{s(s^2 - 1^2)(s + 2)}{4!}\, \delta^4 f_0 + \cdots$$

$$+ \frac{s(s^2 - 1^2) \cdots (s^2 - \overline{m - 1}^2)(s + m)}{(2m)!}\, \delta^{2m} f_0$$

$$or \quad + \frac{s(s^2 - 1^2) \cdots (s^2 - m^2)}{(2m + 1)!}\, \delta^{2m+1} f_{-\frac{1}{2}}$$

$$+ E_s \quad\quad (4.4.5)$$

where $\quad E_s = h^{2m+1} \dfrac{s(s^2 - 1^2) \cdots (s^2 - m^2)}{(2m + 1)!}\, f^{(2m+1)}(\xi)$

$$or \quad E_s = h^{2m+2} \frac{s(s^2 - 1^2) \cdots (s^2 - m^2)(s + m + 1)}{(2m + 2)!}\, f^{(2m+2)}(\xi)$$

$$(4.4.6)$$

according as the formula is terminated with even or odd differences. This formula utilizes the *backward* zigzag difference path in Fig. 4.7 and is known as *Gauss's backward formula*.

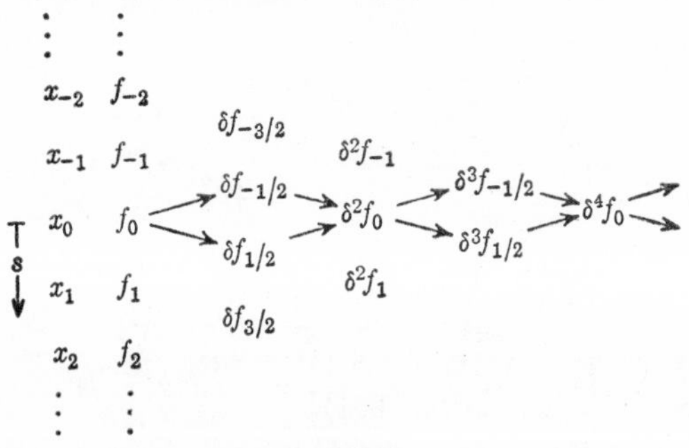

FIG. 4.7

When terminated with an *even* difference, of order $2m$, *both* formulas yield the polynomial agreeing with $f(x)$ at $x_0, x_{\pm 1}, \ldots, x_{\pm m}$, and hence *are completely equivalent in that case.* However, when terminated with **an** *odd* difference, of order $2m + 1$, the forward formula gives the polynomial agreeing with $f(x)$ at $x_0, x_{\pm 1}, \ldots, x_{\pm m}$, and x_{m+1}, whereas the backward formula yields agreement at the first $2m + 1$ points and at x_{-m-1}. In this latter case, when seeking $f(\bar{x})$, the forward formula would be expected to afford somewhat better results when $\bar{x}$ is between x_0 and x_1, whereas the backward formula would generally be preferred when $\bar{x}$ is between x_0 and x_{-1}.

With the notation (4.3.10), the Gaussian forward formula can be written in the more compact form

$$f_s \approx f_0 + \binom{s}{1} \delta f_{\frac{1}{2}} + \binom{s}{2} \delta^2 f_0 + \binom{s+1}{3} \delta^3 f_{\frac{1}{2}} + \binom{s+1}{4} \delta^4 f_0 + \cdots,$$
$$(4.4.7)$$

whereas the corresponding backward formula becomes

$$f_s \approx f_0 + \binom{s}{1} \delta f_{-\frac{1}{2}} + \binom{s+1}{2} \delta^2 f_0 + \binom{s+1}{3} \delta^3 f_{-\frac{1}{2}}$$
$$+ \binom{s+2}{4} \delta^4 f_0 + \cdots. \quad (4.4.8)$$

Neither of these formulas is of frequent practical use, but from them other more useful formulas may be derived.

4.5. Stirling's Formula. When interpolations are to be effected for values of $\bar{x}$ near an interior point x_0, say, between $x_0 - \frac{1}{2}h$ and $x_0 + \frac{1}{2}h$, a formula of frequent use may be obtained by forming the *mean* of the Gaussian forward and backward formulas and so introducing a *symmetry* about the abscissa x_0:

$$f_s = f_0 + \frac{s}{2} (\delta f_{\frac{1}{2}} + \delta f_{-\frac{1}{2}}) + \frac{s}{2 \cdot 2!} [(s-1) + (s+1)] \delta^2 f_0$$
$$+ \frac{s(s^2 - 1^2)}{2 \cdot 3!} (\delta^3 f_{\frac{1}{2}} + \delta^3 f_{-\frac{1}{2}})$$
$$+ \frac{s(s^2 - 1^2)}{2 \cdot 4!} [(s-2) + (s+2)] \delta^4 f_0 + \cdots$$
$$+ \frac{s(s^2 - 1^2) \cdots (s^2 - \overline{m-1}^2)}{2 \cdot (2m)!} [(s-m) + (s+m)] \delta^{2m} f_0$$
$$or \quad + \frac{s(s^2 - 1^2) \cdots (s^2 - m^2)}{2 \cdot (2m+1)!} (\delta^{2m+1} f_{\frac{1}{2}} + \delta^{2m+1} f_{-\frac{1}{2}})$$
$$+ E_s. \quad (4.5.1)$$

It is then convenient to introduce symbols for the mean odd differences which appear in this formula. The notation

$$\mu f(x) \equiv \frac{1}{2} \left[f\left(x + \frac{h}{2}\right) + f\left(x - \frac{h}{2}\right) \right] \quad (4.5.2)$$

is often used, so that, for example, we may write

$$\mu \delta f_0 = \frac{1}{2}(\delta f_{\frac{1}{2}} + \delta f_{-\frac{1}{2}}), \quad \mu \delta^3 f_0 = \frac{1}{2}(\delta^3 f_{\frac{1}{2}} + \delta^3 f_{-\frac{1}{2}}). \quad (4.5.3)$$

With this notation for the so-called *mean central differences* of odd order, (4.5.1) takes the form

$$f_s = f_0 + s\mu\delta f_0 + \frac{s^2}{2!}\delta^2 f_0 + \frac{s(s^2 - 1^2)}{3!}\mu\delta^3 f_0 + \frac{s^2(s^2 - 1^2)}{4!}\delta^4 f_0 + \cdots$$

$$+ \frac{s^2(s^2 - 1^2) \cdots (s^2 - \overline{m - 1^2})}{(2m)!}\delta^{2m} f_0$$

$$or \quad + \frac{s(s^2 - 1^2) \cdots (s^2 - m^2)}{(2m + 1)!}\mu\delta^{2m+1} f_0$$

$$+ E_s. \tag{4.5.4}$$

The result of omitting E_s is known as *Stirling's formula* for interpolation.

Since the errors associated with terminating (4.4.2) and (4.4.5) with an *even* difference are identical, there follows also

$$E_s = h^{2m+1} \frac{s(s^2 - 1^2) \cdots (s^2 - m^2)}{(2m + 1)!} f^{(2m+1)}(\xi) \tag{4.5.5}$$

when $n = 2m$. As in the preceding cases, ξ is intermediate between the largest and smallest of the abscissas involved in the formula (here x_0, $x_{\pm 1}, \ldots, x_{\pm m}$, and x).

However, when $n = 2m + 1$, the mean of the errors (4.4.4) and (4.4.6) takes the form

$$E_s = h^{2m+2} \frac{s(s^2 - 1^2) \cdots (s^2 - m^2)}{2(2m + 2)!} [(s - m - 1)f^{(2m+2)}(\xi_1)$$

$$+ (s + m + 1)f^{(2m+2)}(\xi_2)], \tag{4.5.6}$$

where both ξ_1 and ξ_2 lie inside the interval including x_0, $x_{\pm 1}, \ldots$, $x_{\pm(m+1)}$, and x. Thus, when Stirling's formula is terminated with an *odd* difference, the error term does not take a simple form similar to (4.5.5).

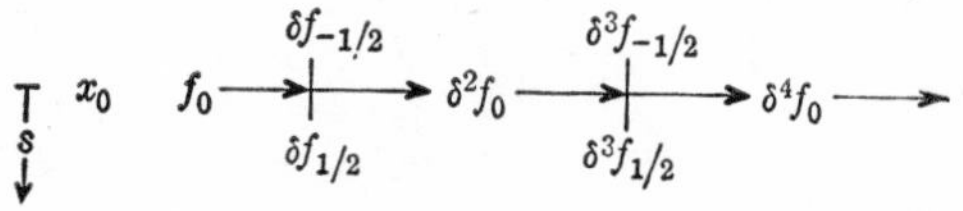

FIG. 4.8

It should be noticed that the interpolation polynomial of degree $2m + 1$, which is yielded by the formula in this case, agrees with $f(x)$ at the $2m + 1$ points x_0, $x_{\pm 1}, \ldots, x_{\pm m}$, but that an additional $(2m + 2)$th point of agreement (which would serve to specify the polynomial) is not known.

The Stirling formula is equivalent to either Gaussian formula when terminated with even differences. But even in this case its form is more convenient because of the fact that the coefficients of the differences of even order are even functions of s, whereas the coefficients of the mean differences of odd order are odd functions of s. With the notation of

(4.3.10), it can be expressed in the more compact form

$$f_s \approx f_0 + \binom{s}{1} \mu \delta f_0 + \frac{s}{2}\binom{s}{1} \delta^2 f_0 + \binom{s+1}{3} \mu \delta^3 f_0$$
$$+ \frac{s}{4}\binom{s+1}{3} \delta^4 f_0 + \cdots . \quad (4.5.7)$$

A brief table of the coefficients is presented in §4.12. More extensive tables can be found in the literature (see references in Appendix B).

4.6. Bessel's Formula. Whereas Stirling's formula is principally intended for interpolation near a tabular entry x_0, the need frequently arises for a formula designed for interpolation over the interval, say, between x_0 and x_1. In order to obtain a formula in which the array of differences involved is symmetric about a horizontal line midway between x_0 and x_1, we again make use of the Gaussian forward formula,

$$f_s = f_0 + s\,\delta f_\frac{1}{2} + \frac{s(s-1)}{2!}\,\delta^2 f_0 + \frac{s(s-1)(s+1)}{3!}\,\delta^3 f_\frac{1}{2} + \cdots , \quad (4.6.1)$$

which involves the differences along the forward zigzag of Fig. 4.9, and combine it with a formula which involves the differences along the backward zigzag of that figure. The latter formula may be obtained most

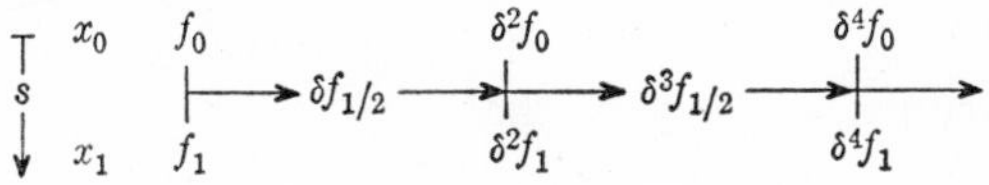

FIG. 4.9

easily by noticing that, if s were to be measured from x_1, that formula would be obtained by advancing all subscripts in the Gaussian backward formula by unity. Hence, if s is to be measured from x_0 in both formulas, we must advance the subscripts in (4.4.5) by unity and, at the same time, replace s by $s-1$, to give the result

$$f_s = f_1 + (s-1)\,\delta f_\frac{1}{2} + \frac{(s-1)s}{2!}\,\delta^2 f_1 + \frac{(s-1)s(s-2)}{3!}\,\delta^3 f_\frac{1}{2} + \cdots .$$
$$(4.6.2)$$

The mean of (4.6.1) and (4.6.2) then takes the form

$$f_s = \mu f_\frac{1}{2} + (s - \tfrac{1}{2})\,\delta f_\frac{1}{2} + \frac{s(s-1)}{2!}\,\mu \delta^2 f_\frac{1}{2} + \frac{s(s-1)(s-\frac{1}{2})}{3!}\,\delta^3 f_\frac{1}{2} + \cdots$$
$$+ \frac{s(s^2 - 1^2)\,\cdots\,(s^2 - \overline{m-1}^2)(s-m)}{(2m)!}\,\mu \delta^{2m} f_\frac{1}{2}$$
$$or \quad + \frac{s(s^2 - 1^2)\,\cdots\,(s^2 - \overline{m-1}^2)(s-m)(s-\frac{1}{2})}{(2m+1)!}\,\delta^{2m+1} f_\frac{1}{2}$$
$$+ E_s, \quad (4.6.3)$$

and is known as *Bessel's formula.*

When terminated with an *odd* difference, of order $2m + 1$, both (4.6.1) and (4.6.2) yield the polynomial of degree $2m + 1$ agreeing with $f(x)$ when $x = x_0$, $x_{\pm 1}$, . . . , $x_{\pm m}$, and x_{m+1}. Hence the same statement applies to Bessel's formula, and the error in that case is consequently identical with (4.4.4),

$$E_s = h^{2m+2} \frac{s(s^2 - 1^2) \cdots (s^2 - m^2)(s - m - 1)}{(2m + 2)!} f^{(2m+2)}(\xi), \quad (4.6.4)$$

when $n = 2m + 1$. However, when Bessel's formula is terminated with even differences the error term is obtained as the mean of (4.4.3) and the first form of (4.4.6) with s replaced by $s - 1$, noticing that the parameter ξ is not generally the same in the two expressions, in the less simple form

$$E_s = h^{2m+1} \frac{s(s^2 - 1^2) \cdots (s^2 - \overline{m - 1}^2)(s - m)}{2(2m + 1)!} [(s + m)f^{(2m+1)}(\xi_1)$$
$$+ (s - m - 1)f^{(2m+1)}(\xi_2)] \quad (4.6.5)$$

when $n = 2m$, where ξ_1 and ξ_2 lie inside the interval including x_0, $x_{\pm 1}$, . . . , $x_{\pm m}$, x_{m+1}, and x.

A brief table of the coefficients appearing in (4.6.3) is given in §4.12. More extensive tables are available in the literature (see Appendix B). Whereas this form therefore is the one most often used in practice, the symmetry about the mid-point of the interval (x_0, x_1) becomes more evident if we write $s = t + \frac{1}{2}$, so that

$$t = \frac{x - \frac{1}{2}(x_0 + x_1)}{h} = s - \frac{1}{2}, \quad (4.6.6)$$

and hence t is distance measured from that mid-point in units of h. It is readily verified that Bessel's formula then takes the equivalent form

$$f_{t+\frac{1}{2}} = \mu f_{\frac{1}{2}} + t \, \delta f_{\frac{1}{2}} + \frac{t^2 - \frac{1}{4}}{2!} \mu \delta^2 f_{\frac{1}{2}} + \frac{t(t^2 - \frac{1}{4})}{3!} \delta^3 f_{\frac{1}{2}}$$
$$+ \frac{(t^2 - \frac{1}{4})(t^2 - \frac{9}{4})}{4!} \mu \delta^4 f_{\frac{1}{2}} + \frac{t(t^2 - \frac{1}{4})(t^2 - \frac{9}{4})}{5!} \delta^5 f_{\frac{1}{2}} + \cdots \quad (4.6.7)$$

where the terminating term and the corresponding error term are obtainable by introducing (4.6.6) into the forms given in (4.6.3) to (4.6.5). Thus we see that the coefficients of mean even differences are even functions of t, whereas the coefficients of odd differences are odd functions of t.

An important special case results, by setting $s = \frac{1}{2}$ in (4.6.3) or $t = 0$ in (4.6.7), in the form

$$f_{\frac{1}{2}} = \frac{1}{2}(f_0 + f_1) - \frac{1}{16}(\delta^2 f_0 + \delta^2 f_1) + \frac{3}{256}(\delta^4 f_0 + \delta^4 f_1) - \frac{5}{2048}(\delta^6 f_0 + \delta^6 f_1)$$
$$+ \cdots + (-1)^m \frac{[1 \cdot 3 \cdots (2m - 1)]^2}{2^{2m+1}(2m)!} (\delta^{2m} f_0 + \delta^{2m} f_1) + E_{\frac{1}{2}}, \quad (4.6.8)$$

where
$$E_{\frac{1}{2}} = (-1)^m \frac{[1 \cdot 3 \cdots (2m + 1)]^2}{2^{2m+2}(2m + 2)!} f^{(2m+2)}(\xi), \quad (4.6.9)$$

and where $x_0 - mh < \xi < x_1 + mh$. This formula is known as the formula for *interpolating to halves* and is particularly useful in subtabulation of data.

With the notation of (4.3.10), Bessel's formula (4.6.3) can also be written in the form

$$
f_s \approx \mu f_{\frac{1}{2}} + (s - \tfrac{1}{2})\, \delta f_{\frac{1}{2}} + \binom{s}{2} \mu \delta^2 f_{\frac{1}{2}} + \frac{s - \frac{1}{2}}{3} \binom{s}{2} \delta^3 f_{\frac{1}{2}}
$$
$$
+ \binom{s+1}{4} \mu \delta^4 f_{\frac{1}{2}} + \frac{s - \frac{1}{2}}{5} \binom{s+1}{4} \delta^5 f_{\frac{1}{2}} + \cdots \qquad (4.6.10)
$$

4.7. Everett's Formulas. In many tabulations, auxiliary tables of central differences of even orders (usually δ^2 and δ^4) are provided. In order to obtain an interpolation formula which involves only central differences of even order, we may, for example, start with the Gauss forward formula, terminated with an *odd* difference and written in the form

$$
f_s = (f_0 + s\, \delta f_{\frac{1}{2}}) + \frac{s(s-1)}{2!}\left(\delta^2 f_0 + \frac{s+1}{3} \delta^3 f_{\frac{1}{2}}\right)
$$
$$
+ \frac{s(s^2 - 1^2)(s-2)}{4!}\left(\delta^4 f_0 + \frac{s+2}{5} \delta^5 f_{\frac{1}{2}}\right) + \cdots
$$
$$
+ \frac{s(s^2 - 1^2) \cdots (s^2 - \overline{m-1}^2)(s-m)}{(2m)!}\left(\delta^{2m} f_0 + \frac{s+m}{2m+1} \delta^{2m+1} f_{\frac{1}{2}}\right) + E_s
$$
$$
(4.7.1)
$$

where

$$
E_s = h^{2m+2}\, \frac{s(s^2 - 1^2) \cdots (s^2 - m^2)(s - m - 1)}{(2m+2)!}\, f^{(2m+2)}(\xi). \qquad (4.7.2)
$$

If we now make use of the relations

$$
\delta f_{\frac{1}{2}} = f_1 - f_0, \qquad \delta^3 f_{\frac{1}{2}} = \delta^2 f_1 - \delta^2 f_0, \qquad \cdots , \qquad (4.7.3)
$$

this formula becomes

$$
f_s = (1 - s) f_0 - \frac{s(s-1)(s-2)}{3!} \delta^2 f_0 - \frac{(s+1)s(s-1)(s-2)(s-3)}{5!} \delta^4 f_0
$$
$$
- \cdots - \frac{(s+m-1)(s+m-2) \cdots (s-m-1)}{(2m+1)!} \delta^{2m} f_0
$$
$$
+ s f_1 + \frac{(s+1)s(s-1)}{3!} \delta^2 f_1 + \frac{(s+2)(s+1)s(s-1)(s-2)}{5!} \delta^4 f_1
$$
$$
+ \cdots + \frac{(s+m)(s+m-1) \cdots (s-m)}{(2m+1)!} \delta^{2m} f_1 + E_s, \qquad (4.7.4)
$$

where E_s is given by (4.7.2). The interpolation formula resulting from neglect of E_s is known as *Everett's first formula* (or frequently merely as *Everett's formula*).

In place of using the differences $\mu\delta^{2r}f_{\frac{1}{2}}$ and $\delta^{2r+1}f_{\frac{1}{2}}$ which are present in Bessel's formula, it uses the differences $\delta^{2r}f_0$ and $\delta^{2r}f_1$. However, it is seen that the result of terminating Bessel's formula with the $(2m+1)$th difference must give a result identical with that of terminating Everett's first formula with the two $(2m)$th differences, for *both* of these formulas are equivalent to the Gauss forward formula terminated with the $(2m+1)$th difference, as may be verified directly by comparison of the error terms.

Whereas the same number of *terms* must be evaluated in using the two formulas just mentioned, if tables are available which include differences of orders, say, two and four, then the use of the Everett formula permits a calculation taking into account all differences through the fifth without the need of differencing on the part of the computer.

A brief table of the coefficients is provided in §4.12 (see references in Appendix B for more elaborate tables).

In a similar way, a formula involving only differences of *odd* order can be obtained from the Gauss forward formula terminated with an *even* difference,

$$f_s = f_0 + s\left(\delta f_{\frac{1}{2}} + \frac{s-1}{2}\delta^2 f_0\right) + \frac{s(s^2-1^2)}{3!}\left(\delta^3 f_{\frac{1}{2}} + \frac{s-2}{4}\delta^4 f_0\right) + \cdots$$
$$+ \frac{s(s^2-1^2)\cdots(s^2-m^2)}{(2m+1)!}\left(\delta^{2m+1}f_{\frac{1}{2}} + \frac{s-m-1}{2m+2}\delta^{2m+2}f_0\right) + E_s,$$

$$(4.7.5)$$

where $\qquad E_s = h^{2m+3}\dfrac{s(s^2-1^2)\cdots(s^2-\overline{m+1}^2)}{(2m+3)!}f^{(2m+3)}(\xi),\qquad (4.7.6)$

by writing

$$\delta^2 f_0 = \delta f_{\frac{1}{2}} - \delta f_{-\frac{1}{2}}, \qquad \delta^4 f_0 = \delta^3 f_{\frac{1}{2}} - \delta^3 f_{-\frac{1}{2}}, \qquad \cdots. \qquad (4.7.7)$$

The result takes the form

$$f_s = f_0 + \frac{(s+1)s}{2!}\delta f_{\frac{1}{2}} + \frac{(s+2)(s+1)s(s-1)}{4!}\delta^3 f_{\frac{1}{2}} + \cdots$$
$$+ \frac{(s+m+1)(s+m)\cdots(s-m)}{(2m+2)!}\delta^{2m+1}f_{\frac{1}{2}}$$
$$- \frac{s(s-1)}{2!}\delta f_{-\frac{1}{2}} - \frac{(s+1)s(s-1)(s-2)}{4!}\delta^3 f_{-\frac{1}{2}} - \cdots$$
$$- \frac{(s+m)(s+m-1)\cdots(s-m-1)}{(2m+2)!}\delta^{2m+1}f_{-\frac{1}{2}} + E_s, \quad (4.7.8)$$

where E_s is given by (4.7.6). The result of neglecting E_s is known as *Everett's second formula* (often also as *Steffensen's formula*), but has not found much favor in practice. The result of terminating it with the $(2m + 1)$th differences is equivalent to that of terminating *Stirling's* formula with the $(2m + 2)$th difference. A brief table of its coefficients is provided in §4.12.

If we introduce the notation of (4.3.10), Everett's first formula can be put in the form

$$f_s \approx (1 - s)f_0 + \binom{(1 - s) + 1}{3} \delta^2 f_0 + \binom{(1 - s) + 2}{5} \delta^4 f_0 + \cdots$$
$$+ sf_1 + \binom{s + 1}{3} \delta^2 f_1 + \binom{s + 2}{5} \delta^4 f_1 + \cdots, \quad (4.7.9)$$

so that the coefficients of one line are obtained by replacing s by $1 - s$ in those of the other line, whereas Everett's second formula becomes

$$f_s \approx f_0 + \binom{s + 1}{2} \delta f_{\frac{1}{2}} + \binom{s + 2}{4} \delta^3 f_{\frac{1}{2}} + \cdots$$
$$- \binom{-s + 1}{2} \delta f_{-\frac{1}{2}} - \binom{-s + 2}{4} \delta^3 f_{-\frac{1}{2}} - \cdots, \quad (4.7.10)$$

so that one set of coefficients is obtained from the other by replacing s by $-s$.

4.8. Use of Interpolation Formulas. As was mentioned earlier, the Newton formulas with forward and backward differences are most appropriate for calculation near the beginning and end, respectively, of a tabulation, and their use is mainly restricted to such situations.

The Gaussian forward and backward formulas terminated with an *even* difference are equivalent to each other, and to the Stirling formula, terminated with the same difference. The Gaussian forward formula terminated with an *odd* difference is equivalent to the Bessel formula terminated with the same difference. The Gaussian backward formula launched from x_0, and terminating with an odd difference, is equivalent to the Bessel formula launched from x_{-1}, terminated with the same difference. Thus, in place of using a Gaussian formula, one may always use an equivalent formula of either Stirling or Bessel, for which the coefficients are extensively tabulated.

Reference to (4.5.4) shows that the coefficients of all differences of *even* order in Stirling's formula involve s^2 as a factor. Thus, for interpolation near x_0, it may be expected that the result of terminating that formula with a *mean odd difference* $\mu \delta^{2m+1} f_0$ will be nearly as accurate, on the average, as the result of retaining one additional difference. However, the relative complexity of the remainder term (4.5.6) in that case is somewhat of a disadvantage when a precise error bound is required.

A comparison of (4.5.6) and (4.6.4) shows that, in addition to common factors, the Stirling error involves the factor

$$\tfrac{1}{2}[(m + 1 + s)f^{(2m+2)}(\xi_2) - (m + 1 - s)f^{(2m+2)}(\xi_1)],$$

whereas the Bessel error involves the factor

$$-(m + 1 - s)f^{(2m+2)}(\xi_1).$$

If it is known only that $|f^{(2m+2)}(x)| \leqq M$ for $x_{-m-1} \leqq x \leqq x_{m+1}$, the Stirling factor can be guaranteed only not to exceed $(m + 1)M$ in magnitude, whereas the Bessel factor cannot exceed $(m + 1 - s)M$ in magnitude, if extrapolation is excluded. Thus, from the point of view of *predictable* error bounds, Bessel's formula actually displays a slight advantage when the highest difference to be retained is *odd*, in spite of the fact that Stirling's formula then makes use of information afforded by an additional ordinate.† In any case, the Stirling formula is most efficient (in general) for small s, say, for $-\tfrac{1}{4} \leqq s \leqq \tfrac{1}{4}$, that is, for calculation between $x_0 - h/4$ and $x_0 + h/4$.

A similar comparison of (4.5.5) and (4.6.5) indicates that, whereas the result of truncating the Bessel formula with a *mean even difference* makes use of more information than does the Stirling formula truncated with the corresponding ordinary even difference, the use of the latter formula may actually be slightly preferable from the point of view of predictable error bounds when the highest difference to be retained is even. In any case, the Bessel formula is most efficient (in general) near $s = \tfrac{1}{2}$, say for $\tfrac{1}{4} \leqq s \leqq \tfrac{3}{4}$, that is, for calculation between $x_0 + h/4$ and $x_1 - h/4$.

In a series of calculations based on a given set of data, it is inconvenient to shift from one of these two formulas to the other, and one of the two must be chosen. Given a set of data, a decision would be made first as to the highest difference which was to be retained. If that difference were of even order, Stirling's formula perhaps would be recommended; if it were of odd order, Bessel's formula might be preferred.§ However, the difference in accuracy between the two formulas is usually small, so that the choice is usually dictated by personal preference.

Everett's first formula is particularly useful when auxiliary tables of certain even differences accompany the given data; Everett's second for-

---

† If it is known (for example) that $f^{(2m+2)}(x)$ is of constant sign in the relevant interval, the advantage clearly is generally reversed.

§ The fallibility of such generalizations is illustrated by a comparison of the results of Probs. 18 and 19.

mula would be useful if its coefficients were tabulated and if auxiliary odd differences were available.

To illustrate the use of these formulas, we consider the following difference table, based on five-place data taken from a table of $f(x) = \sin x$, where the differences are given in units of the fifth place and where the figures in parentheses are auxiliary mean central differences used in the calculations to be described:

x	$f(x)$	Δ	Δ^2	Δ^3	Δ^4	Δ^5
1.0	0.84147					
		4974				
1.1	0.89121		−891			
		4083		−40		
1.2	0.93204	(3617.5)	−931	(−36)	8	
	(0.94780)	3152	(−947)	−32	(9)	2
1.3	0.96356		−963		10	
		2189		−22		1
1.4	0.98545		−985		11	
		1204		−11		−3
1.5	0.99749		−996		8	
		208		−3		4
1.6	0.99957		−999		12	
		−791		9		
1.7	0.99166		−990			
		−1781				
1.8	0.97385					

A convenient check on the differencing effected in any difference table consists in the fact that *the sum of the entries in any column of differences should equal the difference between the last and first entries of the preceding column.* To see that this is so, suppose that the entries in a certain column, reading downward, are $u_1, u_2, u_3, \ldots, u_r$. Then the corresponding entries in the next column to the right are $(u_2 - u_1)$, $(u_3 - u_2)$, $\ldots$, $(u_{r-1} - u_{r-2})$, and $(u_r - u_{r-1})$, and the sum of these quantities evidently "telescopes" into $u_r - u_1$.

Because of the irregular fluctuation of the fifth differences in the given table, we would suppose that they are not significant but that they principally reflect the propagated effects of round-off errors present in the given data (see also §4.9). In fact, it would be suspected that the fluctuation of the fourth differences about their mean value of about 10 is also principally due to these inherent errors in the original data. Thus, not more than the first four differences are to be used here. Whether these differences are sufficient, and whether they are all *needed*, could be determined from the error term associated with the formula to be used, if knowledge of the analytical form of $f(x)$ were presumed.

In order to interpolate for $f(1.02)$, we would use Newton's forward-difference formula, with $s = 0.2$:

$$f(1.02) \approx 0.84147 + 0.2(0.04974) + \frac{(0.2)(-0.8)}{2}(-0.00891)$$
$$+ \frac{(0.2)(-0.8)(-1.8)}{6}(-0.00040)$$
$$+ \frac{(0.2)(-0.8)(-1.8)(-2.8)}{24}(0.00008)$$
$$\doteq 0.84147 + 0.009948 + 0.000713 - 0.000019 - 0.000003$$
$$= 0.852109 \doteq 0.85211,$$

which is correct to five places.

The interpolation for $f(1.75)$ would be accomplished by use of Newton's backward-difference formula, with $s = -0.5$:

$$f(1.75) \approx 0.97385 + (-0.5)(-0.01781) + \frac{(-0.5)(0.5)}{2}(-0.00990)$$
$$+ \frac{(-0.5)(0.5)(1.5)}{6}(0.00009) + \frac{(-0.5)(0.5)(1.5)(2.5)}{24}(0.00012)$$
$$\doteq 0.97385 + 0.008905 + 0.001238 - 0.000006 - 0.000005$$
$$= 0.983982 \doteq 0.98398,$$

the rounded value being in error by defect of one unit in the fifth place.

In order to interpolate for $f(1.22)$, we could use either Stirling's formula or Bessel's formula, with $x_0 = 1.2$ and $s = 0.2$ in either case. Since the formula is to terminate with even differences (and also since the interpolant is nearer $s = 0$ than $s = \frac{1}{2}$), Stirling's formula might be preferred. After inserting the mean odd differences indicated in parentheses in the row $x = 1.2$ of the difference table, the use of Stirling's formula gives

$$f(1.22) \approx 0.93204 + 0.2(0.036175) + \frac{0.04}{2}(-0.00931)$$
$$+ \frac{(0.2)(-0.96)}{6}(-0.00036) + \frac{(0.04)(-0.96)}{24}(0.00008)$$
$$\doteq 0.93204 + 0.007235 - 0.000186 + 0.000012 - 0.0000001$$
$$= 0.9391009 \doteq 0.93910,$$

whereas, after inserting appropriate mean even differences in the table, the use of Bessel's formula gives

$$f(1.22) \approx 0.94780 + (-0.3)(0.03152) + \frac{(0.2)(-0.8)}{2}(-0.00947)$$
$$+ \frac{(0.2)(-0.8)(-0.3)}{6}(-0.00032)$$
$$+ \frac{(0.2)(-0.96)(-1.8)}{24}(0.00009)$$
$$\doteq 0.94780 - 0.009456 + 0.000758 - 0.000003 + 0.000001$$
$$= 0.939100 \doteq 0.93910,$$

both results being correct to five places. We see that both formulas would give results correct to five places if only third differences were retained.

In a table providing δ^2 and δ^4, the entries used in the interpolation for $x = 1.22$ by Everett's first formula would read

x	$f(x)$	δ^2	δ^4
1.2	0.93204	−931	8
1.3	0.96356	−963	10

and the calculation would be of the form

$$f(1.22) \approx 0.8(0.93204) - \frac{(0.2)(-0.8)(-1.8)}{6}(-0.00931)$$
$$- \frac{(1.2)(0.2)(-0.8)(-1.8)(-2.8)}{120}(0.00008)$$
$$+ 0.2(0.96356) + \frac{(1.2)(0.2)(-0.8)}{6}(-0.00963)$$
$$+ \frac{(2.2)(1.2)(0.2)(-0.8)(-1.8)}{120}(0.00010)$$
$$\doteq 0.745632 + 0.000447 + 0.000001$$
$$+ 0.192712 + 0.000308 + 0.000001$$
$$= 0.939101 \doteq 0.93910,$$

in agreement with the preceding results. The additional computation here is because of the fact that Everett's formula with fourth differences actually incorporates the effects of the first *five* differences. In this case, the retention of only the two second differences would have been sufficient.

Since the analytical expression for $f(x)$ is known, this situation could have been predicted by reference to the error formula (4.7.2) which, with $h = 0.1$, $s = 0.2$, and $m = 1$, gives

$$E = 10^{-4} \frac{(0.2)(-0.98)(-1.8)}{24} f^{iv}(\xi)$$
$$\doteq 1.44 \times 10^{-6} f^{iv}(\xi).$$

Since here $f^{iv}(x) = \sin x$, there follows $|f^{iv}(\xi)| \leq 1$, so that (if no round-off errors were present) the error resulting from terminating Everett's first formula with second differences would be less than two units in the sixth place. Similar error estimates could have been obtained, in advance, with reference to the other calculations. Moreover, the calculations are

considerably simplified when use is made of tabulated values of the coefficients (see §4.12).

Formulas for numerical differentiation and integration may be obtained
by differentiating and integrating any of the interpolation formulas (see
Probs. 5, 11, and 13). However, these formulas can be obtained somewhat more systematically by operational methods, and their treatment
is postponed to the following chapter.

4.9. Propagation of Inherent Errors. In addition to the truncation
errors, for which certain analytical expressions have been given, the
effects of round-off errors in the given data, and in the computation,
must be taken into account. The latter generally can be regulated by
retaining one or more extra figures in the intermediate calculation. It
thus remains to investigate the way in which round-off errors in the given
data affect the interpolation process.

The error in the interpolant, corresponding to such inherent errors,
clearly is merely a linear combination of the errors in the ordinates
involved in the interpolation. When the interpolation polynomial is of
degree n and is determined by exact fit to the given data at $n + 1$ points,
the constants of combination are the Lagrange coefficients considered
in Chap. 3. In particular, if the error in each given ordinate cannot
exceed ϵ, then the error in the interpolant cannot exceed the product of
ϵ and the sum of the absolute values of the relevant Lagrange coefficients.
Three-point coefficients, corresponding to retention of second differences,
are tabulated to tenths in §3.4, whereas a similar table of five-point
coefficients, corresponding to retention of fourth differences, is presented
in §4.12. Use of the latter table shows, for example, that the error in an
interpolation at an abscissa midway between the third and fourth of the
five relevant abscissas, due only to data errors not exceeding ϵ in magnitude, cannot exceed 1.4ϵ in magnitude.

The Stirling formula, when terminated with a mean odd difference,
and the Bessel formula, when terminated with a mean even difference,
are not based on interpolation polynomials which fit the data at $n + 1$
points, and hence must be analyzed separately. This is an additional
reason for avoiding the termination of the Stirling and Bessel formulas
with *mean* differences, when precise error estimates are desired.

The presence of round-off errors in given data is also of importance
in connection with the question as to the number of differences which
should be *retained* in an interpolation. For this reason, it is of interest
to study the *propagation* of the effects of such errors into the differences
themselves.

Suppose first that a single initial entry is in error by an excess e, due
perhaps to rounding. Then, if all other initial entries are assumed to be
exact, it is seen that the effects of this error will be propagated into the

irst five differences of the difference table as follows:

f	Δ	Δ²	Δ³	Δ⁴	Δ⁵
—					
	—				e
—		—		e	
	—		e		-5e
—		e		-4e	
	e		-3e		10e
e		-2e		6e	
	-e		3e		-10e
—		e		-4e	
	—		-e		5e
—		—		e	
	—				-e
—		—		—	

This characteristic distribution along a column, in which the successive errors alternate in sign and, indeed, vary along the column of rth differences as the binomial coefficients associated with $(1 - x)^r$, frequently erves to permit one to discover and correct a gross error in a table.

f	Δ	Δ²	Δ³
1.203		18	
	221		18
1.424		36	
	257		18
1.681		54	
	311		22
1.992		76	
	387		6
2.379		82	
	469		30
2.848		112	
	581		14
3.429		126	
	707		18
4.136		144	

Thus, for example, the third differences in the accompanying table appear o fluctuate irregularly. Their mean value is 18, and the successive deviations from the mean, reading downward, are 0, 0, 4, −12, +12, −4,). Thus an excess $e = 4$ in the last place is indicated in the entry 2.379, which occupies the row separating the maximum deviations. The corrected value is 2.375. A fourth differencing would have given the entries), 4, −16, 24, −16, 4, from which the same conclusion would be drawn. When several errors are present, their discovery may be much more difficult.

Suppose now that *all* initial entries may be in error by amounts between $-e$ and e. The most unfavorable situation, with regard to effects on differences, is that in which the successive errors are as large as possible but are of alternating sign. The error-propagation table, through fourth differences, then appears as follows:

f	Δ	Δ^2	Δ^3	Δ^4
e		$-4e$		$16e$
	$-2e$		$8e$	
$-e$		$4e$		$-16e$
	$2e$		$-8e$	
e		$-4e$		$16e$
	$-2e$		$8e$	
$-e$		$4e$		$-16e$
	$2e$		$-8e$	
e		$-4e$		$16e$

Thus, it follows that errors varying between $-e$ and e in the initial data will lead to errors varying between $-2^r e$ and $2^r e$ in the rth differences. Here, for example, if the initial data are correctly rounded to k decimal places, $e = 5 \times 10^{-k-1}$.

Because of this possible error growth, it usually happens in practice that calculated differences beyond a certain order are no longer significant. That is, there exists a certain "noise level" such that the effects of initial round-offs are of the same order of magnitude as the differences which would have been obtained had the initial data been exact. If the initial data are rounded, from exactly known data, to k decimal places, then round-off errors of magnitude $2^{r-1}/10^k$ are possible in the rth differences. Hence rth differences of magnitude appreciably smaller than $2^{r-1}/10^k$ are likely to consist largely of "noise." Thus, since $k = 5$ in the data used for the examples of the preceding section, "noise" of magnitude 1, 2, 4, 8, and 16 units in the fifth place *could* occur in the respective differences of order one through five, although the *probability* of noise of nearly maximum magnitude in the rth difference is clearly small and will decrease rapidly as r increases. In any case, it would be expected that, since the fifth differences in that table are small relative to the permissible noise, they are completely meaningless, so that the fluctuation of the fourth differences about their mean may also lack significance, in the sense that the replacement of those differences by their mean value would lead to errors in interpolation of the same order as the errors which are present in the *given* data.

4.10. Throwback Techniques. A useful procedure, due to Comrie, frequently permits a computer effectively to take into account a neglected difference by modifying certain of the differences actually retained in an interpolation formula.

In illustration, Everett's first formula, terminated with fourth differences, can be expressed in the form

$$f_s \approx (1 - s)f_0 + sf_1 - \frac{s(s - 1)(s - 2)}{6}\left[\delta^2 f_0 + \frac{(s + 1)(s - 3)}{20}\delta^4 f_0\right]$$
$$+ \frac{(s + 1)s(s - 1)}{6}\left[\delta^2 f_1 + \frac{(s + 2)(s - 2)}{20}\delta^4 f_1\right]. \quad (4.10.1)$$

In the interval $0 \leqq s \leqq 1$, the factors

$$\frac{(s + 1)(s - 3)}{20} \quad \text{and} \quad \frac{(s + 2)(s - 2)}{20}$$

both vary only from $-\frac{3}{20}$ to $-\frac{4}{20}$. This fact suggests that these factors be replaced by a constant value over that interval in (4.10.1). The value suggested by Comrie, -0.184, differs only slightly from the *mean* value $(-\frac{11}{60})$ of each factor.† Hence, if we define the *modified second difference*

$$\bar{\delta}^2 f_k = \delta^2 f_k - 0.184\delta^4 f_k, \quad (4.10.2)$$

Everett's formula with fourth differences may be approximated by the formula

$$f_s \approx (1 - s)f_0 + sf_1 - \frac{s(s - 1)(s - 2)}{6}\bar{\delta}^2 f_0 + \frac{(s + 1)s(s - 1)}{6}\bar{\delta}^2 f_1.$$
$$(4.10.3)$$

It is conventional to speak of (4.10.2) as "throwing back the fourth difference on the second."

The error associated with the introduction of this approximation is given by

$$-\left[\binom{s + 1}{5} + 0.184\binom{s}{3}\right]\delta^4 f_0 + \left[\binom{s + 2}{5} + 0.184\binom{s + 1}{3}\right]\delta^4 f_1,$$
$$(4.10.4)$$

and calculation shows that, when $0 \leqq s \leqq 1$, this sum is not larger in magnitude than $0.00122M$, where M is the larger of $|\delta^4 f_0|$ and $|\delta^4 f_1|$. Hence, if $\delta^4 f_0$ and $\delta^4 f_1$ do not exceed 400 units in the last decimal place retained in the over-all calculation, the error committed in the throwback cannot exceed $\frac{1}{2}$ unit in that place; if $\delta^4 f_0$ and $\delta^4 f_1$ are of common sign, then 1000 units are permissible (see Prob. 24).

If the same throwback (4.10.2) is effected in Bessel's formula, so that $\mu\delta^2 f_{\frac{1}{2}}$ is replaced by $\mu\bar{\delta}^2 f_{\frac{1}{2}}$, and differences beyond the third are omitted, the

† The figure $(\sqrt{2} + 3)/24 \doteq 0.184$ was obtained by Comrie as that value of the factor for which the magnitude of the maximum error due to throwback is least in the case of *Bessel's* formula. The same figure is conventionally used with the Everett formula (see also Probs. 23 and 24).

effect of the omitted fourth difference is properly taken into account, in the same sense, if it does not exceed 1000 units in the last decimal place retained.

Generalized techniques, relevant to higher differences or to two or more differences, have also been devised by Comrie. Similar techniques have been given (see Lidstone [134]) for Stirling's formula.

4.11. Interpolation Series. Reference has already been made to the fact that the interpolation formulas considered in this chapter generally do not converge as the number n of differences retained is increased without limit, while the spacing h is held fixed. In this section we consider a simple example which illustrates this fact, and state certain known results.

If the Newton forward-difference formula (4.3.2) were considered as an infinite series, it would be expressed in the form

$$f(x) = f(0) + x \frac{\Delta f(0)}{1!h} + x(x - h) \frac{\Delta^2 f(0)}{2!h^2} + \cdots$$

$$= f(0) + \sum_{k=1}^{\infty} \frac{\Delta^k f(0)}{k!h^k} x(x - h) \cdots (x - \overline{k - 1}h), \quad (4.11.1)$$

where we have supposed that the origin has been chosen such that $x_0 = 0$. Similarly, the Stirling "interpolation series" would be expressible in the form

$$f(x) = f(0) + \frac{x}{h}\left[\mu\delta f(0) + \frac{x}{2h} \delta^2 f(0) \right] + \cdots$$

$$= f(0) + \sum_{k=1}^{\infty} \frac{1}{(2k - 1)!h^{2k-1}}\left[\mu\delta^{2k-1}f(0) + \frac{x}{2kh} \delta^{2k}f(0) \right]$$

$$\cdot [x(x^2 - h^2)(x^2 - 4h^2) \cdots (x^2 - \overline{k - 1}^2 h^2)], \quad (4.11.2)$$

and the remaining formulas would correspond to similar interpolation series. The basic problem considered here is that of determining when such a series converges to the generating function $f(x)$.

In the special case when

$$f(x) = e^{ax}, \quad (4.11.3)$$

there follows

$$\Delta f(x) = e^{a(x+h)} - e^{ax} = (e^{ah} - 1)f(x), \quad \cdots, \quad \Delta^r f(x) = (e^{ah} - 1)^r f(x),$$

and hence also

$$\Delta^r f(0) = (e^{ah} - 1)^r. \quad (4.11.4)$$

Thus the formal Newton interpolation series for e^{ax} may be obtained in the orm

$$e^{ax} = 1 + \sum_{k=1}^{\infty} \frac{(e^{ah} - 1)^k}{k!h^k} [x(x - l) \cdots (x - \overline{k - 1}h)]. \quad (4.11.5)$$

This series *terminates*, and represents e^{ax} correctly, when x is zero or a positive integral multiple of h. In order to investigate its convergence when the series is infinite, we notice first that the ratio of successive terms in this series is given by

$$\frac{e^{ah} - 1}{h(k + 1)} (x - kh),$$

and that, as $k \to \infty$, this ratio tends to $-(e^{ah} - 1)$, for all values of x. Thus we may deduce that the series (4.11.5) *converges* if $|e^{ah} - 1| < 1$ or $e^{ah} < 2$, whereas, if $x \neq 0, h, 2h, \ldots$, it *diverges* when $|e^{ah} - 1| > 1$ or $e^{ah} > 2$.

When $e^{ah} = 2$, the series reduces to

$$1 + \sum_{k=1}^{\infty} \frac{x(x - h) \cdots (x - \overline{k - 1}h)}{k!h^k}$$

$$\equiv 1 + \sum_{k=1}^{\infty} \frac{(-1)^k}{k!} \left[\left(k - \frac{x}{h} - 1 \right) \left(k - \frac{x}{h} - 2 \right) \cdots \left(-\frac{x}{h} \right) \right],$$

the successive terms of which alternate in sign when k is sufficiently large. Now the kth term can be written, in terms of the gamma function, in the form

$$(-1)^k \frac{\Gamma(k - x/h)}{\Gamma(-x/h)k!}.$$

By making use of the fact that $\Gamma(k + u)$ is approximated by $k!k^{u-1}$, for large k, we find that this last ratio is approximated by

$$(-1)^k \frac{k^{-x/h-1}}{\Gamma(-x/h)}$$

when k is large, and hence that it tends to zero as $k \to \infty$ if and only if $x > -h$.

It follows that *the series* (4.11.5) *converges for all finite values of x if $ah < \log 2$ and diverges for all values of x which differ from $0, h, 2h, \ldots$ if $ah > \log 2$, and that, if $ah = \log 2$, the series converges when and only when $x > -h$.* It can be proved that, when the series converges, the convergence is indeed to e^{ax}.

If x is considered as a *complex* variable (but a is real), the preceding developments are unchanged except for the fact that, when $ah = \log 2$, the region of convergence is that half of the complex x plane for which the *real part* of x is greater than $-h$.   If also a is complex, the conditions $ah \lesssim \log 2$ must be replaced by $|e^{ah} - 1| \lesssim 1$.

We see, therefore, that, if the Newton forward-difference formula were used for interpolating e^{ax} where $a > 0$, with a spacing h larger than $(\log 2)/a$, the successive interpolates corresponding to the incorporation of more and more data would eventually begin to oscillate with increasing amplitude about the true value.   Thus, whereas the retention of an additional term of the interpolation formula would generally improve the accuracy of the interpolation up to a certain stage, there would exist a point beyond which additional terms would correspond to *loss* of accuracy. (A similar situation was encountered in §3.7.)   For $ah < \log 2$ (in particular, for negative a), this situation would not arise.   In the intermediate case when $ah = \log 2$, convergence would follow if and only if the formula were not used for backward *extrapolation* beyond $x = -h$.

These results are particularly remarkable in view of the fact that e^{ax} is such a well-behaved function that its *Taylor* series converges for *all* (real or complex) values of x.

A similar analysis, in the case when Stirling's formula is used instead, leads to the fact that here the corresponding interpolation series converges for all x when $ah < 2 \log (1 + \sqrt{2})$ and diverges (when it does not terminate) for all x in all other cases, including the case when

$$ah = 2 \log (1 + \sqrt{2}).$$

If a is complex, the corresponding condition is $|\sinh (ah/2)| < 1$.

In the general case, it is known that, if the *Stirling* series converges for *any* value of x in addition to $x = 0$, $\pm h$, $\pm 2h$, . . . (for which it terminates), then it converges for *all* finite values of x (real or complex). Hence, conversely, if it diverges for any finite value of x, it diverges always unless it terminates.   In the language of the theory of functions of a complex variable, the Stirling series cannot converge to $f(x)$ for *any* x (except those for which it terminates) unless $f(x)$ is a so-called *entire function*, that is, a function which is analytic at all finite points of a complex x plane, or, equivalently, a function whose Taylor series converges everywhere.

But, even though this be the case, the series *still* may not converge (as in the preceding example, where $f(x) = e^{ax}$).   It is also necessary that $|f(re^{i\theta})| < Me^{ar}$ for large r, where M and a are constants such that $ah < \pi$.   If these conditions are not satisfied, the Stirling series will *diverge* everywhere except where it terminates.   On the other hand, if $f(x)$ is an entire function, and if $|f(re^{i\theta})| < Me^{ar}$ for large r, where M and a are constants such that $ah < 2 \log (1 + \sqrt{2})$, then the series will *converge* everywhere.   Similar statements apply to the series associated with Bessel's formula.

In the case of the *Newton* series, with forward differences, it is known that, if the series converges to $f(x)$ for any value of x, say $\bar{x}$, in addition to $x = 0, h, 2h, \ldots$, for which it terminates, then it converges for all values of x such that the real part of x is greater than the real part of $\bar{x}$. Unless $f(x)$ is analytic in some half plane $\mathrm{Re}(x) > \alpha$, and also $|f(re^{i\theta})| < Me^{ar}$ for large r, where M and a are constants such that $ah < \pi/2$, the series will diverge except when it terminates. If $f(x)$ is analytic in such a half plane and if *also* $|f(re^{i\theta})| < Me^{ar}$ for large r, where M and a are constants such that $ah < \log 2$, then the series will converge everywhere in that half plane. (For proofs of these statements, see Nörlund [13, 168].)

Thus, for example, the function $f(x) = 1/(1 + x^2)$ is analytic when x is real, but it possesses poles when $x = \pm i$. Hence the Stirling series will diverge for all values of x. Since this function is analytic in the half plane $x > 0$, and since it is dominated in magnitude by *any* exponential function Me^{ar} $(a > 0)$ as $r \to \infty$, the Newton series will converge in that half plane. Nevertheless, if both series are launched from the same point, the error in the Stirling series will at first decrease much more rapidly than that associated with the Newton series, as additional terms are incorporated into the calculation. *Eventually*, the result of adding still more terms to the Stirling series will *increase* its error, whereas the error in the Newton series will continue to decrease. However, this point of diminishing return in the Stirling formula is likely to be preceded either by a stage at which the truncation error has decreased below the tolerance imposed or by a stage at which the "noise level" is reached, so that the effects of round-off errors would cause the remaining higher differences to be undependable in any case.

Thus, as in many other practical situations, it is quite possible to obtain more accurate results by terminating an ultimately *divergent* process *at an appropriate stage* than by terminating a *convergent* process at a corresponding stage.

It is evident that, since each partial sum of either the Newton or Stirling series represents a polynomial approximation to $f(x)$ corresponding to collocation at the points involved, the two sequences of approximations differ only in that the former results from the successive introduction of the ordinates at $x = 0, h, 2h, \ldots, kh, \ldots$, all of which lie on the half line $0 \leqq x < \infty$, whereas the latter successively introduces the ordinates at the points $\cdots, -kh, \ldots, -h, 0, h, \ldots, kh, \ldots$, in such a way that symmetry is preserved about $x = 0$. Thus, the convergence or divergence of the sequence of approximations truly depends upon the sequence of data introduced, rather than upon the type of polynomial interpolation formula employed. Whereas an indication of the existence of an unfavorable situation is usually afforded by an inspection of a relevant *difference* table, such numerical evidence is not available when *Lagrangian* methods are used.†

4.12. Tables of Interpolation Coefficients. This section provides brief tables of coefficients relevant to the interpolation formulas which have been considered. For more elaborate tables, the references cited in §4.13 should be consulted.

LAGRANGE FIVE-POINT INTERPOLATION
(see §3.4 for three-point coefficients)
$$f_s \approx L_{-2}(s)f_{-2} + L_{-1}(s)f_{-1} + L_0(s)f_0 + L_1(s)f_1 + L_2(s)f_2$$
for negative s, use lower column labels

s	$L_{-2}(s)$	$L_{-1}(s)$	$L_0(s)$	$L_1(s)$	$L_2(s)$	
.0	.000000	.000000	1.000000	.000000	.000000	.0
.1	.007838	−.059850	.987525	.073150	−.008663	−.1
.2	.014400	−.105600	.950400	.158400	−.017600	−.2
.3	.019338	−.136850	.889525	.254150	−.026163	−.3
.4	.022400	−.153600	.806400	.358400	−.033600	−.4
.5	.023438	−.156250	.703125	.468750	−.039063	−.5
.6	.022400	−.145600	.582400	.582400	−.041600	−.6
.7	.019338	−.122850	.447525	.696150	−.040163	−.7
.8	.014400	−.089600	.302400	.806400	−.033600	−.8
.9	.007838	−.047850	.151525	.909150	−.020663	−.9
1.0	.000000	.000000	.000000	1.000000	.000000	−1.0
1.1	−.008663	.051150	−.146475	1.074150	.029838	−1.1
1.2	−.017600	.102400	−.281600	1.126400	.070400	−1.2
1.3	−.026163	.150150	−.398475	1.151150	.123338	−1.3
1.4	−.033600	.190400	−.489600	1.142400	.190400	−1.4
1.5	−.039063	.218750	−.546875	1.093750	.273438	−1.5
1.6	−.041600	.230400	−.561600	.998400	.374400	−1.6
1.7	−.040163	.220150	−.524475	.849150	.495338	−1.7
1.8	−.033600	.182400	−.425600	.638400	.638400	−1.8
1.9	−.020663	.111150	−.254475	.358150	.805838	−1.9
2.0	.000000	.000000	.000000	.000000	1.000000	−2.0
	$L_2(s)$	$L_1(s)$	$L_0(s)$	$L_{-1}(s)$	$L_{-2}(s)$	s

NOTE: All coefficients become exact if each terminal 8 is replaced by 75, and each terminal 3 by 25.

† The sequences of interpolation polynomials considered here correspond to the incorporation of successive ordinates which eventually are at unboundedly increasing distances from the point of interpolation. Whereas the sequence generated by fitting ordinates at points which divide a fixed finite interval (a,b) into n equal parts and allowing n to increase without limit generally is more tractable, there actually exist functions which are continuous in (a,b) but for which this sequence *diverges everywhere* in (a,b).

Newton Interpolation

$$f_s \approx f_0 + s\,\Delta f_0 + C_2(s)\,\Delta^2 f_0 + C_3(s)\,\Delta^3 f_0 + C_4(s)\,\Delta^4 f_0 + C_5(s)\,\Delta^5 f_0$$
$$f_{n-s} \approx f_n - s\,\nabla f_n + C_2(s)\,\nabla^2 f_n - C_3(s)\,\nabla^3 f_n + C_4(s)\,\nabla^4 f_n - C_5(s)\,\nabla^5 f_n$$

(s positive for interpolation)

s	$C_2(s)$	$C_3(s)$	$C_4(s)$	$C_5(s)$
−1.0	1.00000	−1.00000	1.00000	−1.00000
−.9	.85500	−.82650	.80584	−.78972
−.8	.72000	−.67200	.63840	−.61286
−.7	.59500	−.53550	.49534	−.46562
−.6	.48000	−.41600	.37440	−.34445
−.5	.37500	−.31250	.27344	−.24609
−.4	.28000	−.22400	.19040	−.16755
−.3	.19500	−.14950	.12334	−.10607
−.2	.12000	−.08800	.07040	−.05914
−.1	.05500	−.03850	.02984	−.02447
0	.00000	.00000	.00000	.00000
.1	−.04500	.02850	−.02066	.01612
.2	−.08000	.04800	−.03360	.02554
.3	−.10500	.05950	−.04016	.02972
.4	−.12000	.06400	−.04160	.02995
.5	−.12500	.06250	−.03906	.02734
.6	−.12000	.05600	−.03360	.02285
.7	−.10500	.04550	−.02616	.01727
.8	−.08000	.03200	−.01760	.01126
.9	−.04500	.01650	−.00866	.00537
1.0	.00000	.00000	.00000	.00000

Stirling Interpolation

$$f_s \approx f_0 + s\,\mu\delta f_0 + C_2(s)\,\delta^2 f_0 + C_3(s)\,\mu\delta^3 f_0 + C_4(s)\,\delta^4 f_0$$

s	$C_2(s)$	$C_3(s)$	$C_4(s)$	s
0	.00000	.00000	.00000	0
.1	.00500	−.01650†	−.00041	−.1
.2	.02000	−.03200†	−.00160	−.2
.3	.04500	−.04550†	−.00341	−.3
.4	.08000	−.05600†	−.00560	−.4
.5	.12500	−.06250†	−.00781	−.5
.6	.18000	−.06400†	−.00960	−.6
.7	.24500	−.05950†	−.01041	−.7
.8	.32000	−.04800†	−.00960	−.8
.9	.40500	−.02850†	−.00641	−.9
1.0	.50000	.00000	.00000	−1.0

† Change sign when reading s from right-hand column.

BESSEL INTERPOLATION

$$f_s \approx \mu f_{\frac{1}{2}} + (s - \tfrac{1}{2}) \, \delta f_{\frac{1}{2}} + C_2(s) \, \mu \delta^2 f_{\frac{1}{2}} + C_3(s) \, \delta^3 f_{\frac{1}{2}} + C_4(s) \, \mu \delta^4 f_{\frac{1}{2}} + C_5(s) \, \delta^5 f_{\frac{1}{2}}$$

s	$C_2(s)$	$C_3(s)$	$C_4(s)$	$C_5(s)$	s
0	.00000	.00000	.00000	.00000	1.0
.1	−.04500	.00600†	.00784	−.00063†	.9
.2	−.08000	.00800†	.01440	−.00086†	.8
.3	−.10500	.00700†	.01934	−.00077†	.7
.4	−.12000	.00400†	.02240	−.00045†	.6
.5	−.12500	.00000	.02344	.00000	.5

† Change sign when reading s from right-hand column.

EVERETT INTERPOLATION

$$f_s \approx (1 - s)f_0 + C_2(s) \, \delta^2 f_0 + C_4(s) \, \delta^4 f_0$$
$$+ s f_1 + C_2(1 - s) \, \delta^2 f_1 + C_4(1 - s) \, \delta^4 f_1$$

s	$C_2(s)$	$C_4(s)$
0	.00000	.00000
.1	−.02850	.00455
.2	−.04800	.00806
.3	−.05950	.01044
.4	−.06400	.01165
.5	−.06250	.01172
.6	−.05600	.01075
.7	−.04550	.00890
.8	−.03200	.00634
.9	−.01650	.00329
1.0	.00000	.00000

STEFFENSEN INTERPOLATION

$$f_s \approx f_0 + C_1(s) \, \delta f_{\frac{1}{2}} + C_3(s) \, \delta^3 f_{\frac{1}{2}}$$
$$- C_1(-s) \, \delta f_{-\frac{1}{2}} - C_3(-s) \, \delta^3 f_{-\frac{1}{2}}$$

s	$C_1(s)$	$C_3(s)$
−.5	−.12500	.02344
−.4	−.12000	.02240
−.3	−.10500	.01934
−.2	−.08000	.01440
−.1	−.04500	.00784
0	.00000	.00000
.1	.05500	−.00866
.2	.12000	−.01760
.3	.19500	−.02616
.4	.28000	−.03360
.5	.37500	−.03906

4.13. Supplementary References. Davis [246] includes tables of the interpolation coefficients relevant to the first six differences in the formulas of Newton, Stirling, Bessel, and Everett with spacing 0.01 over (0,1), to 11 places, together with tables of corresponding coefficients for numerical differentiation. Other tabulations are listed in the Index of Mathematical Tables [242]. Davis also lists formulas which provide approximations to the results of inverting truncated Newton and Everett formulas and which are useful for inverse interpolation in some cases, although the use of one of the methods outlined in §2.8 (see also Prob. 26) is often to be preferred. Salzer [258, 260] gives tables of the relevant coefficient functions. Miller [151] gives a valuable discussion of the use of difference tables in the detection of errors. See Comrie [244, 245] and Lidstone [134] for additional throwback techniques. Interpolation in two-way tables can be effected by first applying one of the formulas treated in this chapter (or in Chaps. 2 and 3) to interpolate with respect to one variable and then using another formula (or the same formula, if it is appropriate) to interpolate the results with respect to the second variable (see Prob. 20). Formulas essentially permitting the two processes to be effected at the same time are considered in Probs. 55 to 58 of Chap. 5 and are treated in detail by Pearson [180]. See also Steffensen [18] and Willers [21]. The two latter references include some corresponding formulas for two-way integration (*cubature*). See also Probs. 53 and 54 of Chap. 5 and the detailed treatments of Irwin [121] and Radon [189]. For discussions of the convergence of sequences of polynomial approximations, and related matters, see Nörlund [13, 168], Bernstein [35], Jackson [123], Feldheim [75], and de la Vallée Poussin [229].

PROBLEMS

Section 4.2

1. Show that

$$\Delta^r f_k = \nabla^r f_{k+r} = \delta^r f_{k+r/2}, \qquad \nabla^r f_k = \Delta^r f_{k-r} = \delta^r f_{k-r/2},$$
$$\delta^r f_k = \Delta^r f_{k-r/2} = \nabla^r f_{k+r/2},$$
$$\Delta(f_{k-1}\,\Delta g_{k-1}) = \nabla(f_k\,\Delta g_k) = \Delta(f_{k-1}\,\nabla g_k) = \nabla(f_k\,\nabla g_{k+1}),$$
$$\Delta\nabla f_k = \nabla\Delta f_k = \delta^2 f_k.$$

2. Show that

$$\Delta(f_k g_k) = f_k\,\Delta g_k + g_{k+1}\,\Delta f_k, \qquad \Delta(f_k^2) = (f_k + f_{k+1})\,\Delta f_k,$$
$$\Delta\left(\frac{f_k}{g_k}\right) = \frac{g_k\,\Delta f_k - f_k\,\Delta g_k}{g_k g_{k+1}}, \qquad \Delta\left(\frac{1}{f_k}\right) = -\frac{\Delta f_k}{f_k f_{k+1}}.$$

3. Show that

$$\Delta^r\left(\frac{1}{x}\right) = \frac{(-1)^r r!\,h^r}{x(x+h)\,\cdots\,(x+rh)},$$
$$\Delta\cos(\omega x + \alpha) = 2\sin\frac{\omega h}{2}\cos\left(\omega x + \alpha + \frac{\omega h}{2} + \frac{\pi}{2}\right),$$
$$\Delta^r\cos(\omega x + \alpha) = \left(2\sin\frac{\omega h}{2}\right)^r\cos\left(\omega x + \alpha + \frac{r\omega h}{2} + \frac{r\pi}{2}\right).$$

Section 4.3

4. Calculate approximate values of $f(x) = \sin x$ for $x = 0.50(0.02)0.70$ and for $1.50(0.02)1.70$, by applying the appropriate Newtonian formula to the following rounded data:

x	0.5	0.7	0.9	1.1	1.3	1.5	1.7
$f(x)$	0.47943	0.64422	0.78333	0.89121	0.96356	0.99749	0.99166

5. Obtain the formulas

$$hf'_s = \Delta f_0 + \tfrac{1}{2}(2s - 1)\,\Delta^2 f_0 + \tfrac{1}{6}(3s^2 - 6s + 2)\,\Delta^3 f_0 + \tfrac{1}{12}(2s^3 - 9s^2 + 11s - 3)\,\Delta^4 f_0 + \tfrac{1}{120}(5s^4 - 40s^3 + 105s^2 - 100s + 24)\,\Delta^5 f_0 + \cdots$$

and

$$\frac{1}{h}\int_{x_0}^{x_0+sh} f(x)\,dx = sf_0 + \tfrac{1}{2}s^2\,\Delta f_0 + \tfrac{1}{12}s^2(2s - 3)\,\Delta^2 f_0 + \tfrac{1}{24}s^2(s - 2)^2\,\Delta^3 f_0 + \tfrac{1}{720}s^2(6s^3 - 45s^2 + 110s - 90)\,\Delta^4 f_0 + \tfrac{1}{1440}s^2(2s^4 - 24s^3 + 105s^2 - 200s + 144)\,\Delta^5 f_0 + \cdots,$$

and also obtain corresponding formulas for hf'_{n+s} and for $h^{-1}\int_{x_n-sh}^{x_n} f(x)\,dx$ in terms of backward differences.

6. Use the data of Prob. 4 and the results of Prob. 5 to obtain approximate values of $f'(0.6)$, $f'(1.6)$, $f''(0.6)$, $f''(1.6)$, and of

$$\int_{0.5}^{0.6} f(x)\,dx, \qquad \int_{1.6}^{1.7} f(x)\,dx.$$

Section 4.4

7. Calculate approximate values of $f(1.0)$ from the data of Prob. 4, first by use of Gauss's forward formula launched from $x = 0.9$, and second by use of the backward formula launched from $x = 1.1$.

8. By specializing Sheppard's rules for the formation of interpolation formulas to the case when the relevant abscissas are at a uniform spacing h, show that *the coefficient of the kth difference encountered in a continuous difference path can be obtained by dividing by k! the product of k factors, each of which represents the distance between the abscissa of the interpolant and one of the abscissas lying in the region of determination of the preceding difference in the path, in units of the spacing,* if the result of truncating the interpolation formula with the kth difference is to yield exact results at all points involved in its formation. Also, illustrate the use of this rule by writing down the forward and backward formulas of Newton and Gauss.

9. Show that the result of truncating the Gauss forward formula with the fourth difference can be written in the form

$$f_s \approx f_0 + s\left\{\delta f_{\frac{1}{2}} + \frac{s-1}{2}\left[\delta^2 f_0 + \frac{s+1}{3}\left(\delta^3 f_{\frac{1}{2}} + \frac{s-2}{4}\,\delta^4 f_0\right)\right]\right\},$$

where the evaluation of the formula is conveniently effected from right to left, and write the backward formula, as well as the two Newton formulas, in similar forms.

Section 4.5

10. Use Stirling's formula to calculate approximate values of $f(x)$ for

$$x = 1.00(0.02)1.20$$

from the data of Prob. 4.

11. Obtain the formulas

$$hf'_s = \mu\delta f_0 + s\,\delta^2 f_0 + \tfrac{1}{6}(3s^2 - 1)\,\mu\delta^3 f_0 + \tfrac{1}{12}s(2s^2 - 1)\,\delta^4 f_0$$
$$+ \tfrac{1}{120}(5s^4 - 15s^2 + 4)\,\mu\delta^5 f_0 + \tfrac{1}{360}s(3s^4 - 10s^2 + 4)\,\delta^6 f_0 + \cdots$$

and

$$\frac{1}{h}\int_{x_0-hs}^{x_0+hs} f(x)\,dx = 2sf_0 + \tfrac{1}{3}s^3\,\delta^2 f_0 + \tfrac{1}{180}s^3(3s^2 - 5)\,\delta^4 f_0$$
$$+ \tfrac{1}{7560}s^3(3s^4 - 21s^2 + 28)\,\delta^6 f_0 + \cdots,$$

and use them to calculate approximate values of $f'(1.1)$, $f'(1.0)$, $f''(1.1)$, $f''(1.0)$, and of

$$\int_{1.0}^{1.2} f(x)\,dx, \qquad \int_{0.9}^{1.3} f(x)\,dx,$$

from the data of Prob. 4.

Section 4.6

12. Use Bessel's formula to calculate approximate values of $f(x)$ for

$$x = 0.90(0.02)1.10$$

from the data of Prob. 4.

13. Obtain the formulas

$$hf'_{t+\frac{1}{2}} = \delta f_{\frac{1}{2}} + t\,\mu\delta^2 f_{\frac{1}{2}} + \tfrac{1}{24}(12t^2 - 1)\,\delta^3 f_{\frac{1}{2}} + \tfrac{1}{24}t(4t^2 - 5)\,\mu\delta^4 f_{\frac{1}{2}}$$
$$+ \tfrac{1}{1920}(80t^4 - 120t^2 + 9)\,\delta^5 f_{\frac{1}{2}} + \cdots$$

and

$$\frac{1}{h}\int_{x_{\frac{1}{2}}-th}^{x_{\frac{1}{2}}+th} f(x)\,dx = 2t\,\mu f_{\frac{1}{2}} + \tfrac{1}{12}t(4t^2 - 3)\,\mu\delta^2 f_{\frac{1}{2}}$$
$$+ \tfrac{1}{2880}t(48t^4 - 200t^2 + 135)\,\mu\delta^4 f_{\frac{1}{2}} + \cdots,$$

where $x_{\frac{1}{2}} \equiv (x_0 + x_1)/2$, and use them to calculate approximate values of $f'(1.1)$, $f'(1.0)$, $f''(1.1)$, $f''(1.0)$, and of

$$\int_{0.9}^{1.1} f(x)\,dx, \qquad \int_{0.7}^{1.3} f(x)\,dx,$$

from the data of Prob. 4.

Section 4.7

14. Use Everett's first formula to obtain approximate values of $f(x) = \sin x$ for $x = 1.00(0.02)1.20$ from the following data:

x	$f(x)$	δ^2	δ^4
0.9	0.78333	-3123	125
1.1	0.89121	-3553	141
1.3	0.96356	-3842	155

15. Use Everett's second formula to obtain approximate values of $f(x) = \sin x$ for $x = 1.00(0.02)1.20$ from the following data:

x	$f(x)$	δ^3
0.9	0.78333	
		-430
1.1	0.89121	
		-289
1.3	0.96356	

16. By integrating Everett's first formula, obtain the formula

$$\frac{1}{h}\int_{x_0}^{x_1} f(x)\,dx = \mu f_{\frac{1}{2}} - \tfrac{1}{12}\mu\delta^2 f_{\frac{1}{2}} + \tfrac{11}{720}\mu\delta^4 f_{\frac{1}{2}} - \tfrac{191}{60480}\mu\delta^6 f_{\frac{1}{2}} + \cdots$$

and verify that it follows also from the result of Prob. 13. Show that it can be expressed in the alternative form

$$\frac{1}{h}\int_{x_0}^{x_1} f(x)\,dx = \tfrac{1}{2}(f_0 + f_1) - \tfrac{1}{12}(\mu\delta f_1 - \mu\delta f_0) + \tfrac{11}{720}(\mu\delta^3 f_1 - \mu\delta^3 f_0)$$
$$- \tfrac{191}{60480}(\mu\delta^5 f_1 - \mu\delta^5 f_0) + \cdots$$

and deduce *Gauss's sum formula* (see also §5.9) in the form

$$\frac{1}{h}\int_{x_0}^{x_r} f(x)\,dx = h(\tfrac{1}{2}f_0 + f_1 + f_2 + \cdots + f_{r-1} + \tfrac{1}{2}f_r) - \tfrac{1}{12}(\mu\delta f_r - \mu\delta f_0)$$
$$+ \tfrac{11}{720}(\mu\delta^3 f_r - \mu\delta^3 f_0) - \tfrac{191}{60480}(\mu\delta^5 f_r - \mu\delta^5 f_0) + \cdots$$

Section 4.8

17. Sketch the function $\pi(x) = x(x-1)(x-2)(x-3)(x-4)$ over the range $-1 \leqq x \leqq 5$. Noticing that the error associated with the approximation of $f(x)$ by the result of retaining fourth differences in either of Newton's or Gauss's interpolation formulas is of the form $\pi(x)f^{v}(\xi)/120$ for some ξ, if $f^{v}(x)$ is continuous, when the ordinates at $x = 0, 1, 2, 3,$ and 4 are employed, and assuming that Newton's formulas would be used principally in $(0,1)$ and $(3,4)$, whereas central-difference formulas would be used principally in $(1,3)$, account for the fact that the former are sometimes erroneously said to be "less accurate" than the latter. If interpolations were effected in the interval $(1,3)$ by both Newton and Gauss formulas, based on the five ordinates at $x = 0, 1, 2, 3,$ and 4, and if no round-offs were committed, how would the results actually compare in accuracy? What evidence is afforded by the graph with respect to the general relative dependability of interpolation and extrapolation?

18. If $f(x) = (1 + x)^5$, determine the Stirling and Bessel approximations over $(0,1)$ corresponding to a spacing $h = 1$, with $x_0 = 0$ and $x_1 = 1$, and corresponding to the successive retention of differences through the first, second, third, and fourth. Then calculate the error in each of these eight approximations for $x = 0.0(0.2)1.0$, retaining only one decimal place, and plot the error curves in a common graph. Thus show that, in this example, the following facts are true over (0.1):

(a) The Stirling mean first-difference approximation is better than that which also incorporates the second difference over most of the range, and the mean third-difference approximation is better than that which also incorporates the fourth difference over the entire range.

(b) The Bessel mean second-difference approximation is better than that which also incorporates the third difference over half the range.

(c) The Stirling mean first-difference approximation is better than the three Bessel approximations which employ the first difference, the mean second difference, and/or the third difference, near $x = \tfrac{1}{2}$ as well as near $x = 0$.

(d) The Bessel fourth-difference approximation is much better than all the others and is followed successively by the Stirling third-difference and the Stirling fourth-difference approximations.

(Compare the results of Prob. 19.)

19. Proceed as in Prob. 18 with $f(x) = \cos(\pi x/8)$, retaining five decimal places. Thus show that, in this example, the following facts are true over $(0,1)$:

(a) The Stirling zeroth-difference approximation is better than the Bessel first-difference approximation over half the range, whereas the Bessel mean zeroth-difference approximation is better than the Stirling mean first-difference approximation over the remainder of the range.

(b) The Bessel mean second-difference approximation is better than that which also incorporates the third difference over half the range.

(c) The Stirling second-difference approximation is better than the Bessel third-difference approximation over most of the range.

(d) The Stirling fourth-difference approximation is better than all the others and is followed successively by the Bessel fourth-difference and the Stirling second-difference approximations.

(Compare the results of Prob. 18.)

20. The following data represent rounded four-place values of the elliptic-integral function $E(x,y) = \int_0^y \sqrt{1 - \sin^2 x \sin^2 t}\ dt$:

x \\ y	50°	54°	58°	62°
50°	0.8134	0.8060	0.7988	0.7920
52°	0.8414	0.8332	0.8251	0.8174
54°	0.8690	0.8598	0.8508	0.8422
56°	0.8962	0.8859	0.8759	0.8663

Determine an approximation to $E(52°,51°)$ by (a) interpolating horizontally to obtain $E(52°,y)$ for $y = 50°(2°)56°$ and then interpolating these values vertically, (b) interpolating vertically then horizontally, and (c) interpolating directly along a diagonal. Also interpolate as accurately as possible for $E(55.4°,53.1°)$ by any method.

Section 4.9

21. Construct a difference table, corresponding to the results of rounding true values of $f(x) = x^3$ for $x = 1.0(0.1)3.0$ to two decimal places, and study the propagated effects of the round-off errors. Also compare the mean absolute values of the third, fourth, and fifth differences with the ideal values, and show that a more regular difference array would result from an *improper* rounding of the values corresponding to $x = 1.4$ and $x = 2.6$ by one unit.

22. Certain of the following 20 consecutive values, corresponding to equally spaced arguments, are incorrect because of typical copying errors. Locate the errors and correct them.

17278	48818	79779	112630
23424	54440	86249	119398
29585	60723	92752	126246
35764	67041	99318	133180
41964	73398	105937	140206

Section 4.10

23. Show that the additional error $R(s)$ introduced into Bessel's formula, by replacing $\mu\delta^2 f_{\frac{1}{2}}$ by $\mu(\delta^2 f_{\frac{1}{2}} - k\delta^4 f_{\frac{1}{2}})$ and neglecting $\mu\delta^4 f_{\frac{1}{2}}$ otherwise, can be expressed in the form

$$R(s) = \tfrac{1}{24}[(s^2 - s)^2 + (12k - 2)(s^2 - s)]\ \mu\delta^4 f_{\frac{1}{2}},$$

and that the extreme values of the coefficient of $\mu\delta^4 f_{\frac{1}{2}}$ for $0 \leqq s \leqq 1$ occur when $s = \frac{1}{2}$ and when $s^2 - s = 1 - 6k$ and are given by $(3 - 16k)/128$ and $-(1 - 6k)^2/24$, respectively. Show also that the requirement that the extreme values be of equal magnitude and opposite sign (so that the maximum additional error is minimized) gives $k = (3 + \sqrt{2})/24 \doteq 0.184$, and that $R(s)$ then varies between the limits $\pm(3 - 2\sqrt{2})\,\mu\delta^4 f_{\frac{1}{2}}/384 \doteq \pm 0.00045\mu\delta^4 f_{\frac{1}{2}}$.

24. Show that the additional error $R(s)$ introduced into Everett's first formula, by replacing $\delta^2 f_0$ and $\delta^2 f_1$ by $\delta^2 f_0 - k\,\delta^4 f_0$ and $\delta^2 f_1 - k\,\delta^4 f_1$ and neglecting fourth differences otherwise, is identical with that associated with Bessel's formula when $\delta^4 f_0 = \delta^4 f_1$, and hence deduce that, if k is assigned the same value as for Bessel's formula (Prob. 23), then the additional error cannot exceed 0.00045 times the larger of $|\delta^4 f_0|$ and $|\delta^4 f_1|$ if the two fourth differences have the same sign. Show also that, if those differences are equal in magnitude and of opposite sign, then $R(s)$ is given by

$$R(s) = \pm \frac{2s-1}{15}\left[3\binom{s+1}{4} + 5k\binom{s}{2}\right]\delta^4 f_0$$
$$= \pm \tfrac{1}{1920}[t^5 - 10t^3 + 9t + 80k(t^3 - t)]\,\delta^4 f_0 \qquad (t = 2s - 1),$$

and show that the maximum additional error for $0 \leqq s \leqq 1$ is smaller than $0.00122|\delta^4 f_0|$ in magnitude. Thus deduce that $|R(s)| < 0.00122M$ in the general case, where M is the larger of $|\delta^4 f_0|$ and $|\delta^4 f_1|$.

25. Solve Prob. 14 by using the throwback technique.

26. Show that Everett's modified second-difference formula can be expressed in the form

$$s \approx \frac{1}{f_1 - f_0}\left\{(f_s - f_0) + \frac{s(s-1)}{6}[(s-2)\bar{\delta}^2 f_0 - (s+1)\,\bar{\delta}^2 f_1]\right\}$$

for *inverse interpolation* between f_0 and f_1, when f_s is given. Use it iteratively, first replacing s by zero in the coefficients in the right-hand member to calculate an initial approximation to the required value of s, and then successively introducing each new approximation into the right-hand member to obtain the next one, to determine approximately the value of x for which $f(x) = 0.9$, with the data of Prob. 14.

Section 4.11

27. Show that the error corresponding to the truncation of the series in (4.11.5) with the nth term is of the form

$$E_n(x) = \frac{a^{n+1}}{(n+1)!}\,x(x - h)\;\cdots\;(x - nh)e^{a\xi_n},$$

for some ξ_n, and deduce that, if $x < nh$, the errors $E_n(x)$ and $E_{n+1}(x)$ are of opposite sign, so that the error is smaller than the first term omitted and of the same sign (see Prob. 5 of Chap. 1). Under the assumption that $e^{ah} > 2$, so that (4.11.5) diverges, show also that the term corresponding to the $(k + 1)$th difference is smaller than the preceding one so long as k does not exceed k_0, where k_0 is the integral part of $[(e^{ah} - 1)x + h]/[h(e^{ah} - 2)]$.

28. Illustrate the results of Prob. 27 by calculating successive approximations to e^x from successive partial sums of the Newton interpolation series (4.11.5) with $a = 1$ and $h = 1$, when $x = 0.5$. In particular, show that the best approximation is afforded by retention of only two differences, that a consideration of the first neglected term gives the result $1.49009 < e^{0.5} < 1.80717$, and that the *mean* of these limits differs from the true value by less than one unit in the fourth decimal place.

29. If $f(x) = e^{ax}$, show that

$$\delta^{2r} f(0) = \left(2\sinh\frac{ah}{2}\right)^{2r}, \qquad \mu\delta^{2r+1} f(0) = \left(2\sinh\frac{ah}{2}\right)^{2r}\sinh ah,$$

and deduce that the formal Stirling series centered at $x = 0$ is of the form

$$e^{ax} = 1 + \frac{x}{h} \sinh ah + \frac{x^2}{2!h^2}\left(2 \sinh \frac{ah}{2}\right)^2$$
$$+ \frac{x(x^2 - h^2)}{3!h^3}\left(2 \sinh \frac{ah}{2}\right)^2 \sinh ah + \frac{x^2(x^2 - h^2)}{4!h^4}\left(2 \sinh \frac{ah}{2}\right)^4 + \cdots$$

30. Calculate six successive approximations to the value of e^x when $x = 0.5$ by use of Stirling's formula centered at $x = 0$, with $h = 1$, and investigate the trend of the successive deviations from the true value. (Notice that the infinite Stirling series itself is convergent in this case.)

31. By successively equating the even and odd parts of the two members of the expansion of Prob. 29, and taking $h = 1$, deduce the formal expansions

$$\cosh ax = 1 + \frac{x^2}{2!}\beta^2 + \frac{x^2(x^2 - 1^2)}{4!}\beta^4 + \frac{x^2(x^2 - 1^2)(x^2 - 2^2)}{6!}\beta^6 + \cdots$$

and

$$\frac{\sinh ax}{\sinh a} = x + \frac{x(x^2 - 1^2)}{3!}\beta^2 + \frac{x(x^2 - 1^2)(x^2 - 2^2)}{5!}\beta^4 + \cdots = \frac{1}{\beta}\frac{\sinh ax}{\cosh (a/2)}$$

where $\beta = 2 \sinh (a/2)$. Show also that these series converge when $|\beta| < 2$.

32. Show that the formal Bessel-series representation of $f(x) = e^{ax}$, centered at $x = h/2$, is of the form

$$e^{ax} = e^{ah/2}\left[\cosh \frac{ah}{2} + \frac{2x - h}{2h}\beta + \frac{x(x - h)}{2!h^2}\beta^2 \cosh \frac{ah}{2} \right.$$
$$\left. + \frac{x(x - h)(2x - h)}{2 \cdot 3!h^3}\beta^3 + \cdots \right],$$

where $\beta = 2 \sinh (ah/2)$. Also, by taking $h = 1$, replacing x by $x + \frac{1}{2}$, and successively equating the even and odd parts of the result, deduce the expansions

$$\frac{\cosh ax}{\cosh (a/2)} = 1 + \frac{x^2 - \frac{1}{4}}{2!}\beta^2 + \frac{(x^2 - \frac{1}{4})(x^2 - \frac{9}{4})}{4!}\beta^4 + \cdots$$

and

$$\sinh ax = x\beta + \frac{x(x^2 - \frac{1}{4})}{3!}\beta^3 + \frac{x(x^2 - \frac{1}{4})(x^2 - \frac{9}{4})}{5!}\beta^5 + \cdots = \frac{\beta}{2}\frac{\sinh ax}{\sinh (a/2)},$$

where $\beta = 2 \sinh (a/2)$, and show that these series converge when $|\beta| < 2$.

CHAPTER 5

OPERATIONS WITH FINITE DIFFERENCES

5.1. Introduction. The purpose of this chapter is twofold: first, to indicate the power and simplicity of operational methods in deriving a variety of formulas which are useful in various aspects of numerical analysis, and, second, to display certain such formulas for convenient reference and for use in following chapters.

The operational methods which are illustrated supply only the formulas themselves and do not furnish the relevant error term, which therefore must be obtained independently. Many of the formulas could also be obtained by differentiating or integrating an appropriate interpolation formula, although it often would be somewhat more difficult to obtain the rule of formation of the general term in the expansion. However, in such cases, it is clearly possible to deduce the desired *error term* by differentiating or integrating the known error term relevant to the parent formula.

In addition to formulas for numerical differentiation and integration, generally expressed in terms of forward, backward, or central differences, there are included certain formulas which are useful in subtabulation (§5.7) and approximate summation of series (§§5.8, 5.9).

The concluding sections (§§5.11, 5.12) deal with the problem of determining an expression for the error term relevant to a formula for numerical integration, when the coefficients in the formula are known.

5.2. Difference Operators. For many purposes, it is convenient to think of the symbols, Δ, ∇, and δ, defined in the preceding chapter, as *operators*, which transform a given function $f(x)$ into related functions, according to the laws

$$\Delta f(x) = f(x+h) - f(x), \qquad \nabla f(x) = f(x) - f(x-h),$$
$$\delta f(x) = f\left(x + \frac{h}{2}\right) - f\left(x - \frac{h}{2}\right). \tag{5.2.1}$$

Also, in addition to the *averaging operator* μ, such that

$$\mu f(x) = \frac{1}{2}\left[f\left(x + \frac{h}{2}\right) + f\left(x - \frac{h}{2}\right)\right], \tag{5.2.2}$$

128

we define the *shifting operator* E such that

$$Ef(x) = f(x + h),\tag{5.2.3}$$

and *differential* and *integral operators* D and J with the properties

$$Df(x) = f'(x)\tag{5.2.4}$$

and

$$Jf(x) = \int_x^{x+h} f(t)\, dt.\tag{5.2.5}$$

In all these operators except D, the *spacing* h is implied. When a more explicit notation is needed, the spacing may be indicated as a subscript, so that, for example, we could write $\delta_{2h}f(x)$ for $f(x + h) - f(x - h)$.

Positive integral powers of the operators are defined by iteration. Also, we define the *zeroth* power of any operator as the *identity operator* 1, which leaves any function unchanged. For the operator E, the power E^α is defined for *any* α so that

$$E^\alpha f(x) = f(x + \alpha h),\tag{5.2.6}$$

assuming the existence of $f(x + \alpha h)$.

We say that two operators, say L_1 and L_2, are *equal* if $L_1 f(x) = L_2 f(x)$ for any function $f(x)$ for which the operations are defined.

It is easily verified that the seven operators defined here possess the *distributive, commutative,* and *associative* properties shared by real numbers, so that, if L_1, L_2, and L_3 are any of these operators, there follows

$$L_1(L_2 + L_3) = L_1 L_2 + L_1 L_3, \qquad L_2 L_1 = L_1 L_2,$$
$$(L_1 L_2) L_3 = L_1 (L_2 L_3), \qquad (L_1 + L_2) + L_3 = L_1 + (L_2 + L_3).\tag{5.2.7}$$

The exponential law $L^m L^n = L^{m+n}$ is also readily established for each of these operators.

In particular, to show that D and J are commutative, we make the calculations

$$DJf(x) = \frac{d}{dx} \int_x^{x+h} f(t)\, dt = f(x + h) - f(x) = \int_x^{x+h} \frac{df(t)}{dt}\, dt = JDf(x),$$

and so deduce also that

$$DJ = JD = \Delta.\tag{5.2.8}$$

We may define L^{-1} as an operator such that

$$LL^{-1} = 1,\tag{5.2.9}$$

so that, if $L^{-1}g = f$, then $LL^{-1}g = Lf$ or $g = Lf$, and refer to L^{-1} as an *inverse* of L. It is important, however, to notice that the inverse operator L^{-1} may not be uniquely defined. For if $\omega(x)$ is any function which is *annihilated* by L, so that $L\omega(x) = 0$, and if one interpretation of $L^{-1}g(x)$ is $f(x)$, so that $Lf(x) = g(x)$, then another one is $f(x) + \omega(x)$, since also

$\mathbf{L}[f(x) + \omega(x)] = g(x)$. That is, we may write $\mathbf{L}^{-1}\mathbf{L}f = f + \omega$, where ω is *any* function annihilated by $\mathbf{L}$. Conversely, if $\mathbf{L}^{-1}\mathbf{L}f = f + \omega$, then it must follow that $\mathbf{L}\mathbf{L}^{-1}\mathbf{L}f = \mathbf{L}f + \mathbf{L}\omega$ or $\mathbf{L}f = \mathbf{L}f + \mathbf{L}\omega$, so that $\mathbf{L}\omega$ *must* vanish.

If no function is annihilated by an operator $\mathbf{L}$, there follows

$$\mathbf{L}^{-1}\mathbf{L} = \mathbf{L}\mathbf{L}^{-1} = 1,$$

and $\mathbf{L}^{-1}$ is then said to be a *proper* inverse. Thus, whereas no function is annihilated by $\mathbf{E}$, the operators Δ, ∇, and δ annihilate any function of period h, $\mathbf{J}$ annihilates the derivative of any such function, and $\mathbf{D}$ annihilates any constant. Further, μ annihilates any so-called *odd-harmonic* function of period $2h$, that is, any function $f(x)$ for which

$$f(x + h) = -f(x).$$

Hence, care must be taken with respect to the *order* of operations involving the inverses of those operators.

In the case of the operator $\mathbf{D}$, it is seen that $\mathbf{D}^{-1}$ corresponds to the formation of an indefinite integral or "antiderivative," and the situation described corresponds to the fact that, whereas the derivative of that integral is the original function, the integral of the derivative involves an arbitrary additive constant. On the other hand, it should be noticed that $\Delta\mathbf{D}^{-1}f(x)$ *is* uniquely determined, since Δ annihilates the arbitrary constant. In fact, if we write $\mathbf{D}^{-1}f(x) = F(x) + C$, we see that

$$\Delta\mathbf{D}^{-1}f(x) = F(x + h) - F(x) = \mathbf{J}f(x),$$

so that we may write also

$$\Delta\mathbf{D}^{-1} = \mathbf{J}. \tag{5.2.10}$$

This result follows also by using (5.2.8) to deduce that

$$\Delta\mathbf{D}^{-1} = \mathbf{J}\mathbf{D}\mathbf{D}^{-1} = \mathbf{J}.$$

In the present chapter, we will be concerned principally with applying operators to *polynomials*. In this connection, we may notice that *each of the operators Δ, ∇, δ, and $\mathbf{D}$ reduces the degree of any polynomial,* and that the same statement is true of any positive integral powers of these operators. We will refer to such operators as *delta operators*. It should be noticed that $\mathbf{E}$, μ, and $\mathbf{J}$ are *not* delta operators.

From the definitions given, we may obtain the relations

$$\Delta = \mathbf{E} - 1, \qquad \nabla = 1 - \mathbf{E}^{-1}, \qquad \delta = \mathbf{E}^{\frac{1}{2}} - \mathbf{E}^{-\frac{1}{2}}, \qquad \mu = \tfrac{1}{2}(\mathbf{E}^{\frac{1}{2}} + \mathbf{E}^{-\frac{1}{2}}), \tag{5.2.11}$$

whereas (5.2.8) leads also to the relation

$$\mathbf{D}\mathbf{J} = \mathbf{J}\mathbf{D} = \mathbf{E} - 1, \tag{5.2.12}$$

so that these operators are simply expressed in terms of **E**.

Further, if r is any nonnegative integer, there follows

$$\Delta^r = E^r \nabla^r = E^{r/2} \delta^r$$

$$= (E - 1)^r = E^r - \frac{r}{1!} E^{r-1} + \frac{r(r-1)}{2!} E^{r-2} - \cdots$$

$$+ (-1)^{r-1} \frac{r}{1!} E + (-1)^r$$

and hence, by applying these equal operators to $y(x_k) \equiv y_k$, we obtain the useful formulas

$$\Delta^r y_k = y_{k+r} - \binom{r}{1} y_{k+r-1} + \binom{r}{2} y_{k+r-2} - \cdots$$

$$+ (-1)^{r-1} \binom{r}{1} y_{k+1} + (-1)^r y_k,$$

$$\nabla^r y_k = y_k - \binom{r}{1} y_{k-1} + \binom{r}{2} y_{k-2} - \cdots$$

$$+ (-1)^{r-1} \binom{r}{1} y_{k-r+1} + (-1)^r y_{k-r},$$

$$\delta^r y_k = y_{k+r/2} - \binom{r}{1} y_{k+r/2-1} + \cdots$$

$$+ (-1)^{r-1} \binom{r}{1} y_{k-r/2+1} + (-1)^r y_{k-r/2}. \quad (5.2.13)$$

These relations permit the calculation of an arbitrary difference as a linear combination of ordinates, without the formation of a difference table or the calculation of differences of lower order, the coefficients of successive ordinates being merely binomial coefficients prefixed by alternating signs.

From the relations of (5.2.11), we may properly deduce the relations

$$E - \Delta = 1, \quad E(1 - \nabla) = 1, \quad (E^{\frac{1}{2}} - \tfrac{1}{2}\delta)^2 - \tfrac{1}{4}\delta^2 = 1, \quad E^{\frac{1}{2}} - \tfrac{1}{2}\delta - \mu = 0,$$

after which the formal symbolism of elementary algebra suggests the forms

$$E = 1 + \Delta, \quad E = \frac{1}{1 - \nabla}, \quad E^{\frac{1}{2}} = (1 + \tfrac{1}{4}\delta^2)^{\frac{1}{2}} + \tfrac{1}{2}\delta, \quad \mu = (1 + \tfrac{1}{4}\delta^2)^{\frac{1}{2}}.$$

$$(5.2.14)$$

While the first form requires no explanation, the term $1/(1 - \nabla)$ can be interpreted at this stage only as representing the *inverse* of the operator $1 - \nabla$, that is, as an alternative notation for the operator $(1 - \nabla)^{-1}$ such that

$$(1 - \nabla)(1 - \nabla)^{-1} = 1, \quad (5.2.15)$$

whereas the derivation of the third form shows that $(1 + \tfrac{1}{4}\delta^2)^{\frac{1}{2}}$ is to represent an operator such that its *iterate* is the operator $1 + \tfrac{1}{4}\delta^2$,

$$[(1 + \tfrac{1}{4}\delta^2)^{\frac{1}{2}}]^2 = 1 + \tfrac{1}{4}\delta^2. \quad (5.2.16)$$

If we now suppose that the function upon which the operations are to be effected is a *polynomial* $p_n(x)$, of degree n, we may obtain a more useful interpretation of these operators. For, if t is a variable, we have the identity

$$(1 - t)(1 + t + t^2 + \cdots + t^n) = 1 - t^{n+1},$$

for any nonnegative integer n. Clearly, it is proper to replace t by ∇ (or by the symbol representing any other distributive operator), to give

$$(1 - \nabla)(1 + \nabla + \nabla^2 + \cdots + \nabla^n) = 1 - \nabla^{n+1}. \qquad (5.2.17)$$

Since the operator ∇^{n+1} will *annihilate* $p_n(x)$, the operator in (5.2.17) is equivalent to the unit operator for any $p_n(x)$. Since the inverse of $1 - \nabla$ is uniquely defined by (5.2.15), it follows that we may write

$$(1 - \nabla)^{-1} = 1 + \nabla + \nabla^2 + \cdots + \nabla^n$$

when only polynomials of degree n or less are to be affected by the operator. More generally, we are justified in writing

$$E = (1 - \nabla)^{-1} = 1 + \nabla + \nabla^2 + \cdots = \sum_{k=0}^{\infty} \nabla^k \qquad (5.2.18)$$

when the class of *all* polynomials is included, since the finite number of required terms, for which the exponent of ∇ does not exceed the degree of the polynomial, is present, and the remaining terms each annihilate that polynomial.

In a similar way, it is easily seen that if we retain only the terms which involve powers of δ which do not exceed n in the formal expansion

$$(1 + \tfrac{1}{4}\delta^2)^{\frac{1}{2}} = 1 + \tfrac{1}{8}\delta^2 - \tfrac{1}{128}\delta^4 + \cdots,$$

the resultant *polynomial* in δ possesses the property that its square differs from $1 + \tfrac{1}{4}\delta^2$ by the product of δ^{n+1} and a polynomial in δ, and hence is equivalent to $1 + \tfrac{1}{4}\delta^2$ for any $p_n(x)$. Clearly the *negative* of the indicated expansion also has this property. However, the result of applying the expanded form of the third relation in (5.2.14) to any arbitrarily chosen function (say a constant) shows that the former alternative is the proper one, so that we are justified in writing

$$E^{\frac{1}{2}} = (1 + \tfrac{1}{4}\delta^2)^{\frac{1}{2}} + \tfrac{1}{2}\delta = 1 + \tfrac{1}{2}\delta + \tfrac{1}{8}\delta^2 - \cdots \qquad (5.2.19)$$

when we deal only with polynomials.

It then follows that we may write

$$E^s = (1 + \Delta)^s = (1 - \nabla)^{-s} = [(1 + \tfrac{1}{4}\delta^2)^{\frac{1}{2}} + \tfrac{1}{2}\delta]^{2s} \qquad (5.2.20)$$

when s is any integer, where each right-hand member may be expanded in a series of powers of the relevant delta operator when we are dealing only with polynomials. The extension to the more general case when s is any rational number offers no difficulties. It is also possible to give a rigorous direct justification of the use of these expansions when s is irrational, although the required arguments are somewhat more subtle.

The first two equivalences in (5.2.20) are, in fact, seen to be symbolic representations of the relations

$$p(x_0 + sh) = \sum_{k=0}^{\infty} \binom{s}{k} \Delta^k p(x_0) = \sum_{k=0}^{\infty} \binom{-s}{k} \nabla^k p(x_0), \quad (5.2.21)$$

to which the previously established Newton forward- and backward-difference formulas (4.3.11) and (4.3.13) reduce when $f(x)$ is replaced by a polynomial $p(x)$, since only a finite number of terms then do not vanish and since the remainder term also vanishes. This fact can be considered as constituting an indirect proof of the validity of (5.2.20) when s is unrestricted.

As was discussed in §4.11, the series in (5.2.21) frequently do not converge when $p(x)$ is replaced by a function $f(x)$ other than a polynomial; they must be truncated, say, after $n + 1$ terms, and the appropriate error term (4.3.6) or (4.3.9) then must be added. However, the *coefficients* in the formula are not dependent upon the nature of $f(x)$, and the present operational methods serve to determine those coefficients in a simple and systematic way.

The equivalence of the extreme members of (5.2.20) can be expressed in a variety of forms, such as

$$\mathbf{E}^s = [(1 + \tfrac{1}{4}\delta^2)^{\frac{1}{2}} + \tfrac{1}{2}\delta]^{2s} = [1 + \tfrac{1}{2}\delta^2 + \delta(1 + \tfrac{1}{4}\delta^2)^{\frac{1}{2}}]^s$$
$$= (1 + \tfrac{1}{2}\delta^2 + \mu\delta)^s = (1 + \mathbf{E}^{\frac{1}{2}}\delta)^s = (1 - \mathbf{E}^{-\frac{1}{2}}\delta)^{-s}. \quad (5.2.22)$$

The operational formula obtained by expanding the first or second of these expressions would correspond to an interpolation employing the central differences $\delta^{2m+1}f(x_0)$ as well as the central differences of even order. Since the former differences are generally not available in *tabular* work, this formula would be of limited use. The Stirling formula could be obtained by expanding the third expression and afterward replacing μ^{2m} by $(1 + \delta^2/4)^m$ and μ^{2m+1} by $\mu(1 + \delta^2/4)^m$. The two Gaussian formulas could be obtained from the remaining two expressions. Since the results have been obtained in the preceding chapter (see also Prob. 5), these calculations are omitted here, and other derivations are indicated in the following sections.

In the remainder of this chapter we shall proceed, in general, as though we were concerned only with polynomials, and we shall indicate this fact by writing $p(x)$ in place of $f(x)$. Formulas to be obtained will then have been established as *identities* for any polynomial $p(x)$, in which case all relevant series of delta operators will effectively terminate. The determination of the proper error term to be introduced when the formula is applied to a function of more general type, after a *truncation* of the series involved, is then to be considered in each case as a separate problem.

5.3. Differentiation Formulas. In order to obtain formulas for numerical differentiation, by operational methods, it is necessary to relate $\mathbf{D}$ to other delta operators. For this purpose, we notice that the familiar formula of the Taylor-series expansion

$$p(x + h) = p(x) + \frac{h}{1!} p'(x) + \frac{h^2}{2!} p''(x) + \cdots + \frac{h^n}{n!} p^{(n)}(x) + \cdots$$

$$(5.3.1)$$

(which certainly is valid for any polynomial) can be written in the operational form

$$\mathbf{E}p(x) = \left(1 + \frac{h\mathbf{D}}{1!} + \frac{h^2\mathbf{D}^2}{2!} + \cdots + \frac{h^n\mathbf{D}^n}{n!} + \cdots\right) p(x).$$

Since the series in parentheses is the expansion of the function $e^{h\mathbf{D}}$, we deduce the curious relationship

$$\mathbf{E} = e^{h\mathbf{D}}, \qquad (5.3.2)$$

which is to be interpreted as an abbreviation of the statement that the operators $\mathbf{E}$ and $1 + h\mathbf{D}/1! + \cdots + (h\mathbf{D})^n/n!$ are equivalent when applied to any polynomial $p_n(x)$ of degree n, for any n.

Further, we obtain the additional relations

$$h\mathbf{D} = \log \mathbf{E} = \log (1 + \Delta) = -\log (1 - \nabla)$$

$$= 2 \log [(1 + \tfrac{1}{4}\delta^2)^{\frac{1}{2}} + \tfrac{1}{2}\delta] \equiv 2 \sinh^{-1} \frac{\delta}{2}. \qquad (5.3.3)$$

Here, for example, the symbolic relation $h\mathbf{D} = \log (1 + \Delta)$ asserts that the operators $h\mathbf{D}$ and $P_n(\Delta) \equiv \Delta - \Delta^2/2 + \cdots + (-1)^{n+1}\Delta^n/n$ are equivalent for any $p_n(x)$. Its validity can be verified directly by noticing that since Δ and $h\mathbf{D}/1! + \cdots + (h\mathbf{D})^n/n!$ have been shown to be equivalent for any $p_n(x)$, we may replace Δ by this last operator in the polynomial $P_n(\Delta)$. The result will differ from $h\mathbf{D}$ by a polynomial of the form $a_1(h\mathbf{D})^{n+1} + \cdots + a_n(h\mathbf{D})^{2n}$, which will annihilate $p_n(x)$.

In terms of *forward* differences, we thus deduce the formula

$$p_0' = \frac{1}{h} \log (1 + \Delta) p_0 = \frac{1}{h} (\Delta - \tfrac{1}{2}\Delta^2 + \tfrac{1}{3}\Delta^3 - \cdots) p_0. \quad (5.3.4)$$

By iteration, there follows also

$$p_0^{(r)} = \frac{1}{h^r} [\log (1 + \Delta)]^r p_0$$

$$= \frac{1}{h^r} (1 - \tfrac{1}{2}\Delta + \tfrac{1}{3}\Delta^2 - \cdots)^r \Delta^r p_0$$

$$= \frac{1}{h^r} \left[\Delta^r - \frac{r}{2}\Delta^{r+1} + \frac{r(3r+5)}{24}\Delta^{r+2} - \frac{r(r+2)(r+3)}{48}\Delta^{r+3} + \cdots \right] p_0. \tag{5.3.5}$$

The coefficients in this expansion are expressible in terms of the so-called *Stirling numbers of the first kind*, which may be denoted by $S_k^{(r)}$, and which are then defined by the relation

$$\frac{[\log (1 + \Delta)]^r}{r!} = \sum_{k=r}^{\infty} \frac{S_k^{(r)}}{k!} \Delta^k, \tag{5.3.6}$$

so that (5.3.5) can be written in the form

$$p_0^{(r)} = \frac{1}{h^r} \left[\frac{S_r^{(r)}}{1} + \frac{S_{r+1}^{(r)}}{r+1}\Delta + \frac{S_{r+2}^{(r)}}{(r+1)(r+2)}\Delta^2 + \cdots \right] \Delta^r p_0. \tag{5.3.7}$$

In a completely similar way, the corresponding *backward*-difference formulas are obtained in the form

$$p_n' = -\frac{1}{h}\log (1 - \nabla) p_n = \frac{1}{h}(\nabla + \tfrac{1}{2}\nabla^2 + \tfrac{1}{3}\nabla^3 + \cdots) p_n \tag{5.3.8}$$

and

$$p_n^{(r)} = \frac{1}{h^r}(1 + \tfrac{1}{2}\nabla + \tfrac{1}{3}\nabla^2 + \cdots)^r \nabla^r p_n$$

$$= \frac{1}{h^r}\left(\nabla^r + \frac{r}{2}\nabla^{r+1} + \frac{r(3r+5)}{24}\nabla^{r+2} + \frac{r(r+2)(r+3)}{48}\nabla^{r+3} + \cdots \right) p_n$$

$$\equiv \frac{1}{h^r}\left[\frac{S_r^{(r)}}{1} - \frac{S_{r+1}^{(r)}}{r+1}\nabla + \frac{S_{r+2}^{(r)}}{(r+1)(r+2)}\nabla^2 - \cdots \right] \nabla^r p_n. \tag{5.3.9}$$

From the last form of (5.3.3), there follows symbolically

$$p_0' = \left[\frac{2}{h}\sinh^{-1}\frac{\delta}{2} \right] p_0, \tag{5.3.10}$$

and several types of *central*-difference expansions are possible. Since the right-hand member is an *odd* function of δ, its expansion in powers of δ would involve odd central differences, which are not generally useful in tabular interpolation.

To obtain a result equivalent to that of differentiating the Stirling formula, and evaluating the result at x_0, we require an expansion involving *mean* odd central differences. Hence, by multiplying the right-hand member by μ and dividing by its equivalent $\sqrt{1 + \delta^2/4}$, we obtain the form

$$p_0' = \frac{2\mu}{h} \frac{\sinh^{-1} \delta/2}{\sqrt{1 + \delta^2/4}} \, p_0$$

$$= \frac{\mu}{h} \left(\delta - \frac{1^2}{3!} \delta^3 + \frac{1^2 \cdot 2^2}{5!} \delta^5 - \cdots \right) p_0. \qquad (5.3.11)$$

This formula is useful for calculating the derivative at interior tabular points, whereas (5.3.4) and (5.3.8) would be required at end points of the tabulation. Intermediate values are then conveniently interpolated from these values.

Higher derivatives of *even* order $2m$ are obtained by use of the operator $\mathbf{D}^{2m}$, where $\mathbf{D}$ is expressed as in (5.3.10),

$$\mathbf{D} = \frac{2}{h} \sinh^{-1} \frac{\delta}{2}$$

$$= \frac{1}{h} \left(\delta - \frac{1^2}{2^2 \cdot 3!} \delta^3 + \frac{1^2 \cdot 3^2}{2^4 \cdot 5!} \delta^5 - \frac{1^2 \cdot 3^2 \cdot 5^2}{2^6 \cdot 7!} \delta^7 + \cdots \right), \qquad (5.3.12)$$

whereas higher derivatives of *odd* order $2m + 1$ are obtained by multiplying the operator in (5.3.11) by $\mathbf{D}^{2m}$. Thus, for example, we may obtain the formula

$$p_0'' = \frac{1}{h^2} \left(\delta - \frac{1^2}{2^2 \cdot 3!} \delta^3 + \frac{1^2 \cdot 3^2}{2^4 \cdot 5!} \delta^5 - \frac{1^2 \cdot 3^2 \cdot 5^2}{2^6 \cdot 7!} \delta^7 + \cdots \right)^2 p_0$$

$$= \frac{1}{h^2} (\delta^2 - \tfrac{1}{12}\delta^4 + \tfrac{1}{90}\delta^6 - \tfrac{1}{560}\delta^8 + \cdots) p_0. \qquad (5.3.13)$$

Other formulas obtainable in this way may be listed as follows:

$$p_0''' = \frac{\mu}{h^3} (\delta^3 - \tfrac{1}{4}\delta^5 + \tfrac{7}{120}\delta^7 - \cdots) p_0, \qquad (5.3.14)$$

$$p_0^{\mathrm{iv}} = \frac{1}{h^4} (\delta^4 - \tfrac{1}{6}\delta^6 + \tfrac{7}{240}\delta^8 - \cdots) p_0, \qquad (5.3.15)$$

$$p_0^{\mathrm{v}} = \frac{\mu}{h^5} (\delta^5 - \tfrac{1}{3}\delta^7 + \cdots) p_0. \qquad (5.3.16)$$

The error term to be introduced in each case, when $p(x)$ is replaced by a function $f(x)$ which is not a polynomial, so that the series must be terminated with, say, rth differences, can be determined by use of the results of §3.3, if it is noticed that the result of this truncation corresponds to the differentiation of a polynomial of degree r which agrees with $f(x)$ at $x_0, x_1, \ldots, x_r$ in the case of (5.3.5), at $x_n, x_{n-1}, \ldots, x_{n-r}$ in the case of (5.3.9), and at x_0, $x_{\pm 1}$, . . . , $x_{\pm m}$ in the case of the central-difference formulas, where $m = r/2$ if r is even, and $m = (r + 1)/2$ if r is odd.   In the case of the forward- and backward-difference formulas, when the differentiation is effected at an end point of the range, formula (3.3.20) is valid.   However, in the central-difference formulas, the more complicated formula (3.3.15) cannot be avoided.   In practice, unless the analytical definition of $f(x)$ is known and is of sufficiently simple form to permit the determination and estimation of corresponding analytical expressions for the higher derivatives involved in those error terms, one generally must estimate the error by considering the magnitude of the first term omitted, realizing that this estimate is not necessarily a dependable one.   The importance of *inherent* errors in numerical differentiation has already been emphasized in §3.8.

Formulas for differentiation at a point midway between two tabular points are obtained by writing $\mathbf{D}$ in the form (5.3.12) and operating on $p_{\frac{1}{2}}$.   In addition, in order to obtain *ordinary* odd central differences and mean *even* central differences at $s = \frac{1}{2}$, we must multiply the expansion by the unit operator $\mu/\sqrt{1 + \delta^2/4}$ in calculating derivatives of *even* order, whereas in the preceding case this device was necessary when calculating derivatives of *odd* order.   Thus we have, symbolically,

$$p_{\frac{1}{2}}^{(2m)} = \frac{\mu}{\sqrt{1 + \delta^2/4}} \left[\frac{2}{h} \sinh^{-1} \frac{\delta}{2} \right]^{2m} p_{\frac{1}{2}} \qquad (5.3.17)$$

and

$$p_{\frac{1}{2}}^{(2m+1)} = \left[\frac{2}{h} \sinh^{-1} \frac{\delta}{2} \right]^{2m+1} p_{\frac{1}{2}}. \qquad (5.3.18)$$

In particular, when $m = 0$ in (5.3.17), we thus rederive (4.6.8) in the form

$$p_{\frac{1}{2}} = \mu(1 - \tfrac{1}{8}\delta^2 + \tfrac{3}{128}\delta^4 - \tfrac{5}{1024}\delta^6 + \tfrac{35}{32768}\delta^8 - \cdots)p_{\frac{1}{2}} \qquad (5.3.19)$$

and obtain also derivative formulas which may be listed as follows:

$$p_{\frac{1}{2}}' = \frac{1}{h} (\delta - \tfrac{1}{24}\delta^3 + \tfrac{3}{640}\delta^5 - \tfrac{7}{7168}\delta^7 + \cdots)p_{\frac{1}{2}}, \qquad (5.3.20)$$

$$p_{\frac{1}{2}}'' = \frac{\mu}{h^2} (\delta^2 - \tfrac{5}{24}\delta^4 + \tfrac{259}{5760}\delta^6 - \tfrac{3229}{322560}\delta^8 + \cdots)p_{\frac{1}{2}}, \qquad (5.3.21)$$

$$p_{\frac{1}{2}}''' = \frac{1}{h^3} (\delta^3 - \tfrac{1}{8}\delta^5 + \tfrac{37}{1920}\delta^7 - \cdots)p_{\frac{1}{2}}, \qquad (5.3.22)$$

$$p_{\frac{1}{2}}^{\text{iv}} = \frac{\mu}{h^4} (\delta^4 - \tfrac{7}{24}\delta^6 + \tfrac{47}{640}\delta^8 - \cdots)p_{\frac{1}{2}}, \qquad (5.3.23)$$

$$p_{\frac{1}{2}}^{\text{v}} = \frac{1}{h^5} (\delta^5 - \tfrac{5}{24}\delta^7 + \cdots)p_{\frac{1}{2}}. \qquad (5.3.24)$$

In certain applications, it is desirable to express differences at a point in terms of derivatives at that point.   This is the inverse of the problem just considered. Thus, in order to express forward differences in terms of derivatives, we again refer to (5.3.3) and obtain the relation

$$\Delta^r = (e^{h\mathbf{D}} - 1)^r = \left(\frac{h\mathbf{D}}{1!} + \frac{h^2\mathbf{D}^2}{2!} + \cdots\right)^r. \qquad (5.3.25)$$

Thus there follows

$$\Delta^r p_0 = \left[(h\mathbf{D})^r + \frac{r}{2}(h\mathbf{D})^{r+1} + \frac{r(3r+1)}{24}(h\mathbf{D})^{r+2} \right.$$
$$\left. + \frac{r^2(r+1)}{48}(h\mathbf{D})^{r+3} + \cdots\right]p_0. \qquad (5.3.26)$$

The coefficients in this formula are expressible in terms of the so-called *Stirling numbers of the second kind*, which may be denoted by $\mathcal{S}_k^{(r)}$, and are then defined by the relation

$$\frac{(e^{h\mathbf{D}} - 1)^r}{r!} = \sum_{k=r}^{\infty} \frac{\mathcal{S}_k^{(r)}}{k!}(h\mathbf{D})^k, \qquad (5.3.27)$$

so that (5.3.26) can be written in the form

$$\Delta^r p_0 = \left[\frac{\mathcal{S}_r^{(r)}}{1} + \frac{\mathcal{S}_{r+1}^{(r)}}{r+1}(h\mathbf{D}) + \frac{\mathcal{S}_{r+2}^{(r)}}{(r+1)(r+2)}(h\mathbf{D})^2 + \cdots\right](h\mathbf{D})^r p_0.$$
$$(5.3.28)$$

By comparing the relation

$$(-\nabla)^r = (e^{-h\mathbf{D}} - 1)^r \qquad (5.3.29)$$

with (5.3.25), we see that a corresponding formula for *backward* differences can be obtained by replacing Δ by $-\nabla$ and $\mathbf{D}$ by $-\mathbf{D}$ in (5.3.26) or (5.3.28).

Similar formulas involving *central* differences are readily obtained from the relations

$$\delta = 2\sinh\frac{h\mathbf{D}}{2}, \qquad \mu = \cosh\frac{h\mathbf{D}}{2}, \qquad \mu\delta = \sinh h\mathbf{D}. \quad (5.3.30)$$

Thus, for example, there follows

$$\mu\delta p_0 = [(h\mathbf{D}) + \tfrac{1}{6}(h\mathbf{D})^3 + \tfrac{1}{120}(h\mathbf{D})^5 + \cdots]p_0 \qquad (5.3.31)$$
and
$$\delta^2 p_0 = [(h\mathbf{D})^2 + \tfrac{1}{12}(h\mathbf{D})^4 + \tfrac{1}{360}(h\mathbf{D})^6 + \cdots]p_0. \qquad (5.3.32)$$

5.4. Newtonian Integration Formulas. For the purpose of obtaining formulas for numerical integration, we may make use of (5.2.10),

$$\mathbf{J} = \Delta\mathbf{D}^{-1}, \qquad (5.4.1)$$

combined with one of the relations of (5.3.3).

Thus, to obtain a formula involving *forward* differences for the approximation of the integral

$$\int_{x_0}^{x_0+rh} f(x)\ dx,$$

we may notice first that, when $f(x) = p(x)$ is a polynomial, this integral can be expressed as

$$(1 + \mathbf{E} + \mathbf{E}^2 + \cdots + \mathbf{E}^{r-1})\mathbf{J}p_0 = \frac{\mathbf{E}^r - 1}{\mathbf{E} - 1}\,\mathbf{J}p_0.$$

Hence, by expressing $\mathbf{E}$ and $\mathbf{D}$ in terms of Δ, there follows, symbolically,

$$\int_{x_0}^{x_0+rh} p(x)\ dx = h\left[\frac{(1+\Delta)^r - 1}{\Delta}\right]\left[\frac{\Delta}{\log\,(1+\Delta)}\right]p_0. \qquad (5.4.2)$$

The expansion of the first operator is easily found to be

$$\frac{(1+\Delta)^r - 1}{\Delta} = \sum_{i=0}^{\infty}\binom{r}{i+1}\Delta^i, \qquad (5.4.3)$$

whereas the expansion of the second factor may be written in the form

$$\frac{\Delta}{\log\,(1+\Delta)} = \sum_{j=0}^{\infty} c_j\Delta^j, \qquad (5.4.4)$$

the first nine coefficients of which are

$$c_0 = 1, \quad c_1 = \tfrac{1}{2}, \quad c_2 = -\tfrac{1}{12}, \quad c_3 = \tfrac{1}{24}, \quad c_4 = -\tfrac{19}{720}, \quad c_5 = \tfrac{3}{160},$$
$$c_6 = -\tfrac{863}{60480}, \quad c_7 = \tfrac{275}{24192}, \quad c_8 = -\tfrac{33953}{3628800}. \qquad (5.4.5)$$

Hence the operator involved in (5.4.2) can be expressed in the form

$$\sum_{i=0}^{\infty}\sum_{j=0}^{\infty} c_j\binom{r}{i+1}\Delta^{i+j} = \sum_{k=0}^{\infty}\left[\sum_{i=0}^{\infty} c_{k-i}\binom{r}{i+1}\right]\Delta^k. \qquad (5.4.6)$$

Thus, if we write

$$\alpha_k^{(r)} \equiv \sum_{i=0}^{k} c_{k-i}\binom{r}{i+1} = c_k\binom{r}{1} + c_{k-1}\binom{r}{2} + \cdots, \qquad (5.4.7)$$

where the series terminates when the subscript of c vanishes *or* when the arguments of the binomial coefficient become equal, the required formula becomes

$$\int_{x_0}^{x_0+rh} p(x)\ dx = h\left(\sum_{k=0}^{\infty} \alpha_k^{(r)}\Delta^k\right)p_0. \qquad (5.4.8)$$

In particular, in the case $r = 1$, there follows $\alpha_k = c_k$ and (5.4.8) becomes

$$\int_{x_0}^{x_0+h} p(x)\, dx = h(1 + \tfrac{1}{2}\Delta - \tfrac{1}{12}\Delta^2 + \tfrac{1}{24}\Delta^3 - \tfrac{19}{720}\Delta^4 + \tfrac{3}{160}\Delta^5 + \cdots)\, p_0.$$

$$(5.4.9)$$

In the case $r = 2$, there follows $\alpha_k = 2c_k + c_{k-1}$, and we may obtain the formula

$$\int_{x_0}^{x_0+2h} p(x)\, dx = 2h(1 + \Delta + \tfrac{1}{6}\Delta^2 + 0\Delta^3 - \tfrac{1}{180}\Delta^4 + \tfrac{1}{180}\Delta^5 + \cdots)p_0.$$

$$(5.4.10)$$

Further, in the case $r = -1$, there follows

$$\alpha_k = -c_k + c_{k-1} - c_{k-2} + \cdots + (-1)^{k+1}c_0,$$

and (5.4.8) becomes

$$\int_{x_0-h}^{x_0} p(x)\, dx = h(1 - \tfrac{1}{2}\Delta + \tfrac{5}{12}\Delta^2 - \tfrac{3}{8}\Delta^3 + \tfrac{251}{720}\Delta^4 - \tfrac{95}{288}\Delta^5 + \cdots)p_0.$$

$$(5.4.11)$$

This formula amounts to the result of using the Newton formula to extrapolate $f(x) = p(x)$ backward over the interval $(x_0 - h,\ x_0)$ and integrating the result over that interval.

Similar formulas are easily obtained in terms of *backward* differences, for the purpose of integrating a function over r intervals terminating at the *end* of a tabulation. It may be seen that *the formula for integrating from $x_n - rh$ to x_n can be obtained from* (5.4.8) *by replacing Δ by $-\nabla$ and p_0 by p_n.* Thus, for example, one has

$$\int_{x_n-h}^{x_n} p(x)\, dx = h(1 - \tfrac{1}{2}\nabla - \tfrac{1}{12}\nabla^2 - \tfrac{1}{24}\nabla^3 - \tfrac{19}{720}\nabla^4 - \tfrac{3}{160}\nabla^5 - \cdots)p_n$$

$$(5.4.12)$$

and

$$\int_{x_n}^{x_n+h} p(x)\, dx = h(1 + \tfrac{1}{2}\nabla + \tfrac{5}{12}\nabla^2 + \tfrac{3}{8}\nabla^3 + \tfrac{251}{720}\nabla^4 + \tfrac{95}{288}\nabla^5 + \cdots)p_n,$$

$$(5.4.13)$$

the last formula being useful for integration over an interval beyond the range of tabulation and playing an important role in the numerical solution of differential equations.

In each case, the error term to be introduced when $p(x)$ is replaced by $f(x)$, and the series is truncated with the nth difference, can be expressed in the form given by (3.3.5). Thus, in the case of (5.4.8), there follows

$$E_n = \frac{1}{(n+1)!} \int_{x_0}^{x_r} (x - x_0)(x - x_1) \cdots (x - x_n)f^{(n+1)}(\xi)\, dx, \quad (5.4.14)$$

where ξ depends upon x and lies between x_0 and the larger of x_r and x_n, and an analogous term applies to the formula with backward differences.

When $r = 1$, or when r is a negative integer, the coefficient of $f^{(n+1)}$ in (5.4.14), which has been denoted by $\pi(x)$, does not change sign in the interval of integration, and the second law of the mean can then be applied to give the more useful form

$$E_n = \frac{f^{(n+1)}(\eta)}{(n+1)!} \int_{x_0}^{x_r} \pi(x)\, dx \qquad (r \leqq 1). \qquad (5.4.15)$$

A reference to the form of Newton's interpolation formula, from which the preceding formulas may be obtained by integration, shows that, *when (5.4.15) applies, the error term is obtained by replacing $\Delta^k p_0$ or $\nabla^k p_n$ by $h^k f^{(k)}(\eta)$ in the first nonvanishing term omitted.* Thus, for example, we may deduce from (5.4.12) that

$$\int_{x_n-h}^{x_n} f(x)\, dx = h(1 - \tfrac{1}{2}\nabla - \tfrac{1}{12}\nabla^2)f_n - \frac{h^4}{24} f'''(\eta),$$

where $x_n - 2h < \eta < x_n$.

In those cases when $n = r$, so that the number of differences retained is equal to the number of h intervals in the range of integration, the formulas reduce to Newton-Cotes formulas when expressed in terms of the ordinates, and the error terms can be supplied by reference to the results of §3.5. Thus, for example, we may deduce from (5.4.10) that

$$\int_{x_0}^{x_0+2h} f(x)\, dx = 2h(1 + \Delta + \tfrac{1}{6}\Delta^2)f_0 - \frac{h^5}{90} f^{\text{iv}}(\eta),$$

where $x_0 < \eta < x_0 + 2h$, and the formula is equivalent to *Simpson's rule.*

If the terms involving Δ and Δ^2 in (5.4.10) are expressed explicitly in terms of the ordinates p_0, p_1, and p_2, the result takes the form

$$\int_{x_0}^{x_0+2h} p(x)\, dx = \frac{h}{3} (p_0 + 4p_1 + p_2) - \frac{h}{90} (\Delta^4 - \Delta^5 + \tfrac{37}{42}\Delta^6 - \cdots)p_0,$$

$$(5.4.16)$$

which may be considered as Simpson's rule with "correction terms" expressed in terms of forward differences, for use at the beginning of a tabulation. The corresponding formula with backward differences is

$$\int_{x_n-2h}^{x_n} p(x)\, dx = \frac{h}{3} (p_n + 4p_{n-1} + p_{n-2}) - \frac{h}{90} (\nabla^4 + \nabla^5 + \tfrac{37}{42}\nabla^6 + \cdots)p_n.$$

$$(5.4.17)$$

5.5. Newtonian Formulas for Repeated Integration. It frequently happens that the *second* derivative of a function $F(x)$ is known,

$$F''(x) = f(x), \qquad (5.5.1)$$

and that $F(x)$, and perhaps also $F'(x)$, are required at a set of equally spaced points $x_0, x_1, \ldots, x_n$, with the values $F(x_0) \equiv F_0$ and $F'(x_0) \equiv F'$ prescribed in advance. In order to treat this problem operationally without being concerned with remainder terms, we again imagine that F and f are replaced by polynomials and denote this fact by writing P and p for F and f, respectively.

If $P''(x)$ is tabulated at the points $x_0, \ldots, x_n$, it is clear that use may be made, say, of (5.4.9), written in the form

$$P'_{k+1} = P'_k + h(1 + \tfrac{1}{2}\Delta - \tfrac{1}{12}\Delta^2 + \tfrac{1}{24}\Delta^3 - \tfrac{19}{720}\Delta^4 + \tfrac{3}{160}\Delta^5 - \cdots)P''_k, \qquad (5.5.2)$$

where h is the spacing, to obtain a corresponding tabulation of $P'(x)$, after which the same formula may be used again, in the form

$$P_{k+1} = P_k + h(1 + \tfrac{1}{2}\Delta - \tfrac{1}{12}\Delta^2 + \tfrac{1}{24}\Delta^3 - \tfrac{19}{720}\Delta^4 + \tfrac{3}{160}\Delta^5 - \cdots)P'_k, \qquad (5.5.3)$$

to determine the desired tabulation of $P(x)$. Clearly, the formula (5.4.12) could be used instead and would be *needed* near the end of the tabulation if the value of P''_k were not available for $k > n$.

This procedure involves the formation of difference arrays relative to both $P'(x)$ and $P''(x)$. In order to avoid the necessity of two such arrays, we may transform (5.5.1) into the form

$$P_{k+1} = P_k + hP'_k + \int_{x_k}^{x_{k+1}} \int_{x_k}^{x} p(t)\, dt\, dx \qquad (5.5.4)$$

and seek an operator θ such that

$$\int_{x_k}^{x_{k+1}} \int_{x_k}^{x} p(t)\, dt\, dx = \theta p_k. \qquad (5.5.5)$$

Thus θ must be such that

$$(\mathrm{E} - 1 - h\mathrm{D})P_k = \theta p_k = \theta \mathrm{D}^2 P_k$$

and hence

$$\theta = \frac{\mathrm{E} - 1 - h\mathrm{D}}{\mathrm{D}^2} = h^2\, \frac{\mathrm{E} - 1 - \log \mathrm{E}}{(\log \mathrm{E})^2}. \qquad (5.5.6)$$

In terms of the operator Δ, there then follows

$$\theta = h^2\, \frac{\Delta - \log (1 + \Delta)}{[\log (1 + \Delta)]^2} = h^2 \left[\frac{\Delta - \log (1 + \Delta)}{\Delta^2} \right] \left[\frac{\Delta}{\log (1 + \Delta)} \right]^2$$

$$= h^2(\tfrac{1}{2} - \tfrac{1}{3}\Delta + \tfrac{1}{4}\Delta^2 - \cdots)(1 + \tfrac{1}{2}\Delta - \tfrac{1}{12}\Delta^2 + \cdots)^2$$

$$= h^2(\tfrac{1}{2} + \tfrac{1}{6}\Delta - \tfrac{1}{24}\Delta^2 + \tfrac{1}{45}\Delta^3 - \tfrac{7}{480}\Delta^4 + \tfrac{107}{10080}\Delta^5 + \cdots), \qquad (5.5.7)$$

so that (5.5.4) takes the form

$$P_{k+1} = P_k + hP'_k + h^2(\tfrac{1}{2} + \tfrac{1}{6}\Delta - \tfrac{1}{24}\Delta^2 + \tfrac{1}{45}\Delta^3 - \tfrac{7}{480}\Delta^4 + \tfrac{107}{10080}\Delta^5$$
$$+ \cdots)P''_k. \qquad (5.5.8)$$

Thus, if (5.5.2) and (5.5.8) are used for the calculation of values of $P'(x)$ and $P(x)$, only the differences of $P''(x)$ are needed.

In a similar way, the formula

$$P_{k+1} = P_k + hP'_{k+1} - h^2(\tfrac{1}{2} - \tfrac{1}{6}\nabla - \tfrac{1}{24}\nabla^2 - \tfrac{1}{45}\nabla^3 - \tfrac{7}{480}\nabla^4 - \tfrac{107}{10080}\nabla^5$$
$$+ \cdots)P''_{k+1} \qquad (5.5.9)$$

can be derived for use near the end of a tabulation of $P''(x)$, in conjunction with (5.4.12), written in the form

$$P'_{k+1} = P'_k + h(1 - \tfrac{1}{2}\nabla - \tfrac{1}{12}\nabla^2 - \tfrac{1}{24}\nabla^3 - \tfrac{19}{720}\nabla^4 - \tfrac{3}{160}\nabla^5 - \cdots)P''_{k+1}.$$
$$(5.4.12')$$

In those cases when values of P' are not required, we may derive a more useful formula by noticing that

$$\nabla^2 D^{-2} P''(x) = \nabla^2 P(x), \qquad (5.5.10)$$

where the factor ∇^2 is inserted to annihilate the arbitrary linear function of x which would correspond to the (improper) inverse operator D^{-2}. Hence there follows also

$$\nabla^2 P_k = h^2 \left[\frac{\nabla}{-\log(1-\nabla)} \right]^2 P''_k$$
$$= h^2(1 - \tfrac{1}{2}\nabla - \tfrac{1}{12}\nabla^2 - \cdots)^2 P''_k$$

or

$$\nabla^2 P_k = h^2(1 - \nabla + \tfrac{1}{12}\nabla^2 + 0\nabla^3 - \tfrac{1}{240}\nabla^4 - \tfrac{1}{240}\nabla^5 - \cdots)P''_k. \qquad (5.5.11)$$

Thus, since $\nabla^2 P_k \equiv P_k - 2P_{k-1} + P_{k-2}$, this formula permits the determination of P_k from two preceding values of P. It should be noticed that the determination of P_k makes use of P''_k.

Another formula, in which only *preceding* values of P'' are needed, is obtained by operating on both sides of (5.5.11) by E, and replacing E by $(1 - \nabla)^{-1}$ in the right-hand member, to give

$$\nabla^2 P_{k+1} = h^2(1 + \nabla + \nabla^2 + \cdots)(1 - \nabla + \tfrac{1}{12}\nabla^2 + \cdots)P''_k$$
$$= h^2(1 + 0\nabla + \tfrac{1}{12}\nabla^2 + \tfrac{1}{12}\nabla^3 + \tfrac{19}{240}\nabla^4 + \tfrac{3}{40}\nabla^5 + \cdots)P''_k.$$
$$(5.5.12)$$

In fact, a whole series of formulas of either type can be obtained, for example, by operating on both members of (5.5.11) or (5.5.12) by $a_0 + a_1\nabla + a_2\nabla^2 + \cdots$, where the a's are arbitrary constants.

Such formulas are particularly useful in the numerical solution of differential equations (see §6.12), which include (5.5.1) as a very special case.

In order to illustrate the use of these formulas in connection with (5.5.1), we consider a simple example. It is supposed that the values of F'' listed in the table are known and that the values $F(1) = 0$ and $F'(1) = 1$ are prescribed.

x	F	F'	F''	$\Delta F''$	$\Delta^2 F''$	$\Delta^3 F''$
1.0	0	1.000	1.000			
				331		
1.1	0.1055	1.1160	1.331		66	
				397		6
1.2	0.2244		1.728		72	
				469		6
1.3	0.3606		2.197		78	
				547		6
1.4	.		2.744		84	
				631		
1.5	.		3.375			

In order to determine $F_1 \equiv F(1.1)$ and $F'_1 \equiv F'(1.1)$, we use the approximate relations resulting from replacing P by F in (5.5.8) and (5.5.2):

$$F_1 \approx 0 + (0.1)(1) + 0.01[\tfrac{1}{2}(1.000) + \tfrac{1}{6}(0.331) - \tfrac{1}{24}(0.066) + \tfrac{1}{45}(0.006)]$$
$$\doteq 0.1055,$$
$$F'_1 \approx 1 + 0.1[1.000 + \tfrac{1}{2}(0.331) - \tfrac{1}{12}(0.066) + \tfrac{1}{24}(0.006)] \doteq 1.1160.$$

Formula (5.5.8) is then used again to determine F_2. For the evaluation of F_3, sufficiently many *backward* differences are available for the use of (5.5.9) or (5.5.11). Hence, unless values of F' are required, F'_2 need not be calculated, and F_3 may be determined by (5.5.11):

$$F_3 \approx 2F_2 - F_1 + h^2(F''_3 - \nabla F''_3 + \tfrac{1}{12}\nabla^2 F''_3)$$
$$= 0.3433 + 0.01[2.197 - 0.469 + \tfrac{1}{12}(0.072)] \doteq 0.3606.$$

From this stage onward, use may be made exclusively of (5.5.11).

In this example, the given data are exact values of F'' corresponding to $F''(x) = x^3$, from which there follows $F(x) = 0.05x^5 + 0.75x - 0.8$, and the results are correct to the places given. Since here the third difference of $F''(x)$ is constant, *exact* values would have been obtained if no intermediate round-offs had been effected. A check on the calculation, which would be useful if the last difference retained were *not* constant, would be afforded by the use of (5.5.12).

5.6. Central-difference Integration Formulas. The most useful integration formulas involving *central* differences are those in which the differences are evaluated at the center of the range of integration, and the integral is expressed in the form

$$\int_{x_0-mh}^{x_0+mh} f(x)\ dx.$$

n terms of the operator J defined in (5.2.5), this integral can be expressed
n the symbolic form

$$(E^{-m} + E^{-m+1} + \cdots + E^{m-1})Jp_0 = \frac{E^m - E^{-m}}{E - 1}\,Jp_0$$

$$= \frac{e^{mhD} - e^{-mhD}}{\Delta}\,\Delta D^{-1}p_0,$$

when $f(x) = p(x)$ is a polynomial, and hence we may write

$$\int_{x_0 - mh}^{x_0 + mh} p(x)\,dx = 2\frac{\sinh mhD}{D}\,p_0. \tag{5.6.1}$$

In order to obtain an expansion in central differences, we first obtain
he expansion

$$2\frac{\sinh mhD}{D} = 2mh\left[1 + \frac{m^2(hD)^2}{6} + \frac{m^4(hD)^4}{120} + \frac{m^6(hD)^6}{5040} + \cdots\right],$$

and then replace hD by its expansion given in (5.3.12), to give

$$2\frac{\sinh mhD}{D} = 2mh\left[1 + \frac{m^2\delta^2}{6}\left(1 - \tfrac{1}{24}\delta^2 + \tfrac{3}{640}\delta^4 + \cdots\right)^2\right.$$

$$\left. + \frac{m^4\delta^4}{120}\left(1 - \tfrac{1}{24}\delta^2 + \cdots\right)^4 + \frac{m^6\delta^6}{5040} + \cdots\right],$$

f, say, only coefficients of differences of order less than eight are desired.
Hence we may obtain the formula

$$\int_{x_0 - mh}^{x_0 + mh} p(x)\,dx = 2mh\left[1 + \frac{m^2}{6}\delta^2 + \frac{m^2(3m^2 - 5)}{360}\delta^4\right.$$

$$\left. + \frac{m^2(3m^4 - 21m^2 + 28)}{15120}\delta^6 + \cdots\right]p_0. \tag{5.6.2}$$

In the special cases $m = 1$ and $m = 2$, the relevant formulas are of the
forms

$$\int_{x_0 - h}^{x_0 + h} p(x)\,dx = 2h(1 + \tfrac{1}{6}\delta^2 - \tfrac{1}{180}\delta^4 + \tfrac{1}{1512}\delta^6 - \tfrac{23}{226800}\delta^8 - \cdots)p_0 \tag{5.6.3}$$

and

$$\int_{x_0 - 2h}^{x_0 + 2h} p(x)\,dx = 4h(1 + \tfrac{2}{3}\delta^2 + \tfrac{7}{90}\delta^4 - \tfrac{2}{945}\delta^6 + \tfrac{13}{56700}\delta^8 - \cdots)p_0. \tag{5.6.4}$$

Formula (5.6.3) can also be expressed in the form

$$\int_{x_0 - h}^{x_0 + h} p(x)\,dx = \frac{h}{3}(f_{-1} + 4f_0 + f_1) - \frac{h}{90}(\delta^4 - \tfrac{5}{42}\delta^6 + \tfrac{23}{1260}\delta^8 - \cdots)p_0. \tag{5.6.5}$$

and so considered as *Simpson's rule* with "correction terms" expressed i
terms of central differences.

It is known (see Steffensen [18]) that, if $p(x)$ is replaced by $f(x)$ i
(5.6.2) and the formula is truncated with the difference of order $2k$, the
the error term to be introduced can be expressed in the convenient form

$$
E_{2k} = h^{2k+3} \frac{f^{(2k+2)}(\eta)}{(2k+2)!} \int_{x_0-mh}^{x_0+mh} x(x^2 - x_1^2)(x^2 - x_2^2) \cdots (x^2 - x_k^2)\, dx
$$

$$(5.6.6)$$

where $x_0 - mh < \eta < x_0 + mh$ if $k \le m$ and $x_0 - kh < \eta < x_0 + kh$ i
$k \ge m$. Reference to the Stirling interpolation formula, from which the
preceding formulas may be obtained by integration, shows that *this error
term is obtained by replacing $\delta^{2k+2}p_0$ by $h^{2k+2}f^{(2k+2)}(\eta)$ in the first nonvanish
ing term omitted.*

An important formula, relating to repeated integration, is obtained
by noticing that, since

$$\delta^2 \mathbf{D}^{-2} P''(x) = \delta^2 P(x),$$

and since we have the expansion

$$
\frac{\delta^2}{\mathbf{D}^2} = h^2(1 - \tfrac{1}{12}\delta^2 + \tfrac{1}{90}\delta^4 - \tfrac{1}{560}\delta^6 + \cdots)^{-1}
$$

$$
= h^2[1 + (\tfrac{1}{12}\delta^2 - \tfrac{1}{90}\delta^4 + \tfrac{1}{560}\delta^6 + \cdots) + (\tfrac{1}{12}\delta^2 - \tfrac{1}{90}\delta^4 + \cdots)^2
$$

$$
+ (\tfrac{1}{12}\delta^2 + \cdots)^3 + \cdots]
$$

from (5.3.12) and (5.3.13), there follows

$$\delta^2 P_k = h^2(1 + \tfrac{1}{12}\delta^2 - \tfrac{1}{240}\delta^4 + \tfrac{31}{60480}\delta^6 - \cdots)P_k''. \qquad (5.6.7)$$

Because of the fact that only differences of even order are involved,
this formula is usually preferable to (5.5.11) for advancing a step-by-step
double integration of a given tabulated function, over the portion of the
range in which the requisite central differences are available.

The formula (5.6.7) also will be used in the numerical solution of
boundary-value problems governed by certain second-order differential
equations (§6.17), whereas the analogous formulas (5.5.11) and (5.5.12)
are to be used for corresponding initial-value problems (§6.12).

5.7. Subtabulation. In many situations it is desirable to determine,
from a given difference table based on the spacing h, a new set of differences based on a new spacing ρh. This problem would occur, for example, if a function were initially tabulated for increments of 0.1 in x and it
were required to *subtabulate* the function for increments of 0.01, in which
case $\rho = 0.1$. Whereas this subtabulation clearly could be effected by
the use of an appropriate interpolation formula, it is often more convenient to form certain new differences, based on the new spacing, and to

build up the table by addition, as will be illustrated at the end of this section. The problem also arises when a finite-difference method is used in a step-by-step numerical solution of a differential equation, in which case a halving of the interval is desirable when the rate of change of the solution being determined increases.

In order to obtain formulas for such purposes, we designate the shifting operator relative to the new spacing ρh by E_1, and notice that, since E_1 effects an h shift ρ times, there follows

$$E_1 = E^\rho.$$

If we designate the forward-difference operator relative to ρh by Δ_1, there then follows

$$1 + \Delta_1 = (1 + \Delta)^\rho \tag{5.7.1}$$

and hence we obtain the desired transformation in the symbolic form

$$\Delta_1^r = [(1 + \Delta)^\rho - 1]^r$$
$$= \left[\rho\Delta + \frac{\rho(\rho - 1)}{2!} \Delta^2 + \frac{\rho(\rho - 1)(\rho - 2)}{3!} \Delta^3 + \cdots \right]^r. \tag{5.7.2}$$

The leading terms in this expansion can be obtained in the form

$$\Delta_1^r = \rho^r \left\{ \Delta^r + \frac{r(\rho - 1)}{2} \Delta^{r+1} + \frac{r(\rho - 1)}{24} [4(\rho - 2) + 3(r - 1)(\rho - 1)]\Delta^{r+2} \right.$$
$$+ \frac{r(\rho - 1)}{48} [2(\rho - 2)(\rho - 3) + 4(r - 1)(\rho - 1)(\rho - 2)$$
$$\left. + (r - 1)(r - 2)(\rho - 1)^2]\Delta^{r+3} + \cdots \right\}. \tag{5.7.3}$$

In particular, in the important case $\rho = \frac{1}{2}$, so that the spacing is *halved*, this formula becomes

$$\Delta_1^r = \left(\frac{1}{2}\Delta - \frac{1}{2^2 \cdot 2!} \Delta^2 + \frac{1 \cdot 3}{2^3 \cdot 3!} \Delta^3 - \frac{1 \cdot 3 \cdot 5}{2^4 \cdot 4!} \Delta^4 + \cdots \right)^r$$
$$= 2^{-r} \left[\Delta^r - \frac{r}{4} \Delta^{r+1} + \frac{r(r + 3)}{32} \Delta^{r+2} - \frac{r(r + 4)(r + 5)}{384} \Delta^{r+3} + \cdots \right], \tag{5.7.4}$$

whereas the formula reduces in the case $\rho = \frac{1}{10}$ to

$$\Delta_1^r = 10^{-r} \left[\Delta^r - \frac{9r}{20} \Delta^{r+1} + \frac{3r(27r + 49)}{800} \Delta^{r+2} \right.$$
$$\left. - \frac{3r(81r^2 + 441r + 580)}{16000} \Delta^{r+3} + \cdots \right]. \tag{5.7.5}$$

In order to illustrate an appropriate technique, we again consider the data tabulated in §4.8, where a difference table is constructed with spacing $h = 0.1$, and suppose that the data are to be subtabulated by tenths, that is, with a new spacing 0.01. Here, with $\rho = 0.1$, Eq. (5.7.5) gives the formulas

$$\Delta_1 = 0.1\Delta - 0.045\Delta^2 + 0.0285\Delta^3 - 0.0206625\Delta^4 + \cdots ,$$
$$\Delta_1^2 = 0.01\Delta^2 - 0.009\Delta^3 + 0.007725\Delta^4 - \cdots ,$$
$$\Delta_1^3 = 0.001\Delta^3 - 0.00135\Delta^4 + \cdots ,$$
$$\Delta_1^4 = 0.0001\Delta^4 + \cdots ,$$

$$(5.7.6)$$

through fourth differences, where the coefficients have been expressed exactly, for convenient reference. In units of the fifth place, the new forward differences relative to $x = 1.0$ and $x = 1.1$ are found as follows:

$x = 1.0$: $\Delta_1 = 536.2$, $\Delta_1^2 = -8.5$, $\Delta_1^3 = -0.05$, $\Delta_1^4 = 0.0008 \approx 0.$
$x = 1.1$: $\Delta_1 = 449.1$, $\Delta_1^2 = -8.9$, $\Delta_1^3 = -0.05$, $\Delta_1^4 = 0.001 \approx 0.$

Thus, we may suppose that the third differences are constant (within the accuracy indicated) over the first range, and we may set up the *underlined* entries in the following table:

x	f	Δf	$\Delta^2 f$	$\Delta^3 f$
1.00	0.84147			
		536.2		
1.01	0.846832		−8.5	
		527.7		−0.05
1.02	0.852109		−8.6	
		519.1		−0.05
1.03	0.857300		−8.6	
		510.5		−0.05
1.04	0.862405		−8.6	
		501.9		−0.05
1.05	0.867424		−8.7	
		493.2		−0.05

The remaining entries are then filled in by addition, proceeding from right to left, and the results round, correctly to five places, to known rounded values of $f(x) = \sin x$.

The decimal parts of units in the fifth place are retained in order to reduce the danger of propagated effects of round-off errors. Since here the errors are propagated to the left, and since (see §4.9) then errors of magnitude e in the rth difference could lead to errors of magnitude $2^r e$ in the calculated values of f, it follows that if no errors of one-half unit are to be so introduced, the round-off errors in the rth differences should be smaller than 2^{-r-1} units in that place. Hence, for this reason alone, at least one extra place should be retained in the intermediate subtabulation of f and in the first two differences, two extra places in each of the next three differences, and so forth.

If *backward* differences are used, we see that (5.7.1) must be replaced by

$$1 - \nabla_1 = (1 - \nabla)^p,$$

and hence *all the formulas of this section are transformed to corresponding formulas for backward differences by replacing* Δ_1 *by* $-\nabla_1$ *and* Δ *by* $-\nabla$.

Formulas using *central* differences may also be found in the literature (see Prob. 16).

5.8. Summation. The Euler-Maclaurin Sum Formula. The problem of evaluating a sum

$$\sum_{\nu=m}^{k-1} f(x_0 + \nu h) = f_m + f_{m+1} + \cdots + f_{k-1} \qquad (k > m),$$

where $f_\nu \equiv f(x_0 + \nu h)$, is closely related to the problem of determining a function $F(x)$ such that

$$\Delta F(x) = f(x), \tag{5.8.1}$$

since, if any such function $F(x)$ is known, there follows immediately

$$\sum_{\nu=m}^{k-1} f_\nu = (F_{m+1} - F_m) + (F_{m+2} - F_{m+1}) + \cdots$$
$$+ (F_{k-1} - F_{k-2}) + (F_k - F_{k-1})$$
$$= F_k - F_m \equiv [F_\nu]_m^k. \tag{5.8.2}$$

It should be noticed that the upper limit in the last term exceeds by unity the upper limit in the original sum.

If we invert (5.8.1) in the symbolic form $F_k = \Delta^{-1}f_k$, it follows that we may write

$$\Delta^{-1}f_k = C + \sum_{\nu=m}^{k-1} f_\nu, \qquad \sum_{\nu=M}^{k-1} f_\nu = [\Delta^{-1}f_\nu]_M^k, \tag{5.8.3}$$

where C is an arbitrary constant and m is an arbitrarily fixed integer such that $m \leq M < k$. Thus we may refer to $\Delta^{-1}f_k$ as an *indefinite sum* of f_k and may correspondingly consider indefinite summation to be the inverse of the process of differencing, just as indefinite integration is the inverse of differentiation. As was noted previously, to any one inverse $\Delta^{-1}f(x)$ we may add any function $\omega_h(x)$ which is of period h, since any such function is annihilated by Δ. However, if only values of x which differ from some fixed value x_0 by integral multiples of h are involved, then, for that set of values of x, the additive function $\omega_h(x)$ reduces to the constant C, which itself disappears in *definite* summation between limits.

A simple formula for summing any *polynomial* $p(x)$ is obtained by writing

$$\sum_{k=0}^{r-1} p_k = (1 + \mathbf{E} + \mathbf{E}^2 + \cdots + \mathbf{E}^{r-1})p_0 = \frac{\mathbf{E}^r - 1}{\mathbf{E} - 1} p_0 = \frac{(1 + \Delta)^r - 1}{\Delta} p_0$$

$$= \left[r + \frac{r(r-1)}{2!} \Delta + \frac{r(r-1)(r-2)}{3!} \Delta^2 + \cdots \right] p_0. \qquad (5.8.4)$$

Thus, for example, in order to sum the series $1^2 + 2^2 + \cdots + r^2$, we may take $p(x) = (x + 1)^2$, $x_0 = 0$, and $h = 1$. With $p_0 = 1$, $\Delta p_0 = 3$, $\Delta^2 p_0 = 2$, $\Delta^3 p_0 = \cdots = 0$, Eq. (5.8.4) gives

$$1^2 + 2^2 + \cdots + r^2 = r \cdot 1 + \frac{r(r-1)}{2!} \cdot 3 + \frac{r(r-1)(r-2)}{3!} \cdot 2$$

$$= \tfrac{1}{6} r(r+1)(2r+1).$$

The formula (5.8.4) is principally useful for the finite summation of a polynomial of degree n small relative to the number of terms r, so that the number of terms in the transformed series is small relative to the original number. In order to obtain a formula which is of more general usefulness in finite or infinite summation, as well as in numerical integration, we again first restrict attention to a polynomial $p(x)$. From the relation

$$\Delta p(x) = \mathbf{D}\mathbf{J}p(x), \qquad (5.8.5)$$

we may deduce also that

$$hp(x) = \left(\frac{h\mathbf{D}}{e^{h\mathbf{D}} - 1} \right) \mathbf{J}p(x). \qquad (5.8.6)$$

The coefficients B_k in the expansion

$$\frac{h\mathbf{D}}{e^{h\mathbf{D}} - 1} = \sum_{\nu=0}^{\infty} \frac{B_\nu}{\nu!} (h\mathbf{D})^\nu \qquad (5.8.7)$$

are the so-called *Bernoulli numbers*, which occur in many fields of mathematics.[†] It is found that $B_3 = B_5 = B_7 = \cdots = 0$, and the following additional values may be listed:

$$B_0 = 1, \quad B_1 = -\tfrac{1}{2}, \quad B_2 = \tfrac{1}{6}, \quad B_4 = -\tfrac{1}{30}, \quad B_6 = \tfrac{1}{42},$$
$$B_8 = -\tfrac{1}{30}, \quad B_{10} = \tfrac{5}{66}, \quad B_{12} = -\tfrac{691}{2730}, \quad B_{14} = \tfrac{7}{6}, \qquad (5.8.8)$$
$$B_{16} = -\tfrac{3617}{510}, \quad B_{18} = \tfrac{43867}{798}, \quad B_{20} = -\tfrac{174611}{330}.$$

[†] The notation B_k is sometimes used for the present B_{2k}.

Hence, with this notation, (5.8.6) can be expressed in the form

$$hp(x) = \sum_{\nu=0}^{\infty} \frac{B_\nu}{\nu!} h^\nu \, \mathbf{D}^\nu \mathbf{J} p(x)$$

or

$$hp(x) = \int_x^{x+h} p(t)\, dt + \sum_{\nu=1}^{\infty} \frac{B_\nu}{\nu!} h^\nu \, \mathbf{D}^\nu \mathbf{J} p(x). \qquad (5.8.9)$$

By using (5.8.5) to replace $\mathbf{D}^\nu \mathbf{J} p(x)$ by $\mathbf{D}^{\nu-1}[p(x+h) - p(x)]$, we may express this result in the more explicit form

$$p(x) = \frac{1}{h} \int_x^{x+h} p(t)\, dt + \sum_{\nu=1}^{\infty} \frac{B_\nu}{\nu!} h^{\nu-1}[p^{(\nu-1)}(x+h) - p^{(\nu-1)}(x)]. \quad (5.8.10)$$

If we write (5.8.10) for

$$x = x_0, \; x_1 \equiv x_0 + h, \; \ldots, \; x_{r-1} \equiv x_0 + (r-1)h,$$

and sum the results, noticing the "telescoping" of the resultant terms in brackets, we deduce the identity

$$\sum_{k=0}^{r-1} p_k = \frac{1}{h} \int_{x_0}^{x_r} p(x)\, dx + \sum_{\nu=1}^{\infty} \frac{B_\nu}{\nu!} h^{\nu-1}[p_r^{(\nu-1)} - p_0^{(\nu-1)}], \quad (5.8.11)$$

where $p_k \equiv p(x_k)$ and $p_k^{(\nu-1)} \equiv p^{(\nu-1)}(x_k)$. This result is usually known as the *Euler-Maclaurin sum formula* for a polynomial, although that name is also sometimes applied instead to (5.8.10), which leads to (5.8.11), or to still another formula, which generalizes (5.8.11).

It can be written in a somewhat more convenient form by making use of the fact that all Bernoulli numbers with odd subscripts greater than unity are zero. Thus, if we extract the term corresponding to $\nu = 1$, and afterward replace ν by $2i$, we obtain the form

$$\sum_{k=0}^{r} p_k = \frac{1}{h} \int_{x_0}^{x_r} p(x)\, dx + \frac{1}{2}(p_0 + p_r) + \sum_{i=1}^{\infty} \frac{B_{2i}}{(2i)!} h^{2i-1}[p_r^{(2i-1)} - p_0^{(2i-1)}].$$

$$(5.8.12)$$

If the degree of the polynomial $p(x)$ is $2m$ or $2m + 1$, the series terminates when $i = m$.

When $f(x)$ is *not* a polynomial, the result of replacing $p(x)$ by $f(x)$ in the series (5.8.12) must be terminated, say, with $i = m$, and an appropriate error term must be introduced, so that we write

$$\sum_{k=0}^{r} f_k = \frac{1}{h} \int_{x_0}^{x_r} f(x) \, dx + \frac{1}{2} (f_0 + f_r) + \sum_{i=1}^{m} \frac{B_{2i}}{(2i)!} h^{2i-1}[f_r^{(2i-1)} - f_0^{(2i-1)}] + E_m.$$

(5.8.13)

It is known (see Prob. 23) that this error term is expressible in the form

$$E_m = r \frac{B_{2m+2} h^{2m+2}}{(2m+2)!} f^{(2m+2)}(\xi),$$ (5.8.14)

where $x_0 < \xi < x_r$, when r is finite.   When $r \to \infty$ and also $x_r \to \infty$, this form becomes indeterminate and must be replaced by a somewhat more elaborate one.

We see that this result relates a given *sum* and an *integral* in terms of an associated sum of m terms and a corresponding error term, where m can be chosen at pleasure.   It is useful both in numerical integration and in numerical summation of series.

As a particular case, we may let $r \to \infty$, assuming that $f(x)$ is such that the sum and the integral *converge* as $r \to \infty$, and that f and its first $2m + 2$ derivatives tend to zero as $x \to \infty$.   The resultant formula is then

$$\sum_{k=0}^{\infty} f_k = \frac{1}{h} \int_{a}^{\infty} f(x) \, dx + \frac{1}{2} f_0 - \frac{h}{12} f_0' + \frac{h^3}{720} f_0''' - \frac{h^5}{30240} f_0^v + \cdots$$

$$- \frac{B_{2m}}{(2m)!} h^{2m-1} f_0^{(2m-1)} + E_m, \quad (5.8.15)$$

where $f_k \equiv f(a + kh)$.

Thus, for $f(x) = 1/x^2$ and $h = 1$, we have

$$\frac{1}{a^2} + \frac{1}{(a+1)^2} + \frac{1}{(a+2)^2} + \cdots = \frac{1}{a} + \frac{1}{2a^2} + \frac{1}{6a^3} - \frac{1}{30a^5} + \cdots$$

$$+ \frac{B_{2m}}{a^{2m+1}} + E_m, \quad (5.8.16)$$

since here $f_0^{(2m-1)} = -(2m)!/a^{2m+1}$.   Whereas the series on the left converges rather slowly, the terms on the right decrease rapidly when a is fairly large.   Thus, if we take $a = 100$, there follows

$$\frac{1}{100^2} + \frac{1}{101^2} + \frac{1}{102^2} + \cdots = 10^{-2} + \frac{1}{2} \times 10^{-4} + \frac{1}{6} \times 10^{-6}$$

$$- \frac{1}{30} \times 10^{-10} + E_4,$$

and the retention of only the first three terms on the right gives

$$\frac{1}{100^2} + \frac{1}{101^2} + \frac{1}{102^2} + \cdots = 0.0100501667,$$

correctly to 10 places.   Nearly 2×10^{10} terms of the *original* series would be needed to supply this accuracy!

It is of interest to notice that B_{2i} was shown by Euler to be expressible in the form

$$B_{2i} = \frac{2(-1)^{i-1}(2i)!}{(2\pi)^{2i}} \left(1 + \frac{1}{2^{2i}} + \frac{1}{3^{2i}} + \cdots \right) \qquad (i \geqq 1). \quad (5.8.17)$$

Thus, since $(2i)!$ ultimately grows more rapidly than a^{2i} for *any* fixed a, it follows that, whereas B_{2i} at first decreases with i, ultimately B_{2i} increases more rapidly than a^{2i} for any fixed a, as i increases without limit.   Hence it is evident that the result of omitting E_m in the right-hand member of (5.8.16) will not *converge* as $m \to \infty$.   The expression (5.8.14) is of no use when $r \to \infty$.†   However, a test, described below, shows indeed that here E_m decreases in magnitude until m is approximately equal to πa, after which it begins to increase unboundedly in magnitude and to oscillate in sign.   In the case $a = 100$, this would mean that the retention of additional terms would continue to improve the approximation until more than 300 terms were taken.   However, in the case $a = 1$, for which the left-hand member of (5.8.16) has the known value $\pi^2/6 \doteq 1.64493$, in accordance with (5.8.17), the right-hand member becomes

$$1 + \tfrac{1}{2} + \tfrac{1}{6} - \tfrac{1}{30} + \tfrac{5}{42} - \tfrac{1}{30} + \tfrac{5}{66} - \tfrac{691}{2730} + \tfrac{7}{6} - \tfrac{3617}{510} + \cdots .$$

Here the error E associated with the truncation of this series after n terms varies with n as is indicated in the accompanying table.

This type of phenomenon, in which the successive members of a sequence of approximations first approach nearer and nearer to the desired result, and then begin to oscillate about it with ever-increasing amplitude, arises very frequently in numerical analysis.   Whereas such a situation *can* often be brought about by prolonged propagation of *round-off* errors (*and is usually attributed to this cause by computers!*), we have seen here, and in §§3.7 and 4.11, that it can also result from successively progressing to procedures of "higher-order accuracy," and hence eventually using *too many* terms of a divergent (but asymptotic) series, even though it be assumed

n	E
1	0.645
2	0.145
3	−0.022
4	0.012
5	−0.012
6	0.021
7	−0.055
8	0.198
9	−0.968
10	6.124

† Notice, however, that it merely becomes of indeterminate form since, as $x_r \to \infty$, the upper range of permissible values of ξ increases without bound, and $f^{(2m+2)}(\xi) \to 0$ as $\xi \to \infty$.

that *no* round-off errors are introduced. Additional situations of this type will be encountered in other chapters.

In the general summation formula of (5.8.13), it can be shown (see Steffensen [18]) that, if $f^{(2m+2)}(x)$ and $f^{(2m+4)}(x)$ do not change sign for $x_0 < x < x_r$, then E_m is numerically smaller than the first neglected term and is of the same sign. This rule applies to the special case of (5.8.16). More generally, if it is known only that $f^{(2m+2)}$ does not change sign, then it can be shown that E_m is numerically smaller than *twice* the first neglected term and of the same sign (see Prob. 23 and Steffensen [18]).

The fact that rules of this type apply rather frequently to interpolation series and to allied series makes the procedure of using the *first omitted term* as a basis for estimating the order of magnitude of the error somewhat less hazardous in connection with such series than with *convergent* series more often encountered in other fields.

A formula similar to (5.8.13), but summing instead the ordinates midway between the successive ordinates involved in (5.8.13), is sometimes called the *second Eulerian sum formula* (see Steffensen [18]) and is of the form

$$\sum_{k=0}^{r-1} f_{k+1/2} = \frac{1}{h} \int_{x_0}^{x_r} f(x)\, dx - \sum_{i=1}^{m} \frac{(1 - 2^{1-2i})B_{2i}h^{2i-1}}{(2i)!} [f_r^{(2i-1)} - f_0^{(2i-1)}] + E_m$$

(5.8.18)

where
$$E_m = -r \frac{(1 - 2^{-1-2m})B_{2m+2}h^{2m+2}}{(2m+2)!} f^{(2m+2)}(\xi).$$
(5.8.19)

Whereas the first formula is useful for either numerical summation or numerical integration, the second is used chiefly for integration, in the form

$$\int_{x_0}^{x_r} f(x)\, dx = h(f_{\frac{1}{2}} + f_{\frac{3}{2}} + \cdots + f_{r-1/2}) + \frac{h^2}{24}(f_r' - f_0')$$
$$- \frac{7h^4}{5760}(f_r''' - f_0''') + \cdots. \quad (5.8.20)$$

A comparison of (5.8.14) and (5.8.19) shows that the second formula is slightly more accurate than the first, on the average, when truncated with the same number of "correction terms."

Here, again, if $f^{(2m+2)}(x)$ and $f^{(2m+4)}(x)$ are of constant sign in (x_0, x_r), the error is numerically smaller than the first neglected term and is of the same sign. If only $f^{(2m+2)}(x)$ is known to be of constant sign, then E_m can be shown to be numerically smaller than *three times* the first neglected term and of the same sign.

It may be seen that the "correction terms" in both (5.8.13) and (5.8.20) all vanish if, say, $f(x)$ is *periodic*, of period $x_r - x_0$, although the error term naturally remains (see, for example, Prob. 30 of Chap. 3).†

5.9. Formulas of Gregory and Gauss. Euler's Transformation. The Euler-Maclaurin sum formula (5.8.12) can be written in the form

$$\int_{x_0}^{x_r} p(x)\, dx = h(\tfrac{1}{2}p_0 + p_1 + p_2 + \cdots + p_{r-1} + \tfrac{1}{2}p_r) - \frac{h^2}{12}\,(p_r' - p_0')$$

$$+ \frac{h^4}{720}\,(p_r''' - p_0''') - \frac{h^6}{30240}\,(p_r^{\mathrm{v}} - p_0^{\mathrm{v}}) + \cdots , \quad (5.9.1)$$

for a polynomial, and hence can be considered as the *trapezoidal rule* with "correction terms" expressed in terms of derivatives of $p(x)$ evaluated at the ends of the interval.

A more frequently useful formula is obtained if the derivatives at x_0 are expressed in terms of forward differences, by using (5.3.5), and if those at x_r are expressed in terms of backward differences, by using (5.3.9):

$$hp_0' = \Delta p_0 - \tfrac{1}{2}\Delta^2 p_0 + \tfrac{1}{3}\Delta^3 p_0 - \tfrac{1}{4}\Delta^4 p_0 + \tfrac{1}{5}\Delta^5 p_0 - \cdots ,$$
$$hp_r' = \nabla p_r + \tfrac{1}{2}\nabla^2 p_r + \tfrac{1}{3}\nabla^3 p_r + \tfrac{1}{4}\nabla^4 p_r + \tfrac{1}{5}\nabla^5 p_r + \cdots ,$$
$$h^3 p_0''' = \Delta^3 p_0 - \tfrac{3}{2}\Delta^4 p_0 + \tfrac{7}{4}\Delta^5 p_0 - \cdots ,$$
$$h^3 p_r''' = \nabla^3 p_r + \tfrac{3}{2}\nabla^4 p_r + \tfrac{7}{4}\nabla^5 p_r + \cdots ,$$
$$h^5 p_0^{\mathrm{v}} = \Delta^5 p_0 - \cdots ,$$
$$h^5 p_r^{\mathrm{v}} = \nabla^5 p_r + \cdots .$$

The result of this substitution is of the form

$$\int_{x_0}^{x_r} p(x)\, dx = h(\tfrac{1}{2}p_0 + p_1 + p_2 + \cdots + p_{r-1} + \tfrac{1}{2}p_r)$$

$$- \frac{h}{12}\,(\nabla p_r - \Delta p_0) - \frac{h}{24}\,(\nabla^2 p_r + \Delta^2 p_0) - \frac{19h}{720}\,(\nabla^3 p_r - \Delta^3 p_0)$$

$$- \frac{3h}{160}\,(\nabla^4 p_r + \Delta^4 p_0) - \frac{863h}{60480}\,(\nabla^5 p_r - \Delta^5 p_0) - \cdots , \quad (5.9.2)$$

and is known as *Gregory's formula*. If no differences beyond the rth are retained, only values of the integrand in the interval of integration are involved. The error term associated with the substitution of $f(x)$ for $p(x)$, and subsequent truncation of the series, is rather complicated.

On the other hand, if we replace the derivatives at x_0 and at x_r in (5.9.1) by mean *central* differences at those points, by use of the formulas obtained in §5.3, of the form

$$hp' = \mu\delta p - \tfrac{1}{6}\mu\delta^3 p + \tfrac{1}{30}\mu\delta^5 p - \cdots ,$$
$$h^3 p''' = \mu\delta^3 p - \tfrac{1}{4}\mu\delta^5 p + \cdots ,$$
$$h^5 p^{\mathrm{v}} = \mu\delta^5 p - \cdots ,$$

† For significant applications of these formulas in such cases, see Y. L. Luke, Simple Formulas for the Evaluation of Some Higher Transcendental Functions, *J. Math. and Phys.*, **34**:298–307 (1956).

we obtain the formula

$$\int_{x_0}^{x_r} p(x)\, dx = h(\tfrac{1}{2}p_0 + p_1 + p_2 + \cdots + p_{r-1} + \tfrac{1}{2}p_r) - \frac{h}{12}(\mu\delta p_r - \mu\delta p_0)$$

$$+ \frac{11h}{720}(\mu\delta^3 p_r - \mu\delta^3 p_0) - \frac{191h}{60480}(\mu\delta^5 p_r - \mu\delta^5 p_0) + \cdots . \quad (5.9.3)$$

This formula, associated with the name of *Gauss*, has the property that its leading coefficients decrease more rapidly than do those in Gregory's formula. However, it has the disadvantage that it always involves values of the integrand which lie outside the range of integration.

It is known (see Steffensen [18]) that the error term to be introduced in (5.9.3), when $p(x)$ is replaced by $f(x)$ and the series is truncated with differences of order $2k - 1$, is obtained by replacing the contents of the parentheses in the *first omitted term* by $rh^{2k+3}f^{(2k+2)}(\xi)$, where ξ lies between the extreme relevant values of x.

Both these formulas can also be derived directly by operational methods (see Probs. 28 and 29).

The formulas (5.9.1) to (5.9.3) are expressed in a form suitable for approximate evaluation of the relevant integral. When the integral can be evaluated otherwise, and the formulas are to be used instead, say, for approximate *summation* of an infinite series, they may be expressed in the form

$$\sum_{k=0}^{\infty} f_k = \frac{1}{h}\int_{x_0}^{\infty} f(x)\, dx + \begin{cases} \tfrac{1}{2}(f_0 - \tfrac{1}{6}hf_0' + \tfrac{1}{360}h^3 f_0''' - \cdots), & (5.9.4) \\ \tfrac{1}{2}(f_0 - \tfrac{1}{6}\Delta f_0 + \tfrac{1}{12}\Delta^2 f_0 - \cdots), & (5.9.5) \\ \tfrac{1}{2}(f_0 - \tfrac{1}{6}\mu\delta f_0 + \tfrac{11}{360}\mu\delta^3 f_0 - \cdots), & (5.9.6) \end{cases}$$

where $f_k \equiv f(x_0 + kh)$, when applied formally to a function $f(x)$, under the assumptions that $f(x)$ and its derivatives vanish as $x \to \infty$, and that the series and integral are convergent.

If the terms f_k are of constant sign and decrease slowly in magnitude, so that the given series converges slowly, the successive terms in the transformed series generally decrease rapidly in magnitude, at least up to a certain stage. Thus these series, while generally asymptotic, are often useful for calculation in such cases. However, since the right-hand member of (5.9.6) involves values of $f_k \equiv f(x_0 + kh)$ for negative k, it cannot be used if values needed are undefined, and it is inefficient if f_k changes rapidly with k when k is negative.

These transformations are usually not useful when the terms in the given series fluctuate in sign. However, in those situations when the signs of successive terms steadily alternate, there exist more appropriate transformations, of similar type, which possess the additional advantage that their use does not involve the evaluation of an integral. Their formal derivation is simply effected by noticing that the operational relation

$$p_0 - p_1 + p_2 - p_3 + \cdots \equiv (1 - \mathbf{E} + \mathbf{E}^2 - \cdots)p_0 = \frac{1}{1 + \mathbf{E}}\, p_0$$

$$(5.9.7)$$

is valid for any polynomial $p(x)$, and that we have also

$$\frac{1}{1 + \mathbf{E}} = \frac{1}{2}\left(1 - \tanh\frac{h\mathbf{D}}{2}\right) = \frac{1}{2 + \Delta} = \frac{1}{2} - \frac{\mu\delta}{4 + \delta^2}. \qquad (5.9.8)$$

Hence, by formally replacing p by f in (5.9.7) and expanding the operator $1/(1 + \mathbf{E})$ in accordance with (5.9.8), we obtain the relations

$$\sum_{k=0}^{\infty} (-1)^k f_k = \begin{cases} \frac{1}{2}(f_0 - \frac{1}{2}hf_0' + \frac{1}{24}h^3 f_0''' - \frac{1}{240}h^5 f_0^{v} + \frac{17}{40320}h^7 f_0^{vii} - \cdots), \\ \hfill (5.9.9) \\ \frac{1}{2}(f_0 - \frac{1}{2}\Delta f_0 + \frac{1}{4}\Delta^2 f_0 - \cdots + (-1)^r 2^{-r}\,\Delta^r f_0 + \cdots), \\ \hfill (5.9.10) \\ \frac{1}{2}(f_0 - \frac{1}{2}\mu\delta f_0 + \frac{1}{8}\mu\delta^3 f_0 - \cdots \\ \qquad\qquad + (-1)^{r-1}2^{-2r-1}\,\mu\delta^{2r+1}f_0 + \cdots). \quad (5.9.11) \end{cases}$$

The second relation (5.9.10), expressed in terms of forward differences, is often known as *Euler's transformation*.† It is known (see Hardy [102]) that the transformed series in (5.9.10) will converge whenever the given series does so, and to the same sum. Indeed, the transformed series may converge when the parent series does not, in which case the sum of the transformed series is often called the *Euler sum* of the parent series.

The other two transformed series, (5.9.9) and (5.9.11), are generally asymptotic, but the rate of effective convergence of the leading terms is often more rapid. As in (5.9.6), terms on the right in (5.9.11) may be undefined after a certain stage.

In illustration, if only the first four terms of the series

$$S = 1 - \frac{1}{2} + \frac{1}{3} - \frac{1}{4} + \cdots + (-1)^{n+1}\frac{1}{n} + \cdots \quad (= \log 2) \quad (5.9.12)$$

are summed initially, to give

$$S = \tfrac{7}{12} + (\tfrac{1}{5} - \tfrac{1}{6} + \tfrac{1}{7} - \cdots),$$

the use of (5.9.9) to (5.9.11), with $f(x) = 1/x$, $x_0 = 5$, and $h = 1$, is found to give the relations

$$S = \tfrac{7}{12} + \begin{cases} \frac{1}{10} + \frac{1}{100} - \frac{1}{5000} + \frac{1}{62500} - \frac{17}{6250000} + \cdots, & (5.9.13) \\ \frac{1}{10} + \frac{1}{120} + \frac{1}{840} + \frac{1}{4480} + \frac{1}{20160} + \cdots, & (5.9.14) \\ \frac{1}{10} + \frac{1}{96} - \frac{1}{1344} + \frac{5}{21504} - \frac{5}{18232} + \cdots, & (5.9.15) \end{cases}$$

† This transformation is closely related to that considered in Probs. 7 and 8 of Chap. 1.

after an appropriate tabulation and differencing of the ordinates f_k in the last two cases.

Retention of five terms of the transformed series in (5.9.13) yields an approximation to $\log 2 \doteq 0.693147183$ with an error smaller than 6×10^{-7}, whereas the same truncation of the Euler series (5.9.14) is in error by about 2×10^{-5}. If additional terms were retained in these two series, the second would continue to converge indefinitely, whereas the oscillation of the first series eventually (after about nine terms) would begin to increase unboundedly. A consideration of the series (5.9.15) shows that, whereas retention of successive terms through the fourth increases the accuracy of the approximation, until the error is decreased to about 9×10^{-5}, the retention of the fifth "correction term" increases the error in magnitude. In addition, since the sixth term would intro-duce the ordinate f_{-5}, which is *infinite*, the series is undefined beyond this stage in the present case.

More efficient transformations would have been effected by summing more than four terms of the given series in advance.

A useful variant of the Euler transformation (5.9.10), which also yields a convergent series when the parent series converges, is expressible in the form†

$$\sum_{k=0}^{\infty} (-1)^k f_k = \frac{1}{2} \sum_{k=0}^{n} \frac{(-1)^k}{2^k} \Delta^k f_0 + \frac{(-1)^{n+1}}{2^{n+1}} \sum_{k=0}^{\infty} (-1)^k \Delta^{n+1} f_k. \quad (5.9.16)$$

The right-hand member can be interpreted as the result of truncating the Euler formula with nth differences and expressing the error term as an infinite series of $(n + 1)$th differences. In particular, if $\Delta^{n+1} f_k$ is of con-stant sign for $k \geqq 0$ and tends steadily to zero as $k \to \infty$, we may deduce that the truncation error in the Euler formula (5.9.10) is smaller in magnitude than *twice* the first omitted term and is of the same sign. This situation will exist if $f^{(n+1)}(x)$ is of constant sign when $x \geqq x_0$ and if it tends steadily to zero as $x \to \infty$.

The Euler transformation is most efficient when the alternating series $f_0 - f_1 + f_2 - \cdots$ converges very slowly, so that f_k tends to zero, say, like $1/k$ as $k \to \infty$. When f_k tends to zero, say, like r^k $(r < 1)$, so that the series simulates an alternating geometric series, a useful generalization results from writing

$$f_k = r^k g_k, \quad (5.9.17)$$

where r may be identified, for example, with a representative value of

† This formula can be obtained by operational methods or, rigorously, by n iter-ations of the transformation considered in Prob. 7 of Chap. 1.

f_{k+1}/f_k or with its limit as $k \to \infty$. The formal symbolic relation

$$f_0 - f_1 + f_2 - f_3 + \cdots = (1 - E + E^2 - E^3 + \cdots)f_0$$

then becomes

$$f_0 - f_1 + f_2 - f_3 + \cdots = (1 - rE + r^2E^2 - r^3E^3 + \cdots)g_0$$
$$= \frac{1}{1 + rE} g_0 = \frac{1}{(1 + r) + r\Delta} g_0$$

and yields the formula

$$\sum_{k=0}^{\infty} (-1)^k f_k = \frac{1}{1 + r} \left[g_0 - \frac{r}{1 + r} \Delta g_0 + \left(\frac{r}{1 + r} \right)^2 \Delta^2 g_0 - \cdots \right],$$

$$(5.9.18)$$

which reduces to (5.9.10) when r is taken to be unity. For any fixed $r > 0$, the right-hand member will converge when the left-hand member does so.

Other generalizations of a similar nature are readily devised. Thus, if we write $f_k = c_k g_k$, we may derive the formal relation

$$\sum_{k=0}^{\infty} (-1)^k f_k = \left[\phi(1) + \frac{\phi'(1)}{1!} \Delta + \frac{\phi''(1)}{2!} \Delta^2 + \cdots \right] g_0 \qquad (f_k = c_k g_k),$$

$$(5.9.19)$$

where $\phi(x)$ is the function possessing the expansion

$$\phi(x) = \sum_{k=0}^{\infty} (-1)^k c_k x^k \qquad (5.9.20)$$

when $|x|$ is small. Here c_k is to be determined so that g_k tends to vary slowly with increasing k and, desirably, so that $\phi(x)$ is identifiable in closed form.

A related class of transformations, which frequently accelerate the convergence of alternating series, deals directly with the sequence of *partial sums* S_k, such that

$$S_k = f_0 - f_1 + f_2 - f_3 + \cdots + (-1)^k f_k, \qquad (5.9.21)$$

and replaces the sequence $S_0, S_1, \ldots, S_k, \ldots$ by a new sequence $T_0, T_1, \ldots, T_k, \ldots$, where

$$T_k = \frac{w_0 S_k + w_1 S_{k-1} + \cdots + w_k S_0}{w_0 + w_1 + \cdots + w_k}, \qquad (5.9.22)$$

with a suitable definition of the weighting coefficients $w_0, w_1, \ldots, w_k$, after which the transformation may be iterated. It is known (see **Hardy**

[102]) that the T sequence will converge to the same limit as does the S sequence if the conditions

$$w_0 > 0, \qquad w_r \geqq 0 \ (1 \leqq r \leqq k), \qquad \lim_{k \to \infty} \frac{w_k}{w_0 + w_1 + \cdots + w_k} = 0$$

$$(5.9.23)$$

are satisfied.

The choices $w_0 = w_1 = \cdots = w_k = 1$ and

$$w_0 = w_1 = 1, \qquad w_2 = w_3 = \cdots = w_k = 0$$

are most often used, the latter often being particularly efficient (when the f's are positive), and they are associated with the names of Cesàro and Hutton, respectively.

5.10. Special Integration Formulas.   By starting with any integration formula, we may form a new one by adding a multiple of a difference, say $\delta^{2r}f_0$, *and subtracting the same multiple of* $h^{2r}f^{(2r)}(\xi)$, *where ξ is between* $x_0 - rh$ *and* $x_0 + rh$, *from the remainder term.*   Two rather well known formulas, which may be derived in this way, are next considered briefly.

The Newton-Cotes seven-point formula (3.5.15) can be written in the form

$$\int_{x_0-3h}^{x_0+3h} f(x)\, dx = \frac{h}{140} (41f_{-3} + 216f_{-2} + 27f_{-1} + 272f_0 + 27f_1 + 216f_2$$

$$+ 41f_3) - \frac{9h^9}{1400} f^{\text{viii}}(\xi_1), \quad (5.10.1)$$

where $x_0 - 3h < \xi_1 < x_0 + 3h$.   In addition, we have the relation

$$\frac{h}{140} \delta^6 f_0 = \frac{h}{140} (f_{-3} - 6f_{-2} + 15f_{-1} - 20f_0 + 15f_1 - 6f_2 + f_3). \quad (5.10.2)$$

If (5.10.2) is added to (5.10.1), and $\delta^6 f_0$ is replaced by $h^6 f^{\text{vi}}(\xi_2)$ in the result, the formula

$$\int_{x_0-3h}^{x_0+3h} f(x)\, dx = \frac{3h}{10} (f_{-3} + 5f_{-2} + f_{-1} + 6f_0 + f_1 + 5f_2 + f_3)$$

$$- \frac{h^7}{1400} [10f^{\text{vi}}(\xi_2) + 9h^2 f^{\text{viii}}(\xi_1)], \quad (5.10.3)$$

known as *Weddle's rule*, is obtained.   It is notable chiefly because of the simplicity of its coefficients, but can be used only when the interval of integration can be conveniently divided into *six* subintervals.   Also, its accuracy is usually inferior to that of (5.10.1), and its error term is more complicated.

If the ordinates f_{-1} and f_1 are eliminated between (5.10.1) and (5.10.2), by subtracting $\frac{9}{5}$ times the latter from the former, and $\delta^6 f_0$ is again replaced by $h^6 f^{vi}(\xi_2)$, the formula

$$\int_{x_0-3h}^{x_0+3h} f(x)\, dx = \frac{h}{100}\,(28f_{-3} + 162f_{-2} + 220f_0 + 162f_2 + 28f_3)$$
$$+ \frac{9h^7}{1400}\,[2f^{vi}(\xi_2) - h^2 f^{viii}(\xi_1)], \quad (5.10.4)$$

known as *Hardy's rule*, is obtained. For equal integration ranges, its accuracy is usually somewhat superior to the Newton-Cotes *five*-point formula, but it again requires ordinates which divide the range into six equal parts.†

As a further example, suppose that values of $f(x_0 \pm h)$ and $f(x_0 \pm 2h)$ are obtained by observation, but that the value of $f(x_0)$ cannot be measured, and that the integral of $f(x)$ over $(x_0 - 2h, x_0 + 2h)$ is to be approximated. To obtain an appropriate formula, we may write down the Newton-Cotes five-point formula in the form

$$\int_{x_0-2h}^{x_0+2h} f(x)\, dx = \frac{2h}{45}\,(7f_{-2} + 32f_{-1} + 12f_0 + 32f_1 + 7f_2) - \frac{8h^7}{945} f^{vi}(\xi_1),$$
$$(5.10.5)$$

and note that

$$\frac{2h}{45}\,\delta^4 f_0 = \frac{2h}{45}\,(f_{-2} - 4f_{-1} + 6f_0 - 4f_1 + f_2). \qquad (5.10.6)$$

The ordinate f_0 is then eliminated by subtracting twice the second expression from the first, and replacing $\delta^4 f_0$ by $h^4 f^{iv}(\xi_2)$, to give the formula

$$\int_{x_0-2h}^{x_0+2h} f(x)\, dx = \frac{2h}{9}\,(f_{-2} + 8f_{-1} + 8f_1 + f_2) + \frac{4h^5}{945}\,[21f^{iv}(\xi_2) - 2h^2 f^{vi}(\xi_1)].$$
$$(5.10.7)$$

The same formula, with the error term expressed in the somewhat less tractable form

$$\tfrac{1}{24} \int_{x_0-2h}^{x_0+2h} (x^2 - h^2)(x^2 - 4h^2) f^{iv}(\xi)\, dx,$$

would be obtained by determining the Lagrange interpolation polynomial which agrees with $f(x)$ at the four relevant points, and integrating it over the given integral.

5.11. Error Terms in Integration Formulas. This section presents methods of obtaining expressions for the error term to be inserted in a

---

† The error comparisons with Newton-Cotes formulas are based on the supposition that $h^2 f^{viii}$ is small relative to f^{vi}. In those cases when $h^2 f^{viii}$ is comparable with or large relative to f^{vi}, as may happen when $f(x)$ possesses a singularity in the complex plane, near the path of integration, these conclusions may not follow. In such cases, the use of a simpler *composite* formula, such as that of the parabolic rule, may yield better results than *any* of these more elaborate formulas (see §3.7).

formula for numerical integration, obtained (by operational methods or otherwise) in such a way that it reduces to an identity when applied to a *polynomial* of sufficiently low degree, in those cases when the formula is applied to a function of more general type. The methods are readily modified to the consideration of formulas for interpolation or for numerical differentiation as well.

For present purposes, it is convenient to suppose that the formula is expressed explicitly in terms of ordinates, rather than differences or divided differences. Also, in order to include a class of formulas to be developed in Chap. 8, as well as those so far considered, we suppose that the formula is of the rather general form

$$\int_a^b w(x)f(x)\,dx = \sum_{k=0}^n W_k f(x_k) + R, \qquad (5.11.1)$$

where $w(x)$ is a prescribed *weighting function*, which is *unity* in the formulas so far considered and which is *nonnegative* in (a,b) in most other applications; where $x_0, x_1, \ldots, x_n$ are $n + 1$ abscissas, not necessarily equally spaced; and where $W_0, W_1, \ldots, W_n$ are the corresponding so-called *weighting coefficients*.

It is supposed that the required error R is zero when $f(x)$ is any polynomial of degree N or less. If also R is *not* zero when $f(x)$ is a polynomial of degree $N + 1$, then N is called the *degree of precision* of the integration formula. However, we suppose here only that the degree of precision is *at least* N, where N is a known positive integer. We also assume explicitly that $w(x) \geqq 0$ in (a,b).

We may transpose Eq. (5.11.1) into the form

$$\mathbf{R}[f(x)] = \int_a^b w(x)f(x)\,dx - \sum_{k=0}^n W_k f(x_k), \qquad (5.11.2)$$

where the notation $\mathbf{R}[f(x)]$ is used to indicate that the *operation* involved in the right-hand member has been effected on $f(x)$. Our hypothesis, therefore, is that

$$\mathbf{R}[x^r] = 0 \qquad (r = 0, 1, 2, \ldots, N). \qquad (5.11.3)$$

In order to treat situations in which some of the abscissas lie outside the integration range (a,b), we suppose that the abscissas are ordered in increasing algebraic order and denote the smaller of x_0 and a by A and the larger of x_n and b by B, so that all relevant values of x lie in the interval $I \equiv (A,B)$. Attention is restricted to those functions which possess $N + 1$ continuous derivatives in (A,B).

Then, for any values of x and $\bar{x}$ in (A,B), we can write

$$f(x) = f(\bar{x}) + \frac{f'(\bar{x})}{1!}(x - \bar{x}) + \frac{f''(\bar{x})}{2!}(x - \bar{x})^2 + \cdots$$
$$+ \frac{f^{(N)}(\bar{x})}{N!}(x - \bar{x})^N + \frac{f^{(N+1)}(\xi)}{(N+1)!}(x - \bar{x})^{N+1}, \quad (5.11.4)$$

where, for any fixed $\bar{x}$ in I, ξ depends upon x, but lies in (A,B). Since the first $N + 1$ terms in the right-hand member comprise a polynomial of degree N, which is *annihilated* by the operator in (5.11.2), the error $R[f(x)]$ is the same as the error term corresponding to the remainder term

$$E_N(x) = \frac{f^{(N+1)}(\xi)}{(N+1)!}(x - \bar{x})^{N+1}, \quad (5.11.5)$$

and hence

$$(N+1)! R[f(x)] = \int_a^b w(x)(x - \bar{x})^{N+1}f^{(N+1)}(\xi)\, dx$$
$$- \sum_{k=0}^{n} W_k(x_k - \bar{x})^{N+1}f^{(N+1)}(\xi_k), \quad (5.11.6)$$

where $\xi, \xi_0, \xi_1, \ldots, \xi_n$ all lie inside (A,B).

This form of the error term is generally not a very useful one. However, if we denote the maximum value of $|f^{(N+1)}(x)|$ in (A,B) by M, and notice that $|x - \bar{x}| \leq (B - A)/2$ in (A,B) when $\bar{x} = (A + B)/2$, it permits the crude estimate

$$|R| \leq \frac{ML^{N+1}}{2^{N+1}(N+1)!}\left[\int_a^b w(x)\, dx + \sum_{k=0}^{n} |W_k|\right] \quad (5.11.7)$$

where $\quad L = B - A, \quad |f^{(N+1)}(x)| \leq M$ in (A,B). $\quad (5.11.8)$

Since $R = 0$ in (5.11.1) when $f(x) = 1$, there follows

$$\int_a^b w(x)\, dx = \sum_{k=0}^{n} W_k. \quad (5.11.9)$$

Hence, in those cases *when all the weights W_i are nonnegative*, the error bound (5.11.7) can be expressed in the simpler form

$$|R| \leq \frac{ML^{N+1}}{2^N(N+1)!}\int_a^b w(x)\, dx, \quad (5.11.10)$$

where $L = b - a$ when none of the abscissas lies outside (a,b).

This error bound, while of simple form, is often extremely conservative. In order to obtain a more useful form, we may replace the remainder (5.11.5) by the integral form

$$E_N(x) = \frac{1}{N!}\int_{\bar{x}}^{x}(x - s)^N f^{(N+1)}(s)\, ds, \quad (5.11.11)$$

which possesses the advantage that no unknown parameter, corresponding to the ξ in (5.11.5), appears (see §1.7). If we identify $\bar{x}$ with A, the relation (5.11.6) is then replaced by the form

$$N! \, \mathrm{R}[f(x)] = \int_a^b w(x) \int_A^x (x - s)^N f^{(N+1)}(s) \, ds \, dx$$
$$- \sum_{k=0}^n W_k \int_A^{x_k} (x_k - s)^N f^{(N+1)}(s) \, ds. \quad (5.11.12)$$

In order to express this result in more convenient form, it is useful to introduce the notation

$$(x - s)_+^k = \begin{cases} (x - s)^k & \text{when } x > s, \\ 0 & \text{when } x \leqq s, \end{cases} \quad (5.11.13)$$

in accordance with which (5.11.12) can be written in the form

$$N! \, \mathrm{R}[f(x)] = \int_a^b w(x) \int_A^B (x - s)_+^N f^{(N+1)}(s) \, ds \, dx$$
$$- \sum_{k=0}^n W_k \int_A^B (x_k - s)_+^N f^{(N+1)}(s) \, ds. \quad (5.11.14)$$

Since the integration limits are now constant, the order of integration is readily reversed, to give

$$N! \, \mathrm{R}[f(x)] = \int_A^B f^{(N+1)}(s) \left[\int_a^b (x - s)_+^N w(x) \, dx - \sum_{k=0}^n W_k(x_k - s)_+^N \right] ds$$

or, equivalently,

$$\mathrm{R}[f(x)] = \int_A^B G(s) f^{(N+1)}(s) \, ds, \quad (5.11.15)$$

where $G(s)$ is defined by the equation

$$N! \, G(s) = \int_a^b (x - s)_+^N w(x) \, dx - \sum_{k=0}^n W_k(x_k - s)_+^N, \quad (5.11.16)$$

and may be called the *influence function* (or "kernel function") for the integration formula (5.11.1), relevant to N.†

It is useful to notice that $G(s)$ *can be considered as the error in* (5.11.1) *when* $f(x)$ *is identified with* $(x - s)_+^N/N!$. The definition can also be expressed in the more explicit form

$$N! \, G(s) = \begin{cases} \int_a^b (x - s)^N w(x) \, dx & (s \leqq a) \\ \int_s^b (x - s)^N w(x) \, dx & (a \leqq s \leqq b) \\ 0 & (s \geqq b) \end{cases} - \sum_{x_k \geqq s} W_k(x_k - s)^N,$$

$$(5.11.17)$$

† This form appears to be due to Peano and Rémès. See Sard [205] and Milne [10, 153].

where the notation in the right-hand member indicates that the sum is to be taken over those values of k for which $x_k \geqq s$. It is easily seen that $G(s)$ vanishes for all values of s outside the interval (A,B) over which the integration is effected in (5.11.15).

In illustration, we consider the simple integration formula

$$\int_{-1}^{1} f(x)\, dx = f(\alpha) + f(-\alpha) + R \qquad (0 \leqq \alpha \leqq 1), \quad (5.11.18)$$

where α is a fixed constant. It is seen that $R = 0$ for $f(x) = 1$ and for $f(x) = x$, but that $R \neq 0$ for $f(x) = x^2$ unless $\alpha^2 = \frac{1}{3}$. Thus we have always $N = 1$, and also $N > 1$ when $\alpha^2 = \frac{1}{3}$. Here

$$(A,B) = (a,b) = (-1,1)$$

and $w(x) = 1$. The use of (5.11.16) or (5.11.17) gives

$$1!\,G(s) = \int_{-1}^{1} (x - s)_+ \, dx - (-\alpha - s)_+ - (\alpha - s)_+$$

$$= \left[\frac{(x - s)_+^2}{2} \right]_{-1}^{1} - (-\alpha - s)_+ - (\alpha - s)_+$$

$$\equiv \int_{s}^{1} (x - s)\, dx - \sum_{x_k \geqq s} (x_k - s), \qquad (5.11.19)$$

when $|s| \leqq 1$, so that

$$G(s) = \frac{(1 - s)^2}{2} - \sum_{x_k \geqq s} (x_k - s), \qquad (5.11.20)$$

where $x_0 = -\alpha$ and $x_1 = +\alpha$. Hence there follows

$$G(s) = \begin{cases} \dfrac{(1 - s)^2}{2} - (-\alpha - s) - (\alpha - s) = \dfrac{(1 + s)^2}{2} & (-1 \leqq s \leqq -\alpha), \\[2ex] \dfrac{(1 - s)^2}{2} - (\alpha - s) = \dfrac{s^2 + (1 - 2\alpha)}{2} & (-\alpha \leqq s \leqq \alpha), \\[2ex] \dfrac{(1 - s)^2}{2} & (\alpha \leqq s \leqq 1), \end{cases}$$

$$(5.11.21)$$

and, with $G(s)$ so defined, the error R in (5.11.18) can be expressed in the form

$$R = \int_{-1}^{1} G(s) f''(s)\, ds. \qquad (5.11.22)$$

We may notice that this function $G(s)$ is made up of the arcs of three parabolas which join continuously at the transition points, coinciding with the abscissas employed in (5.11.18). However, the slope $G'(s)$ decreases abruptly by unity as each such point is crossed in the positive direction. Also, in each subinterval we have $G''(s) = 1$.

If $\alpha \leqq \frac{1}{2}$, $G(s)$ vanishes only at the ends $s = \pm 1$, and at $s = 0$ in the special case $\alpha = \frac{1}{2}$, and is otherwise *positive* in $(-1,1)$. Hence, in this case, the second law of the mean may be invoked to permit (5.11.22) to be written in the form

$$R = f''(\xi) \int_{-1}^{1} G(s) \, ds = \frac{1 - 3\alpha^2}{3} f''(\xi) \qquad (0 \leqq \alpha \leqq \tfrac{1}{2}), \quad (5.11.23)$$

where $|\xi| < 1$. When $\alpha = 1$, there follows merely $G(s) = (s^2 - 1)/2$ for $-1 \leqq s \leqq 1$. In this case $G(s)$ is *negative* throughout the interior of the interval, so that the law of the mean again can be applied, and (5.11.23) also holds in this case,

$$R = f''(\xi) \int_{-1}^{1} \frac{s^2 - 1}{2} \, ds = -\tfrac{2}{3} f''(\xi) \qquad (\alpha = 1). \quad (5.11.24)$$

If $\frac{1}{2} < \alpha < 1$, $G(s)$ changes sign at $s = \pm \sqrt{2\alpha - 1}$, and (5.11.22) cannot be transformed in this way. However, in any case it *can* be deduced that

$$|R| \leqq |f''|_{\max} \int_{-1}^{1} |G(s)| \, ds. \quad (5.11.25)$$

In the special case in which $\alpha = \sqrt{3}/3$ in (5.11.18), R vanishes also for $f(x) = x^2$ and for $f(x) = x^3$, but does not vanish for $f(x) = x^4$. Hence the degree of precision is then three, and we may obtain a more useful formula by taking $N = 3$, in accordance with which

$$24G(s) = \begin{cases} (1 + s)^4 & (-1 \leqq s \leqq -\alpha), \\ s^4 + 6(1 - 2\alpha)s^2 + (1 - 4\alpha^3) & (-\alpha \leqq s \leqq \alpha), \\ (1 - s)^4 & (\alpha \leqq s \leqq 1), \end{cases} \quad (5.11.26)$$

where $\alpha = \sqrt{3}/3$. It is easily verified that $G(s)$ is continuous and that it vanishes only at the ends of the interval, so that the second law of the mean may be invoked to give

$$R = f^{\text{iv}}(\xi) \int_{-1}^{1} G(s) \, ds = \tfrac{1}{135} f^{\text{iv}}(\xi),$$

and hence there follows

$$\int_{-1}^{1} f(x) \, dx = f\left(-\frac{\sqrt{3}}{3}\right) + f\left(\frac{\sqrt{3}}{3}\right) + \tfrac{1}{135} f^{\text{iv}}(\xi), \quad (5.11.27)$$

where $|\xi| < 1$.†

This example may serve to indicate the use of the influence function in other cases. From the definition (5.11.17), it is easily seen that $G(s)$

---

† This remarkable formula is a member of the class of so-called *Gaussian quadrature* formulas, to be considered in §8.5, as well as the class of *Chebyshev quadrature* formulas, to be treated in §8.13.

and its first $N - 1$ derivatives are continuous at the transition points
and that they all vanish at the end points, $x = A$ and $x = B$, of the interval of integration in (5.11.15). Further, it is found from (5.11.17) that

$$(-1)^N G^{(N)}(s) = \int_s^b w(x)\,dx - \sum_{x_k \geqq s} W_k \qquad (5.11.28)$$

and

$$G^{(N+1)}(s) = (-1)^{N+1} w(s) \qquad (5.11.29)$$

in each subinterval, with the convention that $w(x)$ is to be taken as
zero when x is outside (a,b) in both (5.11.28) and (5.11.29). Thus,
$(-1)^N G^{(N)}(s)$ increases abruptly by W_i as s increases through the ith
abscissa, but is continuous inside each subinterval.

It may be seen that, if $G(s)$ does not change sign in (A,B), the use of
the second law of the mean shows that (5.11.15) is expressible in the form

$$\mathbf{R}[f(x)] = Kf^{(N+1)}(\xi) \qquad (A < \xi < B), \qquad (5.11.30)$$

where K is independent of $f(x)$. In particular, if we take $f(x) = x^{N+1}$
there follows

$$\mathbf{R}[x^{N+1}] = (N + 1)!K.$$

Thus K is determined, and, from (5.11.30), we deduce that

$$\mathbf{R}[f(x)] = \frac{f^{(N+1)}(\xi)}{(N + 1)!}\,\mathbf{R}[x^{N+1}] \qquad (5.11.31)$$

if $G(s)$ does not change sign in (A,B).

In illustration, we have seen that the $G(s)$ associated with (5.11.18)
does not change sign in the cases when $0 \leqq \alpha \leqq \frac{1}{2}$ or when $\alpha = 1$, and
that then $N = 1$. Thus, in place of evaluating the integral involved in
(5.11.23) in those cases, we can use (5.11.31) to obtain the same result
more easily:

$$\mathbf{R}[f(x)] = \frac{f''(\xi)}{2!} \left[\int_{-1}^1 x^2\,dx - \alpha^2 - (-\alpha)^2 \right] = \frac{1 - 3\alpha^2}{3}\,f''(\xi).$$

However, the initial labor of determining $G(s)$ and actually investigating whether or not it changes sign in (A,B) may be appreciable when N
is moderately large. The preceding simple example shows that the
requirement that the weights W_i be positive is not sufficient to guarantee
that $G(s)$ will be of constant sign.

A third form of the error term, complementing the alternatives (5.11.6)
and (5.11.15), can be obtained by replacing $f(x)$ by the sum of the polynomial $y_n(x)$, which agrees with it at the $n + 1$ points $x_0, x_1, \ldots, x_n$
involved in the integration formula, and the appropriate remainder term
(2.6.1), so that we write

$$f(x) = y_n(x) + \pi(x)f[x_0,x_1, \ldots ,x_n,x], \qquad (5.11.32)$$

where, as before,

$$\pi(x) = (x - x_0)(x - x_1) \cdots (x - x_n). \qquad (5.11.33)$$

If we suppose that the degree of precision of (5.11.1) is at least equal to n, as is true for most of the useful formulas, the polynomial $y_n(x)$ is annihilated by the operator in (5.11.2). Since also the remainder term in (5.11.32) vanishes when $x = x_i$, for $i = 0, 1, \ldots, n$, there follows simply

$$R[f(x)] = \int_a^b w(x)\pi(x)f[x_0, x_1, \ldots, x_n, x] \, dx. \qquad (5.11.34)$$

In many cases, there exists a function $V(x)$ such that

$$w(x)\pi(x) = \frac{d^r V(x)}{dx^r}, \qquad (5.11.35)$$

where $V(x)$ and its first $r - 1$ derivatives vanish for both $x = a$ and $x = b$, for some positive integer r. Under this assumption, the result of integrating (5.11.34) by parts r times is seen to be

$$R[f(x)] = (-1)^r \int_a^b V(x) \frac{d^r}{dx^r} f[x_0, \ldots, x_n, x] \, dx$$

and, after making use of (2.3.9) and (3.3.14), combined in the form

$$\frac{d^r}{dx^r} f[x_0, x_1, \ldots, x_n, x] = \frac{r!}{(n + r + 1)!} f^{(n+r+1)}(\eta), \qquad (5.11.36)$$

where η is interior to the interval limited by the largest and smallest of the $n + 2$ arguments on the left, there follows

$$R[f(x)] = \frac{(-1)^r r!}{(n + r + 1)!} \int_a^b V(x) f^{(n+r+1)}(\eta) \, dx. \qquad (5.11.37)$$

If also $V(x)$ is of constant sign in (a,b), this result can be further simplified to the form

$$R[f(x)] = \frac{(-1)^r r! f^{(n+r+1)}(\xi)}{(n + r + 1)!} \int_a^b V(x) \, dx, \qquad (5.11.38)$$

where ξ lies between the smaller of a and x_0 and the larger of b and x_n. In addition, by integrating by parts r times, and again making use of (5.11.35) and of the assumed properties of $V(x)$, we find that

$$\int_a^b V(x) \, dx = \frac{(-1)^r}{r!} \int_a^b [x^r + u_{r-1}(x)] V^{(r)}(x) \, dx$$

$$= \frac{(-1)^r}{r!} \int_a^b [x^r + u_{r-1}(x)] w(x) \pi(x) \, dx,$$

where $u_{r-1}(x)$ is an arbitrary polynomial of degree $r - 1$ or less. Hence (5.11.38) is also expressible in the equivalent form

$$R[f(x)] = \frac{f^{(n+r+1)}(\xi)}{(n + r + 1)!} \int_a^b x^r w(x)\pi(x) \, dx, \qquad (5.11.39)$$

where x^r can be replaced by any convenient polynomial of degree r in which the coefficient of x^r is unity, if so desired.

This result will be of particular usefulness in Chap. 8. In the case of the formula (5.11.18), it is found that

$$w(x)\pi(x) = x^2 - \alpha^2 = \frac{d}{dx} [\tfrac{1}{3}x^3 - \alpha^2 x + (\tfrac{1}{3} - \alpha^2)],$$

where the constant of integration is determined so that the function in brackets vanishes when $x = -1$. That function will also vanish when $x = +1$ if $\alpha^2 = \tfrac{1}{3}$, in which case there follows further

$$w(x)\pi(x) = \frac{d^2}{dx^2} [\tfrac{1}{12}(1 - x^2)^2],$$

so that we may take $V(x) = (1 - x^2)^2/12$ in that case. The use of (5.11.38) or (5.11.39), with $n = 1$ and $r = 2$, leads again to the result given in (5.11.27).

It may be noticed that, *if (5.11.38) or (5.11.39) is valid, the degree of precision of the relevant integration formula is $n + r$.*

In order to express in a different form the conditions permitting the use of (5.11.38) or (5.11.39), we may make use of Theorem 12 of §1.7 to show that, if $V^{(r)}(x) = w(x)\pi(x)$ and if $V, V', \ldots, V^{(r-1)}$ vanish at $x = a$, there follows

$$V(x) = \frac{1}{(r - 1)!} \int_a^x (x - s)^{r-1} w(s)\pi(s) \, ds \qquad (5.11.40)$$

and also the requirements that $V, V', \ldots, V^{(r-1)}$ also vanish at $x = b$ take the form

$$\int_a^b (b - s)^k w(s)\pi(s) \, ds = 0 \qquad (k = 0, 1, 2, \ldots, r - 1). \quad (5.11.41)$$

Further, if we assume that the degree of precision of (5.11.1) is $n + r$, where $r \geq 1$, it follows that the right-hand member of (5.11.34) will vanish when $f(x)$ is any polynomial of degree $n + r$ or less, or, equivalently, when the divided difference $f[x_0, x_1, \ldots, x_n, x]$, of order $n + 1$, is any polynomial of degree $r - 1$ or less. But this situation implies the truth of (5.11.41).

Hence we may deduce that *if the degree of precision of the integration formula* (5.11.1) *is* $n + r$, *where* $r \geqq 1$, *and if the function*

$$V(x) = \frac{1}{(r-1)!} \int_a^x (x-s)^{r-1} w(s)\pi(s) \, ds$$

does not change sign in (a,b), *then the error* R *is given by* (5.11.38) *o* (5.11.39).

5.12. Other Representations of Error Formulas. If the degree o precision of (5.11.1) is exactly n, where $n + 1$ ordinates are used, the function $V(x)$ defined by (5.11.35) will not vanish at both ends of the interval (a,b) when $r \geqq 1$, so that (5.11.38) and (5.11.39) then are no valid. Whereas the use of the G function of the preceding section gen erally involves the individual consideration of each of the ranges (x_k, x_{k+1}) and whereas the vanishing of $\pi(x)$ at each abscissa x_k would require the same subdivision of (a,b) before the second law of the mean could be used in connection with (5.11.34), it may be possible to define V functions which are appropriate to subintervals comprising several such ranges, and so to obtain a more useful form of the remainder with decreased labor.

In illustration, the formula approximating the integral of $f(x)$ over $(0,3)$ in terms of the three ordinates at $x = 0, 1, 2$, with $w(x) = 1$, would possess the error term

$$R = \int_0^3 \pi(x)f[0,1,2,x] \, dx, \qquad \pi(x) = x(x-1)(x-2), \quad (5.12.1)$$

if its degree of precision were at least two, by (5.11.34). Here we have

$$\pi(x) = x^3 - 3x^2 + 2x = \tfrac{1}{4}(x^4 - 4x^3 + 4x^2)' = \tfrac{1}{4}[x^2(x-2)^2]',$$

so that the function $V(x) = x^2(x-2)^2/4$ is appropriate for the sub-interval $(0,2)$. In the remaining subinterval $(2,3)$, $\pi(x)$ does not change sign. Hence we may deduce that

$$
\begin{aligned}
R &= -\int_0^2 V(x)f[0,1,2,x,x] \, dx + \int_2^3 \pi(x)f[0,1,2,x] \, dx \\
&= -\frac{f^{\text{iv}}(\xi_1)}{4!} \int_0^2 V(x) \, dx + \frac{f'''(\xi_2)}{3!} \int_2^3 \pi(x) \, dx \\
&= -\tfrac{1}{90} f^{\text{iv}}(\xi_1) + \tfrac{3}{8} f'''(\xi_2),
\end{aligned}
\qquad (5.12.2)
$$

where both ξ_1 and ξ_2 lie inside $(0,3)$.

In other cases, the function $Q(x)$ defined by the relations

$$Q'(x) = \frac{w(x)\pi(x)}{x - x_k}, \qquad Q(A_k) = 0 \qquad (5.12.3)$$

or, equivalently,

$$Q(x) = \int_{A_k}^x \frac{w(t)\pi(t)}{t - x_k} \, dt, \qquad (5.12.4)$$

where x_k is one of the abscissas, may have the property that it does not change sign over the subinterval (A_k,x_k) of the range (a,b), when A_k is suitably chosen.   In view of the identity

$$(x - x_k)f[x_0, \ldots ,x_k, \ldots ,x_n,x]$$
$$= f[x_0, \ldots ,x_{k-1},x_{k+1}, \ldots ,x_n,x] - f[x_0, \ldots ,x_n], \quad (5.12.5)$$

where the second term on the right is independent of x, we can write

$$\int_{A_k}^{x_k} w(x)\pi(x)f[x_0, \ldots ,x_n,x]\, dx$$
$$= \int_{A_k}^{x_k} Q'(x)\{f[x_0, \ldots ,x_{k-1},x_{k+1}, \ldots ,x_n,x] - f[x_0, \ldots ,x_n]\}\, dx$$
$$= [Q(x)\{f[x_0, \ldots ,x_{k-1},x_{k+1}, \ldots ,x_n,x] - f[x_0, \ldots ,x_n]\}]_{A_k}^{x_k}$$
$$\qquad - \int_{A_k}^{x_k} Q(x)f[x_0, \ldots ,x_{k-1},x_{k+1}, \ldots ,x_n,x,x]\, dx,$$
$$(5.12.6)$$

after an integration by parts.   Now $Q(x)$ vanishes when $x = A_k$, and its coefficient in the integrated term vanishes when $x = x_k$.   Since also $Q(x)$ is assumed not to change sign in (A_k,x_k), the second law of the mean is applicable to the second term, and there follows

$$\int_{A_k}^{x_k} w(x)\pi(x)f[x_0, \ldots ,x_n,x]\, dx = -\frac{f^{(n+1)}(\xi)}{(n+1)!}\int_{A_k}^{x_k} Q(x)\, dx. \quad (5.12.7)$$

Also, if we notice that $\int Q(x)\, dx = \int Q(x)\, d(x - x_k)$, and integrate by parts, there follows

$$\int_{A_k}^{x_k} Q(x)\, dx = [(x - x_k)Q(x)]_{A_k}^{x_k} - \int_{A_k}^{x_k} (x - x_k)Q'(x)\, dx$$
$$= - \int_{A_k}^{x_k} w(x)\pi(x)\, dx,$$

so that (5.12.7) becomes

$$\int_{A_k}^{x_k} w(x)\pi(x)f[x_0, \ldots ,x_n,x]\, dx = \frac{f^{(n+1)}(\xi)}{(n+1)!}\int_{A_k}^{x_k} w(x)\pi(x)\, dx. \quad (5.12.8)$$

Thus, in spite of the fact that $\pi(x)$ may change sign in (A_k,x_k), it follows that the result of *formally* applying the law of the mean to the left-hand member of (5.12.8), and *then* using (5.11.36), with $r = 0$, yields a correct result *when the function $Q(x)$ defined by* (5.12.3) *or* (5.12.4) *does not change sign in* (A_k,x_k).

We may notice also that if, instead, $Q(x)$ does not change sign between $x = A_k$ and $x = B_k$, and if $Q(B_k) = 0$, there follows also

$$\int_{A_k}^{B_k} w(x)\pi(x)f[x_0, \ldots ,x_n,x]\, dx = \frac{f^{(n+1)}(\xi)}{(n+1)!}\int_{A_k}^{B_k} w(x)\pi(x)\, dx, \quad (5.12.9)$$

by a slight modification of the same argument.

As a first example, we notice that the error term relevant to the Newton-Cotes four-point formula of closed type with $h = 1$,

$$\int_0^3 f(x)\,dx = \tfrac{3}{8}[f(0) + 3f(1) + 3f(2) + f(3)] + R, \quad (5.12.10)$$

is of the form

$$R = \int_0^3 \pi(x)f[0,1,2,3,x]\,dx, \quad \pi(x) = x(x-1)(x-2)(x-3). \quad (5.12.11)$$

Here the use of the function $V(x)$ is found to be inappropriate. However, we find that

$$\frac{\pi(x)}{x-3} = \tfrac{1}{4}[x^2(x-2)^2]',$$

so that the function $Q(x) = x^2(x-2)^2/4$, corresponding to the choice $A_k = 0$ in (5.12.3), is nonnegative for $0 \leq x \leq 3$ (as well as for all other real values of x). Hence (5.12.8) applies, with $A_k = 0 \equiv a$ and $x_k = 3 \equiv b$, and it yields

$$R = \frac{f^{iv}(\xi)}{4!} \int_0^3 \pi(x)\,dx = -\tfrac{3}{80}f^{iv}(\zeta), \quad (5.12.12)$$

in accordance with (3.5.12).

As a second example, we consider the Newton-Cotes two-point formula of open type with $h = 1$,

$$\int_0^3 f(x)\,dx = \tfrac{3}{2}[f(1) + f(2)] + R, \quad (5.12.13)$$

for which we may write

$$R = \int_0^3 \pi(x)f[1,2,x]\,dx, \quad \pi(x) = (x-1)(x-2). \quad (5.12.14)$$

Again the use of $V(x)$ is inappropriate. However, we have

$$\frac{\pi(x)}{x-2} = x - 1 = \tfrac{1}{2}[x(x-2)]',$$

corresponding to the choice $x_k = 2$, $A_k = 0$ in (5.12.3), so that (5.12.8) applies over (0,2). Since $\pi(x)$ does not change sign in (2,3), we may write

$$R = \frac{f''(\xi_1)}{2!} \int_0^2 \pi(x)\,dx + \frac{f''(\xi_2)}{2!} \int_2^3 \pi(x)\,dx$$
$$= \tfrac{1}{3}f''(\xi_1) + \tfrac{5}{12}f''(\xi_2)$$

and, since the numerical coefficients are of the same sign, we may combine he terms in the form

$$R = \tfrac{3}{4}f''(\xi), \tag{5.12.15}$$

a accordance with (3.5.18).†

The V and Q methods, *when applicable*, are usually considerably more onvenient than the more general G method of §5.11, which generally ntails the determination and analysis of n or more distinct functions each a polynomial of degree $N + 1$ if $w(x) = 1$] when $n + 1$ ordinates re involved. However, it must be noticed that the V and Q methods re not applicable in those cases when the degree of precision of the inte-ration formula is less than n.

Formulas which involve values of certain *derivatives* of $f(x)$ as well as he value of $f(x)$ itself, at certain points, may be considered as limits of ormulas in which $r + 1$ abscissas coalesce into a single abscissa, corre-ponding to which the values of $f, f', \ldots,$ and $f^{(r)}$ are used. Thus, for example, if the coefficients W_0, W_1, W_2, and C_1 are determined in such a vay that the formula

$$\int_{-1}^{1} w(x)f(x) \, dx \approx W_0 f(-1) + W_1 f(0) + W_2 f(1) + C_1 f'(0) \tag{5.12.16}$$

s exact for $f(x) = 1, x, x^2,$ and x^3, and so for any polynomial of degree three or less, the error term will be of the form

$$R = \int_{-1}^{1} w(x)(x + 1)x^2(x - 1)f[-1,0,0,1,x] \, dx. \tag{5.12.17}$$

Here the second law of the mean applies directly and gives the simpler result

$$R = \frac{f^{iv}(\xi)}{4!} \int_{-1}^{1} w(x)x^2(x^2 - 1) \, dx, \tag{5.12.18}$$

which yields

$$R = -\tfrac{1}{90}f^{iv}(\xi) \tag{5.12.19}$$

in the special case $w(x) = 1$.

However, for the formula

$$\int_{-1}^{1} f(x) \, dx \approx W_0 f(-1) + W_1 f(0) + W_2 f(1) + C_2 f'(1), \tag{5.12.20}$$

with the weighting coefficients determined by the same requirements, there follows

$$R = \int_{-1}^{1} (x + 1)x(x - 1)^2 f[-1,0,1,1,x] \, dx, \tag{5.12.21}$$

† The same methods apply, in particular, to all Newton-Cotes formulas which employ an even number of ordinates, whereas the V method succeeds when an odd number of ordinates is used. The methods are based on analyses given by Steffensen in those cases.

and, since here $\pi(x)$ changes sign at $x = 0$, another approach is needed. Since also the function $\int_{-1}^{x} \pi(t)\, dt$ does not vanish when $x = 1$, the method fails. On the other hand, since

$$\frac{\pi(x)}{x - 1} = x(x^2 - 1) = \tfrac{1}{4}[(x^2 - 1)^2]',$$

the function $Q(x) = (x^2 - 1)^2/4$ is appropriate with $A_k = -1$, $x_k = 1$ and Eq. (5.12.8) gives

$$R = \frac{f^{\mathrm{iv}}(\xi)}{4!} \int_{-1}^{1} \pi(x)\, dx = -\tfrac{1}{90} f^{\mathrm{iv}}(\xi). \qquad (5.12.22)$$

The fact that (5.12.19) and (5.12.22) are both identical with the error term relevant to Simpson's rule (for which $W_0 = W_2 = \tfrac{1}{3}$, $W_1 = \tfrac{4}{3}$, and $C_1 = 0$ or $C_2 = 0$) suggests that both (5.12.16) and (5.12.20) will reduce to Simpson's rule in the case $w(x) = 1$, when the weights are determined in such a way that the degree of precision is at least three, that is, that the weights C_1 and C_2 will be required to vanish. A direct derivation will confirm this suspicion.

The direct derivation of the error formula relevant to Simpson's rule itself, over $(-1,1)$, is effected most easily by the V method, since here

$$R = \int_{-1}^{1} \pi(x) f[-1,0,1,x]\, dx$$

where $\qquad \pi(x) = x(x^2 - 1) = \tfrac{1}{4}[(x^2 - 1)^2]' \equiv V'(x).$

Thus there follows

$$R = -\tfrac{1}{4} \int_{-1}^{1} (x^2 - 1)^2 f[-1,0,1,x,x]\, dx = -\frac{f^{\mathrm{iv}}(\xi)}{4 \cdot 4!} \int_{-1}^{1} (x^2 - 1)^2\, dx$$
$$= -\tfrac{1}{90} f^{\mathrm{iv}}(\xi).$$

5.13. Supplementary References. The use of symbolic methods essentially dates from Boole [50]. See also Steffensen [18], Michel [149], and Bickley [39]. For Comrie's method of "bridging differences" in subtabulation, see Hartree [2]. The polynomials and numbers of Bernoulli, Euler, and Stirling are treated in Fort [82], where collateral references are given. Hardy [102] treats summation of divergent series; for recent accounts of methods for accelerating the convergence of series, see Szasz [219], Cherry [55], and Rosser [198]. Many series whose sums are known are listed by Jolley [125]. General expressions for remainder formulas are given by Peano [177, 178], Rémès [193], Sard [205], and Milne [153]. See also Birkhoff [43], von Mises [157], Radon [188], Daniell [67], and Householder [3].

PROBLEMS

Section 5.2

1. Obtain the formal relations

$$\mu = \tfrac{1}{2}(E^{\frac{1}{2}} + E^{-\frac{1}{2}}) = \frac{2 + \Delta}{2\sqrt{1 + \Delta}} = \frac{2 - \nabla}{2\sqrt{1 - \nabla}} = \sqrt{1 + \tfrac{1}{4}\delta^2}$$

and construct a table expressing each of the operators E, Δ, ∇, δ, and μ similarly in terms of each of the operators E, Δ, ∇, and δ.

2. Establish the relations

$$\Delta = E\nabla, \qquad \nabla = E^{-1}\Delta, \qquad E^{-\frac{1}{2}}\Delta = E^{\frac{1}{2}}\nabla = \delta, \qquad \Delta\nabla = \nabla\Delta = \Delta - \nabla = \delta^2,$$
$$\mu\delta = \tfrac{1}{2}(\Delta + \nabla), \qquad E^{\pm\frac{1}{2}} = \mu \pm \tfrac{1}{2}\delta, \qquad \mu^2 = 1 + \tfrac{1}{4}\delta^2.$$

Section 5.3

3. Express each of the operators E, Δ, ∇, δ, μ, and $\mu\delta$ in terms of hD.

4. Express the operator $h^{-1}J$ in terms of E, Δ, ∇, δ, and hD.

5. Show that the interpolation formulas of Stirling, Bessel, and Everett can be obtained operationally by rewriting the relation $E^s = e^{shD}$ in the forms

$$E^s = \cosh shD + \frac{\sinh shD}{\cosh \tfrac{1}{2}hD}\,\mu,$$

$$E^s = E^{t+\frac{1}{2}} = \left(\frac{\cosh thD}{\cosh \tfrac{1}{2}hD}\,\mu + \sinh thD\right)E^{\frac{1}{2}},$$

and
$$E^s = \frac{\sinh shD}{\sinh hD}\,E + \frac{\sinh (1 - s)hD}{\sinh hD},$$

respectively, and expanding the right-hand members in powers of $\delta = 2 \sinh \tfrac{1}{2}hD$ by using the results of Probs. 31 and 32 of Chap. 4 with a replaced by hD and x by s or t. Why would the corresponding expansion of the simpler relation

$$E^s = e^{shD} = \cosh shD + \sinh shD$$

be of limited usefulness?

6. From the following rounded values of the function $f(x) = \sin x$, calculate approximate values of $f'(x)$ and $f''(x)$ at each tabular point and compare the results with rounded true values:

x	0.5	0.7	0.9	1.1	1.3	1.5	1.7
$f(x)$	0.47943	0.64422	0.78333	0.89121	0.96356	0.99749	0.99166

Section 5.4

7. Using the data of Prob. 6, calculate the approximate value of $\int_{0.5}^{x} f(x)\,dx$ for $x = 0.7$, 0.9, and 1.1, and the approximate value of $\int_{x}^{1.7} f(x)\,dx$ for $x = 1.1$, 1.3, and 1.5. From these results determine approximate values of the integral taken over each tabular interval.

Section 5.5

8. Using the data of Prob. 6, calculate approximate values of the quantities

$$\int_{0.5}^{0.7} \int_{0.5}^{x} f(t)\, dt\, dx, \qquad \int_{1.5}^{1.7} \int_{1.5}^{x} f(t)\, dt\, dx.$$

9. If $F''(x) = \log \tan x$, and if $F(1) = 0$ and $F'(1) = 1$, calculate approximate values of $F(x)$ for $x = 1.00(0.02)(1.10)$, using only tabulated five-place values of $\log \tan x\ [\equiv (\log 10)(\log_{10} \tan x)]$ for $x \geqq 1$.

10. Show that, if the operator θ is defined by the relation

$$\int_{x_k}^{x_k + rh} \int_{x_k}^{x} p(t)\, dt\, dx = \theta p_k,$$

then

$$\theta = \frac{E^r - 1 - rh\mathbf{D}}{\mathbf{D}^2} = h^2 \left[\frac{(1 + \Delta)^r - 1 - r \log (1 + \Delta)}{\Delta^2} \right] \left[\frac{\Delta}{\log (1 + \Delta)} \right]^2,$$

and determine the first three coefficients in the expansion of the operator θ in powers of Δ, as functions of r.

11. Show that the right-hand member of the result of operating on the equal members of (5.5.12) by $1 + a_1 \nabla + a_2 \nabla^2$ is independent of ∇^3 if and only if $a_1 = -1$, that the result is equivalent to (5.5.11) if also $a_2 = 0$, and that a particularly convenient choice is that for which $a_2 = \frac{1}{3}$, leading to the formula

$$P_{k+1} - P_k - P_{k-2} + P_{k-3} = 3h^2(1 - \nabla + \tfrac{5}{12}\nabla^2 + 0\nabla^3 + \tfrac{17}{720}\nabla^4 + \tfrac{17}{720}\nabla^5 + \cdots)P_k''.$$

(This formula is used in §6.12.)

Section 5.6

12. Using the data of Prob. 6, calculate approximate values of

$$\int_{1.1 - 0.2m}^{1.1 + 0.2m} f(x)\, dx$$

for $m = 1, 2,$ and 3.

13. Derive the operational relation

$$\int_{x_0}^{x_0 + h} p(x)\, dx = h\mu \frac{\tanh \frac{1}{2}h\mathbf{D}}{\frac{1}{2}h\mathbf{D}} p_{\frac{1}{2}}$$

and obtain the expansion in powers of δ in the form

$$\int_{x_0}^{x_0 + h} p(x)\, dx = h[\mu - \tfrac{1}{12}\mu\delta^2 + \tfrac{11}{720}\mu\delta^4 - \tfrac{191}{60480}\mu\delta^6 + \cdots]p_{\frac{1}{2}}.$$

14. Use the result of Prob. 13 and the data of Prob. 6 to calculate approximate values of the integral $\int_{x}^{x+0.2} f(x)\, dx$ for $x = 0.9$ and 1.1.

Section 5.7

15. Subtabulate the data of Prob. 6 for $x = 0.50(0.02)0.70$ and $x = 1.50(0.02)1.70$.

16. If δ' represents the central-difference operator relative to the spacing $h' = \rho h$, show that

$$\frac{\delta'}{\delta} = \frac{\sinh \frac{1}{2}\rho h\mathbf{D}}{\sinh \frac{1}{2}h\mathbf{D}}$$

and obtain the expansion of the right-hand member in powers of $\delta = 2 \sinh \frac{1}{2}h\mathbf{D}$ (see Prob. 32 of Chap. 4, with $x = \rho/2$, $a = h\mathbf{D}$, and $\beta = \delta$), thus deducing the relation

$$\delta' = 2\rho \left[\frac{\delta}{2} - \frac{1}{3!} (1^2 - \rho^2) \left(\frac{\delta}{2}\right)^3 + \frac{1}{5!} (1^2 - \rho^2)(3^2 - \rho^2) \left(\frac{\delta}{2}\right)^5 - \cdots \right].$$

Show also that

$$\frac{\mu'\delta'}{\mu\delta} = \frac{\sinh \rho h\mathbf{D}}{\sinh h\mathbf{D}}$$

and obtain the expansion of the right-hand member in powers of δ (see Prob. 31 of Chap. 4, with $x = \rho$, $a = h\mathbf{D}$, and $\beta = \delta$), thus deducing the relation

$$(\mu\delta)' \equiv \mu'\delta' = \rho \left[\mu\delta - \frac{1}{3!} (1^2 - \rho^2)\mu\delta^3 + \frac{1}{5!} (1^2 - \rho^2)(2^2 - \rho^2)\mu\delta^5 - \cdots \right].$$

17. In the case of subtabulation to tenths ($\rho = \frac{1}{10}$), deduce from the results of Prob. 16 the formulas

$$(\mu\delta)' = 0.1\mu\delta - 0.0165\mu\delta^3 + 0.00329175\mu\delta^5 - \cdots ,$$
$$\delta'^2 = 0.01\delta^2 - 0.000825\delta^4 + \cdots ,$$
$$(\mu\delta^3)' = 0.001\mu\delta^3 - 0.0002475\mu\delta^5 + \cdots ,$$
$$\delta'^4 = 0.0001\delta^4 - \cdots ,$$
$$(\mu\delta^5)' = 0.00001\mu\delta^5 - \cdots ,$$

when differences of order greater than five are neglected, and use these formulas to subtabulate the data of Prob. 6 for $x = 0.90(0.02)1.10$.

18. Suppose that mean values of $f(x)$ are known over each of the ranges $(x_k - h/2,$ $x_k + h/2)$ ($k = 0, 1, 2, \ldots$), where $x_{k+1} - x_k = h$, and that approximate mean values over ranges of length $2\rho h$, again centered about the points x_k, are required. With the notations

$$m_k = \frac{1}{h} \int_{x_k - h/2}^{x_k + h/2} f(x) \, dx, \qquad m'_k = \frac{1}{2\rho h} \int_{x_k - \rho h}^{x_k + \rho h} f(x) \, dx,$$

derive the operational relation

$$m'_k = \frac{1}{2\rho} \frac{\sinh \rho h\mathbf{D}}{\sinh \frac{1}{2}h\mathbf{D}} m_k,$$

and deduce the formula

$$m'_k = \left[1 - \frac{1}{3!} (\tfrac{1}{4} - \rho^2)\delta^2 + \frac{1}{5!} (\tfrac{1}{4} - \rho^2)(\tfrac{9}{4} - \rho^2)\delta^4 - \cdots \right] m_k.$$

(See Prob. 32 of Chap. 4, with $x = \rho$, $a = h\mathbf{D}$, and $\beta = \delta$.) In particular, deduce the formula

$$f_k = \left[1 - \frac{1^2}{3!} \left(\frac{\delta}{2}\right)^2 + \frac{1^2 \cdot 3^2}{5!} \left(\frac{\delta}{2}\right)^4 - \cdots \right] m_k.$$

Section 5.8

19. The *Bernoulli polynomial* $B_k(x)$, of kth degree, is defined as the coefficient of $u^k/k!$ in the expansion

$$\frac{ue^{xu}}{e^u - 1} = \sum_{\nu=0}^{\infty} \frac{u^\nu}{\nu!} B_\nu(x).$$

(a) By differentiating the equal members of this relation, deduce the differential recurrence formula

$$B_k'(x) = kB_{k-1}(x) \qquad (k = 1, 2, \ldots),$$

and show also that $B_0(x) = 1$.

(b) By making use of the identity

$$\frac{(-u)e^{-xu}}{e^{-u} - 1} = \frac{ue^{(1-x)u}}{e^u - 1},$$

prove that

$$B_k(1 - x) = (-1)^k B_k(x).$$

Also, by integrating the equal members of the defining relation over $(0,1)$, deduce that

$$\int_0^1 B_k(x)\, dx = 0 \qquad (k > 0)$$

and use this result, together with the recurrence formula of (a), to show that

$$B_0(x) = 1, \qquad B_1(x) = x - \tfrac{1}{2}, \qquad B_2(x) = x^2 - x + \tfrac{1}{6}, \qquad B_3(x) = x^3 - \tfrac{3}{2}x^2 + \tfrac{1}{2}x,$$

and so forth.

(c) In accordance with (5.8.7), the kth *Bernoulli number* B_k is defined by the relation $B_k \equiv B_k(0)$. Show that

$$\frac{u}{e^u - 1} + \frac{u}{2} = \frac{u}{2} \coth \frac{u}{2}$$

is an even function of u, and hence deduce that $B_1 = -\tfrac{1}{2}$ and that $B_{2m+1} = 0$ when $m \geq 1$.

(d) Use the identity

$$\frac{ue^{u/2}}{e^u - 1} = 2\,\frac{u/2}{e^{u/2} - 1} - \frac{u}{e^u - 1}$$

to deduce that

$$B_k(\tfrac{1}{2}) = (2^{1-k} - 1)B_k.$$

20. Use appropriate results of Prob. 19 to show that $B_{2m+1}(x)$ vanishes when $x = 0$, $\tfrac{1}{2}$, and 1. Show also that, if it vanishes at any point inside $(0,1)$ in addition to $x = \tfrac{1}{2}$, then it must vanish at at least two such points. Then deduce that this situation is impossible by using Rolle's theorem to show that its existence would imply that $B_{2m+1}'(x) = (2m + 1)B_{2m}(x)$ vanishes at least four times inside $(0,1)$, that $B_{2m-1}(x)$ vanishes at least two points inside $(0,1)$, in addition to $x = \tfrac{1}{2}$, and hence that $B_{2m-3}(x), \ldots, B_3(x)$ have the same property, thus establishing a contradiction since $B_3(x) = x(x - \tfrac{1}{2})(x - 1)$. Show further that the function $\beta_{2m+2}(x) \equiv B_{2m+2}(x) - B_{2m+2}$ vanishes at the ends of the interval $(0,1)$, and that its vanishing anywhere inside $(0,1)$ would contradict the preceding result. Hence deduce that *the function* $\beta_{2m+2}(x) \equiv B_{2m+2}(x) - B_{2m+2}$ *vanishes at* $x = 0$ *and at* $x = 1$, *is of constant sign in* $(0,1)$, *and takes on its extreme value in that interval at* $x = \tfrac{1}{2}$.

21. Use successive integrations by parts to show that

$$\int_0^1 [B_{2m+2}(s) - B_{2m+2}]F^{(2m+2)}(s)\, ds = [\{B_{2m+2}(s) - B_{2m+2}\}F^{(2m+1)}(s)$$
$$- B_{2m+2}'(s)F^{(2m)}(s) + \cdots + B_{2m+2}^{(2m)}(s)F'(s) - B_{2m+2}^{(2m+1)}(s)F(s)]_0^1$$
$$+ \int_0^1 B_{2m+2}^{(2m+2)}(s)F(s)\, ds.$$

'hen by using results of Prob. 19, deduce the formula

$$\tfrac{1}{2}[F(1) + F(0)] = \int_0^1 F(s)\, ds + \sum_{i=1}^{m} \frac{B_{2i}}{(2i)!}\, [F^{(2i-1)}(1) - F^{(2i-1)}(0)] + E,$$

where

$$E = -\frac{1}{(2m+2)!} \int_0^1 [B_{2m+2}(s) - B_{2m+2}] F^{(2m+2)}(s)\, ds.$$

22. By summing the results of increasing the argument of F successively by 0, 1, , ..., and $r-1$, in Prob. 21, obtain the formula

$$\sum_{=0}^{r} F(k) = \int_0^r F(s)\, ds + \tfrac{1}{2}[F(0) + F(r)] + \sum_{i=1}^{m} \frac{B_{2i}}{(2i)!}\, [F^{(2i-1)}(r) - F^{(2i-1)}(0)] + E_m(r),$$

where

$$E_m(r) = -\frac{1}{(2m+2)!} \int_0^1 [B_{2m+2}(s) - B_{2m+2}]\left[\sum_{k=0}^{r-1} F^{(2m+2)}(s+k)\right] ds.$$

23. Show that the error term in Prob. 22 can be written in the form

$$E_m(r) = -r\frac{F^{(2m+2)}(\xi)}{(2m+2)!} \int_0^1 [B_{2m+2}(s) - B_{2m+2}]\, ds = r\frac{B_{2m+2}}{(2m+2)!}\, F^{(2m+2)}(\xi)$$

or some ξ such that $0 < \xi < r$, if $F^{(2m+2)}$ is continuous in that interval, and also that, f $F^{(2m+2)}(s)$ *does not change sign for* $0 < s < r$, the error term can be expressed in the orm

$$E_m(r) = -\frac{B_{2m+2}(\eta) - B_{2m+2}}{(2m+2)!} \sum_{k=0}^{r-1} [F^{(2m+1)}(k+1) - F^{(2m+1)}(k)]$$

$$= -\frac{B_{2m+2}(\eta) - B_{2m+2}}{(2m+2)!} [F^{(2m+1)}(r) - F^{(2m+1)}(0)],$$

or some η such that $0 < \eta < 1$. Further, use the results of Probs. 20 and 19(d) o show that this term is numerically smaller than twice the first term neglected n the expansion of Prob. 22 and is of the same sign. [Notice that this expansion s reduced to that of (5.8.13) if $F(s)$ is identified with $f(x_0 + hs)$, with the substitution $x_0 + hs = x$.]

24. Show that, if the first $N-1$ terms of the series

$$S \equiv 1 + \frac{1}{2^2} + \frac{1}{3^2} + \cdots + \frac{1}{n^2} + \cdots = \frac{\pi^2}{6} \doteq 1.644934$$

re summed directly, and if the Euler-Maclaurin sum formula is used to approximate he remainder, there follows

$$S = \left[1 + \frac{1}{2^2} + \frac{1}{3^2} + \cdots + \frac{1}{(N-1)^2}\right]$$

$$+ \left[\frac{1}{N} + \frac{1}{2N^2} + \frac{1}{6N^3} - \frac{1}{30N^5} + \frac{1}{42N^7} - \cdots + \frac{B_{2m}}{N^{2m+1}}\right] + E_m(N).$$

Then determine N and m in such a way that the number of terms to be retained is minimized, assuming successively that approximations which round correctly to 5, 10, and 20 decimal places are required.

25. Suppose that neither $\sum_{0}^{r} F(k)$ nor $\int_0^r F(s)\,ds$ necessarily converges as $r \to \infty$ but that their difference tends to a limit C, so that

$$C = \lim_{r \to \infty} \left[\sum_{k=0}^{r} F(k) - \int_0^r F(s)\,ds \right],$$

and that $F(s)$ and all its derivatives tend to zero as $s \to \infty$. Show that the Euler-Maclaurin expansion of Prob. 22 then can be written in the form

$$\sum_{k=0}^{r} F(k) = \int_0^r F(s)\,ds + C + \tfrac{1}{2}F(r) + \sum_{i=1}^{m} \frac{B_{2i}}{(2i)!} F^{(2i-1)}(r) + \bar{E}_m(r),$$

where

$$\bar{E}_m(r) = E_m(r) - E_m(\infty)$$

$$= \frac{1}{(2m+2)!} \int_0^1 [B_{2m+2}(s) - B_{2m+2}]\left[\sum_{k=r}^{\infty} F^{(2m+2)}(s+k) \right] ds,$$

and also obtain results analogous to those of Prob. 23 in this case.   Show further that

$$C = \tfrac{1}{2}F(0) - \sum_{i=1}^{m} \frac{B_{2i}}{(2i)!} F^{(2i-1)}(0) + E_m(\infty),$$

where $$E_m(\infty) = \frac{B_{2m+2}(\eta) - B_{2m+2}}{(2m+2)!} F^{(2m+1)}(0) \qquad (0 < \eta < 1),$$

if $F^{(2m+2)}(s)$ does not change sign for $0 < s < \infty$.

26. Use the result of Prob. 25 to deduce the asymptotic expansion

$$1 + \frac{1}{2} + \frac{1}{3} + \cdots + \frac{1}{n} = \log n + C + \frac{1}{2n} - \frac{1}{12n^2} - \cdots - \frac{B_{2m}}{(2m)n^{2m}} + \cdots,$$

where $$C = \lim_{n \to \infty} \left(\sum_{k=1}^{n} \frac{1}{k} - \log n \right),$$

assuming the existence of this limit.   Also show that

$$C = \frac{1}{2} + \frac{1}{12} - \frac{1}{120} + \cdots + \frac{B_{2m}}{2m} + E_m,$$

where $$E_m = -\frac{B_{2m+2}(\eta) - B_{2m+2}}{2m+2} \qquad (0 < \eta < 1),$$

and that E_m is of the same sign as the first neglected term and is less than twice as large.   Finally, determine the best approximation to C obtainable from this expansion and determine C to five places by equating the two members of the former expansion when $n = 10$.   (The constant C involved here is known as *Euler's constant* and is known to round to 0.5772156649.)

27. Use an appropriate modification of the result of Prob. 25 to deduce the asymptotic expansion

$$\log n! \equiv \log 1 + \log 2 + \cdots + \log n$$
$$= (n + \tfrac{1}{2}) \log n + K - n + \frac{1}{12n} - \frac{1}{360n^3} + \cdots + \frac{B_{2m}}{2m(2m - 1)n^{2m-1}}$$
$$+ \cdots ,$$

where
$$K = \lim_{n \to \infty} [\log n! - (n + \tfrac{1}{2}) \log n + n],$$

assuming the existence of this limit, and show that

$$K = 1 - \frac{1}{12} + \frac{1}{360} - \cdots - \frac{B_{2m}}{2m(2m - 1)} + E_m,$$

where E_m is of the same sign as the first neglected term and is less than twice as large. Also, calculate an approximate value of K from this expansion, and determine K to five places by setting $n = 10$ in the former one and using the fact that $\log 10! \doteq 15.104412$. The true value of K is known to be $\tfrac{1}{2} \log 2\pi \doteq 0.91894$. Assuming this fact, deduce *Stirling's asymptotic formula for the factorial*, in the form

$$n! = \sqrt{2\pi n}\, n^n e^{-n} \left(1 + \frac{1}{12n} + \frac{1}{288n^2} - \cdots \right).$$

Section 5.9

28. Deduce the Gauss summation formula by writing $\delta^{2r}p_{\frac{1}{2}} = \delta^{2r-1}p_1 - \delta^{2r-1}p_0$ in the formula of Prob. 13 and summing the resultant equal members for $k = 0, 1, \ldots, r - 1$.

29. Show that

$$\int_{x_0}^{x_r} p(x)\, dx - h(p_0 + p_1 + \cdots + p_r) = \frac{h}{1 - \mathbf{E}} [(1 - \mathbf{E}^r)h^{-1}\mathbf{J} - (1 - \mathbf{E}^{r+1})]p_0$$
$$= h \left[\frac{h^{-1}\mathbf{J} - 1}{1 - \mathbf{E}} p_0 - \frac{h^{-1}\mathbf{J} - \mathbf{E}}{1 - \mathbf{E}} p_r \right]$$

and, by expressing the operator affecting p_0 in terms of Δ and that affecting p_r in terms of ∇, deduce the Gregory summation formula in the operational form

$$\frac{1}{h} \int_{x_0}^{x_r} p(x)\, dx = (p_0 + p_1 + \cdots + p_{r-1} + p_r) - \frac{\phi(\Delta) - 1}{\Delta} p_0 - \frac{\phi(-\nabla) - 1}{(-\nabla)} p_r,$$

where
$$\phi(u) = \frac{u}{\log (1 + u)} = \sum_{k=0}^{\infty} c_k u^k,$$

with the notation of (5.4.4).

30. Use the data given in Prob. 27 of Chap. 3 to obtain approximate values of the integral

$$\sqrt{\frac{2}{\pi}} \int_0^1 e^{-t^2/2}\, dt$$

by means of the Euler-Maclaurin, Gregory, and Gauss formulas.

31. Apply both the Gregory and Gauss formulas to the approximate summation of the **series**

$$\sum_{k=1}^{\infty} \frac{k}{(2k+1)^3}$$

to five places, after summing an appropriate number of terms in advance.

32. Use each of the formulas (5.9.9) to (5.9.11) to sum the series

$$\sum_{k=1}^{\infty} \frac{(-1)^k}{k^2 + 4}$$

to five places, after summing an appropriate number of terms in advance.

33. Determine the *Euler sum* of each of the following divergent series:

(a) $1 - 1 + 1 - 1 + \cdots + (-1)^n + \cdots$.
(b) $1 - 2 + 3 - 4 + \cdots + (-1)^{n-1}n + \cdots$.
(c) $1 - 2 + 4 - 8 + \cdots + (-1)^n 2^n + \cdots$.

Also verify that the three series can be obtained formally by setting $x = 1$ in the power-series expansions of $(1 + x)^{-1}$, $(1 + x)^{-2}$, and $(1 + 2x)^{-1}$, respectively, and that the Euler sum in each case is the value taken on by the generating function when $x = 1$.

Section 5.10

34. Calculate the approximate value of

$$\int_{0.5}^{1.7} \sin x \, dx$$

from the data of Prob. 6, using Weddle's rule and Hardy's rule.

35. Calculate five approximate values of

$$\int_{0}^{6} \frac{dx}{1 + x^2},$$

using the Newton-Cotes seven-point formula, the formulas of Weddle and Hardy, and the parabolic and trapezoidal rules, with $h = 1$, and compare the results with the true value $\tan^{-1} 6 \doteq 1.406$.

Section 5.11

36. Show that $(x - s)_+^n$ is a continuous function of x and s if $n > 0$, and that

$$\int_{a}^{b} (x - s)_+^n \, dx = \frac{(x - s)_+^{n+1}}{n + 1} \Big|_{a}^{b} \quad (n \neq -1), \qquad \frac{\partial}{\partial x} (x - s)_+^n = n(x - s)_+^{n-1}.$$

37. Derive (5.11.17) from (5.11.16) and, under the assumption that the degree of precision of (5.11.1) is at least N, show also that $G(s)$ vanishes when s is outside (A,B), where A and B are the smallest and largest of $x_0, x_1, \ldots, x_n, a$, and b.

38. Obtain the influence function $G(s)$ for which

$$\int_{-1}^{1} F(x) \, dx = \tfrac{1}{3}[F(-1) + 4F(0) + F(1)] + \int_{-1}^{1} G(s)F^{iv}(s) \, ds,$$

in the form

$$G(s) = -\tfrac{1}{72}(1 - |s|)^3(1 + 3|s|) \qquad (|s| \leq 1),$$

and show that

$$\int_{-1}^{1} G(s)F^{iv}(s)\, ds = -\tfrac{1}{90}F^{iv}(\xi) \qquad (|\xi| < 1).$$

Also, by writing $x = (t - x_0 - h)/h$ and $F(x) = f(t)$, deduce Simpson's rule in the form (3.5.11).

39. Apply integration by parts to the result of Prob. 38, to show that the error in Simpson's rule, as applied to $F(x)$ over the interval $(-1,1)$, can be expressed in the alternative forms

$$\begin{aligned}
R &= -\tfrac{1}{72}\int_{-1}^{1}(1 - |s|)^3(1 + 3|s|)F^{iv}(s)\, ds \\
&= -\tfrac{1}{6}\int_{-1}^{1} s(1 - |s|)^2 F'''(s)\, ds \\
&= \tfrac{1}{6}\int_{-1}^{1}(1 - |s|)(1 - 3|s|)F''(s)\, ds
\end{aligned}$$

and deduce that, when the rule is applied to $f(x)$ over an interval $(x_0, x_0 + 2h)$, there follows

$$|R| \leq \frac{h^5}{90} M_4, \qquad |R| \leq \frac{h^4}{36} M_3, \qquad |R| \leq \frac{8h^3}{81} M_2,$$

where M_k is the maximum value of $|f^{(k)}(x)|$ in $(x_0, x_0 + 2h)$, under the assumption that $f^{(k)}(x)$ exists and is integrable over that interval.

40. Determine W_0, W_1, and W_2, as functions of α, in such a way that the error term in the formula

$$\int_{-1}^{1} F(x)\, dx = W_0 F(-\alpha) + W_1 F(0) + W_2 F(\alpha) + R \qquad (0 < \alpha \leq 1)$$

vanishes when $F(x)$ is an arbitrary polynomial of degree three or less, showing that the resultant formula is of the form

$$\int_{-1}^{1} F(x)\, dx = \frac{1}{3\alpha^2}[F(-\alpha) + 2(3\alpha^2 - 1)F(0) + F(\alpha)] + R,$$

and that its degree of precision is three unless $\alpha = \sqrt{\tfrac{3}{5}}$, and is five in that case. Also, show that the influence function corresponding to $N = 3$ is given by

$$G(s) = \begin{cases} \tfrac{1}{24}(1 - |s|)^4 - \dfrac{1}{18\alpha^2}(\alpha - |s|)^3 & (|s| \leq \alpha), \\ \tfrac{1}{24}(1 - |s|)^4 & (\alpha \leq |s| \leq 1). \end{cases}$$

(Compare Prob. 45.)

41. Show that the function $G(s)$ obtained in Prob. 40 does not change sign in $(-1,1)$ when $\alpha = \tfrac{1}{2}$, and deduce the formula

$$\int_{-1}^{1} F(x)\, dx = \tfrac{2}{3}[2F(-\tfrac{1}{2}) - F(0) + 2F(\tfrac{1}{2})] + \tfrac{7}{720}F^{iv}(\xi),$$

where $|\xi| < 1$. Also transform this result to the Newton-Cotes three-point formula (3.5.19), of open type.

42. Show that the degree of precision of the formula

$$\int_{-1}^{1} F(x)\,dx = \tfrac{1}{15}[7F(1) + 16F(0) + 7F(-1)] - \tfrac{1}{15}[F'(1) - F'(-1)] + R$$

is five, obtain the influence function relative to $N = 5$ in the form

$$G(s) = \tfrac{1}{3600}(1 - |s|)^4(1 + 4|s| + 5s^2),$$

and deduce that

$$R = \tfrac{1}{4725}F^{\text{vi}}(\xi) \qquad (|\xi| < 1).$$

Also, generalize this result by writing $x = (t - x_0 - h)/h$ and $F(x) = f(t)$.

43. Show that the degree of precision of the formula

$$F(1) - 2F(0) + F(-1) = \tfrac{1}{12}[F''(1) + 10F''(0) + F''(-1)] + R$$

is five, and that R can be expressed in the form

$$R = \tfrac{1}{360}\int_{-1}^{1} (1 - |s|)^3(3s^2 - 6|s| - 2)F^{\text{vi}}(s)\,ds = -\tfrac{1}{240}F^{\text{vi}}(\xi) \qquad (|\xi| < 1).$$

44. Assuming that $x_0 \leqq x \leqq x_1$, obtain $g(x,s)$ such that

$$f(x) = f(x_0) + (x - x_0)\frac{f(x_1) - f(x_0)}{h} + \int_{x_0}^{x_1} g(x,s)f''(s)\,ds \qquad (x_1 - x_0 = h)$$

in the form

$$hg(x,s) = \begin{cases} -(s - x_0)(x_1 - x) & (x_0 \leqq s \leqq x), \\ -(x - x_0)(x_1 - s) & (x \leqq s \leqq x_1), \end{cases}$$

and deduce the more familiar form of the error term,

$$R = \tfrac{1}{2}(x - x_0)(x - x_1)f''(\xi) \qquad (x_0 < \xi < x_1).$$

45. Show that the error term relevant to the formula of Prob. 40 can be written in the form

$$R = \int_{-1}^{1} V'(x)F[-\alpha,0,\alpha,x]\,dx,$$

where $V(x) = \tfrac{1}{4}[(x^2 - \alpha^2)^2 - (1 - \alpha^2)^2]$, and deduce that

$$R = \frac{3 - 5\alpha^2}{180} F^{\text{iv}}(\xi) \qquad (|\xi| < 1)$$

when $0 < \alpha^2 \leqq \tfrac{1}{2}$ or $\alpha^2 = 1$. Also show that this result reduces to the results of Probs. 38 and 41 when $\alpha = 1$ and $\tfrac{1}{2}$, respectively, and, by determining α such that the weighting coefficients are equal, deduce the additional formula

$$\int_{-1}^{1} F(x)\,dx = \tfrac{2}{3}\left[F\left(-\frac{\sqrt{2}}{2}\right) + F(0) + F\left(\frac{\sqrt{2}}{2}\right) \right] + \tfrac{1}{360}F^{\text{iv}}(\xi).$$

46. Determine α such that the error term relevant to the formula of Prob. 40 can be written in the form

$$R = \int_{-1}^{1} V'''(x)F[-\alpha,0,\alpha,x]\,dx,$$

where V, V', and V'' vanish for $x = \pm 1$, show that then $V(x)$ is nonpositive in $(-1,1)$, and deduce the formula

$$\int_{-1}^{1} F(x)\, dx = \tfrac{1}{9}[5F(-\sqrt{\tfrac{3}{5}}) + 8F(0) + 5F(\sqrt{\tfrac{3}{5}})] + \tfrac{1}{15750}F^{\mathrm{vi}}(\xi) \qquad (|\xi| < 1).$$

Section 5.12

47. By specializing the Newton-Cotes four-point formula of open type to the interval $(-2,3)$ with $h = 1$, in the form

$$\int_{-2}^{3} F(x)\, dx = \tfrac{5}{24}[11F(-1) + F(0) + F(1) + 11F(2)] + \int_{-2}^{3} \pi(x)F[-1,0,1,2,x]\, dx,$$

where $\pi(x) = x(x^2 - 1)(x - 2)$, and considering the function

$$Q(x) = \int_{-2}^{x} \frac{\pi(t)}{t - 2}\, dt,$$

show that the error can be expressed in the form

$$E = \frac{F^{\mathrm{iv}}(\xi_1)}{4!} \int_{-2}^{2} \pi(x)\, dx + \frac{F^{\mathrm{iv}}(\xi_2)}{4!} \int_{2}^{3} \pi(x)\, dx = \tfrac{95}{144}F^{\mathrm{iv}}(\xi),$$

where ξ_1, ξ_2, and ξ are inside the interval $(-2,3)$.

48. Determine W_1, W_2, and W_3 such that the formula

$$\int_{0}^{2} xF(x)\, dx = W_1F(0) + W_2F(1) + W_3F(2) + R$$

possesses a degree of precision of at least two, and show that the resultant formula takes the form

$$\int_{0}^{2} xF(x)\, dx = \tfrac{2}{3}[2F(1) + F(2)] - \tfrac{2}{45}F'''(\xi) \qquad (0 < \xi < 2).$$

49. Derive the formula

$$\int_{-1}^{1} \frac{F(x)}{\sqrt{1 - x^2}}\, dx = \frac{\pi}{4}[F(-1) + 2F(0) + F(1)] - \frac{\pi}{192}F^{\mathrm{iv}}(\xi) \qquad (|\xi| < 1).$$

50. Show that the error R in Prob. 42 can be written in the form

$$R = \int_{-1}^{1} x^2(1 - x^2)^2 F[-1,-1,0,0,1,1,x]\, dx,$$

and that this form leads again to the result

$$R = \tfrac{1}{4725}F^{\mathrm{vi}}(\xi) \qquad (|\xi| < 1).$$

51. Show that the error R relevant to the Newton-Cotes five-point formula of closed type, as applied to $F(x)$ over $(-2,2)$, can be expressed in the form

$$R = \int_{-2}^{2} V'(x)F[-2,-1,0,1,2,x]\, dx,$$

where
$$V(x) = \int_{-2}^{x} t(t^2 - 1)(t^2 - 4)\, dt.$$

Show also that $V(x)$ is an even function, so that $V(-x) = V(x)$, and that $V(2) = 0$. Show further that $V(x)$ increases to a positive maximum value as x increases from -2

to -1, that it then decreases steadily as x increases from -1 to 0, and that

$$V(0) = V(-1) + \int_{-1}^{0} t(t^2 - 1)(t^2 - 4)\, dt = V(-1) - \int_{-2}^{-1} \frac{3+t}{2-t}[t(t^2 - 1)(t^2 - 4)]\, dt$$

$$= \left(1 - \frac{3+\eta}{2-\eta}\right) V(-1) \qquad (-2 < \eta < -1).$$

Hence deduce that $V(0)$ is positive, that $V(x)$ does not change sign in $(-2,2)$, and therefore that

$$R = \frac{F^{\mathrm{vi}}(\xi)}{6!} \int_{-2}^{2} x^2(x^2 - 1)(x^2 - 4)\, dx = -\tfrac{8}{945}F^{\mathrm{vi}}(\xi) \qquad (|\xi| < 2).$$

(A similar analysis, due to Steffensen [18], applies to all Newton-Cotes formulas, of closed type, employing an odd number of ordinates.)

52. For the Newton-Cotes six-point formula of closed type, as applied to $F(x)$ over $(-2,3)$, show that the function $V(x)$ of Prob. 51 serves as an appropriate Q function over $(-2,2)$, so that the error R can be expressed in the form

$$R = \frac{F^{\mathrm{vi}}(\xi_1)}{6!} \int_{-2}^{2} x(x^2 - 1)(x^2 - 4)(x - 3)\, dx + \frac{F^{\mathrm{vi}}(\xi_2)}{6!} \int_{2}^{3} x(x^2 - 1)(x^2 - 4)(x - 3)\, dx$$

$$= -\tfrac{8}{945}F^{\mathrm{vi}}(\xi_1) - \tfrac{863}{60480}F^{\mathrm{vi}}(\xi_2) = -\tfrac{275}{12096}F^{\mathrm{vi}}(\xi) \qquad (-2 < \xi < 3).$$

Supplementary Problems

53. By a double application of Simpson's rule, derive the formula

$$\int_{x_0}^{x_2} \int_{y_0}^{y_2} f(x,y)\, dx\, dy = \frac{hk}{9}\left[(f_{0,0} + f_{0,2} + f_{2,0} + f_{2,2}) + 4(f_{0,1} + f_{1,0} + f_{1,2} + f_{2,1}) + 16f_{1,1}\right] + E,$$

where $x_r \equiv x_0 + rh$, $y_s \equiv y_0 + sk$, and $f_{r,s} \equiv f(x_r,y_s)$, and show that

$$E = -\frac{hk}{45}\left[h^4 \frac{\partial^4 f(\xi_1,\eta_1)}{\partial x^4} + k^4 \frac{\partial^4 f(\xi_2,\eta_2)}{\partial y^4}\right],$$

where ξ_1, ξ_2 lie in (x_0,x_2) and η_1, η_2 in (y_0,y_2). [More elaborate formulas for two-way integration over a rectangle ("cubature formulas") are obtainable by double application of other one-dimensional integration formulas.]

54. By applying the formula of Prob. 53 to subrectangles, and adding the results, derive the two-dimensional generalization of the parabolic rule in the form

$$\int_{x_0}^{x_m} \int_{y_0}^{y_n} f(x,y)\, dx\, dy = \frac{hk}{9}[(f_{0,0} + 4f_{1,0} + 2f_{2,0} + \cdots + f_{m,0})$$

$$+ 4(f_{0,1} + 4f_{1,1} + 2f_{2,1} + \cdots + f_{m,1}) + 2(f_{0,2} + 4f_{1,2} + 2f_{2,2} + \cdots + f_{m,2})$$

$$+ \cdots + (f_{0,n} + 4f_{1,n} + 2f_{2,n} + \cdots + f_{m,n})] + E,$$

where

$$E = -\frac{hk}{90}\left[mh^4 \frac{\partial^4 f(\bar{\xi}_1,\bar{\eta}_1)}{\partial x^4} + nk^4 \frac{\partial^4 f(\bar{\xi}_2,\bar{\eta}_2)}{\partial y^4}\right],$$

when m and n are even integers.

55. Let $\mathbf{E}_x$, $\mathbf{E}_y$, Δ_x, Δ_y, and so forth, designate operators which affect only the variable indicated by the subscript, with uniform spacings h and k implied in the x and y directions, respectively, so that, for example, $\delta_x^2 f_{0,0} \equiv f_{1,0} - 2f_{0,0} + f_{-1,0}$, where $f_{r,s} \equiv f(x_0 + rh, y_0 + sk)$. By writing

$$f_{r,s} = \mathbf{E}_x^r \mathbf{E}_y^s f_{0,0}$$

and referring to the interpolation formulas of Newton, Stirling, Bessel, and Everett, deduce that a variety of two-dimensional interpolation formulas can be obtained by substituting one of the following indicated expansions for each operator, and truncating the result:

$$E^p = 1 + p\Delta + \frac{p(p-1)}{2!}\Delta^2 + \cdots = 1 + p\nabla + \frac{p(p+1)}{2!}\nabla^2 + \cdots$$

$$= 1 + p\mu\delta + \frac{p^2}{2!}\delta^2 + \cdots = \left[\mu + (p-0.5)\delta + \frac{p(p-1)}{2!}\mu\delta^2 + \cdots\right]E^{\frac{1}{2}}$$

$$= \left[(1-p) - \frac{p(p-1)(p-2)}{3!}\delta^2 + \cdots\right] + \left[p + \frac{p(p^2-1)}{3!}\delta^2 + \cdots\right]E.$$

Which pairs of expansions would be appropriate for interpolation near corners of a table? Near the borders? At interior points?

56. By using the Newton forward-difference expansion in both directions in Prob. 55, and retaining only differences through the first in each direction, deduce the approximate formula

$$f_{r,s} \approx (1 + r\Delta_x)(1 + s\Delta_y)f_{0,0}$$
$$= (1-r)(1-s)f_{0,0} + r(1-s)f_{1,0} + s(1-r)f_{0,1} + rsf_{1,1}$$

and show that this formula would yield exact results if $f(x,y)$ were of the form $A + Bx + Cy + Dxy$. Also obtain the formula which neglects the mixed second difference $\Delta_x\Delta_y f_{0,0}$, show that it would yield exact results if f were of the form $A + Bx + Cy$, and specialize both formulas when $r = s = \frac{1}{2}$.

57. By using the Everett expansion in both directions in Prob. 55, and neglecting differences and mixed differences of order greater than three, deduce the approximate formula

$$f_{r,s} \approx (1-r)(1-s)\left[1 - \frac{r(2-r)}{6}\delta_x^2 - \frac{s(2-s)}{6}\delta_y^2\right]f_{0,0}$$
$$+ r(1-s)\left[1 - \frac{1-r^2}{6}\delta_x^2 - \frac{s(2-s)}{6}\delta_y^2\right]f_{1,0}$$
$$+ (1-r)s\left[1 - \frac{r(2-r)}{6}\delta_x^2 - \frac{1-s^2}{6}\delta_y^2\right]f_{0,1}$$
$$+ rs\left[1 - \frac{1-r^2}{6}\delta_x^2 - \frac{1-s^2}{6}\delta_y^2\right]f_{1,1}.$$

Show also that it would yield exact results for

$$f(x,y) = A + B_1x + B_2y + C_1x^2 + C_2xy + C_3y^2 + D_1x^3 + D_2x^2y + D_3xy^2$$
$$+ D_4y^3 + E_1x^3y + E_2xy^3,$$

and specialize the formula when $r = s = \frac{1}{2}$.

58. A table includes the following ordinates and differences, together with a statement that differences of order four or greater are negligible. Use the formula of Prob. 57 to interpolate for $f(6.55, 1.05)$ and for $f(6.524, 1.042)$.

	$y = 1.0$			$y = 1.1$		
x	$f(x,y)$	δ_x^2	δ_y^2	$f(x,y)$	δ_x^2	δ_y^2
6.5	0.9989623	-168	-31	0.9989783	-171	-28
6.6	0.9990866	-147	-28	0.9991026	-150	-26

NUMERICAL SOLUTION OF DIFFERENTIAL EQUATIONS

6.1. Introduction. Many techniques are available for the approximate solution of ordinary differential equations, or of sets of such equations, by numerical methods. This chapter presents a selection of frequently used procedures of various types and illustrates their application. In addition, an indication is given of the troublesome problem of error propagation in stepwise integration processes, and over-all error bounds are obtained in illustrative cases.

Some comments relative to the problem of selecting an appropriate technique are included in the concluding section (§6.19).

Whereas most of the treatments deal with initial-value problems, brief considerations of boundary-value problems (§6.17) and characteristic-value problems (§6.18) are also included.

6.2. Formulas of Open Type. We consider first the problem in which it is desired to obtain a numerical approximate solution of the first-order equation

$$\frac{dy}{dx} = F(x,y) \tag{6.2.1}$$

which takes on a prescribed value y_0 when $x = x_0$,

$$y(x_0) = y_0. \tag{6.2.2}$$

Starting with the known ordinate, it is proposed to calculate successively the ordinates

$$y_1 \equiv y(x_0 + h) \equiv y(x_1), \qquad y_2 \equiv y(x_0 + 2h) \equiv y(x_2), \qquad \cdots ,$$
$$y_n \equiv y(x_0 + nh) \equiv y(x_n), \qquad \cdots , \tag{6.2.3}$$

where h is a suitably chosen spacing.

For this purpose, we may, in particular, make use of the relation

$$y_{n+1} = y_n + \int_{x_n}^{x_n+h} y'(x)\, dx. \tag{6.2.4}$$

Suppose that the ordinates $y_n, y_{n-1}, \ldots, y_1$, and y_0 are known. Then the corresponding values of $y'(x)$ are calculable from the formula

$$y'_k \equiv y'(x_k) = F(x_k,y_k). \tag{6.2.5}$$

If we approximate $y'(x)$ by the polynomial of degree N which takes on the calculated values at the $N + 1$ points $x_n, x_{n-1}, \ldots,$ and x_{n-N}, by making use of the Newton backward-difference formula (4.3.8),

$$y'_{n+s} \approx y'_n + s\nabla y'_n + \frac{s(s + 1)}{2!}\nabla^2 y'_n + \cdots$$
$$+ \frac{s(s + 1)\cdots(s + N - 1)}{N!}\nabla^N y'_n \quad (6.2.6)$$

where
$$s = \frac{x - x_n}{h}, \quad (6.2.7)$$

we may use this polynomial to *extrapolate* $y'(x)$ over the interval $(x_n, x_n + h)$, for the purpose of approximately effecting the integration indicated in (6.2.4).

The result of this calculation is

$$y_{n+1} = y_n + h\int_0^1 y'_{n+s}\, ds \approx y_n + h\sum_{k=0}^N a_k \nabla^k y'_n, \quad (6.2.8)$$

where
$$a_k = \int_0^1 \frac{s(s + 1)\cdots(s + k - 1)}{k!}\, ds, \quad (6.2.9)$$

the leading terms of (6.2.8) being of the form

$$y_{n+1} \approx y_n + h(1 + \tfrac{1}{2}\nabla + \tfrac{5}{12}\nabla^2 + \tfrac{3}{8}\nabla^3 + \tfrac{251}{720}\nabla^4 + \tfrac{95}{288}\nabla^5 + \cdots)y'_n, \quad (6.2.10)$$

in accordance with (5.4.13).

The error term corresponding to truncation with the Nth difference of y'_n is given by h times the integral of the right-hand member of (4.3.9) with $f = y'$, in the form

$$E = h^{N+2}\int_0^1 \frac{s(s + 1)\cdots(s + N)}{(N + 1)!}\, y^{(N+2)}(\eta)\, ds,$$

or, since the coefficient of $y^{(N+2)}$ does not change sign in $(0,1)$,

$$E = a_{N+1}h^{N+2}y^{(N+2)}(\xi), \quad (6.2.11)$$

where $x_{n+1} > \xi > x_{n-N}$. Thus, for example, if only third differences are retained, the error is given by $\tfrac{251}{720}h^5 y^v(\xi)$ where $x_{n+1} > \xi > x_{n-3}$.

More generally, we may use (6.2.6) in the relation

$$y_{n+1} = y_{n-p} + h\int_{-p}^1 y'_{n+s}\, ds, \quad (6.2.12)$$

where p is any positive integer, to express the ordinate following the nth one in terms of the ordinate calculated p steps previously and in terms of, say, $N + 1$ already calculated values of y'. The formulas most frequently used, in addition to (6.2.10) with $p = 0$, are those for which

$p = 1, 3$, and 5, the leading terms of which are of the form

$$y_{n+1} \approx y_{n-1} + h(2 + 0\nabla + \tfrac{1}{3}\nabla^2 + \tfrac{1}{3}\nabla^3 + \tfrac{29}{90}\nabla^4 + \tfrac{14}{45}\nabla^5 + \cdots)y_n', \tag{6.2.13}$$

$$y_{n+1} \approx y_{n-3} + h(4 - 4\nabla + \tfrac{8}{3}\nabla^2 + 0\nabla^3 + \tfrac{14}{45}\nabla^4 + \tfrac{14}{45}\nabla^5 + \cdots)y_n', \tag{6.2.14}$$

and

$$y_{n+1} \approx y_{n-5} + h(6 - 12\nabla + 15\nabla^2 - 9\nabla^3 + \tfrac{33}{10}\nabla^4 + 0\nabla^5 + \cdots)y_n'. \tag{6.2.15}$$

Whereas the error associated with terminating one of these formulas with the Nth difference can be expressed in the form

$$E = h^{N+2} \int_{-p}^{1} \frac{s(s + 1) \cdots (s + N)}{(N + 1)!} \, y^{(N+2)}(\eta) \, ds, \tag{6.2.16}$$

where η lies between x_{n+1} and the smaller of x_{n-p} and x_{n-N}, the fact that the coefficient of $y^{(N+2)}$ changes sign in the integration range when $p > 0$ makes it impossible to apply the law of the mean directly in order to obtain a simple form similar to (6.2.11). Somewhat more complicated forms are obtainable by subdividing the range of integration and applying the law of the mean to each subinterval, or, better, by using one of the methods of §§5.11 and 5.12.

The formulas for which p is an *odd* integer are of particular interest because of the fact that, in each such formula, the coefficient of the pth difference is found to be zero. In these cases, the retention of $p - 1$ differences thus affords the same accuracy as the retention of p differences. Indeed, the cases in which $N = p$ correspond to the use of *Newton-Cotes* formulas of the *open* type, employing an *odd* number of ordinates, in the integration indicated in (6.2.12). Further, the error terms in those cases can be expressed in a form similar to (6.2.11) and are given for $p = 3$ and $p = 5$ in Eqs. (3.5.19) and (3.5.21). Thus, in particular, we have the special formulas

$$y_{n+1} = y_{n-1} + 2hy_n' + \frac{h^3}{3} y'''(\xi), \tag{6.2.17}$$

$$y_{n+1} = y_{n-3} + 4h(y_n' - \nabla y_n' + \tfrac{2}{3}\nabla^2 y_n') + \frac{14h^5}{45} y^{\text{v}}(\xi), \tag{6.2.18}$$

and

$$y_{n+1} = y_{n-5} + 6h(y_n' - 2\nabla y_n' + \tfrac{5}{2}\nabla^2 y_n' - \tfrac{3}{2}\nabla^3 y_n' + \tfrac{11}{20}\nabla^4 y_n') + \frac{41h^7}{140} y^{\text{vii}}(\xi), \tag{6.2.19}$$

where, in each case, ξ lies between the largest and smallest of the arguments involved in that formula. These formulas, and corresponding ones for $p = 7, 9, \ldots$, have the property that, in each case, the retention of differences through the Nth leads to a formula with accuracy "of order $N + 2$," that is, to an error term proportional to h^{N+3}, whereas for the other formulas of the type considered here the accuracy corresponding to the retention of differences through the Nth is of order $N + 1$.†

It is clear that, since a formula employing Nth differences depends upon knowledge of $N + 1$ successive values of y_k, and since initially only y_0 is known, such a formula cannot be used until N additional ordinates have been determined by another method.

Before illustrating the use of such formulas, it is desirable to consider a class of related formulas.

6.3. Formulas of Closed Type.

The formulas derived in the preceding section express y_{n+1} in terms only of previously calculated ordinates and slopes. A set of similar formulas which involve also the unknown slope y'_{n+1} is obtained by replacing the right-hand member of (6.2.6) by the interpolation polynomial agreeing with $y'(x)$ at $x_{n+1}, x_n, \ldots, x_{n-N+1}$:

$$y'_{n+s} \approx y'_{n+1} + (s - 1) \nabla y'_{n+1} + \frac{(s - 1)s}{2!} \nabla^2 y'_{n+1} + \cdots$$
$$+ \frac{(s - 1)s(s + 1) \cdots (s + N - 2)}{N!} \nabla^N y'_{n+1}, \quad (6.3.1)$$

where s is again defined by (6.2.7). If this approximation is introduced into (6.2.12), the results in the cases $p = 0, 1, 3,$ and 5 are obtained in the forms

$$y_{n+1} \approx y_n + h(1 - \tfrac{1}{2}\nabla - \tfrac{1}{12}\nabla^2 - \tfrac{1}{24}\nabla^3 - \tfrac{19}{720}\nabla^4 - \tfrac{3}{160}\nabla^5 - \cdots)y'_{n+1}, \quad (6.3.2)$$

$$y_{n+1} \approx y_{n-1} + h(2 - 2\nabla + \tfrac{1}{3}\nabla^2 + 0\nabla^3 - \tfrac{1}{90}\nabla^4 - \tfrac{1}{90}\nabla^5 - \cdots)y'_{n+1}, \quad (6.3.3)$$

$$y_{n+1} \approx y_{n-3} + h(4 - 8\nabla + \tfrac{20}{3}\nabla^2 - \tfrac{8}{3}\nabla^3 + \tfrac{14}{45}\nabla^4 - 0\nabla^5 - \cdots)y'_{n+1}, \quad (6.3.4)$$

and

$$y_{n+1} \approx y_{n-5} + h(6 - 18\nabla + 27\nabla^2 - 24\nabla^3 + \tfrac{123}{10}\nabla^4 - \tfrac{33}{10}\nabla^5 + \cdots)y'_{n+1}. \quad (6.3.5)$$

The error associated with retaining only Nth differences in a formula relating y_{n+1} and y_{n-p} can be expressed in the form

$$E = h^{N+2} \int_{-p}^{1} \frac{(s - 1)s(s + 1) \cdots (s + N - 1)}{(N + 1)!} y^{(N+2)}(\eta) \, ds, \quad (6.3.6)$$

---

† It is seen that the terminology here is also such that a formula with "accuracy of order m" would yield exact results if the required solution $y(x)$ were a polynomial of degree m or less. When $y(x)$ is *not* such a function, it is not *necessarily* true that an increase in m corresponds to an improvement in the approximation afforded, as was seen in §3.7.

where η lies between x_{n+1} and the smaller of x_{n-p} and x_{n-N}. When $p = 0$, the law of the mean can be used, as in the preceding section, to show that the error is expressible in the form (6.2.11), where a_{N+1} is the numerical coefficient in the first neglected term. In the cases (6.3.3) and (6.3.5), for which p is an odd integer, it is seen that retention of $p + 1$ differences is equivalent to the retention of $p + 2$ differences and that the use of these special formulas corresponds to the use of Newton-Cotes formulas of the *closed* type, employing an odd number of ordinates, for which the error terms are obtainable from (3.5.11) and (3.5.13) when $p = 1$ and $p = 3$. Thus we have the special formulas

$$y_{n+1} = y_{n-1} + 2h(y'_{n+1} - \nabla y'_{n+1} + \tfrac{1}{6}\nabla^2 y'_{n+1}) - \frac{h^5}{90} y^{\mathrm{v}}(\xi), \qquad (6.3.7)$$

and

$$y_{n+1} = y_{n-3} + 4h(y'_{n+1} - 2\nabla y'_{n+1} + \tfrac{5}{3}\nabla^2 y'_{n+1} - \tfrac{2}{3}\nabla^3 y'_{n+1} + \tfrac{7}{90}\nabla^4 y'_{n+1})$$
$$- \frac{8h^7}{945} y^{\mathrm{vii}}(\xi), \quad (6.3.8)$$

for which the retention of Nth differences yields an accuracy of order $N + 2$, whereas the other formulas of the type considered generally yield $(N + 1)$th-order accuracy.

Formulas of the sort derived in this section may be said to be of *closed* type, since the expressions for the required ordinate y_{n+1}, at the point x_{n+1}, involve the unknown slope y'_{n+1} at that point, whereas those of the preceding section involve only *known* slopes at preceding points and are accordingly said to be of *open* type. A comparison of corresponding formulas employing a like number of differences shows that the error terms associated with formulas of closed type possess smaller numerical coefficients. However, since the unknown y_{n+1} is involved (explicitly and implicitly) in *both* members of formulas of closed type, this advantage must be weighed against the fact that, unless $y' \equiv F(x,y)$ is a *linear* function of y, the equation relevant to such a formula generally must be solved for y_{n+1} by iterative methods.

6.4. Start of Solution. Except for the special formula

$$y_{n+1} = y_n + hy'_n + \frac{h^2}{2} y''(\xi), \qquad (6.4.1)$$

obtained by omitting all differences in (6.2.10), and a similar formula of closed type, obtained from (6.3.2), each of the formulas obtained in the preceding sections can be applied only after the calculation of a number of ordinates $y_1, y_2, \ldots, y_r$ equal to the order of the highest difference retained in that formula, in addition to the prescribed ordinate y_0.

One method of starting the solution of the problem

$$\frac{dy}{dx} = F(x,y), \qquad y(x_0) = y_0 \tag{6.4.2}$$

consists in determining the coefficients of a Taylor expansion

$$y_s \equiv y(x_0 + hs) = y_0 + \frac{hy_0'}{1!}s + \frac{h^2y_0''}{2!}s^2 + \cdots + \frac{h^r y_0^{(r)}}{r!}s^r$$

$$+ \frac{h^{r+1}y^{(r+1)}(\xi)}{(r+1)!}s^{r+1} \tag{6.4.3}$$

where $y_0^{(k)} \equiv (d^k y/dx^k)_{x=x_0}$ and $x_0 < \xi < x_0 + hs$, by successively differentiating the basic differential equation or otherwise, under the assumption that a convergent expansion of this type exists, when s is sufficiently small.

Thus, recalling that $d/dx = \partial/\partial x + y'\,\partial/\partial y$, we obtain the relations

$$y' = F(x,y), \qquad y'' = F_x(x,y) + y'F_y(x,y),$$
$$y''' = F_{xx}(x,y) + 2y'F_{xy}(x,y) + y'^2 F_{yy}(x,y) + y''F_y(x,y),$$

and so forth, and hence there follows

$$y_0' = F(x_0,y_0), \qquad y_0'' = F_x(x_0,y_0) + y_0'F_y(x_0,y_0), \tag{6.4.4}$$

and so forth.

Whereas these *general* expressions become quite involved as the order of the required derivative increases, they are not actually needed in practice. In order to illustrate this fact, we consider the specific example

$$\frac{dy}{dx} = x^2 - y, \qquad y(0) = 1, \tag{6.4.5}$$

for which the *exact* solution is readily found to be

$$y = 2 - 2x + x^2 - e^{-x}. \tag{6.4.6}$$

From the given equation, we obtain successively

$$y' = x^2 - y, \qquad y'' = 2x - y', \qquad y''' = 2 - y'', \qquad y^{iv} = -y''',$$
$$y^v = -y^{iv}, \qquad \cdots, \tag{6.4.7}$$

and hence, with $x_0 = 0$, there follows

$$y_0 = 1, \qquad y_0' = -1, \qquad y_0'' = 1, \qquad y_0''' = 1,$$
$$y_0^{iv} = -1, \qquad y_0^v = 1, \qquad y_0^{vi} = -1, \qquad \cdots.$$

Thus, if we take $h = \frac{1}{10}$, Eq. (6.4.3) gives

$$y_s = 1 - \frac{s}{10} + \frac{1}{2}\left(\frac{s}{10}\right)^2 + \frac{1}{6}\left(\frac{s}{10}\right)^3 - \frac{1}{24}\left(\frac{s}{10}\right)^4 + \frac{1}{120}\left(\frac{s}{10}\right)^5$$

$$- \frac{1}{720}\left(\frac{s}{10}\right)^6 + \cdots \tag{6.4.8}$$

and, with $s = 1$, 2, and 3, we obtain

$$y_1 = 0.90516, \qquad y_2 = 0.82127, \qquad y_3 = 0.74918, \qquad (6.4.9)$$

to five places.   Since the successive terms of (6.4.8) alternate in sign from the fourth term onward, and decrease steadily in magnitude, the error due to truncation is smaller in magnitude than the first neglected term and is of the same sign.   Additional ordinates could be obtained to this accuracy by retaining sufficiently many terms in the expansion.   Alternatively, a new expansion could be launched from the point x_3, in the form

$$y_{3+s} = y_3 + \frac{hy_3'}{1!} s + \frac{h^2 y_3''}{2!} s^2 + \cdots ,$$

with y_3 known and y_3', y_3'', $\ldots$ calculable in terms of y_3 from (6.4.7).

It is obvious that the linear example chosen illustrates a particularly simple case, because of the simplicity of the relations (6.4.7) and because of the fact that (6.4.8) is an alternating series and hence is amenable to a precise truncation-error analysis.   More usually, the relations (6.4.7) are replaced by successive equations which increase fairly rapidly in complexity, so that it is usually desirable to abandon this procedure in favor of a more convenient one when sufficiently many starting values have been obtained.   Furthermore, since $y(x)$ itself is not known, it is usually difficult to obtain a reliable estimate of the truncation-error term given in (6.4.3), even though it be known that the series itself is convergent for the value of s under consideration.

Discussion of the convergence (and existence) of (6.4.3) in the general case of the problem (6.4.2), as well as consideration of other types of expansions which can be used when (6.4.3) cannot, must be omitted here (see Ince [120]).   In some cases it is preferable to determine the coefficients in an assumed expansion of the form

$$y(x) = \sum_{k=0}^{\infty} A_k (x - x_0)^k$$

by inserting that expansion in the differential equation and obtaining a recurrence formula to be satisfied by the A's.

A similar method, which has the advantage that the order of the highest derivative required is about half that needed in (6.4.3), but has the disadvantage that each forward step involves an iterative process, is treated in §6.14.

Mention should also be made of *Picard's method*, in which the problem (6.4.2) is first transformed into the *integral equation*

$$y(x) = y_0 + \int_{x_0}^{x} F(x, y(x)) \, dx,$$

and successive *functions* approximating $y(x)$ near $x = x_0$ are generated by the iteration

$$y^{[k+1]}(x) = y_0 + \int_{x_0}^{x} F(x, y^{[k]}(x))\, dx. \tag{6.4.10}$$

The initial approximation $y^{[0]}(x)$ is conveniently taken to be the constant y_0 or the linear function $y_0 + y_0'(x - x_0)$, where y_0' is determined from the differential equation.

Thus, in the preceding example, we would write

$$y^{[k+1]}(x) = 1 + \int_{0}^{x} [x^2 - y^{[k]}(x)]\, dx \tag{6.4.11}$$

and, with $y^{[0]}(x) = 1$, there would then follow

$$y^{[1]}(x) = 1 - x + \tfrac{1}{3}x^3, \qquad y^{[2]}(x) = 1 - x + \tfrac{1}{2}x^2 + \tfrac{1}{3}x^3 - \tfrac{1}{12}x^4,$$
$$\tag{6.4.12}$$

and so forth. The accuracy afforded by a member of the sequence of approximations at a certain number of points x_1, x_2, ... could be estimated by comparing calculated values at those points with values calculated from the preceding approximation, or by use of appropriate analytical methods.

While Picard's method is of great theoretical importance, the explicit evaluation of the integral in (6.4.10) is often impracticable in cases which are less simple than the preceding one. Thus, for the problem $y' = \cos (x + y)$, $y(0) = 1$, the first iteration with $y^{[0]}(x) = 1$ gives $y^{[1]}(x) = 1 - \sin 1 + \sin (x + 1)$, and the second iteration would involve the evaluation of the form

$$y^{[2]}(x) = 1 + \int_{0}^{x} \cos [1 - \sin 1 + x + \sin (x + 1)]\, dx.$$

Also, when $F(x,y)$ is not given analytically, neither this procedure nor the power-series method is directly applicable.

A frequently used class of procedures consists in evaluating the integral of $y' \equiv F(x,y)$ in (6.4.10) approximately, by use of numerical methods. Thus, in particular, if y' is approximated by the Newton forward-difference polynomial-interpolation formula, the results of the integration are obtained by replacing $p(x)$ by $y'(x)$ in (5.4.8), and we have the formulas

$$
\begin{aligned}
y_1 &= y_0 + h[1 + \tfrac{1}{2}\Delta - \tfrac{1}{12}\Delta^2 + \tfrac{1}{24}\Delta^3 - \tfrac{19}{720}\Delta^4 + \cdots]y_0', \\
y_2 &= y_0 + h[2 + 2\Delta + \tfrac{1}{3}\Delta^2 + 0\Delta^3 - \tfrac{1}{90}\Delta^4 + \cdots]y_0', \\
y_3 &= y_0 + h[3 + \tfrac{9}{2}\Delta + \tfrac{9}{4}\Delta^2 + \tfrac{3}{8}\Delta^3 - \tfrac{3}{80}\Delta^4 + \cdots]y_0', \\
y_4 &= y_0 + h[4 + 8\Delta + \tfrac{20}{3}\Delta^2 + \tfrac{8}{3}\Delta^3 + \tfrac{14}{45}\Delta^4 + \cdots]y_0',
\end{aligned}
\tag{6.4.13}
$$

and so forth. Here y_0 is given, and if, say, y_1, y_2, y_3, and y_4 are *estimated*, the corresponding values of y_0', ... , y_4' can be calculated from the differential equation and introduced into the right-hand members to give the new approximations to $y_1, \ldots, y_4$, after which the process may be iterated.

In the case of (6.4.5) we may notice that, since the value $y_0' = -1$ is obtained from the differential equation, the initial approximation $y^{[0]}(x_k) = 1 - x_k$ is appropriate. With $h = 0.1$, the following initial array then may be formed when three additional ordinates are incorporated:

x	y	y'	Δ	Δ^2	Δ^3
0.0	1.00000	-1.00000			
			11000		
0.1	0.90000	-0.89000		2000	
			13000		0
0.2	0.80000	-0.76000		2000	
			15000		
0.3	0.70000	-0.61000			

The use of the first three of Eqs. (6.4.13), retaining third differences, leads to the new array

0.0	1.00000	-1.00000			
			10467		
0.1	0.90533	-0.89533		799	
			11266		-198
0.2	0.82267	-0.78267		601	
			11867		
0.3	0.75400	-0.66400			

Three additional iterations yield results which are unchanged to five places by further iteration and which are correct to those places. The correctness of those values would be checked, in practice, by considering the effects of the neglected fourth differences, sample values of which become available as the calculation is advanced from this stage.

A useful variation of this procedure consists in using *central* differences and in determining ordinates on both sides of the initial point x_0. Thus, by appropriate integration of the *Stirling* interpolation formula, we obtain the relations

$$
\begin{aligned}
y_{-2} &= y_0 + h[-2 + 2\mu\delta - \tfrac{4}{3}\delta^2 + \tfrac{1}{3}\mu\delta^3 - \tfrac{7}{45}\delta^4 + \cdots]y_0', \\
y_{-1} &= y_0 + h[-1 + \tfrac{1}{2}\mu\delta - \tfrac{1}{6}\delta^2 - \tfrac{1}{24}\mu\delta^3 + \tfrac{1}{180}\delta^4 + \cdots]y_0', \\
y_1 &= y_0 + h[1 + \tfrac{1}{2}\mu\delta + \tfrac{1}{6}\delta^2 - \tfrac{1}{24}\mu\delta^3 - \tfrac{1}{180}\delta^4 + \cdots]y_0', \\
y_2 &= y_0 + h[2 + 2\mu\delta + \tfrac{4}{3}\delta^2 + \tfrac{1}{3}\mu\delta^3 + \tfrac{7}{45}\delta^4 + \cdots]y_0'.
\end{aligned}
\tag{6.4.14}
$$

Since here the calculated ordinates are taken as close to the given one as is possible, the convergence of the iterative process is generally more rapid than that associated with the use of (6.4.13) unless the solution displays unfavorable characteristics to the left of the point x_0.† Since truncation with a mean odd difference would not correspond to true collocation, it is desirable to use a symmetrical array of abscissas.

In the case of the preceding example, we may start with the array

x	y	y'	δ	δ^2	δ^3	δ^4
-0.2	1.20000	-1.16000				
			7000			
-0.1	1.10000	-1.09000		2000		
			9000		0	
0.0	1.00000	-1.00000	(10000)	2000	(0)	0
			11000		0	
0.1	0.90000	-0.89000		2000		
			13000			
0.2	0.80000	-0.76000				

when four additional ordinates are used. The mean odd central differences are entered in parentheses. After four iterations, using (6.4.14), we obtain the array

x	y	y'				
-0.2	1.21860	-1.17860				
			8377			
-0.1	1.10483	-1.09483		1106		
			9483		-105	
0.0	1.00000	-1.00000		1001		9
			10484		-96	
0.1	0.90516	-0.89516		905		
			11389			
0.2	0.82127	-0.78127				

which is unchanged, to the five places retained, by further iteration. Thus five-place values of y_{-2}, y_{-1}, y_0, y_1, and y_2 are now available for the advancing calculation. Here the fact that the effect of the fourth differences is negligible supplies fair evidence that sufficiently many ordinates were used.

It is important to notice that the formulas of (6.4.13) or (6.4.14) can also be expressed explicitly in terms of the slopes y'_k, if the use of differences is undesirable, once the number of slopes to be retained has been decided (the corresponding five-slope formulas are given in Milne [155]).

Another class of self-starting methods, which are also useful when $F(x,y)$ is not defined analytically, but which are noniterative, is treated in §§6.15 and 6.16.

6.5. Methods Based on Open-type Formulas. Once at least N additional ordinates, say y_1, y_2, $\cdots$, y_N, are determined, the calculation may be continued by use of one of the formulas, derived in §6.2 or 6.3,

† The calculation of ordinates on both sides of the starting point is also frequently convenient when use is made of power series.

which involves Nth differences. In the case of the example (6.4.5), with the calculated data (6.4.9), the preliminary tabulation may be arranged as in Table 6.1 where, for compactness, the backward difference $\nabla^k y'_n$ is written in the same line as the entry y'_n.

TABLE 6.1

x	y	y'	$\nabla y'$	$\nabla^2 y'$	$\nabla^3 y'$	$\nabla^4 y'$
0.0	1.00000	−1.00000				
0.1	0.90516	−0.89516	10484			
0.2	0.82127	−0.78127	11389	905		
0.3	0.74918	−0.65918	12209	820	−85	

In particular, the *Adams method* uses formula (6.2.10), truncated to a suitable number of terms, for advancing the calculation. (The simplest such procedure, in which *no* differences are retained, is often known as *Euler's method*.) Thus, if third differences are retained, the Adams method next yields

$$y_4 \approx 0.74918 + \tfrac{1}{10}[-0.65918 + \tfrac{1}{2}(0.12209) + \tfrac{5}{12}(0.00820) - \tfrac{3}{8}(0.00085)]$$
$$\doteq 0.68968,$$

after which an additional line

$$0.4 \quad | \quad 0.68968 \quad | \quad -0.52968 \quad | \quad 12950 \quad 741 \quad -79 \quad 6 \qquad (6.5.1)$$

is entered for the purpose of advancing to y_5. If again only third differences are retained, the next line appears as follows:

$$0.5 \quad | \quad 0.64347 \quad | \quad -0.39347 \quad | \quad 13621 \quad 671 \quad -70 \quad 9 \qquad (6.5.2)$$

The fourth difference is carried along as a partial-check column. Since the truncation error in each step is of the form

$$\tfrac{251}{720}h^5 y^\mathrm{v}(\xi),$$

for some ξ, and since $h^4 y^\mathrm{v}(\xi)$ is given by $\nabla^4 y'(\eta)$, for some η, the two available sample values of $\nabla^4 y'$ indicate that $h^4 y^\mathrm{v}$ probably does not vary strongly over the relevant range, so that a fairly dependable estimate of the truncation error committed in each of the steps can be obtained by calculating the contribution $\tfrac{251}{720}h \nabla^4 y'_n$ of the first neglected difference. With $h = 0.1$, this contribution will amount to less than one-half unit in the fifth place if $\nabla^4 y'_n$ does not exceed 14 units in that place.

If use is made instead of formula (6.2.18), in which only *second* differences are retained, the same results are obtained. Here the error estimate again depends upon the fourth difference, the factor $\tfrac{14}{45} \doteq 0.31$ replacing the factor $\tfrac{251}{720} \doteq 0.35$ relevant to the Adams formula with ird differences. Thus, as compared with the Adams method, this method here possesses the advantage that one less difference is needed in the calculation (but not in the error check) and that the coefficients in the formula are somewhat simpler.

It should be emphasized that the errors so far considered are those which would arise in a single step from x_n to x_{n+1} if $y_0, y_1, \ldots, y_n$ were exactly correct and if no round-off errors were introduced in that step. In addition, however, one must consider the cumulative effect of the errors introduced in *preceding* steps. Whereas consideration of the *propagation* of errors is postponed to §§6.7 and 6.8, it may be remarked here that the advantage in stability generally lies with the Adams method. This situation is related to the fact that the ordinates themselves are "loosely coupled" by (6.2.18), in that the ordinate y_k is linked directly only with ordinates of the form y_{k-4i}, where i is an integer, whereas in (6.2.10) all ordinates are directly linked together.

6.6. Methods Based on Closed-type Formulas. The usual method of employing one of the formulas of §6.3 to calculate y_{n+1} consists in first *estimating* y_{n+1}, calculating $y'_{n+1} = F(x_{n+1}, y_{n+1})$ and forming the requisite differences $\nabla^k y'_{n+1}$ corresponding to this estimate, and then calculating an improved estimate of y_{n+1} by use of the formula. The cycle is repeated, if necessary, until two successive estimates agree within the prescribed tolerance. The *initial* estimate, say $y_{n+1}^{(0)}$, may be obtained by use of a formula of *open* type.

Thus, returning to the example considered in the preceding section, line (6.5.1) can be considered as the result of using the Adams method, with third differences, as a "predictor." If now the data in this line are used in (6.3.2), truncated also with third differences, the first *revised* ordinate $y_4^{(1)}$ is given by

$$y_4^{(1)} = 0.74918 + \tfrac{1}{10}[-0.52968 - \tfrac{1}{2}(0.12950) - \tfrac{1}{12}(0.00741) + \tfrac{1}{24}(0.00079)] \doteq 0.68968,$$

which agrees with the initial prediction to the five places retained, so that iteration is not needed.

Suppose, however, that in the more general case the result obtained after sufficiently many iterations of (6.3.2) is denoted by y_{n+1} and that the initial prediction, afforded by (6.2.10), is again denoted by $y_{n+1}^{(0)}$. If only third differences are retained, the *calculated* values of $y_{n+1}^{(0)}$ and y_{n+1} then satisfy the equations

$$
\begin{aligned}
y_{n+1}^{(0)} &= y_n + \frac{h}{24}\,(55y'_n - 59y'_{n-1} + 37y'_{n-2} - 9y'_{n-3}), \\
y_{n+1} &= y_n + \frac{h}{24}\,(9y'_{n+1} + 19y'_n - 5y'_{n-1} + y'_{n-2}),
\end{aligned}
\qquad (6.6.1)
$$

where $y'_k = F(x_k, y_k)$, if the errors due to round-off are neglected. If th
calculated values of $y_1, y_2, \ldots, y_n$ and, accordingly, of $y'_1, y'_2, \ldots,$
were exactly correct, then the *true* ordinate at x_{n+1}, say Y_{n+1}, wou
satisfy the equations

$$Y_{n+1} = y_n + \frac{h}{24}(55y'_n - 59y'_{n-1} + 37y'_{n-2} - 9y'_{n-3}) + \tfrac{251}{720}h^5 y^v(\xi_1),$$

$$Y_{n+1} = y_n + \frac{h}{24}(9Y'_{n+1} + 19y'_n - 5y'_{n-1} + y'_{n-2}) - \tfrac{19}{720}h^5 y^v(\xi_2),$$

(6.6.?

where ξ_1 and ξ_2 both lie between x_{n-3} and x_{n+1}, and it would follow tha

$$Y_{n+1} - y_{n+1}^{(0)} = \tfrac{251}{720}h^5 y^v(\xi_1),$$

$$Y_{n+1} - y_{n+1} = \frac{3h}{8}(Y'_{n+1} - y'_{n+1}) - \tfrac{19}{720}h^5 y^v(\xi_2).$$

(6.6.3

In addition, we have the relation

$$Y'_{n+1} - y'_{n+1} = F(x_{n+1}, Y_{n+1}) - F(x_{n+1}, y_{n+1}) = (Y_{n+1} - y_{n+1})F_y(x_{n+1}, \eta_{n+1})$$

where η_{n+1} is between y_{n+1} and Y_{n+1}. If now it is assumed that h i
sufficiently small to ensure that

$$\frac{3h}{8}|F_y(x_{n+1}, \eta_{n+1})| \ll 1,$$

(6.6.4

and also that $y^v(x)$ does not vary strongly for $x_{n-3} < x < x_{n+1}$, so tha
$y^v(\xi_1)$ and $y^v(\xi_2)$ can be equated, to a first approximation, Eqs. (6.6.3
lead to the useful approximate relation

$$Y_{n+1} - y_{n+1} \approx \frac{-19}{251 + 19}(y_{n+1} - y_{n+1}^{(0)})$$

or
$$Y_{n+1} - y_{n+1} \approx -\tfrac{19}{270}\gamma_{n+1},$$
(6.6.5

where
$$\gamma_{n+1} = y_{n+1} - y_{n+1}^{(0)}.$$
(6.6.6

Thus, if a column of the differences $\gamma_k \equiv y_k - y_k^{(0)}$ is carried along
in the calculation, the error in the final iterate y_{n+1} which is due to truncation error in the step from x_n to x_{n+1} can be estimated as $-19\gamma_{n+1}/270$
$\approx -\gamma_{n+1}/14$. The reliability of this estimate depends upon the magnitude of hF_y and of hy^{vi} in the relevant range (see also Prob. 24). A
will be seen in §6.9, the condition (6.6.4) is necessary in order to ensure
rapid convergence of the iteration leading from $y_{n+1}^{(0)}$ to y_{n+1}. Also, if the
first neglected difference $\nabla^4 y'_{k+1}$ does not vary rapidly with k, it can be
expected that the same is true of y^v, so that hy^{vi} is probably small relative
to y^v. Accordingly, if the first neglected difference does not vary exces-

vely, if the rate of convergence of the iteration is satisfactory, and if
ɛ never exceeds seven units in the last place retained, then the effect of
ɪe truncation error *in each step* probably does not exceed one-half unit
ι that place.

More generally, if (6.2.10) is used as a predictor for (6.3.2), the factor
= $\frac{270}{19} \approx 14$ corresponding to retention of *third* differences is easily
ɛen to be replaced by 2 for no differences, 6 for first differences, 10 for
ɛcond differences, $\frac{270}{19} \approx 14$ for third differences, and $\frac{502}{27} \approx 18$ when
ɔurth differences are retained. That is, if the difference between the
ɪitial prediction and the final corrected value does not exceed half the
ɑlue listed, in units of the last place retained, then the truncation error
ι *each step* probably does not exceed one-half unit in that place.

We will refer to the method just described as the *modified Adams
ɑethod* (it is also known as *Moulton's method*). The procedure based on
ɛtaining only the *first* difference in (6.3.2) is often called the *modified
ℓuler method*.

Milne's methods differ from the methods just described in that they
ɪse (6.3.7) for iteration and (6.2.18) for prediction, retaining second
ℓifferences, or (6.3.8) for iteration and (6.2.19) for prediction, when
ɔurth differences are retained. The truncation error in the nth step
ɛan be estimated as $-(y_{n+1} - y_{n+1}^{(0)})/29$ in the former case, and as
$-32(y_{n+1} - y_{n+1}^{(0)})/1139 \approx -(y_{n+1} - y_{n+1}^{(0)})/35$ in the latter case. These
ɱethods possess the advantage that the truncation errors in each step
ɑre proportional to h^5 and h^7, respectively, whereas retention of only
ɛecond or only fourth differences in the preceding method corresponds
ɔo truncation errors proportional to h^4 and h^6, respectively. On the other
ɦand, as will be indicated in §6.7, they compare unfavorably with the
ρreceding method with regard to stability.

It is obvious that each of the formulas considered could be expressed
explicitly in terms of the values of the derivative y', in place of differences
of those values, once a decision was made as to the number of differences
which were to be effectively retained. Thus, in particular, the Milne
second-difference procedure can be based on Eqs. (6.2.18) and (6.3.7) or,
equivalently, on the equations

$$y_{n+1} = y_{n-3} + \frac{4h}{3}(2y'_n - y'_{n-1} + 2y'_{n-2}) + \frac{14h^5}{45} y^v(\xi) \qquad (6.6.7)$$

and
$$y_{n+1} = y_{n-1} + \frac{h}{3}(y'_{n+1} + 4y'_n + y'_{n-1}) - \frac{h^5}{90} y^v(\xi), \qquad (6.6.8)$$

where, of course, the values of ξ in the two equations are generally
unequal. The second equation is seen to be equivalent to *Simpson's
rule*. Similarly, the Milne fourth-difference procedure can be specified

by the equations

$$y_{n+1} = y_{n-5} + \frac{3h}{10}\,(11y_n' - 14y_{n-1}' + 26y_{n-2}' - 14y_{n-3}' + 11y_{n-4}')$$

$$+ \frac{41h^7}{140}\,y^{\mathrm{vii}}(\xi) \quad (6.6.9)$$

and

$$y_{n+1} = y_{n-3} + \frac{2h}{45}\,(7y_{n+1}' + 32y_n' + 12y_{n-1}' + 32y_{n-2}' + 7y_{n-3}')$$

$$- \frac{8h^7}{945}\,y^{\mathrm{vii}}(\xi), \quad (6.6.10)$$

which are to be used for prediction and for iteration, respectively.

6.7. The Special Case $F = Ay$. Each of the formulas treated in the preceding sections is expressible in the form

$$y_{n+1} = y_{n-p} + h(\alpha_{-1}y_{n+1}' + \alpha_0 y_n' + \alpha_1 y_{n-1}' + \cdots + \alpha_r y_{n-r}'), \quad (6.7.1)$$

where $\alpha_{-1} = 0$ for the formulas of open type, and where

$$y_k' = F(x_k, y_k). \quad (6.7.2)$$

Formula (6.7.1) corresponds to the retention of $r + 1$ differences in a closed formula or of r differences in an open formula. Thus, in particular, it reduces to an identity if $y(x)$ is a polynomial of degree $r + 2$ or less when $\alpha_{-1} \neq 0$, and of degree $r + 1$ or less when $\alpha_{-1} = 0$.

In the case when the differential equation is of the very special form

$$\frac{dy}{dx} = Ay, \quad (6.7.3)$$

so that $F(x,y) = Ay$, where A is a constant, the relation (6.7.1) takes the form

$$(1 - \alpha_{-1}Ah)y_{n+1} = y_{n-p} + Ah(\alpha_0 y_n + \alpha_1 y_{n-1} + \cdots + \alpha_r y_{n-r}),$$

$$(6.7.4)$$

and is subject to a simple analysis, the results of which are helpful in understanding the propagation of errors in the more general case. It may be noticed that the exact solution of (6.7.3), subject to the condition $y(x_0) = y_0$, is

$$y(x) = y_0 e^{A(x-x_0)}. \quad (6.7.5)$$

In order to fix ideas, we suppose that $r \geqq p$ and so include all the commonly used formulas, such as formulas (6.2.10) and (6.3.2), for which $p = 0$, and the formulas (6.2.17) to (6.2.19) and (6.3.7) and (6.3.8), for which $r = p$. As will be seen, this restriction is easily removed.

The relation (6.7.4) then affords a linear relation among the $r + 2$

ordinates y_{n+1}, y_n, y_{n-1}, . . . , and y_{n-r} (one of which is identical with y_{n-p}) and is known as a *difference equation* of order $r + 1$, under the assumption that $\alpha_{-1} A h \neq 1$ and $\alpha_r \neq 0$. It holds only for $n \geqq r$, the ordinate y_0 being prescribed, and the remaining r initial ordinates y_1, y_2, . . . , y_r supposedly being supplied by an independent calculation.

We may notice that $y_n = \beta^n$ will satisfy (6.7.4), with β constant, if β is determined such that

$$(1 - \alpha_{-1} A h)\beta^{n+1} = \beta^{n-p} + A h(\alpha_0 \beta^n + \alpha_1 \beta^{n-1} + \cdots + \alpha_r \beta^{n-r}),$$

or, after removing the common factor β^{n-r}, such that β satisfies the *characteristic equation*

$$(1 - \alpha_{-1} A h)\beta^{r+1} - A h(\alpha_0 \beta^r + \alpha_1 \beta^{r-1} + \cdots + \alpha_r) - \beta^{r-p} = 0. \tag{6.7.6}$$

Since p and r are nonnegative integers, such that $r - p \geqq 0$, this relation is an algebraic equation of degree $r + 1$ in β and hence possesses $r + 1$ roots β_0, β_1, . . . , β_r, which may be real or complex.

If no roots are repeated, then, from the linearity and homogeneity of the difference equation (6.7.4), it follows that

$$y_n = c_0 \beta_0^n + c_1 \beta_1^n + \cdots + c_r \beta_r^n \tag{6.7.7}$$

satisfies (6.7.4) for arbitrary values of the $r + 1$ independent constants c_0, c_1, . . . , c_r, which are available for satisfying the $r + 1$ initial conditions which prescribe y_0, y_1, . . . , y_r. It can be shown that (6.7.7) then represents the *most general* solution of (6.7.4), when n is restricted to integral values.

If $\beta_1 = \beta_2$, the terms $c_1 \beta_1^n + c_2 \beta_2^n$ are to be replaced by $\beta_1^n(c_1 + c_2 n)$, as is easily verified. Furthermore, if β_1 and β_2 are conjugate complex, so that

$$\beta_1 = \rho e^{i\phi}, \qquad \beta_2 = \rho e^{-i\phi}$$

where $\rho = |\beta_1| = |\beta_2|$, we may replace c_1 and c_2 by $\frac{1}{2}(c_1 + c_2)$ and $\frac{1}{2}i(c_1 - c_2)$, and rewrite the corresponding two terms in (6.7.7) in the more convenient form

$$\rho^n(c_1 \cos n\phi + c_2 \sin n\phi).$$

It remains to investigate the roots of the characteristic equation (6.7.6). We may notice first that, when $h = 0$, the equation reduces to

$$\beta^{r-p}(\beta^{p+1} - 1) = 0,$$

so that $\beta = 0$ is then a root of multiplicity $r - p$, and the remaining $p + 1$

roots are the $(p+1)$th roots of unity. In the complex β plane (Fig. 6.1) $r-p$ roots coincide at the origin, whereas the remaining $p+1$ roots are equally spaced about the unit circle $|\beta|=1$, with one root at the point $\beta = 1$. When h is small, the $r+1$ roots will generally be distinct, with

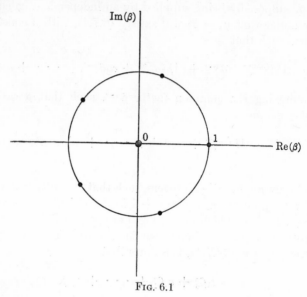

FIG. 6.1

$r-p$ roots *near* the origin, and $p+1$ roots in the *neighborhood* of the unit circle.

In particular, if we denote by β_0 that root which tends to unity as h tends to zero, we may write

$$\beta_0 = 1 + m_1 h + m_2 h^2 + \cdots, \tag{6.7.8}$$

where the coefficients $m_1, m_2, \ldots$ are to be determined in such a way that the result of replacing β by β_0 in (6.7.6), and expanding the result in powers of h, reduces identically to zero. A simple calculation then shows that the result of that substitution is of the form

$$h[(p+1)m_1 - A(\alpha_{-1} + \alpha_0 + \alpha_1 + \cdots + \alpha_r)]$$
$$+ h^2[\cdot\ \cdot\ ] + \cdots = 0,$$

and hence, in particular, that we must have

$$m_1 = \frac{A}{p+1} (\alpha_{-1} + \alpha_0 + \alpha_1 + \cdots + \alpha_r). \tag{6.7.9}$$

But, since the integration formula which led to (6.7.1) certainly gives exact results when applied to the integration of a constant, that is, for

$y'(x) \equiv 1$, we deduce from (6.7.1) the relation

$$\alpha_{-1} + \alpha_0 + \alpha_1 + \cdots + \alpha_r = p + 1, \qquad (6.7.10)$$

and so find that $m_1 = A$. Thus, one root of (6.7.6) can be expressed in the form

$$\beta_0 = 1 + Ah + 0(h^2), \qquad (6.7.11)$$

where the symbol $0(h^2)$ represents a term which is small, of the order h^2, when h is small.

The corresponding part of the solution (6.7.7) is thus of the form

$$c_0(1 + Ah + \cdots)^n = c_0(1 + Ah + \cdots)^{(x_n - x_0)/h},$$

and is approximated by $c_0 e^{A(x_n - x_0)}$ when h is small. Thus we see that this part of the general solution of the *difference* equation tends toward the general solution of the approximated *differential* equation as $h \to 0$ and, indeed, tends toward the *required* solution, for which $y(x_0) = y_0$, if $c_0 \to y_0$ as $h \to 0$.

The remaining r terms in (6.7.7) represent so-called *parasitic solutions* which correspond to the fact that the order of the difference equation exceeds the order of the approximated differential equation by r. For small values of h, we have seen that $r - p$ of the roots β_i will be small in magnitude, relative to unity, and hence that the corresponding terms β_i^n will tend rapidly to zero as the calculation proceeds and n increases.

However, if $p > 0$, there are p roots in addition to β_0 which are of unit absolute value when $h = 0$. If, for $h > 0$, any one of these roots, say β_k, has a magnitude *greater* than unity, then (unless the coefficient c_k happens to vanish) the corresponding term $c_k \beta_k^n$ will increase unboundedly in magnitude as n increases.

In illustration, if use is made of the simplest formula of open type (Euler's formula),

$$y_{n+1} = y_n + hy'_n = (1 + Ah)y_n, \qquad (6.7.12)$$

with $p = r = 0$, the only root is $\beta_0 = 1 + Ah$, and hence the solution is

$$y_n = y_0(1 + Ah)^n = y_0(1 + Ah)^{(x_n - x_0)/h}, \qquad (6.7.13)$$

which does indeed approximate (6.7.5) when h is small.

For the open formula with $p = 0$ and $r = 1$,

$$y_{n+1} = y_n + h(y'_n + \tfrac{1}{2}\nabla y'_n) = y_n + \frac{h}{2}(3y'_n - y'_{n-1})$$
$$= (1 + \tfrac{3}{2}Ah)y_n - \tfrac{1}{2}Ahy_{n-1}, \qquad (6.7.14)$$

the characteristic equation (6.7.6) becomes

$$\beta^2 - (1 + \tfrac{3}{2}Ah)\beta + \tfrac{1}{2}Ah = 0,$$

and yields

$$\beta_0 = \tfrac{1}{2} + \tfrac{3}{4}Ah + \tfrac{1}{2}\sqrt{1 + Ah + \tfrac{9}{4}A^2h^2} = 1 + Ah + \tfrac{1}{2}A^2h^2 + \cdots$$

and

$$\beta_1 = \tfrac{1}{2} + \tfrac{3}{4}Ah - \tfrac{1}{2}\sqrt{1 + Ah + \tfrac{9}{4}A^2h^2} = \tfrac{1}{2}Ah(1 - Ah + \cdots).$$

Thus, for small h, the solution is of the form

$$y_n = c_0(1 + Ah + \cdots)^{(x_n - x_0)/h} + c_1(\tfrac{1}{2}Ah + \cdots)^{(x_n - x_0)/h}. \quad (6.7.15)$$

If c_0 and c_1 are determined such that $y_n = c_0\beta_0^n + c_1\beta_1^n$ reduces to y_0 and y_1 for $n = 0$ and 1, respectively, there follows

$$c_0 = \frac{y_1 - \beta_1 y_0}{\beta_0 - \beta_1}, \qquad c_1 = \frac{\beta_0 y_0 - y_1}{\beta_0 - \beta_1}. \quad (6.7.16)$$

The ordinate y_1 is assumed to be supplied by another method. If we assume that y_1 differs from the true value $y_0 e^{Ah} = y_0[1 + Ah + \cdots]$, at worst, by an amount of order h, it is easily seen that c_0 differs from y_0 and c_1 from zero by an amount at worst of order h. Hence here the parasitic solution is small when h is small, and also it tends to zero as $n \to \infty$ for any fixed value of h which is sufficiently small to make $|\beta_1| < 1$.†

As an example in which $p > 0$, we may notice that if the Simpson's rule formula (6.6.8) is used, in the form

$$y_{n+1} = y_{n-1} + \frac{Ah}{3}(y_{n+1} + 4y_n + y_{n-1}), \quad (6.7.17)$$

Eq. (6.7.6) becomes

$$\left(1 - \frac{Ah}{3}\right)\beta^2 - \frac{4Ah}{3}\beta - \left(1 + \frac{Ah}{3}\right) = 0,$$

with roots expressible in the forms

$$\beta_0 = 1 + Ah + \cdots, \qquad \beta_1 = -1 + \tfrac{1}{3}Ah + \cdots,$$

when h is small. Thus the solution of (6.7.17) is expressible in the form

$$y_n = c_0(1 + Ah + \cdots)^{(x_n - x_0)/h} + (-1)^n c_1(1 - \tfrac{1}{3}Ah + \cdots)^{(x_n - x_0)/h}$$
$$\approx c_0 e^{A(x_n - x_0)} + (-1)^n c_1 e^{-\frac{1}{3}A(x_n - x_0)}, \quad (6.7.18)$$

when h is small.

When A is *positive*, so that the *exact* solution grows exponentially with x, the root β_1 lies inside the circle $|\beta| = 1$, and the parasitic solution accordingly damps out exponentially in magnitude, as the calculation proceeds with increasing n. However, when A is *negative*, so that the

† If $A \geqq 0$, the requirement $|\beta_1| < 1$ is satisfied for all h. However, if $A < 0$, the spacing h must be such that $h < 1/|A|$.

exact solution tends exponentially to zero as x increases, the parasitic solution *increases* exponentially in magnitude and, in addition, alternates in sign from step to step in an advancing calculation.   To a first approximation, c_1 is found to be half the difference between the value of y_1 used in the calculation and the true value $y_0 e^{Ah}$.   However, the value which should be assigned to y_1 in order that c_1 vanish exactly is *not* the true value, but a value which *tends* to the true value as $h \to 0$.   That is, the parasitic solution would be present even though y_0 and y_1 were *exactly* correct.

It is important to notice also that each round-off committed at *any* stage of the advancing calculation will initiate a *new* parasitic solution, of the same type.

In the somewhat more general case when the differential equation is of the form $y' = Ay + Bx + C$, where A, B, and C are constants, a linear function of x is accordingly added to the exponential term present in the true solution when $B = C = 0$.   It is found that the same modification occurs in the solution of the approximating difference equation, so that a linear function of n is merely added to the right-hand member of (6.7.7).   Thus the same parasitic solutions are present, and the preceding discussion again applies, except for the fact that here the true solution will not decrease in magnitude as x increases and when A is negative, but will grow linearly, while the parasitic solutions may grow exponentially.

Finally, in the general case, when we are concerned with an equation of the form $y' = F(x,y)$, we may imagine that $F(x,y)$ is replaced by the linear approximation

$$F(x,y) \approx F(x_n,y_n) + (x - x_n)F_x(x_n,y_n) + (y - y_n)F_y(x_n,y_n)$$

in the neighborhood of a point (x_n,y_n), and so imagine that the differential equation is replaced by the linear equation $y' = A_n y + B_n x + C_n$, where

$$A_n = F_y(x_n,y_n), \qquad B_n = F_x(x_n,y_n),$$
$$C_n = F(x_n,y_n) - x_n F_x(x_n,y_n) - y_n F_y(x_n,y_n).$$

It is then plausible (but not *always* true) that the nature of the error propagated in the numerical solution of the true equation will be simulated by that for the linearized equation, over a short range near x_n. The situations in which no one of the parasitic solutions tends to increase in magnitude as the calculation proceeds from that point are often said to be characterized by *short-range stability*.

In order to illustrate the occurrence of instability, we present in Table 6.2 the results of calculations based on the problem

$$y' + 2y = 2, \qquad y(0) = 2.$$

TABLE 6.2

x	y_M	γ_M	y_A	γ_A	y_T
0.0	2.000	—	2.000	—	2.000
0.5	1.368	—	1.368	—	1.368
1.0	1.132	—	1.135	—	1.135
1.5	1.052	—	1.046	—	1.050
2.0	1.014	−42	1.016	−64	1.018
2.5	1.012	−36	1.005	−17	1.007
3.0	0.995	15	1.002	−10	1.002
3.5	1.011	−33	1.001	−2	1.001
4.0	0.986	40	1.000	−2	1.000
4.5	1.020	−57	1.000	−1	1.000

The entries in the column headed y_M are values determined by the Milne method, using (6.6.7) for prediction and (6.6.8) (Simpson's rule) for actual calculation. The entries γ_M represent the differences between the final results and the initial predictions, and $-\gamma_M/29$ affords the Milne estimate of the truncation error in each step. The entries in the column headed y_A were obtained by the modified Adams method, using (6.2.10) with third differences as a predictor and (6.3.2) with third differences for actual calculation. The estimated truncation error in each step is afforded by $-\gamma_A/14$. The entries in the y_T column are values of the true solution $y(x) = e^{-2x} + 1$, rounded to three decimal places. As has been noted, both numerical procedures introduce truncation errors of order h^5 in each step.

A large spacing is chosen deliberately, and all calculations are rounded to three decimal places, in order to cause the effects of the error propagation to become evident at a relatively early stage of the process. The requisite starting values (above the broken lines) are correct to the places retained.

The tabulation is intended, not only to show the increasing oscillation of the first solution about the true solution, but also to serve as a reminder that the quantity $-\gamma_M/29$ affords only an estimate of the *truncation* error introduced *in each step* but does not, in itself, indicate the manner in which the effects of that error are propagated. Thus, for example, the fact that $-\gamma_M/29$ is smaller than 2 in each step must not be interpreted as indicating that the *accumulated* error at each step is less than 2 units in the last place. In fact, that error is seen to amount to -20 units in $y_M(4.5)$, in the present case.

6.8. Propagated-error Bounds. In actual calculation, the calculated value of y_{n+1} generally will not be given exactly by the right-hand member of the relevant formula (6.7.1), because of the necessity of effecting round-offs. If we replace y_{n+1} by $y_{n+1} + R_n$, where R_n is inserted to count for the effects of round-off in the nth step, Eqs. (6.7.1) and (6.7.2) an be combined in the form

$$y_{n+1} = y_{n-p} + h \sum_{k=-1}^{r} \alpha_k F(x_{n-k}, y_{n-k}) - R_n. \qquad (6.8.1)$$

n the other hand, if we denote the *true* value of the solution of the given roblem when $x = x_k$ by Y_k, we have also the relation

$$Y_{n+1} = Y_{n-p} + h \sum_{k=-1}^{r} \alpha_k F(x_{n-k}, Y_{n-k}) + T_n, \qquad (6.8.2)$$

here we here denote the *truncation* error corresponding to the nth step y T_n.

If we subtract (6.8.1) from (6.8.2) and write

$$\epsilon_n = Y_n - y_n, \qquad E_n = T_n + R_n, \qquad (6.8.3)$$

e find that the error ϵ_n associated with the calculated value y_n satisfies ne difference equation

$$\epsilon_{n+1} = \epsilon_{n-p} + h \sum_{k=-1}^{r} \alpha_k[F(x_{n-k}, Y_{n-k}) - F(x_{n-k}, y_{n-k})] + E_n. \quad (6.8.4)$$

n order to obtain a bound on the magnitude of ϵ_n, we notice first that we aay write

$$F(x_i, Y_i) - F(x_i, y_i) = (Y_i - y_i)F_y(x_i, \eta_i)$$
$$= \epsilon_i F_y(x_i, \eta_i), \qquad (6.8.5)$$

$F_y \equiv \partial F/\partial y$ is continuous, where η_i is between y_i and Y_i, so that (6.8.4) an be written in the form

$$1 - h\alpha_{-1}F_y(x_{n+1}, \eta_{n+1})]\epsilon_{n+1} = \epsilon_{n-p} + h \sum_{k=0}^{r} \alpha_k \epsilon_{n-k} F_y(x_{n-k}, \eta_{n-k}) + E_n.$$

$$(6.8.6)$$

uppose now that, for the range of values of x and y involved in the ver-all calculation, we have

$$|F_y(x, y)| \leq K, \qquad (6.8.7)$$

vhere K is a known constant, and consider the related difference equation

$$(1 - Kh|\alpha_{-1}|)e_{n+1} = e_{n-p} + Kh \sum_{k=0}^{r} |\alpha_k|e_{n-k} + E, \qquad (6.8.8)$$

vhere E is such that

$$|E_n| \leq E \qquad (n = r, r+1, \ldots). \qquad (6.8.9)$$

If $\alpha_{-1} \neq 0$, so that the formula is of closed type, suppose also that h is sufficiently small to ensure that

$$Kh|\alpha_{-1}| < 1. \tag{6.8.10}$$

From (6.8.6) and (6.8.7), we have

$$|1 - h\alpha_{-1}F_y(x_{n+1}, \eta_{n+1})| \, |\epsilon_{n+1}| \leqq |\epsilon_{n-p}| + hK \sum_{k=0}^{r} |\alpha_k| \, |\epsilon_{n-k}| + |E_n|,$$

and hence, if $|\epsilon_n| \leqq e_n$, $|\epsilon_{n-1}| \leqq e_{n-1}$, $\cdots$, $|\epsilon_{n-r}| \leqq e_{n-r}$, there follows also

$$|1 - h\alpha_{-1}F_y(x_{n+1}, \eta_{n+1})| \, |\epsilon_{n+1}| \leqq (1 - Kh|\alpha_{-1}|)e_{n+1},$$

and thus $|\epsilon_{n+1}| \leqq e_{n+1}$. That is, if $|\epsilon_i| \leqq e_i$ for $r + 1$ successive integral values of i, then, by induction, the same is true for all succeeding integral values of i.

Now the error ϵ_0 vanishes except for round-off since $y_0 = Y_0$ is prescribed. Also, again assuming that $r \geqq p$, the errors $\epsilon_1, \ldots, \epsilon_r$ are errors associated with the starting values $y_1, \ldots, y_r$, supplied by an independent analysis. Let $\bar{e}$ be a positive number which is not exceeded in magnitude by any of these initial errors. Then, if e_n is a solution of (6.8.8) which is not smaller than $\bar{e}$ for $n = 0, 1, \ldots, r$, it follows that

$$|\epsilon_n| \leqq e_n$$

for all relevant values of n. That is, any such solution of (6.8.8) will "dominate" the solution of (6.8.4).

Since the nonhomogeneous term E in (6.8.8) is a constant, a *particular* solution of (6.8.8) may be assumed in the form $e_n = -\lambda$, where λ is a constant, and the introduction of this assumption leads to the determination

$$\lambda = \frac{E}{Kh\sigma}, \tag{6.8.11}$$

with the additional abbreviation

$$\sigma \equiv \sum_{k=-1}^{r} |\alpha_k|. \tag{6.8.12}$$

It may be noticed that $\sigma = p + 1$ when all the α's are positive, and that $\sigma \geqq p + 1$ in any case, in virtue of (6.7.10).

To this particular solution may be added any multiple of β^n, where β is determined such that β^n satisfies the homogeneous difference equation obtained by replacing E by zero in (6.8.8), and where β accordingly must satisfy the characteristic equation

$$(1 - Kh|\alpha_{-1}|)\beta^{r+1} - Kh(|\alpha_0|\beta^r + |\alpha_1|\beta^{r-1} + \cdots + |\alpha_{r-1}|\beta + |\alpha_r|)$$
$$- \beta^{r-p} = 0. \tag{6.8.13}$$

ince the left-hand member is negative when $\beta = 1$ and tends to $+\infty$ as $\rightarrow +\infty$, there is a positive real root β_0 which is larger than unity. ndeed, for small values of h, it is found to be expressible in the form

$$\beta_0 = 1 + \frac{Kh\sigma}{p + 1} + 0(h^2). \tag{6.8.14}$$

With this value of β, and the value of λ defined by (6.8.11), it follows hat $e_n = c\beta_0^n - \lambda$ satisfies (6.8.8) for any constant value of c. In addi-ion, since it increases steadily with n, if we determine c in such a way that $_0 = \bar{e}$, so that

$$e_n = \bar{e}\beta_0^n + \lambda(\beta_0^n - 1), \tag{6.8.15}$$

hen we will have $e_n \geqq \bar{e}$ for all $n \geqq 0$. Thus this particular solution of 6.8.8) will dominate the solution of (6.8.4).

Hence, in summary, we deduce that *the error ϵ_n associated with the value f y_n determined by step-by-step calculation based on the formula*

$$y_{n+1} \approx y_{n-p} + h \sum_{k=-1}^{r} \alpha_k F(x_{n-k}, y_{n-k}) \qquad (n \geqq r) \tag{6.8.16}$$

s limited by the inequality

$$|\epsilon_n| \leqq \bar{e}\beta_0^n + \lambda(\beta_0^n - 1), \tag{6.8.17}$$

vhere $\bar{e}$ is the absolute value of the largest error associated with the $r + 1$ tarting values $y_0, y_1, \ldots, y_r$; λ is defined by the equations

$$\lambda = \frac{E}{Kh\sigma}, \qquad \sigma = \sum_{k=-1}^{r} |\alpha_k|; \tag{6.8.18}$$

K *is the maximum value of $|\partial F/\partial y|$ for the range of values of x and y involved n the calculation; E is the absolute value of the maximum total error intro-luced in each step; and β_0 is the positive real root, of the equation*

$$\beta^{n+1} = \beta^{n-p} + Kh \sum_{k=-1}^{r} |\alpha_k|\beta^{n-k}, \tag{6.8.19}$$

vhich exceeds unity.†

In those cases when the coefficients α_k are all *positive*, reference to (6.7.10) shows that (6.8.11) reduces to $\lambda = E/[Kh(p + 1)]$ and that the xpansion (6.8.14) becomes $\beta_0 = 1 + Kh + 0(h^2)$. Also, the character-stic equation (6.8.13) is then equivalent to Eq. (6.7.6), with A replaced by K, and $\beta_0^n \approx \exp[K(x_n - x_0)]$.

† If $\partial F/\partial y$ is known to be negative throughout the calculation, a less conservative bound often can be obtained in a correspondingly simple form. For example, see Probs. 19 and 20.

Of the three constants $\bar{e}$, E, and K, needed for the application of thi error estimate, the first may be estimated initially, and it represents th maximum round-off error associated with the initial values determined before the stepwise calculation is begun, if those values are correctly determined to the number of places retained.

The constant E comprises the maximum error introduced in one step because of round-off and truncation. The latter effect cannot be estimated in advance unless $F(x,y)$ is of a particularly convenient form, but it can be estimated in the course of the calculation by approximating the factor $h^m y^{(m)}(\xi)$ by $h \, \Delta^{m-1} y'$ in the truncation-error term, or by making use of the quantity γ_n defined in §6.6 if one of the methods described in that section is employed.

The constant K can be calculated in advance if the equation is linear since then $\partial F/\partial y$ is independent of y, and it can be estimated in advance (assuming that an analytical expression for $\partial F/\partial y$, in terms of x and y can be obtained) if the range of values of y can be estimated initially Otherwise, sample values of $\partial F/\partial y$ can be tabulated as the calculation proceeds. Thus, for example, in the case of (6.4.5) we have $\partial F/\partial y \equiv -1$ and hence $K = 1$. For the equation $y' = x^2 + y^2$, K would be estimated as the largest value of $2|y|$ encountered in the calculation.†

The maximum effects of errors due to truncation and to round-off can be treated separately. However, because of the more or less random fluctuation in sign of errors due to round-off, any upper bound on the over-all effect of a large number of round-offs, no matter how precise, is likely to be extremely conservative in any actual calculation. On the other hand, the *statistical* analysis of such effects in stepwise integration is rather involved and, in any case, can afford only the *probability* that the over-all effect of round-off errors will not exceed a certain amount.

6.9. Convergence of Iterations. When the formula used is of the closed type, its solution generally must be approximated by iteration, as was seen in §6.6. It is then important to determine conditions under which this iteration converges and to investigate the *rate* of convergence.

If we denote the ith approximation to y_{n+1} by $y_{n+1}^{(i)}$, the iteration is described by the equation

$$y_{n+1}^{(i+1)} = h\alpha_{-1}F(x_{n+1},y_{n+1}^{(i)}) + y_{n-p} + h \sum_{k=0}^{r} \alpha_k F(x_{n-k},y_{n-k}), \quad (6.9.1)$$

† It should be noticed that the estimate $\partial F/\partial y \approx \Delta y'/\Delta y$ (which has been suggested in the literature) is *not* generally significant. Whereas we do have the relation

$$\Delta y_n' \equiv [F(x_{n+1},y_{n+1}) - F(x_{n+1},y_n)] + [F(x_{n+1},y_n) - F(x_n,y_n)]$$
$$\approx F_y(x_{n+1},y_n) \, \Delta y_n + hF_x(x_n,y_n),$$

there is no reason to suppose that the last term is small relative to $\Delta y_n'$.

whereas y_{n+1} itself satisfies the equation

$$y_{n+1} = h\alpha_{-1}F(x_{n+1},y_{n+1}) + y_{n-p} + h\sum_{k=0}^{r}\alpha_k F(x_{n-k},y_{n-k}). \quad (6.9.2)$$

When we subtract (6.9.1) from (6.9.2), and suppress the subscript $n + 1$ in order to simplify the notation, we obtain the relation

$$y - y^{(i+1)} = h\alpha_{-1}(y - y^{(i)})F_y(x,\eta^{(i)}), \quad (6.9.3)$$

where $\eta^{(i)}$ lies between $y_{n+1}^{(i)}$ and y_{n+1}. If, in the neighborhood of (x_{n+1}, y_{n+1}), we have $|F_y(x,y)| \leqq K_{n+1}$, there follows

$$|y - y^{(i+1)}| \leqq h|\alpha_{-1}|K_{n+1}|y - y^{(i)}|, \quad (6.9.4)$$

and also, by induction,

$$|y - y^{(i+1)}| \leqq (h|\alpha_{-1}|K_{n+1})^i|y - y^{(0)}|. \quad (6.9.5)$$

Hence, if h is sufficiently small to ensure that

$$h < \frac{1}{|\alpha_{-1}|K_{n+1}}, \quad (6.9.6)$$

in accordance with (6.8.10), the error in the ith iterate tends to zero as i increases.

The *rate* of convergence is specified by the ratio of the magnitudes of errors of successive iterates, and it is seen that this ratio is approximated by the absolute value of the "convergence factor" ρ_{n+1} such that

$$\rho_n = h\alpha_{-1}F_y(x_n,y_n). \quad (6.9.7)$$

For example, if Milne's method, based on (6.3.7) or (6.6.8), were to be used in dealing with the problem

$$y' = x^2 - y^2, \qquad y(0) = 1,$$

we would notice that, near the beginning of the calculation,

$$F_y = -2y \approx -2.$$

Since here $\alpha_{-1} = \frac{1}{3}$, from (6.6.8), the convergence factor in the early steps would be about $-2h/3$. Thus, with the choice $h = 0.1$, each iterate would tend to deviate from the limiting value by about one-fifteenth of the deviation associated with the preceding iterate.

It should be carefully noticed that the smallness of the difference between successive iterates at a certain stage is a measure only of the degree of approximation to which the *difference equation* employed for the approximate integration is satisfied at that stage, and clearly must not be considered in any sense as a measure of the difference between an iterate and the true solution of the *differential* equation. Indeed, there obviously is no *certainty* that the ultimate result of the iteration, as applied, say, to (6.6.8), will be a better approximation to the true solution of the differential equation than the initial prediction afforded, say, by (6.6.7), although the remainder terms indicate that the odds are about 28 to 1 in its favor.

6.10. Application to Equations of Higher Order. In order to apply one of the preceding methods to a differential equation of higher order, it is often convenient first to replace that equation by an equivalent *set* of equations of the first order. We here illustrate the procedure only in the case of a second-order equation, after which the generalization to higher-order equations, or to sets of simultaneous equations of more general type, will be obvious.

The problem

$$y'' = G(x,y,y'), \qquad y(x_0) = y_0, \qquad y'(x_0) = y_0' \qquad (6.10.1)$$

is equivalent to the problem

$$\begin{aligned} y' &= u, & y(x_0) &= y_0 \\ u' &= G(x,y,u), & u(x_0) &= y_0', \end{aligned} \qquad (6.10.2)$$

which is, in turn, a specialization of the more general problem in which u is replaced by, say, $F(x,y,u)$ in the right-hand member of the first equation.

It is usually convenient, but not necessary, to use the same formula in dealing with the two equations in (6.10.2). The approximate formulation then comprises two relations which are expressible in the general form

$$y_{n+1} = y_{n-p} + h(\alpha_{-1}y_{n+1}' + \alpha_0 y_n' + \alpha_1 y_{n-1}' + \cdots + \alpha_r y_{n-r}') \qquad (6.10.3)$$

and

$$u_{n+1} = u_{n-p} + h(\alpha_{-1}u_{n+1}' + \alpha_0 u_n' + \alpha_1 u_{n-1}' + \cdots + \alpha_r u_{n-r}'), \qquad (6.10.4)$$

or in equivalent forms in terms of backward differences, with

$$y_n' = u_n \qquad (6.10.5)$$

and
$$u_n' = G(x_n, y_n, u_n). \qquad (6.10.6)$$

In any case, the relations (6.10.3) and (6.10.4) apply only for $n \geq r$, the values y_0 and u_0 being given and the values $y_1, \ldots, y_r$ and $u_1, \ldots, u_r$ being obtained by another method (such as the use of power series or of one of the methods to be given in §6.16). The values of $u_0', u_1', \ldots, u_r'$ are calculated in advance, from (6.10.6). If the formula is of *open* type, so that $\alpha_{-1} = 0$, y_{r+1} and u_{r+1} are then calculated directly by use of (6.10.3) and (6.10.4). Next y_{r+1}' is given immediately as u_{r+1}, and u_{r+1}' is calculated as $G(x_{r+1}, y_{r+1}, u_{r+1})$, so that data are then available for advancing by another step.

If the formula is of *closed* type, so that $\alpha_{-1} \neq 0$, an initial prediction $u_{r+1}^{(0)}$ is first obtained (by use of a supplementary formula of open type, by pure estimation, or otherwise) and $y_{r+1}^{(0)}$ is obtained by replacing y'_{r+1} by $u_{r+1}^{(0)}$ in (6.10.3). Next $u'^{(0)}_{r+1}$ is obtained from (6.10.6), with y and u replaced by their zeroth approximations, and the cycle is closed by calculating $u_{r+1}^{(1)}$ from (6.10.4). If the calculated value differs from the initial prediction $u_{r+1}^{(0)}$, the cycle is iterated until agreement is obtained, when the iteration converges. The next step is then taken in the same way.

The iteration is thus described by the equations

$$
\begin{aligned}
y_{n+1}^{(i)} &= y_{n-p} + h(\alpha_{-1}u_{n+1}^{(i)} + \cdots), \\
u'^{(i)}_{n+1} &= G(x_{n+1}, y_{n+1}^{(i)}, u_{n+1}^{(i)}), \\
u_{n+1}^{(i+1)} &= u_{n-p} + h(\alpha_{-1}u'^{(i)}_{n+1} + \cdots),
\end{aligned}
\tag{6.10.7}
$$

where y_{n-p}, u_{n-p}, and all omitted terms remain fixed throughout the iteration. There then follows also

$$
y - y^{(i)} = h\alpha_{-1}(u - u^{(i)})
\tag{6.10.8}
$$

and

$$
u - u^{(i+1)} = h\alpha_{-1}[G(x,y,u) - G(x,y^{(i)},u^{(i)})],
\tag{6.10.9}
$$

where the common subscript $n + 1$ is suppressed throughout. Now if, near $(x_{n+1}, y_{n+1}, u_{n+1})$, it is true that

$$
|G_y(x,y,u)| \leqq K_{n+1}, \qquad |G_u(x,y,u)| \leqq L_{n+1},
\tag{6.10.10}
$$

then we may deduce from (6.10.9) the inequality

$$
|u - u^{(i+1)}| \leqq h|\alpha_{-1}|[K_{n+1}|y - y^{(i)}| + L_{n+1}|u - u^{(i)}|],
\tag{6.10.11}
$$

and hence, making use of (6.10.8),

$$
|u - u^{(i+1)}| \leqq h|\alpha_{-1}|(h|\alpha_{-1}|K_{n+1} + L_{n+1})|u - u^{(i)}|.
\tag{6.10.12}
$$

Thus, convergence will attain if h is so chosen that

$$
h|\alpha_{-1}|(h|\alpha_{-1}|K_{n+1} + L_{n+1}) < 1,
\tag{6.10.13}
$$

and the "convergence factor" ρ_n in the nth step is such that

$$
|\rho_n| \leqq h|\alpha_{-1}|(h|\alpha_{-1}|K + L),
\tag{6.10.14}
$$

where K and L are upper bounds on $|G_y|$ and $|G_u|$. If G does not explicitly involve $u \equiv y'$, it is seen that the convergence factor is of second order in h.

In order to illustrate the procedures, we consider the simple problem

$$
y'' = y + xy', \qquad y(0) = 1, \qquad y'(0) = 0.
\tag{6.10.15}
$$

In order to start the calculation, we first obtain the expressions

$$y'' = y + xy', \qquad y''' = 2y' + xy'', \qquad y^{iv} = 3y'' + xy''', \qquad \cdots,$$

and hence, with $x_0 = 0$,

$$y_0 = 1, \quad y_0' = 0, \quad y_0'' = 1, \quad y_0''' = 0, \quad y_0^{iv} = 3, \quad y_0^{v} = 0, \quad y_0^{vi} = 15, \quad \cdots,$$

so that, with $h = 0.1$, there follows

$$y_s = 1 + \frac{1}{2}\left(\frac{s}{10}\right)^2 + \frac{1}{8}\left(\frac{s}{10}\right)^4 + \frac{1}{48}\left(\frac{s}{10}\right)^6 + \cdots$$

$$y_s' = \frac{s}{10} + \frac{1}{2}\left(\frac{s}{10}\right)^3 + \frac{1}{8}\left(\frac{s}{10}\right)^5 + \cdots.$$

Thus we may obtain, in particular,

$$\begin{aligned} y_1 &= 1.0050, & y_2 &= 1.0202, & y_3 &= 1.0461, & \cdots, \\ y_1' &= 0.1005, & y_2' &= 0.2040, & y_3' &= 0.3138, & \cdots, \end{aligned} \qquad (6.10.16)$$

if only four places are retained. For the purpose of simplicity, we make use of the calculated values of y_1 and y_1', and proceed by using a formula involving only *first* differences.

The preliminary calculation may then be arranged as follows:

x	y	$y' = u$	$\nabla y'$	$\nabla^2 y'$	$y'' = y + xu$	$\nabla y''$	$\nabla^2 y''$
0.0	1.0000	0.0000	—	—	1.0000	—	—
0.1	1.0050	0.1005	1005	—	1.0150	150	—

If the *Adams formula* of the *open* type is used with first differences, there follows

$$y_2 \approx 1.0050 + 0.1[0.1005 + \tfrac{1}{2}(0.1005)] \doteq 1.0201,$$
$$u_2 \approx 0.1005 + 0.1[1.0150 + \tfrac{1}{2}(0.0150)] \doteq 0.2028,$$

and the third line of the calculation is

0.2	1.0201	0.2028	1023	18	1.0607	457	307

$$(6.10.17)$$

Since a second difference $\nabla^2 y''$ of about 300 would contribute about $\frac{5}{12}\cdot\frac{1}{10}\cdot 300 \doteq 12$ units to y', while a second difference $\nabla^2 y'$ of about 18 units would contribute about 0.7 units to y, if we suppose that the neglected second differences relative to x_1 are of the same order of magnitude as those calculated here, we may consider these quantities as rough estimates of the truncation errors in y_2 and u_2, introduced in the step from x_1 to x_2. Further information with regard to the reliability of these estimates would be afforded, in succeeding steps, by a consideration of the extent to which the second differences remain constant. If such errors are not tolerable, and this method is to be used, it is then necessary to calculate one or more additional starting values of y and u, and to retain at least one more difference. In this connection, it should be kept in mind that the errors introduced in each step are propagated into *succeeding* calculations, as was seen in the first-order case in §§6.7 and 6.8, in a manner which depends both upon the problem involved and the integration formula employed.

If, instead, the *Adams formula* of *closed* type is used with first differences, with the open-type formula as a predictor, the value 0.2028 is obtained, as in the preceding method, as the zeroth approximation $u_2^{(0)} \equiv y_2'^{(0)}$. The corresponding difference $\nabla y_2'^{(0)}$ is then entered, $y_2^{(0)}$ is determined by the formula

$$y_2^{(0)} = 1.0050 + 0.1[0.2028 - \tfrac{1}{2}(0.1023)] \doteq 1.0202,$$

and $u_2'^{(0)}$ is determined as $y_2^{(0)} + x_2 y_2'^{(0)} \doteq 1.0608$, so that the third line takes the form

| 0.2 | 1.0202 | 0.2028 | 1023 | — | 1.0608 | 458 | — |

$$(6.10.18)$$

Next the cycle is closed by calculating

$$u_2^{(1)} = 0.1005 + 0.1[1.0608 - \tfrac{1}{2}(0.0458)] \doteq 0.2043.$$

Since this result differs from the initial prediction, the entry 0.2028 in the third line is altered to 0.2043 and the cycle is repeated, at the end of which the third line has been changed to

| 0.2 | 1.0202 | 0.2043 | 1038 | 33 | 1.0611 | 461 | 311 |

$$(6.10.19)$$

Finally, the value $u_2^{(2)}$ is calculated and is found to agree with $u_2^{(1)}$, to four places, so that the iteration is completed.

Reference to (6.3.2) shows that incorporation of the second differences would contribute $-\tfrac{1}{10} \cdot \tfrac{1}{12} \cdot 311 \approx -3$ units to y_2' and $-\tfrac{1}{10} \cdot \tfrac{1}{12} \cdot 33 \approx 0$ units to y_2. A somewhat more dependable estimate of the truncation error introduced in a single step can be obtained by calculating the *initial* approximation $y_{n+1}^{(0)}$ by use of the *open* formula, in place of the closed one, but using the closed formula in subsequent iterations. Since also $u_{n+1}^{(0)}$ is calculated by the open formula, it then follows that if we write

$$\gamma_{n+1} \equiv y_{n+1} - y_{n+1}^{(0)}, \qquad \gamma_{n+1}' \equiv u_{n+1} - u_{n+1}^{(0)},$$

where y_{n+1} and u_{n+1} are the values provided by the closed formula after appropriate iteration, then the desired truncation errors in y_{n+1} and u_{n+1} are approximated respectively by $-\gamma_{n+1}/C$ and $-\gamma_{n+1}'/C$, where C is the numerical factor considered in §6.6, here equal to 6 (see also Prob. 28). It is convenient to tabulate γ_n and γ_n' in place of the two first neglected differences, so that the line (6.10.19) then is replaced by

| 0.2 | 1.0202 | 0.2043 | 1038 | γ 1 | 1.0611 | 461 | γ' 15 |

The estimated truncation errors introduced into the calculated values of y'_2 and y_2 are then $-\frac{15}{6} \approx -3$ units and $-\frac{1}{6} \approx 0$ units, as before.

It may be noticed that the actual errors, obtainable by reference to the rounded true values given in (6.10.16), are indeed correctly predicted, in this case, by the estimates afforded by both procedures.

In a fairly lengthy sequence of steps, however, the *propagation* of errors becomes particularly important. This rather unpleasant problem is considered, for the second-order equation, in the following section.

In this connection, it may be remarked that an elementary analysis quite similar to that of §6.7 permits a study of the situation corresponding to the use of (6.10.3) and (6.10.4) in the numerical solution of an equation of the special form

$$y'' = Ly' + Ky, \tag{6.10.20}$$

where L and K are *constants*. Here the exact solution is of the form

$$y(x) = c_1 e^{A_1 x} + c_2 e^{A_2 x}, \tag{6.10.21}$$

where A_1 and A_2 are the roots of $A^2 - LA - K = 0$ and c_1 and c_2 are determined by the initial conditions, and it is again found that the use of formulas (6.10.3) and (6.10.4) with $p > 0$ introduces "parasitic solutions" which may dominate the part of the solution which simulates the exact solution when A_1 and A_2 are negative or have negative real parts. When $p = 0$, this situation can exist only when excessively large spacings are employed.

In particular, if use is made of Milne's method, based on (6.6.8) and corresponding to $p = 1$, the generated numerical solution is found to be approximated by

$$C_1 e^{A_1 x_k} + C_2 e^{A_2 x_k} + (-1)^k [C_3 e^{-A_1 x_k/3} + C_4 e^{-A_2 x_k/3}] \tag{6.10.22}$$

when $x = x_k$, if the spacing h is small and if round-off errors are neglected, where the C's are determined by the starting values. Thus, for example, if the true solution is of the form

$$y(x_k) = c e^{-a x_k} \cos (b x_k + \omega),$$

where $a > 0$, then the parasitic part of the numerical solution will be approximated by

$$(-1)^k c' e^{a x_k/3} \cos \left[\left(\frac{b x_k}{3} \right) + \omega' \right],$$

and will tend to dominate the desirable part of the numerical solution when x is large.

It is also important to notice that the propagated error generally will possess components simulating both the terms $e^{A_1 x}$ and $e^{A_2 x}$, even when the parasitic solutions are not troublesome. This situation is of particular disadvantage when the initial conditions require that the *exact* solution involve only the term which grows least rapidly (or decays most rapidly).

When the governing differential equation $y'' = G(x,y,y')$ is less simple than (6.10.20), a qualitative analysis of short-range error propagation near a point (x_k, y_k) generally can be obtained by identifying L and K in (6.10.20) with the values of $\partial G/\partial y'$ and $\partial G/\partial y$, respectively, at that point, if those partial derivatives do not vary excessively near that point.

6.11. Propagated-error Bounds. If the *true* values of the solution and its derivative at x_n are denoted by Y_n and U_n, respectively, and if the approximate values are calculated from (6.10.3) and (6.10.4), then we have the relations

$$y_{n+1} = y_{n-p} + h \sum_{k=-1}^{r} \alpha_k u_{n-k} - R_n,$$

$$Y_{n+1} = Y_{n-p} + h \sum_{k=-1}^{r} \alpha_k U_{n-k} + T_n,$$

(6.11.1)

and

$$u_{n+1} = u_{n-p} + h \sum_{k=-1}^{r} \alpha_k G(x_{n-k}, y_{n-k}, u_{n-k}) - R'_n$$

$$U_{n+1} = U_{n-p} + h \sum_{k=-1}^{r} \alpha_k G(x_{n-k}, Y_{n-k}, U_{n-k}) + T'_n,$$

(6.11.2)

where R_n, R'_n, T_n, and T'_n are round-off and truncation errors introduced in the nth step itself. If we write

$$\epsilon_n = Y_n - y_n, \qquad \epsilon'_n = U_n - u_n, \qquad (6.11.3)$$

and

$$E_n = T_n + R_n, \qquad E'_n = T'_n + R'_n, \qquad (6.11.4)$$

we obtain, from (6.11.1) and (6.11.2), the relations

$$\epsilon_{n+1} = \epsilon_{n-p} + h \sum_{k=-1}^{r} \alpha_k \epsilon'_{n-k} + E_n \qquad (6.11.5)$$

and

$$\epsilon'_{n+1} = \epsilon'_{n-p} + h \sum_{k=-1}^{r} \alpha_k (G_{y_{n-k}} \epsilon_{n-k} + G_{y'_{n-k}} \epsilon'_{n-k}) + E'_n, \qquad (6.11.6)$$

where $G_{y_{n-k}}$ and $G_{y'_{n-k}}$ are values of G_y and $G_{y'}$ respectively, for $x = x_{n-k}$, some y between y_{n-k} and Y_{n-k}, and some y' between u_{n-k} and U_{n-k}.

We now suppose that, for all values of x, y, and u involved in the calculation, we have

$$|G_y(x,y,u)| \leq K, \qquad |G_{y'}(x,y,u)| \leq L, \qquad (6.11.7)$$

where K and L are fixed constants, and consider the associated relations

$$e_{n+1} = e_{n-p} + h \sum_{k=-1}^{r} |\alpha_k| e'_{n-k} + E \qquad (6.11.8)$$

and

$$e'_{n+1} = e'_{n-p} + h \sum_{k=-1}^{r} |\alpha_k| (K e_{n-k} + L e'_{n-k}) + E', \qquad (6.11.9)$$

where E and E' are fixed constants such that

$$|E_n| \leq E, \qquad |E'_n| \leq E'. \qquad (6.11.10)$$

Then, by an argument similar to that of §6.8, it follows that if $|\epsilon_n| \leq e_n$ and $|\epsilon'_n| \leq e'_n$ for $n = 0, 1, \ldots, r$, and if

$$h|\alpha_{-1}|(h|\alpha_{-1}|K + L) < 1, \qquad (6.11.11)$$

then $|\epsilon_n| \leq e_n$ and $|\epsilon'_n| \leq e'_n$ for all positive integral values of n.

In order to obtain a solution of (6.11.8) and (6.11.9) with this property, we first seek a *particular* solution in the form $e_n = -\lambda$, $e'_n = -\lambda'$, where λ and λ' are independent of n, and so obtain the determination

$$\lambda = \frac{E' - LE}{Kh\sigma}, \qquad \lambda' = \frac{E}{h\sigma} \qquad (6.11.12)$$

where again

$$\sigma \equiv \sum_{k=-1}^{r} |\alpha_k|. \qquad (6.11.13)$$

Upon this particular solution we may superimpose

$$e_n = A\beta^n, \qquad e'_n = A'\beta^n, \qquad (6.11.14)$$

if the constants A, A', and β are determined so that these expressions satisfy (6.11.8) and (6.11.9) *when E and E' are replaced by zeros* and hence so that

$$A(\beta^{n+1} - \beta^{n-p}) - hA' \sum_{k=-1}^{r} |\alpha_k| \beta^{n-k} = 0 \qquad (6.11.15)$$

and

$$-hKA \sum_{k=-1}^{r} |\alpha_k| \beta^{n-k} + A' \left(\beta^{n+1} - \beta^{n-p} - hL \sum_{k=-1}^{r} |\alpha_k| \beta^{n-k} \right) = 0.$$

$$\qquad (6.11.16)$$

These equations are compatible, with not both A and A' zero, if and only if the determinant of the coefficients of A and A' vanishes, that is, if β satisfies the characteristic equation

$$\begin{vmatrix} \beta^{n+1} - \beta^{n-p} & -h \Sigma|\alpha_k|\beta^{n-k} \\ -hK \Sigma|\alpha_k|\beta^{n-k} & \beta^{n+1} - \beta^{n-p} - hL \Sigma|\alpha_k|\beta^{n-k} \end{vmatrix} = 0. \qquad (6.11.17)$$

Now, when $\beta = 1$, the left-hand member reduces to

$$\begin{vmatrix} 0 & -h\sigma \\ -hK\sigma & -hL\sigma \end{vmatrix} = -h^2\sigma^2 K,$$

and is therefore *negative*. For large positive real values of β, the highest power of β will dominate the expansion, and its coefficient is seen to be

$$\begin{vmatrix} 1 & -h|\alpha_{-1}| \\ -hK|\alpha_{-1}| & 1 - hL|\alpha_{-1}| \end{vmatrix} = 1 - h|\alpha_{-1}|(h|\alpha_{-1}|K + L),$$

which is positive when h is sufficiently small to ensure that

$$h|\alpha_{-1}|(h|\alpha_{-1}|K + L) < 1, \tag{6.11.18}$$

in accordance with (6.11.11). It is interesting to notice that this is also the requirement that (6.10.12) hold for all n, so that the iteration relevant to a closed-type formula is convergent.

Thus, if (6.11.18) is satisfied, there exists (at least) one positive real root of (6.11.17), say β_0, which exceeds unity. If we write

$$\beta_0 = 1 + m_1 h + m_2 h^2 + \cdots,$$

and expand the elements of (6.11.17) in powers of h, there follows

$$\begin{vmatrix} (p+1)m_1 h + \cdots & -h\sigma + \cdots \\ -hK\sigma + \cdots & [(p+1)m_1 - L\sigma]h + \cdots \end{vmatrix} = 0,$$

and hence, in particular, the requirement that the leading coefficient (of h^2) in the expansion vanish leads to the equation

$$(p+1)^2 m_1^2 - (p+1)L\sigma m_1 - K\sigma^2 = 0,$$

the positive root of which is

$$m_1 = \frac{\sigma}{p+1}\frac{L + \sqrt{L^2 + 4K}}{2}. \tag{6.11.19}$$

Thus we have the result

$$\beta_0 = 1 + m_1 h + 0(h^2), \tag{6.11.20}$$

for small h.

When $\beta = \beta_0$, the two equations (6.11.15) and (6.11.16) become equivalent, and either can be used to express A in terms of A'. If we use the former, we find that

$$A' = \frac{A}{\mu} \tag{6.11.21}$$

where

$$\mu = \frac{h \sum_{k=-1}^{r} |\alpha_k|\beta_0^{p-k}}{\beta_0^{p+1} - 1} = \frac{\sigma}{(p+1)m_1} + 0(h). \tag{6.11.22}$$

Thus with β_0 and μ so defined, Eqs. (6.11.8) and (6.11.9) are satisfied by

$$e_n = A\beta_0^n - \lambda, \qquad e_n' = \frac{A}{\mu}\beta_0^n - \lambda', \tag{6.11.23}$$

where λ and λ' are constants defined in (6.11.12), and where A is an *arbitrary* constant. These expressions will dominate the solutions ϵ_n and ϵ_n' of (6.11.5) and (6.11.6) for all n if they do so for $n = 0, 1, \ldots, r$. If we denote the maximum values of $|\epsilon_n|$ and $|\epsilon_n'|$ for $n \leq r$ by $\bar{e}$ and $\bar{e}'$, respectively, it remains only to choose A such that

$$A - \lambda \geqq \bar{e}, \qquad \frac{A}{\mu} - \lambda' \geqq \bar{e}'.$$

Thus, if we take

$$A = \max\left[\left(\bar{e} + \frac{E' - LE}{Kh\sigma}\right), \mu\left(\bar{e}' + \frac{E}{h\sigma}\right)\right], \tag{6.11.24}$$

the expressions defined in (6.11.23) will exceed $\bar{e}$ and $\bar{e}'$, respectively, for $n = 0$ and, since A and μ are positive and $\beta_0 > 1$, will continue to do so for $n > 0$.

It follows finally that, *with A defined by (6.11.24), the errors ϵ_n and ϵ_n' associated with the use of the formulas (6.10.3) and (6.10.4) are limited by the inequalities*

$$|\epsilon_n| \leqq A\beta_0^n - \frac{E' - LE}{Kh\sigma}, \qquad |\epsilon_n'| \leqq \frac{A}{\mu}\beta_0^n - \frac{E}{h\sigma}. \tag{6.11.25}$$

The relative simplicity of these forms is attained at the expense of conservatism of the bounds. Less-conservative bounds would be obtained in a much more complicated form if the *general* solution of (6.11.8) and (6.11.9) were obtained, with $2r + 2$ independent arbitrary constants, and if those constants were determined such that $e_n = |\epsilon_n|$ and $e_n' = |\epsilon_n'|$ for $n = 0, 1, \ldots, r$, or if (6.11.8) and (6.11.9) were replaced by dominating equations of less simple form.

In those cases when the coefficients α_i are nonnegative, so that

$$\sigma = p + 1,$$

in accordance with (6.7.10), Eqs. (6.11.19) and (6.11.20) give

$$\beta_0 = 1 + \frac{h}{2}(L + \sqrt{L^2 + 4K}) + 0(h^2). \tag{6.11.26}$$

Hence there follows

$$\beta_0^n \equiv \beta_0^{(x_n - x_0)/h} = \left[1 + \frac{h}{2}(L + \sqrt{L^2 + 4K}) + \cdots\right]^{(x_n - x_0)/h}$$

$$\approx e^{(L + \sqrt{L^2 + 4K})(x_n - x_0)/2}. \tag{6.11.27}$$

when h is small, so that the dominating functions in (6.11.25) grow in the same way as $\exp\left[\frac{1}{2}(L + \sqrt{L^2 + 4K})x_n\right]$ as n increases.

6.12. Special Second-order Equations. Second-order equations of the special form

$$y'' = G(x,y), \qquad (6.12.1)$$

in which y' is not explicitly involved, arise very frequently in practice. If values of y' are not required, it is desirable to have available methods which do not entail their calculation.

Two formulas having this property were derived, as formulas (5.5.11) and (5.5.12) for repeated integration, in §5.5, and may be written with the present notation in the forms

$$y_{n+1} = 2y_n - y_{n-1} + h^2(1 + 0\nabla + \tfrac{1}{12}\nabla^2 + \tfrac{1}{12}\nabla^3 + \tfrac{19}{240}\nabla^4$$
$$+ \tfrac{3}{40}\nabla^5 + \cdots)y_n'' \qquad (6.12.2)$$

and

$$y_{n+1} = 2y_n - y_{n-1} + h^2(1 - \nabla + \tfrac{1}{12}\nabla^2 + 0\nabla^3 - \tfrac{1}{240}\nabla^4$$
$$- \tfrac{1}{240}\nabla^5 + \cdots)y_{n+1}''. \qquad (6.12.3)$$

The former is of open type, the latter of closed type. In order to use either, a suitable number of preliminary ordinates must be calculated by another method, which takes into account the fact that y and y' are prescribed at $x = x_0$, after which the technique of the ensuing calculation, often known as *Störmer's method*, is evident.

Formulas (6.12.2) and (6.12.3) are each representative of a whole class of similar formulas, one class of open type and the other of closed type, which are analogous to the formulas given in §§6.2 and 6.3. In particular, an additional formula of open type,

$$y_{n+1} = y_n + y_{n-2} - y_{n-3} + 3h^2(1 - \nabla + \tfrac{5}{12}\nabla^2 + 0\nabla^3 + \tfrac{17}{720}\nabla^4$$
$$+ \tfrac{17}{720}\nabla^5 + \cdots)y_n'', \qquad (6.12.4)$$

may be listed (see Prob. 11 of Chap. 5).

Formulas (6.12.3) and (6.12.4) comprise a pair of formulas for both of which the coefficient of the third difference vanishes. If only second differences are retained in these formulas, they become

$$y_{n+1} = y_n + y_{n-2} - y_{n-3} + \begin{cases} 3h^2(y_n'' - \nabla y_n'' + \tfrac{5}{12}\nabla^2 y_n'') \\ \dfrac{h^2}{4}(5y_n'' + 2y_{n-1}'' - 5y_{n-2}'') \end{cases} + \frac{17h^6}{240}\,y^{\mathrm{vi}}(\xi)$$

$$(6.12.5)$$

and

$$y_{n+1} = 2y_n - y_{n-1} + \begin{cases} h^2(y_{n+1}'' - \nabla y_{n+1}'' + \tfrac{1}{12}\nabla^2 y_{n+1}'') \\ \dfrac{h^2}{12}(y_{n+1}'' + 10y_n'' + y_{n-1}'') \end{cases} - \frac{h^6}{240}\,y^{\mathrm{vi}}(\xi),$$

$$(6.12.6)$$

where the coefficients of the remainder terms are the same as those of the omitted fourth differences in the formulas (6.12.3) and (6.12.4). The error term when one of the formulas is truncated with a difference not preceding one with a zero coefficient is of more complicated form.

Milne's method employs (6.12.5) to afford an initial prediction $y_{n+1}^{(0)}$, and (6.12.6) as the basic formula, to be solved for y_{n+1} by iteration. If the factor $\gamma_{n+1} = y_{n+1} - y_{n+1}^{(0)}$ is calculated (as in §6.6), the estimated truncation error in the nth step is seen to be $T_n \approx -\gamma_n/18$. Also, the convergence factor in the iteration at the nth step (see §6.9) is easily found to be approximately $\rho_n \approx \frac{1}{12}h^2 G_y(x_n, y_n)$, so that h should be sufficiently small to ensure that $|\rho_n| \ll 1$.

In order to illustrate the relevant analysis of error *propagation*, we consider the special case in which (6.12.6) is the basis of the method.† With the same notation as was used in earlier developments, it is easily seen that the error ϵ_n associated with the calculated value y_n satisfies a relation of the form

$$\epsilon_{n+1} = 2\epsilon_n - \epsilon_{n-1} + \frac{h^2}{12}\left(G_{y_{n+1}}\epsilon_{n+1} + 10G_{y_n}\epsilon_n + G_{y_{n-1}}\epsilon_{n-1}\right) + E_n, \quad (6.12.7)$$

for $n \geq 1$, where G_{y_r} is an appropriate value of G_y. This relation can also be written in the form

$$\left(1 - \frac{h^2}{12}G_{y_{n+1}}\right)(\epsilon_{n+1} - \epsilon_n) = \epsilon_n - \epsilon_{n-1} + \frac{h^2}{12}[(G_{y_{n+1}} + 10G_{y_n})\epsilon_n$$
$$+ G_{y_{n-1}}\epsilon_{n-1}] + E_n, \quad (6.12.8)$$

so that, if we have

$$|G_y(x,y)| \leq K, \quad (6.12.9)$$

for all relevant values of x and y, and if h is sufficiently small to ensure that

$$\frac{Kh^2}{12} < 1, \quad (6.12.10)$$

there follows

$$\left(1 - \frac{Kh^2}{12}\right)|\epsilon_{n+1} - \epsilon_n| \leq |\epsilon_n - \epsilon_{n-1}| + \frac{Kh^2}{12}(11|\epsilon_n| + |\epsilon_{n-1}|) + |E_n|.$$
$$(6.12.11)$$

If e_n satisfies the relation

$$\left(1 - \frac{Kh^2}{12}\right)(e_{n+1} - e_n) = e_n - e_{n-1} + \frac{Kh^2}{12}(11e_n + e_{n-1}) + E, \quad (6.12.12)$$

where
$$E = |E_n|_{max}, \quad (6.12.13)$$

and if
$$e_0 \geq |\epsilon_0|, \quad e_1 - e_0 \geq |\epsilon_1 - \epsilon_0|, \quad (6.12.14)$$

† The method used for the initial prediction at each step is irrelevant to this analysis.

there follows also $e_1 - e_0 \geq |\epsilon_1| - |\epsilon_0|$ and hence $e_1 - |\epsilon_1| \geq e_0 - |\epsilon_0|$ or $e_1 \geq |\epsilon_1|$. Then, by comparing (6.12.11) and (6.12.12), we find that $e_2 - e_1 \geq |\epsilon_2 - \epsilon_1|$ and hence $e_2 - e_1 \geq |\epsilon_2| - |\epsilon_1|$ or $e_2 \geq |\epsilon_2|$. By induction, there follows $e_n - e_{n-1} \geq |\epsilon_n - \epsilon_{n-1}|$ and $e_n \geq |\epsilon_n|$ for $n = 0$, 1, 2, . . . , so that the error ϵ_n is then dominated by e_n.

The general solution of (6.12.12) is readily found to be of the form

$$e_n = A_0 \beta_0^n + A_1 \beta_1^n - \frac{E}{Kh^2}, \qquad (6.12.15)$$

where β_0 and β_1 are the roots of the equation

$$\left(1 - \frac{Kh^2}{12}\right)\beta^2 - 2\left(1 + \frac{5Kh^2}{12}\right)\beta + \left(1 - \frac{Kh^2}{12}\right) = 0, \quad (6.12.16)$$

and hence

$$\beta_0 = \frac{1}{\beta_1} = \frac{1 + \frac{5}{12}Kh^2 + \sqrt{Kh^2 + \frac{1}{6}K^2h^4}}{1 - \frac{1}{12}Kh^2} = 1 + \sqrt{K}h + 0(h^2).$$

$$(6.12.17)$$

When A_0 and A_1 are determined by the conditions $e_0 = 0$ and $e_1 = |\epsilon_1|$, under the assumption that $\epsilon_0 = 0$, there follows finally

$$|\epsilon_n| \leq e_n$$

where

$$e_n = \frac{E}{Kh^2}\frac{1}{\beta_0 + 1}(\beta_0^n + \beta_0^{1-n} - 1 - \beta_0) + \frac{\beta_0|\epsilon_1|}{\beta_0^2 - 1}(\beta_0^n - \beta_0^{-n}). \qquad (6.12.18)$$

If round-off errors are ignored, we have $E \leq \frac{1}{240}h^6|y^{vi}|_{\max}$. Also, since $\beta_0 = 1 + \sqrt{K}h + 0(h^2)$, and $n = (x_n - x_0)/h$, there follows

$$e_n \approx \frac{h^4}{240K}|y^{vi}|_{\max}\{\cosh[\sqrt{K}(x_n - x_0)] - 1\}$$

$$+ \frac{|\epsilon_1|}{\sqrt{K}h}\sinh[\sqrt{K}(x_n - x_0)], \quad (6.12.19)$$

when h is small. Whereas $|y^{vi}|_{\max}$ is generally not easy to estimate directly, the factor $[h^4|y^{vi}|_{\max}]/240$ can be estimated as $h^{-2}|T_n|_{\max} \approx |\gamma_n|_{\max}/18h^2$ or as $|\nabla^4 y_k''|_{\max}/240$.

Similar but more involved error bounds can be derived in the more general case.

In order to illustrate the calculation and to provide a basis for the considerations of the following section, we apply Milne's method, based on (6.12.5) and (6.12.6), to the problem

$$y'' = xy, \qquad y(0) = 0, \qquad y'(0) = 1, \qquad (6.12.20)$$

for which the exact solution is expressible in the form

$$y = 3^{\frac{1}{3}}\Gamma(\tfrac{4}{3})I_{\frac{1}{3}}(\tfrac{2}{3}x^{\frac{3}{2}}), \qquad (6.12.21)$$

where $I_{\frac{1}{3}}$ is the *modified Bessel function of the first kind, of order* $\frac{1}{3}$. With $h = 0.1$, the calculation can be arranged as in Table 6.3, if differences are used and if five places are retained.

TABLE 6.3

x	y	y''	$\nabla y''$	$\nabla^2 y''$	γ
0.0	0.00000	0.00000			
0.1	0.10001	0.01000	1000		
0.2	0.20013	0.04003	3003	2003	
0.3	0.30068	0.09020	5017	2014	
0.4	0.40214	0.16086	7066	2049	
0.5	0.50523	0.25262	9176	2110	1
0.6	0.61086	0.36652	11390	2214	−1
0.7	0.72017	0.50412	13760	2370	−1
0.8	0.83454	0.66763	16351	2591	−1

The first five lines are easily calculated in advance (only *three* lines are needed), the ordinates being determined by use of a single Taylor series, and the values of y'', determined from the equation $y'' = xy$, and of the differences are entered as shown. If (6.12.5) is used to predict y_5, the prediction is found to be 0.50522; the remainder of the sixth line is then filled in, after which (6.12.6) gives the revised value 0.50523, and the resultant slight modification in the remainder of the line does not call for additional iteration. The value $\gamma_5 = 0.50523 - 0.50522$ is then listed as +1 unit in the fifth place, and the calculation proceeds in the same way in succeeding steps.

Since the truncation error in each step may be estimated as $-\gamma/18$, we may be reasonably confident of the calculated values of y to the places retained (except for the usual uncertainty of one unit in the last place, due to round-off). In fact, the small values of γ may be expected to correspond to the effects of round-off.

Clearly, the alternative forms of (6.12.5) and (6.12.6) may be used instead, without the need for calculation of differences. This procedure possesses an additional advantage in that then only the entries y_{n+1} and y''_{n+1} are modified in successive steps of each *iteration* process. However, whereas these advantages are of particular significance when large-scale computing devices are used, so that simplicity in programming and minimization of storage requirements are of prime importance, they may compare unfavorably in other cases with the advantages which follow from the possibility of detecting gross errors by inspecting the regularity of the trend of the difference columns.

Further, in place of using (6.12.5) to obtain an initial prediction for y_{n+1}, it is possible to *estimate* the second difference $\nabla^2 y''_{n+1}$ and to then fill in the remainder of that line from right to left through y''_{n+1}, after which use may be made of (6.12.6) to initiate the prediction. Thus, in Table 6.3, a glance at the $\nabla^2 y''$ column would suggest the estimate $\nabla^2 y''_8 \approx 0.026$ after the calculation of y_7. However, this procedure would not supply data for the γ column.

It may be noticed that any *linear* equation of the second order, of the form

$$Y'' + P(x)Y' + Q(x)Y = F(x), \tag{6.12.22}$$

can be reduced to the form (6.12.1) by the change of variables

$$Y(x) = e^{-\frac{1}{2}\int P\,dx} y(x), \tag{6.12.23}$$

in accordance with which (6.12.22) takes the form

$$y'' + f(x)y = g(x), \tag{6.12.24}$$

where

$$f(x) = \tfrac{1}{4}\{4Q(x) - 2P'(x) - [P(x)]^2\}, \qquad g(x) = e^{\frac{1}{2}\int P\,dx} F(x). \tag{6.12.25}$$

6.13. Change of Interval. In many cases it is desirable to, say, double or halve the spacing at a certain stage of the advancing calculation. Doubling the spacing presents no difficulties, since it involves only the use of alternate values of previously calculated data, together with a direct calculation of modified differences relevant to the new spacing, if differences are used.

Thus, in illustration, the smallness of the entries in the γ column of Table 6.3 suggests that the same accuracy may be obtained with a doubled spacing $h' = 2h = 0.2$. In fact, reference to the error expression in (6.12.6) shows that the truncation error in each step can be estimated roughly by

$$T_n \approx -\frac{h^6}{240} \frac{\nabla^4 y''_n}{h^4} \approx -0.00004 \nabla^4 y''_n,$$

and it is found that, for the data of Table 6.3, $\nabla^4 y''$ varies from 0.00024 to 0.00065, so that the largest single *truncation* error in the range covered is probably less than about three units in the eighth decimal place. Doubling the spacing h will multiply the truncation error by a factor of the order 2^6 and hence may be expected to lead to a truncation error of less than about one unit in the sixth place in each step. The calculation following the work of Table 6.3, with doubled spacing, is given in Table 6.4.

TABLE 6.4

x	y	y''	$\nabla y''$	$\nabla^2 y''$	γ
0.0	0.00000	0.00000			
0.2	0.20013	0.04003	4003		
0.4	0.40214	0.16086	12083	8080	
0.6	0.61086	0.36652	20566	8483	
0.8	0.83454	0.66763	30111	9545	
1.0	1.08531	1.08531	41768	11657	1
1.2	1.38000	1.65600	57069	15301	3
1.4	1.74164	2.43830	78230	21161	7

After three lines of calculation, the γ column serves a warning that the truncation error per step may have increased at that stage to about one-half unit in the last place retained. Thus (as might have been anticipated in advance from the increasing rate of growth of $\nabla^2 y''$) the advantages of the more rapid calculation were short-lived, and the doubling of the spacing was ill-advised in the present case. However, the results of Table 6.4 may serve to illustrate the somewhat more complicated transition to a *halved* spacing.†

In the present analysis, knowledge of $y(1.3)$ would permit the determination of $y''(1.3)$ and, consequently, $\nabla y''(1.4)$ and $\nabla^2 y''(1.4)$, relative to the *new* spacing $h = 0.1$. Then an iteration, based on (6.12.6), could be initiated by estimating $\nabla^2 y''(1.5)$ and proceeding as was outlined in the preceding section. The value of $y(1.3)$ could be obtained by an interpolation involving certain of the available calculated ordinates. Clearly, care should be taken to obtain this ordinate to the same degree of accuracy as the other ordinates. The use of a difference formula, for this purpose, would entail the calculation of differences of the ordinates themselves, but would be desirable, in order that the accuracy of the interpolation could be estimated.

Another procedure consists in using the formulas derived in §5.7 to transform the tabulated differences $\nabla y''(1.4)$ and $\nabla^2 y''(1.4)$ to corresponding differences relative to the halved spacing. The ordinate $y(1.3)$ can then be determined by rewriting (6.12.6) in the form

$$y_n \approx \tfrac{1}{2}(y_{n+1} + y_{n-1}) - \frac{h^2}{2}\left(y''_{n+1} - \nabla y''_{n+1} + \tfrac{1}{12}\nabla^2 y''_{n+1}\right). \quad (6.13.1)$$

If the difference operators corresponding to the halved spacing are

---

† An obvious alternative consists in merely retaining additional differences in the relevant integration formulas (6.12.3) and (6.12.4). In the present case, however, it is assumed that retention of the advantages of the special formulas (6.12.5) and (6.12.6) is considered to be desirable.

denoted by ∇' and ∇'^2, Eq. (5.7.4) yields the formulas

$$\nabla' = \tfrac{1}{2}\nabla + \tfrac{1}{8}\nabla^2 + \tfrac{1}{16}\nabla^3 + \tfrac{5}{128}\nabla^4 + \tfrac{7}{256}\nabla^5 + \tfrac{21}{1024}\nabla^6 + \tfrac{33}{2048}\nabla^7 + \cdots$$
$$(6.13.2)$$

and

$$\nabla'^2 = \tfrac{1}{4}\nabla^2 + \tfrac{1}{8}\nabla^3 + \tfrac{5}{64}\nabla^4 + \tfrac{7}{128}\nabla^5 + \tfrac{21}{512}\nabla^6 + \tfrac{33}{1024}\nabla^7 + \cdots, \qquad (6.13.3)$$

when Δ is replaced by $-\nabla$ in (5.7.4), in accordance with the results of §5.7. The use of these formulas permits the calculation of the differences relative to $x = 1.4$ in the third line of Table 6.5, after which $\nabla y''$ and y'' are obtained in line two and y'' in line one.

Table 6.5

x	y	y''	$\nabla y''$	$\nabla^2 y''$	γ
1.2	1.38000	1.65600			
1.3	1.55071	2.01592	35992		
1.4	1.74164	2.43830	42238	6246	

A useful check on the accuracy of the modified differences is then afforded by a comparison of the value of $y''(1.2)$ so obtained with that previously obtained in the direct calculation of Table 6.4.

The ordinate $y(1.3)$ is next calculated from (6.13.1). Then if, say, $\nabla^2 y''(1.5)$ is estimated approximately as being *equal* to $\nabla^2 y''(1.4)$, the line

$$1.5 \quad | \quad 1.95701 \quad | \quad 2.92314 \quad | \quad 48484 \quad 6246 \quad | \qquad (6.13.4)$$

is obtained (from right to left), the first approximation to $y(1.5)$ being obtained by use of (6.12.6). When $y''(1.5)$ and its differences are recalculated (from left to right), the next approximation to $y(1.5)$ is obtained from (6.12.6) as 1.95702, and the final form of this line of the calculation reads as follows:

$$1.5 \quad | \quad 1.95702 \quad | \quad 2.93553 \quad | \quad 49723 \quad 7487 \quad | \qquad (6.13.5)$$

Sufficient data are now available for the use of (6.12.5) as a predictor in the next step, if this is desired, after which entries in the γ column are again calculable.

Appropriate modifications of this procedure are easily devised in other cases.

6.14. Use of Higher Derivatives. It is possible to derive a variety of formulas, for the numerical integration of differential equations, which will involve values of certain higher derivatives of the unknown function.

In particular, the Euler-Maclaurin sum formula (5.9.1) can be expressed in the form

$$y_{n+1} - y_{n-p} = h(\tfrac{1}{2}y'_{n+1} + y'_n + y'_{n-1} + \cdots + y'_{n-p+2} + y'_{n-p+1} + \tfrac{1}{2}y'_{n-p})$$
$$- \frac{h^2}{12}(y''_{n+1} - y''_{n-p}) + \frac{h^4}{720}(y^{iv}_{n+1} - y^{iv}_{n-p})$$
$$- \frac{h^6}{30240}(y^{vi}_{n+1} - y^{vi}_{n-p}) + \cdots, \quad (6.14.1)$$

where the error committed by truncation with the term of order h^{2k} is $(p+1)h$ times the term of order h^{2k+2} with the contents of the relevant parentheses replaced by $y^{(2k+3)}(\xi)$, where $x_{n-p} < \xi < x_{n+1}$. Thus, for example, with $p = 0$ we have the formula

$$y_{n+1} = y_n + \frac{h}{2}(y'_{n+1} + y'_n) - \frac{h^2}{12}(y''_{n+1} - y''_n) + \frac{h^5}{720}y^v(\xi), \quad (6.14.2)$$

of closed type, which may be used with any convenient predictor formula (preferably also with an error of order h^5) as in the methods discussed previously.

Formula (6.14.2) can be obtained also as a special case of the so-called *Hermite interpolation formula*, to be discussed in §8.2, and can also be derived by a method of *undetermined coefficients*, in which we write

$$y_{n+1} = y_n + h(\alpha_0 y'_{n+1} + \alpha_1 y'_n) + h^2(\beta_0 y''_{n+1} + \beta_1 y''_n) + E,$$

so that $E = 0$ if $y(x)$ is a constant, and determine α_0, α_1, β_0, and β_1 in such a way that $E = 0$ also when $y(x) = x$, x^2, x^3, and x^4, and hence for *any* polynomial of degree four or less. For this purpose, it is convenient and nonrestrictive to take $h = 1$ and $x_n = 0$, so that the relevant equations become

$$\alpha_0 + \alpha_1 = 1, \quad 2\alpha_0 + 2(\beta_0 + \beta_1) = 1, \quad 3\alpha_0 + 6\beta_0 = 1,$$
$$4\alpha_0 + 12\beta_0 = 1,$$

and yield $\alpha_0 = \alpha_1 = \tfrac{1}{2}$ and $\beta_0 = -\beta_1 = -\tfrac{1}{12}$, in accordance with (6.14.2). The error term can then be determined by the methods of §§5.11 and 5.12, if the formula is first rewritten in the equivalent form

$$\int_0^1 f'(s)\,ds = \tfrac{1}{2}[f'(0) + f'(1)] + \tfrac{1}{12}[f''(0) - f''(1)] + E,$$

where
$$f(s) \equiv y(x_n + sh).$$

Reference to §5.12 then gives

$$E = \int_0^1 \pi(s)f'[0,0,1,1,s]\,ds, \quad \pi(s) = s^2(s - 1)^2,$$

and, since $\pi(s)$ does not change sign, there follows

$$E = \frac{f^v(\eta)}{4!}\int_0^1 \pi(s)\,ds = \tfrac{1}{720}f^v(\eta) = \tfrac{1}{720}h^5 y^v(x_n + \eta h) = \tfrac{1}{720}h^5 y^v(\xi),$$

where $0 < \eta < 1$, and hence $x_n < \xi < x_{n+1}$.

In the same way, a formula of *open* type, involving only y_{n+1}, y_{n-1}, y_n', y_{n-1}', y_n'', and y_{n-1}'', can be obtained in the form

$$y_{n+1} = y_{n-1} + 2hy_{n-1}' + \frac{2h^2}{3}(2y_n'' + y_{n-1}'') + \frac{2h^5}{45}y^v(\xi), \quad (6.14.3)$$

and can be used as a predictor in connection with (6.14.2).

Since (6.14.2) affords an accuracy which is generally better than that associated with the result of retaining fourth-order terms in the Taylor expansion

$$y_{n+1} = y_n + hy_n' + \frac{h^2}{2}y_n'' + \frac{h^3}{6}y_n''' + \frac{h^4}{24}y_n^{iv} + \frac{h^5}{120}y^v(\xi),$$

it is often useful in *starting* the solution when a procedure of fourth order is appropriate and when the calculation of values of y''' and y^{iv} is to be avoided. The formula $y_1 \approx y_0 + hy_0' + \frac{1}{2}h^2y_0''$ can be used for a *prediction* in the first step, after which (6.14.3) is available.

When the differential equation is of second order, Eqs. (6.14.2) and (6.14.3) are to be supplemented by the two equations obtained by replacing y by u, where $u = y'$. Formulas of higher-order accuracy may be obtained if derivatives of order three or more are also employed.

A useful class of formulas, associated with the name of *Obrechkoff*, can be derived by an inverse method in which we first seek a formula for $\int_0^h \phi(x)\, dx$ with an error expressed in the form

$$E = \frac{1}{(2r)!} \int_0^h x^r(x - h)^r \phi^{(2r)}(x)\, dx, \quad (6.14.4)$$

where r is an arbitrarily prescribed integer. If we integrate by parts r times, there follows immediately

$$E = \frac{1}{(2r)!} \int_0^h \phi^{(r)}(x)\, \frac{d^r}{dx^r}\,[x^r(h - x)^r]\, dx,$$

since the integrated terms vanish at both limits, and r additional integrations by parts yield the result

$$E = \int_0^h \phi(x)\, dx - \frac{r!}{(2r)!} \sum_{k=1}^r (-1)^{k-1} \frac{(2r-k)!\,h^k}{(r-k)!\,k!}\,[\phi^{(k-1)}(h)$$

$$+ (-1)^{k-1}\phi^{(k-1)}(0)] \quad (6.14.5)$$

which supplies the required formula after a transposition.

If we write $\phi(x) = y'(x)$, and translate the origin to x_n, the result takes the form

$$y_{n+1} = y_n + \frac{r!}{(2r)!} \sum_{k=1}^{r} (-1)^{k-1} \frac{(2r-k)!\,h^k}{(r-k)!\,k!} [y_{n+1}^{(k)} + (-1)^{k-1} y_n^{(k)}] + E$$

$$(6.14.6)$$

where, after an application of the second mean-value theorem, (6.14.4) becomes

$$E = \frac{y^{(2r+1)}(\xi)}{(2r)!} \int_0^h x^r (x-h)^r \, dx = (-1)^r \frac{h^{2r+1}}{2r+1} \left[\frac{r!}{(2r)!} \right]^2 y^{(2r+1)}(\xi),$$

$$(6.14.7)$$

with $x_n < \xi < x_{n+1}$.

When $r = 2$, this result becomes identical with (6.14.2). However, when $r = 3$ we obtain the formula

$$y_{n+1} = y_n + \frac{h}{2} (y_{n+1}' + y_n') - \frac{h^2}{10} (y_{n+1}'' - y_n'') + \frac{h^3}{120} (y_{n+1}''' + y_n''')$$

$$- \frac{h^7}{100800} y^{\mathrm{vii}}(\xi) \quad (6.14.8)$$

which possesses obvious advantages (in general) over the corresponding formula

$$y_{n+1} = y_n + \frac{h}{2} (y_{n+1}' + y_n') - \frac{h^2}{12} (y_{n+1}'' - y_n'') + \frac{h^4}{720} (y_{n+1}^{\mathrm{iv}} - y_n^{\mathrm{iv}})$$

$$- \frac{h^7}{30240} y^{\mathrm{vii}}(\xi), \quad (6.14.9)$$

obtained from (6.14.1). An appropriate predictor formula can be obtained in the form

$$y_{n+1} = y_{n-1} + 2h(4y_n' - 3y_{n-1}') - \frac{2h^2}{5} (8y_n'' + 7y_{n-1}'')$$

$$+ \frac{2h^3}{15} (7y_n''' - 3y_{n-1}''') + \frac{13h^7}{6300} y^{\mathrm{vii}}(\xi). \quad (6.14.10)$$

An infinite variety of other formulas can be derived by employing data relevant to more than two points for calculation, and to more than three points for prediction. Thus, for example, the three-point formula of highest precision, using first and second derivatives, is readily found to be

$$y_{n+1} - 2y_n + y_{n-1} = \frac{3h}{8} (y_{n+1}' - y_{n-1}') - \frac{h^2}{24} (y_{n+1}'' - 8y_n'' + y_{n-1}'')$$

$$+ \frac{h^8}{60480} y^{\mathrm{viii}}(\xi). \quad (6.14.11)$$

6.15. A Simple Runge-Kutta Method. The methods associated with he names of Runge, Kutta, and others, as applied to the numerical solu- ion of the problem

$$y' = F(x,y), \qquad y(x_0) = y_0, \qquad (6.15.1)$$

effectively replace the result of truncating a Taylor-series expansion of he form

$$y_{n+1} = y_n + hy'_n + \frac{h^2}{2} y''_n + \frac{h^3}{6} y'''_n + \cdots \qquad (6.15.2)$$

oy an approximation in which y_{n+1} is calculated from a formula of the type

$$\begin{aligned}
y_{n+1} = y_n &+ h[\alpha_0 F(x_n,y_n) + \alpha_1 F(x_n + \mu_1 h, y_n + b_1 h) \\
&+ \alpha_2 F(x_n + \mu_2 h, y_n + b_2 h) + \cdots + \alpha_p F(x_n + \mu_p h, y_n + b_p h)].
\end{aligned} \qquad (6.15.3)$$

Here the α's, μ's, and b's are so determined that, if the right-hand member of (6.15.3) were expanded in powers of the spacing h, the coefficients of a certain number of the leading terms would agree with the corresponding coefficients in (6.15.2).

They possess the advantages that they are self-starting but do not require the evaluation of derivatives of $F(x,y)$ and hence can be used (even at the beginning of the solution) when $F(x,y)$ is not given by an analytical expression, and also that a change in spacing is easily effected at any intermediate stage of the calculation. On the other hand, each step involves several evaluations of $F(x,y)$, which may be excessively laborious in hand computation, and also the estimation of errors is less simply accomplished than in the previously described methods.

It is convenient, in order both to simplify the derivation and also to systematize the formulation, to express each of the b's in (6.15.3) as a linear combination of the preceding values of F. Thus, in place of using the notation of (6.15.3), it is desirable to write the approximation in the form

$$y_{n+1} = y_n + \alpha_0 k_0 + \alpha_1 k_1 + \cdots + \alpha_p k_p, \qquad (6.15.4)$$

where $k_0 = hF(x_n,y_n)$,

$$\begin{aligned}
k_1 &= hF(x_n + \mu_1 h, y_n + \lambda_{10} k_0), \\
k_2 &= hF(x_n + \mu_2 h, y_n + \lambda_{20} k_0 + \lambda_{21} k_1), \qquad (6.15.5) \\
&\cdots\cdots\cdots\cdots\cdots\cdots\cdots\cdots\cdots\cdots \\
k_p &= hF(x_n + \mu_p h, y_n + \lambda_{p0} k_0 + \lambda_{p1} k_1 + \cdots + \lambda_{p,p-1} k_{p-1}),
\end{aligned}$$

and where the coefficients α_i, μ_i, and λ_{ij} are to be determined.

Since the actual derivation of such formulas involves considerable algebraic manipulation, we consider in detail only the very simple case $p = 1$, which may serve to illustrate the procedure in the more general case.   Thus, writing μ for μ_1 and λ for λ_{10}, we proceed to determine α_0, α_1, μ, and λ such that

$$y_{n+1} = y_n + \alpha_0 k_0 + \alpha_1 k_1, \qquad (6.15.6)$$

where $k_0 = hF(x_n,y_n),   \qquad   k_1 = hF(x_n + \mu h, y_n + \lambda k_0),   \qquad (6.15.7)$

possesses an expansion in powers of h whose leading terms agree, in so far as is possible, with the leading terms of (6.15.2).

We first obtain the expansion

$$k_1 = h[F + (\mu h F_x + \lambda k_0 F_y) + \tfrac{1}{2}(\mu^2 h^2 F_{xx} + 2\mu\lambda h k_0 F_{xy} + \lambda^2 k_0^2 F_{yy}) + 0(h^3)]$$

$$= hF + h^2(\mu F_x + \lambda F F_y) + \frac{h^3}{2}(\mu^2 F_{xx} + 2\mu\lambda F F_{xy} + \lambda^2 F^2 F_{yy}) + 0(h^4),$$

$$(6.15.8)$$

where $F \equiv F(x_n,y_n)$, $F_x \equiv F_x(x_n,y_n)$, and so forth.   Hence (6.15.6) becomes

$$y_{n+1} = y_n + h(\alpha_0 + \alpha_1)F + h^2\alpha_1(\mu F_x + \lambda F F_y)$$

$$+ \frac{h^3}{2}\alpha_1(\mu^2 F_{xx} + 2\mu\lambda F F_{xy} + \lambda^2 F^2 F_{yy}) + 0(h^4). \quad (6.15.9)$$

On the other hand, with the same abbreviated notation, we obtain from (6.15.1) the relations

$$y' = F, \quad y'' = F_x + F F_y, \quad y''' = F_{xx} + 2F F_{xy} + F^2 F_{yy} + F_y(F_x + F F_y),$$

$$(6.15.10)$$

so that (6.15.2) becomes

$$y_{n+1} = y_n + hF + \frac{h^2}{2}(F_x + F F_y)$$

$$+ \frac{h^3}{6}[F_{xx} + 2F F_{xy} + F^2 F_{yy} + F_y(F_x + F F_y)] + 0(h^4). \quad (6.15.11)$$

Thus, if we identify the coefficients of hF, $h^2 F_x$, and $h^2 F F_y$ in (6.15.9) and (6.15.11), we obtain the three conditions

$$\alpha_0 + \alpha_1 = 1, \qquad \mu\alpha_1 = \tfrac{1}{2}, \qquad \lambda\alpha_1 = \tfrac{1}{2}, \qquad (6.15.12)$$

involving the four adjustable parameters, which are satisfied if and only if

$$\alpha_0 = 1 - c, \qquad \alpha_1 = c, \qquad \mu = \frac{1}{2c}, \qquad \lambda = \frac{1}{2c},$$

where c is an arbitrary nonzero constant.   The expansion (6.15.9) then reduces to

$$y_{n+1} = y_n + hF + \frac{h^2}{2}(F_x + F F_y) + \frac{h^3}{8c}(F_{xx} + 2F F_{xy} + F^2 F_{yy}) + 0(h^4),$$

$$(6.15.13)$$

and reference to (6.15.10) shows that (6.15.13) or, equivalently, (6.15.6) would then be brought into agreement with (6.15.11) or (6.15.2) if a truncation-error term of the form

$$T_n = -\left(\frac{h^3}{8c} - \frac{h^3}{6}\right)[(F_{xx} + 2FF_{xy} + F^2F_{yy}) + F_y(F_x + FF_y)]$$
$$+ \frac{h^3}{8c}F_y(F_x + FF_y) + 0(h^4)$$

or $\qquad T_n = -\dfrac{h^3}{24c}[(3 - 4c)y_n''' - 3F_y(x_n,y_n)y_n''] + 0(h^4) \qquad (6.15.14)$

were added to its right-hand member.

The remaining free parameter c clearly cannot be determined so that T_n is of order h^4, except in trivial special cases. A convenient choice is $c = \frac{1}{2}$, in which case the second abscissa involved in (6.15.6) and (6.15.7) is x_{n+1}, and the formula becomes

$$y_{n+1} = y_n + \tfrac{1}{2}(k_0 + k_1) + T_n, \qquad (6.15.15)$$
where $\qquad k_0 = hF(x_n,y_n), \qquad k_1 = hF(x_n + h,\, y_n + k_0), \qquad (6.15.16)$
and where $\qquad T_n = -\dfrac{h^3}{12}[y_n''' - 3F_y(x_n,y_n)y_n''] + 0(h^4). \qquad (6.15.17)$

If, for all values of x and y involved in the calculation, it is known that

$$|F_y(x,y)| \leqq K, \qquad (6.15.18)$$

then, as in earlier developments, it is readily shown that the propagated error ϵ_n in the nth step is dominated by the solution of the difference equation

$$e_{n+1} = e_n + \frac{hK}{2}e_n + \frac{hK}{2}(e_n + hKe_n) + E$$

or $\qquad e_{n+1} = \left(1 + hK + \dfrac{h^2K^2}{2}\right)e_n + E, \qquad (6.15.19)$

where $\qquad e_0 = 0, \qquad E = |T_n + R_n|_{max}, \qquad hK + \dfrac{h^2K^2}{2} < 1. \qquad (6.15.20)$

Further, it can be shown that (6.15.17) can be replaced by

$$T_n = -\frac{h^3}{12}[y'''(\xi_1) - 3F_y(x_{n+1},\eta)y''(\xi_2)], \qquad (6.15.21)$$

where ξ_1 and ξ_2 are intermediate between x_n and x_{n+1}, and η between y_{n+1} and $y_n + hy_n'$. Thus, if the round-off error R_n is ignored, and if

$$|y''(x)| \leqq M_2, \qquad |y'''(x)| \leqq M_3, \qquad (6.15.22)$$

it follows after a simple calculation that

$$|\epsilon_n| \leqq \frac{h^2(M_3 + 3KM_2)}{12K(1 + \frac{1}{2}hK)}\left[\left(1 + hK + \frac{h^2K^2}{2}\right)^n - 1\right]. \qquad (6.15.23)$$

The formula (6.15.15), using (6.15.16), is of limited accuracy. Indeed, it can be considered to be a modification of the result of retaining only the first difference in (6.3.2),

$$y_{n+1} = y_n + \frac{h}{2}(y_n' + y_{n+1}') - \frac{h^3}{12}y'''(\xi), \qquad (6.15.24)$$

in which the unknown derivative $y_{n+1}' \equiv F(x_{n+1}, y_{n+1})$ is replaced by the approximation $y_{n+1}' \approx F(x_{n+1}, y_n + hy_n')$. This consideration is useful in deriving (6.15.21). The details of the analysis were presented here principally to illustrate the similar but more complicated analysis relevant to formulas of higher-order accuracy, certain of which are listed in the following section.

It is of some importance to notice that the error (6.15.21), associated with (6.15.15) and (6.15.16), depends upon the form of the function $F(x,y)$ as well as upon the solution y itself. This situation is characteristic of formulas of the Runge-Kutta type. For example, whereas the equations $y' = 2(x + 1)$ and $y' = 2y/(x + 1)$ both define the function $y = (x + 1)^2$ when the condition $y(0) = 1$ is imposed, the formula (6.15.15) and (6.15.16) would yield this solution *exactly* when applied to the first equation, if no round-offs were committed, but would not do so when applied to the second form. On the other hand, the formula (6.15.24) would yield exact results when applied to *either* form, or to any *other* first-order equation whose required solution is a polynomial of degree two or less (see also Milne [154, 155]).

At the same time, the mere fact that (6.15.15), with (6.15.16), does not have this last property does not imply that its interpretation as a weakened modification of (6.15.24) is proper in the more general case when the true solution is not such a polynomial. For example, it is easily seen that the use of (6.15.15) and (6.15.16) would yield exact results when applied to the problem $y' = -y/(x + 1)$, $y(0) = 1$, for which the solution is $y = 1/(x + 1)$, whereas the use of (6.15.24) would lead only to an approximation.

6.16. Runge-Kutta Methods of Higher Order. When k_0, k_1, and k_2 are employed in (6.15.4), corresponding to $p = 2$, it is found that the requirement that the expansion of the right-hand member be correct through h^3 terms imposes only six conditions on the eight arbitrary parameters involved, so that a doubly infinite set of such formulas with third-order accuracy can be obtained. One such formula, due to Kutta, is of the form

$$y_{n+1} = y_n + \tfrac{1}{6}(k_0 + 4k_1 + k_2) + 0(h^4), \qquad (6.16.1)$$

where
$$k_0 = hF(x_n, y_n),$$
$$k_1 = hF(x_n + \tfrac{1}{2}h, \ y_n + \tfrac{1}{2}k_0), \qquad (6.16.2)$$
$$k_2 = hF(x_n + h, \ y_n + 2k_1 - k_0).$$

A second, due to Heun, is of the form

$$y_{n+1} = y_n + \tfrac{1}{4}(k_0 + 3k_2) + 0(h^4), \qquad (6.16.3)$$

where
$$k_0 = hF(x_n, y_n),$$
$$k_1 = hF(x_n + \tfrac{1}{3}h, \ y_n + \tfrac{1}{3}k_0), \qquad (6.16.4)$$
$$k_2 = hF(x_n + \tfrac{2}{3}h, \ y_n + \tfrac{2}{3}k_1).$$

These two formulas are generally of about equal accuracy, with each possessing certain obvious computational advantages. Kutta's form is seen to be analogous to the formula of Simpson's rule and would reduce to that formula if F were independent of y.

It is also possible to derive a two-parameter family of formulas of fourth-order accuracy, by retaining an additional k in (6.15.4). The simplest such formula, due to Kutta, is of the form

$$y_{n+1} = y_n + \tfrac{1}{6}(k_0 + 2k_1 + 2k_2 + k_3) + 0(h^5), \qquad (6.16.5)$$

where
$$k_0 = hF(x_n, y_n),$$
$$k_1 = hF(x_n + \tfrac{1}{2}h, \ y_n + \tfrac{1}{2}k_0),$$
$$k_2 = hF(x_n + \tfrac{1}{2}h, \ y_n + \tfrac{1}{2}k_1), \qquad (6.16.6)$$
$$k_3 = hF(x_n + h, \ y_n + k_2),$$

and would also reduce to Simpson's rule if F were independent of y.

Such formulas can also be generalized to the treatment of *simultaneous* equations of the form

$$\frac{dy}{dx} = F(x, y, u),$$
$$\frac{du}{dx} = G(x, y, u), \qquad (6.16.7)$$

where y and u are prescribed when $x = x_0$. In particular, the preceding formula generalizes as follows:

$$y_{n+1} = y_n + \tfrac{1}{6}(k_0 + 2k_1 + 2k_2 + k_3) + 0(h^5),$$
$$u_{n+1} = u_n + \tfrac{1}{6}(m_0 + 2m_1 + 2m_2 + m_3) + 0(h^5), \qquad (6.16.8)$$

where
$$k_0 = hF(x_n, y_n, u_n),$$
$$k_1 = hF(x_n + \tfrac{1}{2}h, \ y_n + \tfrac{1}{2}k_0, \ u_n + \tfrac{1}{2}m_0),$$
$$k_2 = hF(x_n + \tfrac{1}{2}h, \ y_n + \tfrac{1}{2}k_1, \ u_n + \tfrac{1}{2}m_1), \qquad (6.16.9)$$
$$k_3 = hF(x_n + h, \ y_n + k_2, \ u_n + m_2),$$

and
$$m_0 = hG(x_n, y_n, u_n),$$
$$m_1 = hG(x_n + \tfrac{1}{2}h, \ y_n + \tfrac{1}{2}k_0, \ u_n + \tfrac{1}{2}m_0),$$
$$m_2 = hG(x_n + \tfrac{1}{2}h, \ y_n + \tfrac{1}{2}k_1, \ u_n + \tfrac{1}{2}m_1), \qquad (6.16.10)$$
$$m_3 = hG(x_n + h, \ y_n + k_2, \ u_n + m_2).$$

A consideration of this form indicates the way in which other formulas are so generalized.

In particular, when $F = u$, so that (6.16.7) is equivalent to

$$\frac{d^2y}{dx^2} = G(x,y,y'),$$ (6.16.11)

with $u \equiv y'$, (6.16.9) gives

$$k_0 = hy'_n, \qquad k_1 = hy'_n + \frac{h}{2}m_0, \qquad k_2 = hy'_n + \frac{h}{2}m_1, \qquad k_3 = hy'_n + hm_2,$$

and hence (6.16.8) and (6.16.10) reduce to

$$y_{n+1} = y_n + hy'_n + \frac{h}{6}(m_0 + m_1 + m_2) + 0(h^5),$$
$$y'_{n+1} = y'_n + \tfrac{1}{6}(m_0 + 2m_1 + 2m_2 + m_3) + 0(h^5),$$ (6.16.12)

where
$$m_0 = hG(x_n,y_n,y'_n),$$
$$m_1 = hG(x_n + \tfrac{1}{2}h,\ y_n + \tfrac{1}{2}hy'_n,\ y'_n + \tfrac{1}{2}m_0),$$
$$m_2 = hG(x_n + \tfrac{1}{2}h,\ y_n + \tfrac{1}{2}hy'_n + \tfrac{1}{4}hm_0,\ y'_n + \tfrac{1}{2}m_1),$$
$$m_3 = hG(x_n + h,\ y_n + hy'_n + \tfrac{1}{2}hm_1,\ y'_n + m_2).$$ (6.16.13)

The use of this formula is clearly simplified in those cases when G is independent of y'.

Many variations and generalizations of these formulas are present in the literature, some of which afford certain computational advantages in certain situations.

One such modification, due to Gill [94], is of particular usefulness when the computation is to be effected by large-scale calculators, in which the *storage* of data is to be minimized.

No simple expressions are known for the precise truncation errors in the preceding formulas. An *estimate* of the error can be obtained, in practice, in the following way. Let the truncation error associated with a formula of rth-order accuracy, in progressing from the ordinate at x_n to that at $x_{n+1} = x_n + h$, in a single step, be denoted by $C_n h^{r+1}$, and suppose that C_n varies slowly with n and is nearly independent of h when h is small. Then if the true ordinate at x_{n+1} is denoted by Y_{n+1}, the value obtained by two steps starting at x_{n-1} by $y_{n+1}^{(h)}$, and the value obtained by a single step with *doubled* spacing $2h$ by $y_{n+1}^{(2h)}$, there follows approximately

$$Y_{n+1} - y_{n+1}^{(h)} \approx 2C_n h^{r+1},$$
$$Y_{n+1} - y_{n+1}^{(2h)} \approx 2^{r+1}C_n h^{r+1},$$ (6.16.14)

when h is small. The result of eliminating C_n from these approximate relations is then the *extrapolation* formula†

$$Y_{n+1} \approx y_{n+1}^{(h)} + \frac{y_{n+1}^{(h)} - y_{n+1}^{(2h)}}{2^r - 1}.$$ (6.16.15)

† This is another example of so-called *Richardson extrapolation* (see §3.6).

Thus if, at certain stages of the advancing calculation, the newly calculated ordinate y_{n+1} is recomputed from y_{n-1} with a doubled spacing, the truncation error in the originally calculated value is approximated by the result of dividing the difference between the two values by the factor $2^r - 1$, that is, by 3 in (6.15.15), by 7 in (6.16.1) or (6.16.3), and by 15 in the formulas of fourth-order accuracy.

It is apparent that an arbitrary change in spacing can be introduced at any stage of the forward progress, when a method of the Runge-Kutta type is used, without introducing any appreciable complication.

6.17. Boundary-value Problems.   Problems in which the conditions to be satisfied by the solution of a differential equation, of order two or greater, are specified at both ends of an interval in which the solution is required are known as *boundary-value* problems and are generally much less amenable to numerical analysis than are *initial-value* problems, in which all conditions are imposed at one point.   In this section, we consider briefly the application of certain elementary methods to the numerical solution of such problems.   More efficient methods can often be based upon the result of reformulating the problem as an *integral equation* or as a problem in the *calculus of variations*, the treatment of both of which falls outside the scope of this work.

For a *linear* problem, such as one governed by a second-order equation of the form
$$y'' + P(x)y' + Q(x)y = F(x) \qquad (a < x < b), \qquad (6.17.1)$$

and by the end conditions
$$y(a) = A, \qquad y(b) = B, \qquad (6.17.2)$$

where A and B are prescribed, the analysis can be based on the principle of superposition.   Thus, if $u(x)$ is *any* solution of the equation
$$u'' + Pu' + Qu = F \qquad (6.17.3)$$

which satisfies the initial condition
$$u(a) = A, \qquad (6.17.4)$$

and $v(x)$ is any *nontrivial* solution of the equation
$$v'' + Pv' + Qv = 0 \qquad (6.17.5)$$

which satisfies the initial condition
$$v(a) = 0, \qquad (6.17.6)$$

then the function
$$y(x) = u(x) + cv(x) \qquad (6.17.7)$$

satisfies (6.17.1) and the condition $y(a) = A$ for *any* constant value of c.

Further, if P, Q, and F are continuous in (a,b), there cannot exist addi tional functions having this property. Thus, a solution is found if c ca be determined such that

$$u(b) + cv(b) = B. \qquad (6.17.8$$

Unless c can be so determined, no solution exists.

If P, Q, and F are continuous in (a,b), the initial slopes $u'(a)$ and $v'(a$ can be chosen arbitrarily, so long as $v'(a) \neq 0$; the choices $u'(a) = 0$ an $v'(a) = 1$ are frequently convenient. It may be noticed that, if $u(b) = I$ and $v(b) = 0$, then c is arbitrary and infinitely many solutions exist; i $u(b) \neq B$ and $v(b) = 0$, then *no* solution exists. Unless it happens tha $v(b) = 0$, the solution exists uniquely. Any of the previously discusse methods can be used in determining u and v.

In the case of a corresponding nonlinear problem, such as that governe by an equation of the more general form

$$y'' = G(x,y,y') \qquad (a < x < b) \qquad (6.17.9$$

and the end conditions

$$y(a) = A, \qquad y(b) = B, \qquad (6.17.10$$

superposition generally is not valid. One possible procedure consists i defining $u(x,\alpha)$ as the solution of the initial-value problem

$$\begin{aligned} u'' &= G(x,u,u'), \\ u(a) &= A, \qquad u'(a) = \alpha, \end{aligned} \qquad (6.17.11$$

and attempting to determine α such that

$$u(b,\alpha) = B. \qquad (6.17.12$$

For this purpose, $u(b)$ could be determined for two or more trial values of α Then, by linear (or higher-order) inverse interpolation, an "improved" value of α would be obtained, and the process would be iterated unti (6.17.12) is satisfactorily approximated, if the iteration converges.

The process is apt to be tedious, and is complicated by the fact tha small changes in α do not necessarily correspond to small changes i $u(b,\alpha)$. Further, the basic questions of existence and uniqueness of th solution are particularly troublesome in themselves, in the general non linear case. There exists no completely satisfactory general method (numerical or otherwise) for dealing with such problems.

Problems in which the end conditions prescribe y' or a linear combina tion of y and y', or which are expressed in a more complicated way, involve more or less obvious modifications.

Another class of methods, which is usually convenient only when the problem is *linear*, consists in approximating the differential equation by a difference equation and in solving the *simultaneous* set of algebraic

quations resulting from the requirement that this equation be satisfied
t each of a set of equally spaced points in the relevant interval.†

In illustration, any linear second-order equation can be transformed
o an equation of the form

$$y'' + f(x)y = g(x), \tag{6.17.13}$$

s was pointed out at the end of §6.12.   Reference to Eq. (5.6.7) yields
he relation

$$y_{n+1} - 2y_n + y_{n-1} = h^2(1 + \tfrac{1}{12}\delta^2)y_n'' + T_n, \tag{6.17.14}$$

where the truncation error T_n is expressible in the form

$$T_n = -\frac{h^6}{240}y^{vi}(\xi) \qquad (x_{n-1} < \xi < x_{n+1}). \tag{6.17.15}$$

Thus, if we use (6.17.13) to replace y_n'' by $g_n - f_n y_n$, (6.17.14) takes
he form

$$\left(1 + \frac{h^2}{12}f_{n+1}\right)y_{n+1} - 2\left(1 - \frac{5h^2}{12}f_n\right)y_n + \left(1 + \frac{h^2}{12}f_{n-1}\right)y_{n-1}$$
$$= \frac{h^2}{12}(g_{n+1} + 10g_n + g_{n-1}) + T_n. \tag{6.17.16}$$

Now, if the interval (a,b) is divided into $N + 1$ equal parts, in such a
way that $x_0 = a$, $x_1 = a + h$, $\cdots$, $x_N = a + Nh$, $x_{N+1} = b$, where
$\iota = (b - a)/(N + 1)$, we may require the result of ignoring T_n in
6.17.16) to hold for $n = 1, 2, \ldots, N$, and so obtain a set of N simultaneous linear algebraic equations in $y_1, y_2, \ldots, y_N$, of the form

$$\left(1 + \frac{h^2}{12}f_0\right)y_0 - 2\left(1 - \frac{5h^2}{12}f_1\right)y_1 + \left(1 + \frac{h^2}{12}f_2\right)y_2 = \frac{h^2}{12}G_1,$$
$$\left(1 + \frac{h^2}{12}f_1\right)y_1 - 2\left(1 - \frac{5h^2}{12}f_2\right)y_2 + \left(1 + \frac{h^2}{12}f_3\right)y_3 = \frac{h^2}{12}G_2,$$
$$\cdots\cdots\cdots\cdots\cdots\cdots\cdots\cdots\cdots\cdots$$
$$\left(1 + \frac{h^2}{12}f_{N-1}\right)y_{N-1} - 2\left(1 - \frac{5h^2}{12}f_N\right)y_N + \left(1 + \frac{h^2}{12}f_{N+1}\right)y_{N+1} = \frac{h^2}{12}G_N, \tag{6.17.17}$$

where $G(x) \equiv g(x + h) + 10g(x) + g(x - h)$, supplemented by the prescribed conditions $y_0 = A$ and $y_{N+1} = B$.

In virtue of (6.17.15), this procedure is of fifth order, in the sense that
t would afford exact results if $y(x)$ were a polynomial of degree five or
ess. A simpler procedure, of third order, corresponds to the neglect of
second differences in (6.17.14) and hence consists in solving the simulta-

† Such methods are often preferred to step-by-step methods since their use does not
involve stepwise *propagation* of errors.

neous equations

$$y_{n+1} - 2\left(1 - \frac{h^2}{2}f_n\right)y_n + y_{n-1} = h^2 g_n \qquad (n = 1, 2, \ldots, N),$$

(6.17.18)

supplemented by the boundary conditions.

On the other hand, if fourth differences are retained in (5.6.7), the corresponding equations are easily obtained in the form

$$-\frac{h^2}{240}f_{n+2}y_{n+2} + \left(1 + \frac{h^2}{10}f_{n+1}\right)y_{n+1} - 2\left(1 - \frac{97h^2}{240}f_n\right)y_n$$
$$+ \left(1 + \frac{h^2}{10}f_{n-1}\right)y_{n-1} - \frac{h^2}{240}f_{n-2}y_{n-2}$$
$$= \frac{h^2}{240}\left(-g_{n+2} + 24g_{n+1} + 194g_n + 24g_{n-1} - g_{n-2}\right), \quad (6.17.19)$$

and would reduce to identities for $n = 2, 3, \ldots, N - 1$ if $y(x)$ were a polynomial of degree seven or less. For $n = 1$ and $n = N$, Eq. (6.17.19) would involve the irrelevant quantities y_{-1} and y_{N+2}. Two additional "off-center" relations, which would also be satisfied exactly by any polynomial solution of degree seven or less, are thus needed. They may be obtained, for example, by retaining *fifth* differences in the backward-difference formula (5.5.11), relative to $\nabla^2 y_{N+1}$, and in the corresponding forward-difference formula relative to $\Delta^2 y_0$, in the forms†

$$\left(1 + \frac{3h^2}{40}f_0\right)y_0 - 2\left(1 - \frac{209h^2}{480}f_1\right)y_1 + \left(1 + \frac{h^2}{60}f_2\right)y_2$$
$$+ \frac{7h^2}{120}f_3 y_3 - \frac{h^2}{40}f_4 y_4 + \frac{h^2}{240}f_5 y_5$$
$$= \frac{h^2}{240}\left(18g_0 + 209g_1 + 4g_2 + 14g_3 - 6g_4 + g_5\right) \quad (6.17.20)$$

and

$$\frac{h^2}{240}f_{N-4}y_{N-4} - \frac{h^2}{40}f_{N-3}y_{N-3} + \frac{7h^2}{120}f_{N-2}y_{N-2} + \left(1 + \frac{h^2}{60}f_{N-1}\right)y_{N-1}$$
$$- 2\left(1 - \frac{209h^2}{480}f_N\right)y_N + \left(1 + \frac{3h^2}{40}f_{N+1}\right)y_{N+1}$$
$$= \frac{h^2}{240}\left(g_{N-4} - 6g_{N-3} + 14g_{N-2} + 4g_{N-1} + 209g_N + 18g_{N+1}\right). \quad (6.17.21)$$

---

† The same relations can be obtained by using the approximate relations

$$\Delta^6 y''_{-1} = \Delta^6(g_{-1} - f_{-1}y_{-1}) = 0, \qquad \nabla^6 y''_{N+2} = \nabla^6(g_{N+2} - f_{N+2}y_{N+2}) = 0$$

to eliminate the ordinates y_{-1} and y_{N+2} from the equations which correspond to setting $n = 1$ and $n = N$ in (6.17.19).

The $N - 2$ equations (6.17.19), the two equations (6.17.20) and (6.17.21), and the two prescribed end conditions serve to determine (approximately) the values of the $N + 2$ ordinates $y_0, y_1, \ldots, y_N, y_{N+1}$. Here the interval (a,b) must be divided into at least five equal parts.

If the prescribed end condition at $x = a \equiv x_0$ involves $y'(a)$ in place of (or in combination with) $y(a)$, that condition can be replaced by an appropriate approximate one, involving y_0 and y_1, by means of the result of retaining terms through h^n (where n is the order of the procedure used) in the expansion

$$\Delta y_0 = \left(h\mathbf{D} + \frac{1}{2!} h^2\mathbf{D}^2 + \frac{1}{3!} h^3\mathbf{D}^3 + \frac{1}{4!} h^4\mathbf{D}^4 + \cdots \right) y_0,$$

combined with (6.17.13), to give

$$y_1 - y_0 = hy_0' + \frac{h^2}{2}(g_0 - f_0 y_0) + \frac{h^3}{6}(g_0' - f_0' y_0 - f_0 y_0')$$

$$+ \frac{h^4}{24}(g_0'' - f_0'' y_0 - 2f_0' y_0' - f_0 g_0 + f_0^2 y_0) + \cdots$$

or

$$y_1 = y_0 \left[1 - \frac{h^2}{2} f_0 - \frac{h^3}{6} f_0' - \frac{h^4}{24}(f_0'' - f_0^2) - \frac{h^5}{120}(f_0''' - 4f_0' f_0) - \cdots \right]$$

$$+ y_0' \left[h - \frac{h^3}{6} f_0 - \frac{h^4}{12} f_0' - \frac{h^5}{120}(3f_0'' - f_0^2) - \cdots \right]$$

$$+ \left[\frac{h^2}{2} g_0 + \frac{h^3}{6} g_0' + \frac{h^4}{24}(g_0'' - f_0 g_0) \right.$$

$$\left. + \frac{h^5}{120}(g_0''' - 3f_0' g_0 - f_0 g_0') + \cdots \right]. \quad (6.17.22)$$

A similar relation, for use at $x = b \equiv x_{N+1}$, is obtainable from the expansion

$$\nabla y_{N+1} = \left(h\mathbf{D} - \frac{1}{2!} h^2\mathbf{D}^2 + \frac{1}{3!} h^3\mathbf{D}^3 - \frac{1}{4!} h^4\mathbf{D}^4 + \cdots \right) y_{N+1}.$$

6.18. Linear Characteristic-value Problems. When $g(x) \equiv 0$ in (6.17.13), and the prescribed end conditions are of the special form $y(a) = y(b) = 0$, one solution of the problem is clearly the "trivial solution" $y(x) \equiv 0$. It frequently happens that an arbitrary constant parameter λ is linearly involved in the definition of the function $f(x)$ and that it is then desired to determine values of λ for which the problem also admits a *nontrivial* solution. Such values of λ are known as its *characteristic values* (or *eigenvalues*), and the corresponding solutions are called the *characteristic functions* of the problem. The study of their properties and applications comprises an important field of mathematics, and a great variety of methods have been (and are being) devised fo their approximate numerical treatment.

One such method can be based on the result of appropriately specializ ing (6.17.17). Thus, if the problem is of the form

$$y'' + [q(x) + \lambda r(x)]y = 0,$$
$$y(a) = y(b) = 0, \tag{6.18.1}$$

we may replace f by $q + \lambda r$ in (6.17.17), to obtain a set of N equations o the form

$$-2\left[\left(1 - \frac{5h^2}{12} q_1\right) - \frac{5h^2}{12} \lambda r_1\right] y_1 + \left[\left(1 + \frac{h^2}{12} q_2\right) + \frac{h^2}{12} \lambda r_2\right] y_2 = 0,$$

$$\left[\left(1 + \frac{h^2}{12} q_1\right) + \frac{h^2}{12} \lambda r_1\right] y_1 - 2\left[\left(1 - \frac{5h^2}{12} q_2\right) - \frac{5h^2}{12} \lambda r_2\right] y_2$$
$$+ \left[\left(1 + \frac{h^2}{12} q_3\right) + \frac{h^2}{12} \lambda r_3\right] y_3 = 0$$

. . . .

$$\left[\left(1 + \frac{h^2}{12} q_{N-1}\right) + \frac{h^2}{12} \lambda r_{N-1}\right] y_{N-1}$$
$$- 2\left[\left(1 - \frac{5h^2}{12} q_N\right) - \frac{5h^2}{12} \lambda r_N\right] y_N = 0. \tag{6.18.2}$$

This set of homogeneous linear equations will admit a nontrivial solu tion for $y_1, y_2, \ldots, y_N$ if and only if the determinant of the array c coefficients vanishes (see §10.2), a requirement which demands that λ be a root of an algebraic equation of degree N if no one of the values o r vanishes, as is generally the case in practice. For each such value of λ this set of equations becomes redundant and (at least) one equation ca be ignored, after which the remaining equations can be solved for th *ratios* of certain of the ordinates to the remaining one or ones. Excep in unusual cases, only one of the ordinates (but, generally, *any* one) ca be chosen arbitrarily, and the ratios of the remaining ones to that one ar determinate. In this way, approximations to N of the characteristi numbers (generally the N *smallest* ones) of the true problem are obtained together with ordinates of the corresponding characteristic functions defined within a common arbitrary multiplicative factor.

The crudest approximation is obtained by taking $N = 1$, so that onl the central ordinate y_1, at $x = (a + b)/2$, is involved, and $y_0 = y_2 = 0$ Thus only the equation

$$-2\left[\left(1 - \frac{5h^2}{12} q_1\right) - \frac{5h^2}{12} \lambda r_1\right] y_1 = 0$$

is obtained, and the requirement $y_1 \neq 0$ leads to the approximation

$$\lambda = \frac{12}{5h^2r_1}\left(1 - \frac{5h^2q_1}{12}\right) \equiv \lambda_1^{(1)} \qquad \left(h = \frac{b-a}{2}\right) \qquad (6.18.3)$$

to the smallest characteristic number λ_1. The ordinate y_1 is then indeterminate.

When $N = 2$, the two permissible values of λ are found to be the roots of the determinantal equation

$$\begin{vmatrix} -2\left[\left(1 - \frac{5h^2}{12}q_1\right) - \frac{5h^2}{12}\lambda r_1\right] & \left[\left(1 + \frac{h^2}{12}q_2\right) + \frac{h^2}{12}\lambda r_2\right] \\ \left[\left(1 + \frac{h^2}{12}q_1\right) + \frac{h^2}{12}\lambda r_1\right] & -2\left[\left(1 - \frac{5h^2}{12}q_2\right) - \frac{5h^2}{12}\lambda r_2\right] \end{vmatrix} = 0,$$

$$(6.18.4)$$

where $h = (b - a)/3$, and may be denoted by $\lambda_1^{(2)}$ and $\lambda_2^{(1)}$. For each of these calculated values of λ, there follows also, from the first equation,

$$\frac{y_2}{y_1} = 2\frac{(1 - 5h^2q_1/12) - (5h^2r_1/12)\lambda}{(1 + h^2q_2/12) + (h^2r_2/12)\lambda}, \qquad (6.18.5)$$

with y_1 arbitrary. The use of the second equation would lead to an equivalent result.

In illustration, the problem

$$Y'' + 2Y' + \lambda xY = 0, \qquad Y(0) = Y(1) = 0 \qquad (6.18.6)$$

is transformed to the problem

$$y'' - y + \lambda xy = 0, \qquad y(0) = y(1) = 0, \qquad (6.18.7)$$

with the change of variables

$$Y = e^{-x}y, \qquad (6.18.8)$$

in accordance with (6.12.23). With $q(x) = -1$ and $r(x) = x$, Eq. (6.18.3) yields

$$\lambda_1^{(1)} = \tfrac{96}{5}(1 + \tfrac{5}{48}) = \tfrac{106}{5} = 21.2.$$

Equation (6.18.4) becomes

$$\begin{vmatrix} -2\left(\dfrac{399 - 5\lambda}{324}\right) & \dfrac{321 + 2\lambda}{324} \\ \dfrac{321 + \lambda}{324} & -2\left(\dfrac{399 - 10\lambda}{324}\right) \end{vmatrix} = 0,$$

and expands into the relevant *characteristic equation*

$$22\lambda^2 - 2367\lambda + 39627 = 0,$$

to yield a second approximation $\lambda_1^{(2)} \doteq 20.74$ to λ_1 and a first approximation $\lambda_2^{(1)} \doteq 89.38$ to λ_2. Equation (6.18.5) becomes

$$\frac{y_2}{y_1} = \frac{678 - 10\lambda}{321 + 2\lambda}$$

and yields $y_2/y_1 \doteq 1.30$ for $\lambda_1^{(2)}$ and $y_2/y_1 \doteq -0.432$ for $\lambda_2^{(1)}$. Thus, from (6.18.8) there follows $Y(\frac{2}{3})/Y(\frac{1}{3}) \approx 0.93$ in the first "mode" and -0.31 in the second one.

If three interior ordinates were used, to afford improved approximations to λ_1 and λ_2, and a first approximation to λ_3, it would be necessary to expand a determinant of third order and to determine the roots of a cubic equation. Various iterative techniques for determining the roots of the relevant characteristic equation without explicitly expanding the determinant, in such cases, exist in the literature (for example, see Frazer, Duncan, and Collar [88]).

A simpler procedure would be based on the use of (6.17.18), whereas a more elaborate procedure could be based on (6.17.19) to (6.17.21).

Modifications, which are appropriate to situations when a linear combination of y and y' is required to vanish at each end of the interval, may be based on the use of (6.17.22) and a similar equation relevant to $x = b$, with $f = q + \lambda r$ and $g = 0$, in place of the conditions $y_0 = y_{N+1} = 0$.

In the simple special case when $q(x) = 0$ and $r(x) = 1$, so that (6.18.1) reduces to $y'' + \lambda y = 0$, where $y(a) = y(b) = 0$, the exact value of the rth characteristic value is easily found to be

$$\lambda_r = \frac{r^2 \pi^2}{(b - a)^2}.$$

The approximation $\bar{\lambda}_r$ afforded by use of the simpler procedure is known to be

$$\bar{\lambda}_r = \frac{4}{h^2} \sin^2 \left(\frac{h}{2} \sqrt{\lambda_r} \right),$$

whereas that afforded by use of (6.18.2) can be shown to be

$$\bar{\lambda}_r = \frac{4}{h^2} \frac{\sin^2 [(h/2) \sqrt{\lambda_r}]}{1 - \frac{1}{3} \sin^2 [(h/2) \sqrt{\lambda_r}]},$$

where $h = (b - a)/(N + 1)$, from which results the nature of the approximations to the first N characteristic numbers can be determined in the two cases. In particular, the error in the former case is found to be positive and less than $h^2 \lambda_r^2/12$, whereas that in the latter case is positive and less than $h^4 \lambda_r^3/240$. The error associated with the use of the more elaborate seventh-order procedure would be of the order of $h^6 \lambda_r^4$. These facts permit crude preliminary estimates of the requisite number of subdivisions in similar (but less simple) cases.

When only the smallest characteristic number, and the associated mode, is required, the present methods are objectionable since the determination of the Nth approximation essentially entails the formation and solution of an algebraic equation of Nth degree (although, as was mentioned above, some of this labor can be avoided by matrix iteration). In such cases, the use of a variational method, such as that based on *Rayleigh's principle* (see Temple and Bickley [223]), is often preferable.

6.19. Selection of a Method. Whereas a rather large number of methods for dealing with initial-value problems have been outlined in this chapter, it should be remarked that a substantial number of additional variations may also be found in the literature. The problem of deciding which one of these methods is most appropriate, in any specific situation, is a particularly troublesome one because of the large number of factors which may affect the decision.

First of all, the choice will depend upon the nature of the computational device to be used. Thus, for example, a method which is well adapted to the use of a desk calculator may be inconvenient for hand calculation because of the fact that it involves too many operations with multidigit numbers; or it may be inappropriate for a certain large-scale computing device for the reason that each step in the advancing calculation requires the availability of more independent data than can be accommodated in the storage unit of that device, the execution of operations for which the arithmetical unit is not well adapted, or a more involved sequence of operations than can be programed in the control unit. These restrictions vary so considerably from one device to another that no general discussion can be attempted here.

Again, a procedure which involves a large number of iterations of a relatively simple technique may be remarkably well adapted to an automatic high-speed calculator, but its use may entail a prohibitive amount of time when the calculations are to be made by hand.

A procedure which involves a large number of evaluations of a certain function $F(x,y)$ may not be objectionable for hand calculation if $F(x,y)$ is well tabulated, but may require an undesirably complicated program in machine calculation. On the other hand, the situation may be completely reversed if the function is of complicated analytical form and if a routine is available for generating it directly in the computer.

Stability considerations may be of great importance, for a given problem, when a large number of steps is to be taken, but may be much less significant when only a relatively small number of ordinates is required, or when a different problem is dealt with. The computational advantages associated with a simple procedure with relatively large truncation error must be weighed against the fact that the use of that procedure generally requires a small spacing and a correspondingly large number of steps, and hence increases the importance of the effects of round-off errors. At the same time, such a procedure may be preferred to a more elaborate one when its use permits a fairly confident estimate of an upper bound on the total propagated error, whereas such an estimate corresponding to the use of the more elaborate procedure is not readily available.

One may be faced with the problem of choosing the procedure which is most appropriate in the solution of a single differential equation, or that which appears to be best on the average for a wide class of equations.

The methods described in this chapter, for advancing the solution, fall into three broad classes: (1) methods which express the future ordinate as a linear combination of present and/or past ordinates and slopes (§§6.5, 6.6, 6.10, 6.12); (2) methods which also involve the calculation of certain higher derivatives (§6.14); and (3) methods in which the determination of the future ordinate does not involve memory of the past (§§6.15, 6.16).

The Euler procedure and its modification of closed type are the simplest of the procedures in the first class. The Adams method and its closed-type modification and the Milne methods are the most frequently used procedures of higher-order accuracy in this class. In either case, the relevant formulas may be expressed either in terms of differences of slopes or in terms of the slopes themselves. The Milne procedure using a given number of slopes is generally of higher-order accuracy than the corresponding Adams procedure, but it compares unfavorably with the latter from the point of view of stability. Except for the crude Euler method, the procedures in this class are not self-starting.

The methods of the second class are highly efficient when and only when the differential equation is of such a form that analytical relations between higher derivatives of the unknown function and the function itself are readily obtained. If derivatives at only two points are used, the special methods actually treated are effectively self-starting.

The Runge-Kutta methods, of the third class, possess the advantage that, since their use at each stage of the advancing calculation does not require information relevant to past stages, they are completely self-starting and are particularly appropriate when memory requirements are to be minimized. Furthermore, these procedures are inherently stable and are such that a change in spacing is easily effected at any stage of the advance. The principal disadvantage consists in the fact that each forward step entails several evaluations of the "right-hand member" of the differential equation, a fact which may be of considerable importance in hand calculation. In addition, the nonexistence of a tractable expression for the associated truncation error is a source of some inconvenience.

For the purpose of starting a solution, when a method of the first class is to be used for advancing the solution, one may choose among the methods of the second and third classes as well as the methods of §6.4. When the right-hand member of the differential equation is of such a form that the formation of higher derivatives is readily effected, the use of Taylor series (§6.4) or of series which involve values of higher derivatives at two points (§6.14) is often convenient.   Otherwise, resort may be had to one of the iterative methods of §6.4 or to the methods of Runge-Kutta type (§§6.15, 6.16).

6.20. Supplementary References.   Texts on the numerical solution of ordinary differential equations include Levy and Baggot [132], Collatz [58], and Milne [155], each of which presents a useful bibliography. For analytical methods of solution and general theory, see Bateman [32] and Ince [120].   Selected journal references to special numerical methods are included in the present bibliography.   For stability considerations relevant to step-by-step methods, see Todd [224], Rutishauser [200], Mitchell and Craggs [159], and Collatz [59].   Errors are discussed by von Mises [156], Brouwer [51], Tollmien [225, 226], Turton [228], Rademacher [187], Duncan [71], Weissinger [233, 234], Bieberbach [41], Mohr [161], Richter [196], Matthieu [144], and Sterne [217].   Round-off error bias is treated by Huskey and Hartree [119] and Forsythe [79].   For the numerical solution of boundary-value and characteristic-value problems governed by ordinary differential equations, see Collatz [56], Nyström [170], Temple [222], and Fox [83].   Sampling ("Monte Carlo") methods, described, for example, in Householder, Forsythe, and Germond [118] and by Curtiss [66], are intended primarily for the solution of more involved problems, but are also applicable, in principle, to ordinary differential equations.

PROBLEMS

Section 6.2

1. Show that the operator affecting y'_n in the open formula (6.2.12) relating y_{n+1} and y_{n-p} can be obtained by multiplying the one corresponding to $p = 0$ in (6.2.10) by

$$\frac{1 - (1 - \nabla)^{p+1}}{\nabla} = (p + 1) - \frac{(p + 1)p}{2!} \nabla + \cdots,$$

and use this method to derive (6.2.13) to (6.2.15), as well as the formulas corresponding to $p = 2$ and $p = 4$.

2. Verify that the results of terminating (6.2.13) to (6.2.15) with the zeroth, second, and fourth differences, respectively, are Newton-Cotes formulas of open type.

Section 6.3

3. Show that the method used in Prob. 1 also applies to the closed formulas, and derive the formulas relating y_{n+1} and y_{n-p} from (6.3.2) for $p = 1, 2, 3, 4$, and 5 in this way.

4. Verify that the results of terminating (6.3.3) to (6.3.5) with the second, fourth, and sixth differences, respectively, are Newton-Cotes formulas of closed type.

Section 6.4

5. Obtain additional values of y, corresponding to $x = \pm 0.1$ and ± 0.2, for each of the following problems, by use of power series, rounding the results to five decimal places:

(a) $y' + y = 0$, $y(0) = 1$.
(b) $y' + 2xy = 2x^3$, $y(0) = 0$.
(c) $y' + y + xy^2 = 0$, $y(0) = 1$.
(d) $xy' = 1 - y + x^2y^2$, $y(0) = 1$.

[The respective analytical solutions are e^{-x}, $e^{-x^2} - 1 + x^2$, $(2e^x - 1 - x)^{-1}$, and $(\tan x)/x$.]

6. (a) to (d) Proceed as in Prob. 5 by Picard's method.

7. (a) to (d) Proceed as in Prob. 5 by use of Eqs. (6.4.14).

8. Obtain additional starting values of y when $x = 0.1, 0.2, 0.3,$ and 0.4 for the following problem, by use of Eqs. (6.4.13), assuming that only the tabulated values of $\phi(x)$ are available, and rounding the results to five decimal places:

$$y' + xy = \phi(x), \qquad y(0) = 1.$$

x	$\phi(x)$	x	$\phi(x)$
0.0	1.00000	0.6	1.16412
0.1	1.00499	0.7	1.21579
0.2	1.01980	0.8	1.27059
0.3	1.04399	0.9	1.32660
0.4	1.07683	1.0	1.38177
0.5	1.11730		

[Here $\phi(x) \approx \cos x + x \sin x$, and hence $y(x) \approx e^{-x^2/2} + \sin x$.]

Section 6.5

9. (a) to (d) Advance the calculation of the solutions of Prob. 5 to $x = 1$ with $h = 0.1$ by use of the Adams method, rounding all calculated ordinates to five decimal places and estimating the errors.

10. (a) to (d) Proceed as in Prob. 9, using Eq. (6.2.18).

11. Advance the calculations of Prob. 8 to $x = 1$ with $h = 0.1$, (a) by use of the Adams method and (b) by use of (6.2.18), rounding all calculated ordinates to five decimal places and estimating the errors.

Section 6.6

12. (a) to (e) Recalculate the ordinates required in Probs. 9(a) to (d) and 11 by use of the modified Adams method, again retaining five places and estimating the errors.

13. (a) to (e) Proceed as in Prob. 12 by use of Milne's method.

Section 6.7

14. Show that the approximate solution of the problem

$$y' + y = 0, \qquad y(0) = 1$$

afforded by the result of retaining first differences in the formula (6.3.2) would be of the form

$$y_n^{(1)} = \left(\frac{2 - h}{2 + h}\right)^n$$

if no round-offs were effected, and that corresponding to retention of first differences in (6.3.3) would be of the form

$$y_n^{(2)} = \frac{1}{2\sqrt{1+h^2}}[(\sqrt{1+h^2}+h+y_1)(\sqrt{1+h^2}-h)^n$$
$$+ (-1)^n(\sqrt{1+h^2}-h-y_1)(\sqrt{1+h^2}+h)^n],$$

where y_1 is the independently calculated approximation to the true value e^{-h}, whereas the exact solution is given by $y_n = e^{-nh}$.

15. Show that, when h is small, the solutions obtained in Prob. 14 can be expressed in the forms

$$y_n^{(1)} = (e^{-h} - \tfrac{1}{12}h^3 + \cdots)^n$$

and

$$y_n^{(2)} = [(1 - \tfrac{1}{12}h^3 + \cdots) - \tfrac{1}{2}\epsilon(1 - \tfrac{1}{2}h^2 + \cdots)](e^{-h} + \tfrac{1}{6}h^3 + \cdots)^n$$
$$+ (-1)^n[(\tfrac{1}{12}h^3 + \cdots) + \tfrac{1}{2}\epsilon(1 - \tfrac{1}{2}h^2 + \cdots)](e^h - \tfrac{1}{6}h^3 + \cdots)^n,$$

where ϵ represents the error associated with the value employed for y_1, and where omitted terms in each expansion are small, of order h^4.

16. Suppose that a spacing $h = 0.1$ is used in the approximations of Prob. 14, and that the value of y_1 used in the second calculation is assumed to be free of error. Calculate the errors and relative errors in the two approximations for values of n in the neighborhood of 10, 50, and 100, neglecting the effects of round-off errors.

17. Show that, when Milne's second-difference method is used, the parasitic part $u_n \equiv u(x_n)$ of the approximate solution of the problem

$$y' = Ay, \qquad y(0) = y_0,$$

where A is a constant, is approximated by

$$u_n \approx (-1)^n \left[\frac{A^5h^5}{360}y_0 + \tfrac{1}{2}\epsilon\right] e^{-Ax_n/3}$$

when $|Ah|$ is small, where ϵ is the error inherent in y_1.

Section 6.8

18. If the formula

$$y_{n+1} = y_n + h(\alpha_{-1}y_{n+1}' + \alpha_0 y_n')$$

is used for the numerical solution of the problem

$$y' = F(x,y), \qquad y(x_0) = y_0,$$

if $\alpha_{-1} \geq 0$, $\alpha_0 \geq 0$, if $|F_y(x,y)| \leq K$ throughout the calculation leading to y_n, and if $Kh\alpha_{-1} < 1$, show that the error ϵ_n in y_n is bounded by the inequality

$$|\epsilon_n| \leq \frac{E}{Kh}\left[\left(\frac{1+Kh\alpha_0}{1-Kh\alpha_{-1}}\right)^n - 1\right] \approx \frac{E}{Kh}(e^{nKh}-1),$$

where E is the largest error introduced in a single step. Also specialize to the cases $(\alpha_{-1} = 0, \alpha_0 = 1)$, $(\alpha_{-1} = 1, \alpha_0 = 0)$, and $(\alpha_{-1} = \alpha_0 = \tfrac{1}{2})$, showing that E is given by $\tfrac{1}{2}h^2M_2 + R$ in the first two cases and by $\tfrac{1}{12}h^3M_3 + R$ in the third case, where M_k is the maximum value of $|y^{(k)}(x)|$ for $x_0 \leq x \leq x_n$, and where R is the maximum round-off error introduced in a single step.

19. Suppose that $F_y(x,y)$ is known to be negative throughout the calculation considered in Prob. 18, and also that

$$0 < \omega \leqq -F_y(x,y)$$

where ω is a constant. Show that then ϵ_n is dominated by e_n, where

$$(1 + h\omega\alpha_{-1})e_{n+1} = (1 - h\omega\alpha_0)e_n + E \qquad (n = 0, 1, 2, \ldots)$$

and $e_0 = 0$, if $h\omega\alpha_0 < 1$, and deduce the more useful bound

$$|\epsilon_n| \leqq \frac{E}{\omega h}\left[1 - \left(\frac{1 - h\omega\alpha_0}{1 + h\omega\alpha_{-1}}\right)^n\right] \approx \frac{E}{\omega h}\left(1 - e^{-n\omega h}\right)$$

in this case.

20. Suppose that the formula of the Adams method, written in the form

$$y_{n+1} = y_n + h\alpha_{-1}y'_{n+1} + h\alpha_0 y'_n + \sum_{k=1}^{r} \alpha_k y'_{n-k},$$

is applied to the problem

$$y' = F(x,y), \qquad y(x_0) = y_0,$$

where it is known that

$$0 < \omega \leqq -F_y(x,y) \leqq K,$$

where ω and K are constants, and assume also that $\alpha_0 \geqq 0$, $\alpha_{-1} \geqq 0$, and $h\omega\alpha_0 < 1$. Show that, if the maximum error introduced in a single step is E, then the error ϵ_n in y_n is dominated by e_n, where

$$(1 + h\omega\alpha_{-1})e_{n+1} = (1 - h\omega\alpha_0)e_n + hK\sum_{k=1}^{r}|\alpha_k|e_{n-k} + E,$$

if $|\epsilon_k| \leqq e_k$ for $k = 0, 1, 2, \ldots, r$. Show that one solution of this equation is of the form

$$e_n = \frac{E}{h\delta} - c\beta_0^n,$$

where

$$\delta = \omega(\alpha_{-1} + \alpha_0) - K\sum_{k=1}^{r}|\alpha_k|,$$

that it is possible to take β_0 such that $0 < \beta_0 < 1$ if $\delta > 0$, and that then

$$|\epsilon_n| \leqq \bar{e}\beta_0^{n-r} + \frac{E}{h\delta}\left(1 - \beta_0^n\right),$$

where $\bar{e}$ is the absolute value of the largest of the errors $\epsilon_0, \epsilon_1, \ldots, \epsilon_r$.

21. Show that the absolute values of the errors in the calculations of Prob. 14 are dominated by

$$\left(\frac{h^2}{12} + \frac{R}{h}\right)\left[1 - \left(\frac{2 - h}{2 + h}\right)^n\right] \approx \left(\frac{h^2}{12} + \frac{R}{h}\right)\left(1 - e^{-nh}\right)$$

and

$$\left(\frac{h^2}{3} + \frac{R}{h}\right)[(\sqrt{1 + h^2} + h)^n - 1] + |\epsilon|(\sqrt{1 + h^2} + h)^n$$

$$\approx \left(\frac{h^2}{3} + \frac{R}{h}\right)(e^{nh} - 1) + |\epsilon|e^{nh},$$

respectively, where R is the magnitude of the maximum round-off error introduced in a single step and ϵ is the inherent error in y_1, and compare these bounds with the direct error calculations of Prob. 16. (Use the results of Prob. 19 in the first case.)

22, 23. (a) to (e) Calculate values of F_y at appropriate stages of the calculations of Probs. 12 and 13, and obtain corresponding approximate error bounds, considering separately the effects of truncation and round-off errors and using the result of Prob. 20 when it is appropriate. Estimate the truncation error in each step by approximating $h^m y^{(m)}$ by $h \nabla^{m-1} y'_m$ in the appropriate error term.

Section 6.9

24. If C is the numerical factor by which $-\gamma_{n+1}$ should be divided to give an approximation to the truncation error involved in a calculation of y_{n+1}, based on a pair of formulas of open and closed types, when the effect of the term $h\alpha_{-1} F_y(x_{n+1}, \eta_{n+1})$ is neglected (see §6.6), show that the true factor is generally more closely approximated by $C - (C - 1)\rho_{n+1}$, where ρ_{n+1} is the convergence factor in the iteration for y_{n+1}.

25, 26. (a) to (e) Use the data of Probs. 22 and 23 to estimate the convergence factors at relevant stages of the corresponding calculations, and determine whether the use of the result of Prob. 24 appreciably modifies the previously calculated individual truncation-error and over-all-error bounds.

27. Use any numerical step-by-step method for the calculation of approximate values of the solution of each of the following problems for $x = 0.0(0.1)1.0$, with an error which can be reasonably confidently expected to be less than one unit in the fifth decimal place:

(a) $y' = x - y^2$, $y(0) = 1$.

(b) $y' = x + \sin y$, $y(0) = \pi/2$.

(c) $y' = e^{-xy}$, $y(0) = 1$.

Section 6.10

28. Suppose that closed formulas of the type (6.10.3) and (6.10.4) are used for the numerical integration of (6.10.1), that the relevant truncation errors in the nth step are E_2 and E'_2, respectively, and that another pair of formulas of open type is used for prediction of y_{n+1} and u_{n+1}, with truncation errors E_1 and E'_1, respectively. If the predicted values are denoted by $y_{n+1}^{(0)}$ and $u_{n+1}^{(0)}$, the finally calculated values by y_{n+1} and u_{n+1}, and the true values by Y_{n+1} and U_{n+1}, and if the notation

$$\frac{E_2 - E_1}{E_2} = C, \qquad \frac{E'_2 - E'_1}{E'_2} = C'$$

is introduced, show that there follows

$$Y_{n+1} - y_{n+1}^{(0)} = -(C - 1)E_2,$$
$$Y_{n+1} - y_{n+1} = h\alpha_{-1}(U_{n+1} - u_{n+1}) + E_2,$$
$$U_{n+1} - u_{n+1}^{(0)} = -(C' - 1)E'_2,$$
$$U_{n+1} - u_{n+1} = h\alpha_{-1}[G_{y_{n+1}}(Y_{n+1} - y_{n+1}) + G_{y'_{n+1}}(U_{n+1} - u_{n+1})] + E'_2,$$

where $G_{y_{n+1}}$ and $G_{y'_{n+1}}$ are appropriate values of G_y and $G_{y'}$, respectively. By eliminating E_2 and E'_2, express $T_{n+1} \equiv Y_{n+1} - y_{n+1}$ and $T'_{n+1} \equiv U_{n+1} - u_{n+1}$ as linear combinations of $\gamma_{n+1} \equiv y_{n+1} - y_{n+1}^{(0)}$ and $\gamma'_{n+1} \equiv u_{n+1} - u_{n+1}^{(0)}$, and show that, if

$$h|\alpha_{-1}|[h|\alpha_{-1}| \, |G_{y_{n+1}}| + |G_{y'_{n+1}}|] \ll 1,$$

so that also the convergence factor ρ_{n+1} is such that $|\rho_{n+1}| \ll 1$, and if it is assumed that

$C' \approx C \gg 1$, then the approximations

$$T_{n+1} \approx -\frac{1}{C}\,(\gamma_{n+1} + h\alpha_{-1}\gamma'_{n+1}), \qquad T'_{n+1} \approx -\frac{1}{C}\,(\gamma'_{n+1} + h\alpha_{-1}G_{y_{n+1}}\gamma_{n+1})$$

generally provide better estimates than the simpler approximations $T_{n+1} \approx -\gamma_{n+1}/C$ and $T'_{n+1} \approx -\gamma'_{n+1}/C$. In particular, obtain the estimates

$$T_{n+1} \approx -\tfrac{1}{6}(\gamma_{n+1} + \tfrac{1}{20}\gamma'_{n+1}), \qquad T'_{n+1} \approx -\tfrac{1}{6}(\gamma'_{n+1} + \tfrac{1}{20}\gamma_{n+1})$$

for the calculations of the illustrative example of §6.10.

29. Obtain approximate values of the solution of each of the following problems for $x = 0.0(0.1)1.0$, determining appropriate starting values by power-series methods or otherwise, and proceeding by use of the modified Adams method, retaining only *first* differences, estimating the errors introduced in each step, and retaining an appropriate number of decimal places in the calculations:

(a) $y'' - y = 0,\ y(0) = 1,\ y'(0) = -1$.

(b) $y'' + 2y' + 2y = 0,\ y(0) = 1,\ y'(0) = -1$.

(c) $xy'' + y' + xy = 0,\ y(0) = 1,\ y'(0) = 0$.

(d) $y'' + y' + y^2 = x,\ y(0) = 1,\ y'(0) = 0$.

(e) $\begin{cases} u' = x + u - v^2,\ u(0) = 0, \\ v' = x^2 - v + u^2,\ v(0) = 1. \end{cases}$

30. (a) to (e) Repeat the calculations of Prob. 29, retaining differences through the third.

31. (a) to (e) Use the Milne second-difference procedure in place of the modified Adams method in Prob. 29.

Section 6.11

32. Show that, if the formulas

$$y_{n+1} = y_n + h(\alpha_{-1}y'_{n+1} + \alpha_0 y'_n), \qquad u_{n+1} = u_n + h(\alpha_{-1}u'_{n+1} + \alpha_0 u'_n)$$

are used for the numerical solution of (6.10.2), with $\alpha_{-1} \geqq 0$ and $\alpha_0 \geqq 0$, then the errors ϵ_n and ϵ'_n are dominated by

$$e_n = A_0\beta_0^n + A_1\beta_1^n - \frac{E' - LE}{Kh},$$

$$e'_n = \frac{\beta_0 - 1}{h(\alpha_{-1}\beta_0 + \alpha_0)}\,A_0\beta_0^n + \frac{\beta_1 - 1}{h(\alpha_{-1}\beta_1 + \alpha_0)}\,A_1\beta_1^n - \frac{E}{h},$$

respectively, where

$$\beta_{0,1} = \frac{2 + hL(\alpha_0 - \alpha_{-1}) + 2h^2K\alpha_0\alpha_{-1} \pm \sqrt{L^2 + 4Kh}}{2(1 - hL\alpha_{-1} - h^2K\alpha_{-1}^2)}$$

$$= 1 + \frac{h}{2}\,(L \pm \sqrt{L^2 + 4K}) + \cdots,$$

if $hL\alpha_{-1} + h^2K\alpha_{-1}^2 < 1$, where K and L are upper bounds on $|G_y|$ and $|G_{y'}|$, when A_0 and A_1 are assigned any values which ensure that e_n and e'_n are nonnegative for $n \geqq 0$.

33. Show that, if the hypothesis $|G_{y'}| \leqq L$ is replaced by the hypothesis

$$0 < \omega \leqq -G_{y'}$$

in Prob. 32, and if $h^2K\alpha_{-1}^2 < 1 + h\omega\alpha_{-1}$, then L can be replaced by $-\omega$ throughout the relations obtained in that problem.

34. (a) to (e) Use results of Prob. 32 or 33 to obtain approximate error bounds for the calculations of Prob. 29.

35, 36. (a) to (e) Obtain approximate error bounds for the calculations of Probs. 30 and 31.

Section 6.12

37. Suppose that the formula (6.12.3) is used with *no* differences to generate an approximation to e^{-x} as the solution of the problem

$$y'' = y, \qquad y(0) = 1, \qquad y'(0) = -1,$$

with spacing h, and that the value used for y_1 is in error by ϵ, so that $y_1 = e^{-h} - \epsilon$. Show that, if all subsequent calculations were effected without round-off, then the nth calculated ordinate would be given exactly by

$$y_n \equiv y(x_n) = \frac{1 - h^2}{2h} \left(\frac{1}{1 - h} - e^{-h} + \epsilon \right) e^{-n \log (1+h)}$$
$$- \frac{1 - h^2}{2h} \left(\frac{1}{1 + h} - e^{-h} + \epsilon \right) e^{n \log [1/(1-h)]},$$

where $x_n = nh$, and that the approximation

$$y(x_n) \approx \left(1 + \frac{h}{4} + \frac{\epsilon}{2h} \right) e^{-x_n} - \left(\frac{h}{4} + \frac{\epsilon}{2h} \right) e^{x_n}$$
$$= e^{-x_n} - \left(\frac{h}{2} + \frac{\epsilon}{h} \right) \sinh x_n \approx e^{-x_n} - \left(\frac{h}{4} + \frac{\epsilon}{2h} \right) e^{x_n}$$

would hold when h is small and n large, so that the *relative* error in $y(x_n)$ would then be approximated by $(h^2 + 2\epsilon)e^{2x_n}/(4h)$. Show also that the corresponding relative error in the approximation to e^x, with the modified condition $y'(0) = +1$, would be approximated by the constant $(h^2 + 2\epsilon)/(4h)$ when h is small and n large, again neglecting round-offs.

38. Obtain approximate values of the solution of each of the following problems for $x = 0.0(0.1)1.0$, using the Milne procedure (6.12.5) and (6.12.6), and estimating the error introduced in each step:

 (a) $y'' - y = 0$, $y(0) = 1$, $y'(0) = -1$.
 (b) $y'' + xy = 0$, $y(0) = 0$, $y'(0) = 1$.
 (c) $y'' + xy + \frac{1}{6}xy^3 = 0$, $y(0) = 0$, $y'(0) = 1$.
 (d) $y'' + \sin y = x$, $y(0) = \pi/2$, $y'(0) = 0$.

39. (a) to (d) Obtain approximate error bounds for the calculations of Prob. 38.

40. Obtain approximate values of the solution of each of the following problems at the points noted, using the Milne procedure (6.12.5) and (6.12.6) after introducing the transformation (6.12.23), and estimating the error introduced in each step:

 (a) $xY'' + Y' + xY = 0$, $Y(1) = 0.76520$, $Y'(1) = -0.44005$: $[x = 1.0(0.1)2.0]$.
 (b) $Y'' + 2Y' + x^2Y = 0$, $Y(0) = 0$, $Y'(0) = 1$: $[x = 0.0(0.1)1.0]$.
 (c) $Y'' + 2Y' + xY^2 = 0$, $Y(0) = 1$, $Y'(0) = -1$: $[x = 0.0(0.1)1.0]$.

41. Show that the equation $y'' + f(x)y = 0$ is satisfied by

$$y(x) = A(x) \cos \theta(x),$$

where

$$\theta(x) = \int_{x_0}^{x} v(x) \, dx + \omega,$$

if A and v satisfy the equations $A'' - Av^2 + fA = 0$ and $2A'v + Av' = 0$, or hence if

$$A'' + fA = \frac{c^2}{A^3}, \qquad v \equiv \theta' = \frac{c}{A^2},$$

where c and ω are arbitrary constants. Show also that the conditions

$$A(x_0) = A_0, \qquad A'(x_0) = 0, \qquad A''(x_0) = 0,$$

which tend to require that $A(x)$ remain constant near $x = x_0$, are consistent with the conditions $y(x_0) = y_0$ and $y'(x_0) = y_0'$ if A_0 and ω satisfy the relations

$$A_0 \cos \omega = y_0, \qquad A_0 \sin \omega = -\frac{y_0'}{f_0^{\frac{1}{2}}},$$

and if
$$c = f_0^{\frac{1}{2}} A_0^2,$$

under the assumption that $f_0 \equiv f(x_0) > 0$. [This procedure, attributed to Madelung, is often useful when $f(x)$ is large and *positive*, so that $y(x)$ is strongly oscillatory, since $A(x)$ often varies much less rapidly. A similar transformation, which is often useful when $f(x)$ is large and *negative*, and $y(x)$ increases or decreases rapidly, may be obtained analogously by replacing $\cos \theta$ by $\cosh \theta$, $\sinh \theta$, or e^θ in the expression assumed for y, according as the ratio of $|y_0|$ to $|y_0'|/(-f_0)^{\frac{1}{2}}$ is greater than, less than, or equal to unity, respectively.]

42. Use the results of Prob. 41 to show that the solution of the problem

$$y'' + (16 - x^2)y = 0, \qquad y(0) = 1, \qquad y'(0) = 0$$

can be expressed in the form

$$y(x) = A(x) \cos \theta(x),$$

where $A(x)$ is the solution of the problem

$$A'' + (16 - x^2)A = \frac{16}{A^3}, \qquad A(0) = 1, \qquad A'(0) = 0,$$

and where
$$\theta(x) = 4 \int_0^x \frac{dx}{[A(x)]^2}.$$

Also determine $A(x)$, and hence $\theta(x)$ and $y(x)$, for $x = 0.0(0.1)1.0$ to five places, by a numerical method.

Section 6.13

43, 44. (a) to (e) Advance the calculations of Probs. 12 and 13 to $x = 1.2$ with $h = 0.05$, given that $\phi(1.1) \doteq 1.43392$ and $\phi(1.2) \doteq 1.48080$ in Prob. 8.

45, 46, 47. (a) to (e) Advance the calculations of Probs. 29, 30, and 31 to $x = 1.2$ with $h = 0.05$.

48. (a) to (d) Advance the calculations of Prob. 38 to $x = 1.2$ with $h = 0.05$.

Section 6.14

49(a) to (d), **50**(a) to (e), **51**(a) to (d). Obtain approximate solutions of Probs. 5, 29, and 38 for $x = 0.0(0.1)1.0$, by use of (6.14.2) and (6.14.3).

Section 6.15

52. (a) to (e) Obtain approximate values of the solutions of Probs. 5(a) to (d) and 8 for $x = 0.0(0.1)1.0$ by use of (6.15.15) and (6.15.16), and estimate the errors.

Section 6.16

53. (a) to (e) Obtain approximate values of the solutions of Probs. 5(a) to (d) and 8 for $x = 0.0(0.1)1.0$ by use of (6.16.5) and (6.16.6) and estimate the errors.

54(a) to (e), **55**(a) to (d). Obtain approximate values of the solutions of Probs. 29 and 38 for $x = 0.0(0.1)1.0$ by use of (6.16.12) and (6.16.13), and estimate the errors.

Section 6.17

56. Use an appropriate step-by-step method to determine approximate five-place values of $u(x)$ such that $u'' + u = 1$, $u(0) = 0$, $u'(0) = 0$, and of $v(x)$ such that $v'' + v = 0$, $v(0) = 0$, $v'(0) = 1$, for $x = 0.0(0.1)1.0$. Then use these results to determine approximate values of $y(x)$ for $x = 0.0(0.1)1.0$ such that $y''(x) + y(x) = 1$, $y(0) = 0$, $y(1) = 1$, and compare the results with exact values.

57. Use an appropriate step-by-step method to determine approximate five-place values of the solution $u(x,\alpha)$ of the problem

$$u''(x) + u(x) = 1, \qquad u(0) = 0, \qquad u'(0) = \alpha,$$

for $x = 0.0(0.1)1.0$, taking successively $\alpha = 0$ and $\alpha = 1$. Then use linear interpolation to estimate the value of α for which $u(1) = 1$, and investigate the correctness of this estimate by making another corresponding step-by-step calculation (see Prob. 58).

58. Prove that the procedure described in connection with Eqs. (6.17.11) and (6.17.12) would yield an exact result with *linear* interpolation on α if (6.17.11) were a *linear* equation and if no errors were committed in the determination of solutions corresponding to two trial values of α.

59. Obtain approximate values of the solution of the problem

$$y'' + y = 0, \qquad y(0) = 0, \qquad y(1) = 1$$

for $x = 0.0(0.1)1.0$ by use of (6.17.18) with $h = 0.2$.

60. Repeat the calculation of Prob. 59, using (6.17.17) with $h = 0.2$, and compare the two approximations.

61. Repeat the calculation of Prob. 59, using (6.17.19) with $h = 0.2$, together with (6.17.20) and (6.17.21).

62. Use the method of Prob. 59, together with (6.17.22), to deal with the modification of that problem in which the condition $y(0) = 0$ is replaced by the condition $y'(0) = y(0)$.

63. Repeat the calculation of Prob. 62, using the method of Prob. 60, and compare the results with those obtained in Prob. 62.

Section 6.18

64. Determine approximate values of the smallest characteristic value of λ for the problem
$$y'' + \lambda y = 0, \qquad y(0) = y(1) = 0$$

by use of (6.18.3) and (6.18.4), and compare those approximations with the true value π^2, and with corresponding approximations based on the use of (6.17.18) with $N = 1$ and 2.

65. Repeat the calculations of Prob. 64 when the condition $y(0) = 0$ is replaced by the condition $y'(0) = 0$, making use of (6.17.22), in each case, in such a way that the order of the procedure is not reduced, and compare the results which correspond to the use of the approximate condition $\Delta y_0 \equiv y_1 - y_0 = 0$.

66, 67. Repeat the calculations of Probs. 64 and 65, making use of (6.18.2) with $N = 3$.

68 to 71. Deal as in Probs. 64 to 67 with the corresponding modified formulations involving the equation $y'' + \lambda xy = 0$. [The true characteristic numbers in Probs. 68 and 70 are the zeros of the function $J_{\frac{1}{3}}(2\lambda^{\frac{1}{2}}/3)$, the smallest of which rounds to 18.956, whereas those in Probs. 69 and 71 are the zeros of the function $J_{-\frac{1}{3}}(2\lambda^{\frac{1}{2}}/3)$, the smallest of which rounds to 7.8373.]

CHAPTER 7

LEAST-SQUARES POLYNOMIAL APPROXIMATION

7.1. Introduction. There are two classes of situations in which the process of determining an approximation (polynomial or otherwise) to a function by fitting given data exactly at a certain set of discrete points often is a particularly inefficient one.

First, when the function $f(x)$, to be approximated, is specified for *all* values of x in an interval, it is clearly desirable to take many or all of the known values into account, rather than to select an arbitrary set, consisting of the least possible number of discrete values which leads to a determinate set of conditions. This is especially true when $f(x)$ or one of its derivatives possesses known finite discontinuities or "jumps."

Second, and on the opposite extreme, when only a discrete set of approximate values of $f(x)$ is provided, and when the degree of reliability of those values is not well established, it is foolish (and, indeed, inherently dangerous) to attempt to determine a polynomial of high degree which fits the vagaries of such data exactly and hence, in all probability, is represented by a curve which oscillates violently about the curve which represents the true function. In particular, the use of the result for numerical differentiation would be hard to justify.

The so-called method of least squares, which is designed for the treatment of both these classes of problems, is introduced in the present chapter, and its application to the analysis of typical situations is treated. Several of the classical sets of orthogonal polynomials, which are particularly useful in these applications, are introduced, and certain of their properties are discussed.

7.2. The Principle of Least Squares. In place of determining a polynomial approximation $y(x)$, of degree n, to a certain function $f(x)$, by requiring that the values of $y(x)$ at a set of $n + 1$ points agree with known exact or approximate values of $f(x)$ at those points, as was done in preceding chapters, it is often preferable to require that $y(x)$ and $f(x)$ agree *as well as possible* (in some sense) over a domain D of greater extent. This domain may be taken as a continuous interval, when $f(x)$ is specified analytically, or as a set, say, of $N + 1$ points, where $N > n$.

When the available data in D are either exact or of equal reliability, it is frequently assumed that the "best approximation" over D is that one for which the aggregate (sum or integral) of the squared error in D is least. This postulate is often known as *Legendre's principle of least squares*. More generally, if $w(x_i)$ is a measure of the relative precision of the value assigned to $f(x)$ when $x = x_i$, the criterion is modified by requiring that the squared error at x_i be multiplied by the *weight* $w(x_i)$ before the aggregate is calculated.

Suppose first that *exact* values of $f(x)$ are known over a certain domain D, which may consist of a discrete set of points $x_0, x_1, \ldots, x_N$ or of a continuous interval (a,b), and that the approximation is to be of the form

$$f(x) \approx \sum_{k=0}^{n} a_k \phi_k(x) \equiv y(x), \qquad (7.2.1)$$

where $\phi_0(x), \ldots, \phi_n(x)$ are $n + 1$ appropriately chosen functions. In particular, in order to obtain a *polynomial* approximation of degree n, we could take $\phi_0 = 1$, $\phi_1 = x$, $\ldots$, $\phi_n = x^n$, although other choices of the coordinate functions, which would also afford a *basis* for the generation of all polynomials of degree n, are often more convenient, as will be seen. It is supposed that the specified *weighting function* $w(x)$ is non-negative in D,

$$w(x) \geqq 0. \qquad (7.2.2)$$

If we define the *residual* $R(x)$ by the equation

$$R(x) = f(x) - \sum_{k=0}^{n} a_k \phi_k(x) \equiv f(x) - y(x), \qquad (7.2.3)$$

the best approximation (7.2.1), in the least-squares sense, is defined to be that for which the a's are determined so that the *aggregate* (sum or integral) of $w(x)R^2(x)$ over D is as small as possible. It is convenient to denote this aggregate here by $\{wR^2\}$. The requirement

$$\{wR^2\} \equiv \left\{ w\left[f - \sum_{k=0}^{n} a_k \phi_k \right]^2 \right\} = \min \qquad (7.2.4)$$

then imposes the conditions

$$\frac{\partial}{\partial a_r} \left\{ w\left[f - \sum_{k=0}^{n} a_k \phi_k \right]^2 \right\} = 0 \qquad (r = 0, 1, \ldots, n) \qquad (7.2.5)$$

or

$$\left\{ w\phi_r \left[f - \sum_{k=0}^{n} a_k \phi_k \right] \right\} \equiv \{w\phi_r(f - y)\} = 0 \qquad (7.2.6)$$

or

$$\sum_{k=0}^{n} a_k \{w\phi_r\phi_k\} = \{w\phi_r f\} \qquad (r = 0, 1, \ldots, n), \qquad (7.2.7)$$

and hence leads to $n + 1$ simultaneous linear equations in the $n + 1$ unknown parameters $a_0, a_1, \ldots, a_n$. These equations are called the *normal equations* of the process.

It is useful to notice that these conditions can be expressed also in the form

$$\{w(x)\phi_r(x)R(x)\} = 0 \qquad (r = 0, 1, \ldots, n). \tag{7.2.8}$$

Hence, since we have also

$$\{wR^2\} = \{wR \cdot R\} = \left\{ wR \left[f - \sum_{k=0}^{n} a_k \phi_k \right] \right\} = \{wRf\} - \sum_{k=0}^{n} a_k \{w\phi_k R\}, \tag{7.2.9}$$

it follows that, when the coefficients $a_0, \ldots, a_n$ satisfy (7.2.7), the corresponding aggregate squared residual reduces to

$$\{wR^2\}_{\min} = \{wRf\} \equiv \{wf(f - y)\} \equiv \{wf^2\} - \sum_{k=0}^{n} a_k \{w\phi_k f\}. \tag{7.2.10}$$

The smallness of this quantity can be used as a criterion for the efficiency of the approximation over D.

In particular, if the domain D consists only of $n + 1$ discrete points, and if the set of functions S_n generated by the coordinate functions $\phi_0, \ldots, \phi_n$ comprises, say, all polynomials of degree not exceeding n, it is possible to reduce $R(x)$ to *zero* at each point of the domain. Thus here the least-squares procedure reduces to the determination of the polynomial $y(x)$ of degree n which agrees exactly with $f(x)$ at $n + 1$ points, and the minimum value of $\{wR^2\}$ is zero. If the domain consists of $N + 1$ points, where $N > n$, or of a continuous interval, exact fit over all of D is generally impossible and the procedure gives the function of the class considered which affords the best approximate fit under the criterion (7.2.4), in which the weighting function $w(x)$ must be specified.

It is seen from (7.2.7) that the coefficients of the unknowns in the left-hand members of the normal equations are independent of the function $f(x)$ to be approximated, so that they may be precalculated, once the coordinate functions and the weighting function have been selected. Also, since $\{w\phi_i\phi_j\} \equiv \{w\phi_j\phi_i\}$, the coefficient of a_i in the jth equation is equal to that of a_j in the ith equation, so that the array of the coefficients of the a's is symmetrical with respect to its principal diagonal. This fact appreciably reduces the labor in both the formation and the solution of the set of equations (see §10.4).

Clearly, these equations are greatly simplified if the coordinate functions are chosen, in advance, in such a way that

$$\{w\phi_i\phi_j\} = 0 \qquad (i \neq j). \tag{7.2.11}$$

A set of ϕ's having this property over D is said to be an *orthogonal set*, relative to the weighting function $w(x)$, over D. For such a set of coordinate functions, the corresponding set of normal equations (7.2.7) becomes "uncoupled" and takes the form

$$a_r\{w\phi_r^2\} = \{w\phi_r f\} \qquad (r = 0, 1, \ldots, n). \qquad (7.2.12)$$

Since $w(x)$ is nonnegative, the coefficient of a_r cannot vanish,† and we obtain the result

$$a_r = \frac{\{w\phi_r f\}}{\{w\phi_r^2\}} \qquad (r = 0, 1, \ldots, n). \qquad (7.2.13)$$

Further, reference to (7.2.10) and (7.2.12) shows that the corresponding value of $\{wR^2\}$ can be expressed in the alternative form

$$\{wR^2\}_{\min} = \{wf^2\} - \sum_{k=0}^{n} a_k^2\{w\phi_k^2\} \qquad (7.2.14)$$

in this case.

In theoretical work it is often convenient to suppose that the ϕ's have also been *normalized* in such a way that $\{w\phi_i^2\} = 1$, so that (7.2.13) and (7.2.14) are still further simplified. However, this normalization is rarely convenient in practice.

The root-mean-square (RMS) error in the approximation over D, relative to $w(x)$, is defined to be

$$\epsilon_{\text{RMS}} \equiv (f - y)_{\text{RMS}} = \sqrt{\frac{\{wR^2\}}{\{w\}}}. \qquad (7.2.15)$$

Here, in particular, when $w(x) \equiv 1$ the quantity $\{1\}$ represents the length of the interval in the continuous case and the number $(N + 1)$ of points in D in the discrete case.

In the discrete case, it frequently happens that the given data are empirical and correspond accordingly to an "observed function" $\bar{f}(x)$, and that the "true function" $f(x)$ is not known. Here we must replace $f(x)$ by $\bar{f}(x)$ in the preceding developments, and we are in position to calculate only $\bar{\epsilon}_{\text{RMS}} = (\bar{f} - y)_{\text{RMS}}$ over D. The subsequent estimation of the *desired* quantity ϵ_{RMS} is considered in the following section.

7.3. Least-squares Approximation over Discrete Ranges. Before exploiting the convenience afforded by the use of orthogonal functions, we here consider the application of the general least-squares method to the case when the domain D comprises a discrete set of points. The case when D is a continuous interval is treated in a completely analogous way.

In accordance with the results of the preceding section, if an approxima-

† It is assumed that none of the coordinate functions vanishes everywhere in D.

tion of the form

$$f(x) \approx \sum_{k=0}^{n} a_k \phi_k(x) \tag{7.3.1}$$

is to hold over a set of $N + 1$ points $x_0, x_1, \ldots, x_N$, where $N \geqq n$, in the sense that the aggregate weighted squared error is to be a minimum,

$$\sum_{i=0}^{N} w(x_i)[f(x_i) - \sum_{k=0}^{n} a_k \phi_k(x_i)]^2 = \text{min}, \tag{7.3.2}$$

the set of $n + 1$ normal equations (7.2.7) becomes

$$a_0 \sum_{i=0}^{N} w(x_i)\phi_r(x_i)\phi_0(x_i) + a_1 \sum_{i=0}^{N} w(x_i)\phi_r(x_i)\phi_1(x_i) + \cdots$$
$$+ a_n \sum_{i=0}^{N} w(x_i)\phi_r(x_i)\phi_n(x_i)$$
$$= \sum_{i=0}^{N} w(x_i)\phi_r(x_i)f(x_i) \qquad (r = 0, 1, \ldots, n). \tag{7.3.3}$$

These equations can be obtained quite simply, by first writing down the $N + 1$ equations which would require that (7.3.1) be an *equality* at the $N + 1$ points x_i,

$$\begin{aligned} a_0\phi_0(x_0) + a_1\phi_1(x_0) + \cdots + a_n\phi_n(x_0) &= f(x_0), \\ a_0\phi_0(x_1) + a_1\phi_1(x_1) + \cdots + a_n\phi_n(x_1) &= f(x_1), \\ \cdots\cdots\cdots\cdots\cdots\cdots\cdots\cdots\cdots\cdots\cdots\cdots \\ a_0\phi_0(x_N) + a_1\phi_1(x_N) + \cdots + a_n\phi_n(x_N) &= f(x_N). \end{aligned} \tag{7.3.4}$$

The rth normal equation is then obtained by multiplying each equation by the coefficient of a_r in that equation, and by the weight associated with that equation, and by summing the results. Unless there is a reason for proceeding otherwise, the weights are generally taken to be equal and then may be assigned the value unity.

When $N = n$, the problem reduces to that of satisfying the $n + 1$ equations (7.3.4) in $n + 1$ unknowns, and the normal equations are equivalent to the original ones.

As a very simple example, suppose that the problem is that of fitting the equation of a straight line as well as possible (in the least-squares sense) to the following data:

x	0	1	2	3	4
$f(x)$	1.00	3.85	6.50	9.35	12.05

In place of writing out the equations (7.3.4), corresponding to the substitution of these corresponding values into the equation

$$a_0 + a_1 x = f(x),$$ (7.3.5)

we may merely write down the array of the coefficients of a_0 and a_1 and the right-hand members (the "augmented matrix" of the system) in the form

$$\begin{array}{ccc} 1 & 0 & 1.00 \\ 1 & 1 & 3.85 \\ 1 & 2 & 6.50 \\ 1 & 3 & 9.35 \\ 1 & 4 & 12.05 \end{array}$$ (7.3.6)

Under the assumption that all the data are of equal significance, we take all weights equal to unity. The first normal equation then corresponds to the result of adding the elements of the respective columns of (7.3.6), to give the array [5   10   32.75], and the second corresponds to the result of multiplying the elements in each row by the element of that row which lies in the second column, and adding the results, to give the array [10   30   93.10], so that the normal equations are

$$\begin{aligned} 5a_0 + 10a_1 &= 32.75, \\ 10a_0 + 30a_1 &= 93.10, \end{aligned}$$ (7.3.7)

yielding the solution $a_0 = 1.03$, $a_1 = 2.76$, and hence determining the linear approximation

$$f(x) \approx y(x) = 1.03 + 2.76x.$$ (7.3.8)

The values obtained from this approximation at the points $x = 0, 1, 2, 3$, and 4 are 1.03, 3.79, 6.55, 9.31, and 12.07, respectively, and the sum of the squared errors is found to be 0.0090. Thus the RMS error for these five points is about 0.042.

The interpretation of this result must depend upon the context. If the given values are considered to be exact values of a *true* function, then the figure 0.042 represents the RMS deviation of the approximate function $y(x)$ from the true function over the five points for which information is available. In the absence of any further information, this figure would afford the only available estimate of the RMS error over the continuous range $0 \leq x \leq 4$.

On the other hand, if the given ordinates are empirical, and hence properly correspond to an "observed function" $\bar{f}(x)$, the figure 0.042 represents only the RMS error in approximating $\bar{f}(x)$ over the five relevant points. Unless additional information is supplied, or additional assumptions are made, no conclusions can be drawn with respect to the RMS value of the *true* error $f - y$.

However, if it is postulated that the *true* function is such that the residuals at each of the $N + 1$ points *can* be reduced to zero, but that the impossibility of achieving this end in the case at hand is due to the presence of independent random errors in the several observed values, then it is possible to obtain a certain amount of additional information. It is also frequently desirable to estimate the errors in the calculated *coefficients*.

For both these purposes, we examine the general problem in greater detail in the remainder of this section.

Suppose that the right-hand members of (7.3.4) are replaced by values of an observed function $\bar{f}(x)$, and that the *calculated* coefficients are then denoted by $\bar{a}_0, \ldots, \bar{a}_n$, so that those relations become

$$\sum_{k=0}^{n} \bar{a}_k \phi_k(x_i) \approx \bar{f}(x_i) \qquad (i = 0, 1, \ldots, N), \tag{7.3.9}$$

whereas the proper equations are

$$\sum_{k=0}^{n} a_k \phi_k(x_i) = f(x_i) \equiv \bar{f}(x_i) + E(x_i), \tag{7.3.10}$$

where $E(x_i)$ is the error associated with the "observed value" $\bar{f}(x_i)$. The normal equations (7.3.3), associated with (7.3.9), can then be written in the form

$$\sum_{k=0}^{n} c_{rk} \bar{a}_k = v_r \qquad (r = 0, 1, \ldots, n) \tag{7.3.11}$$

where

$$c_{rk} = c_{kr} = \sum_{i=0}^{N} w(x_i) \phi_r(x_i) \phi_k(x_i) \tag{7.3.12}$$

and

$$v_r = \sum_{i=0}^{N} w(x_i) \phi_r(x_i) \bar{f}(x_i). \tag{7.3.13}$$

The corresponding approximation $\Sigma \bar{a}_k \phi_k(x)$ may be denoted by $\bar{y}(x)$, and the residual $\bar{f}(x_i) - \bar{y}(x_i)$ by $\bar{R}(x_i)$.

If we denote by C_{rs} the cofactor of c_{rs} in the coefficient array of (7.3.11),

$$\begin{matrix} c_{00} & c_{01} & \cdots & c_{0n} \\ c_{10} & c_{11} & \cdots & c_{1n} \\ \cdot & \cdot & \cdots & \cdot \\ c_{n0} & c_{n1} & \cdots & c_{nn} \end{matrix} \tag{7.3.14}$$

and define the "reduced cofactor" $\tilde{C}_{rs} = C_{rs}/D$, where D is the determinant of the array, noticing that $\tilde{C}_{sr} = \tilde{C}_{rs}$ because of the symmetry of the array, the solution of the set (7.3.11) can be expressed in the form ee §10.2)

$$\bar{a}_r = \sum_{k=0}^{n} \widetilde{C}_{rk}v_k \qquad (r = 0, 1, \ldots, n). \qquad (7.3.15)$$

order to express the $\bar{a}$'s directly in terms of the given ordinates, we
troduce (7.3.13) into (7.3.15), to obtain

$$\bar{a}_r = \sum_{k=0}^{n} \widetilde{C}_{rk} \sum_{i=0}^{N} w(x_i)\phi_k(x_i)\bar{f}(x_i) = \sum_{i=0}^{N} \left[\sum_{k=0}^{n} \widetilde{C}_{rk}\phi_k(x_i) \right] w(x_i)\bar{f}(x_i).$$

hus, if we introduce the abbreviation

$$\Phi_r(x) = \sum_{k=0}^{n} \widetilde{C}_{rk}\phi_k(x), \qquad (7.3.16)$$

is relation takes the form

$$\bar{a}_r = \sum_{i=0}^{N} w(x_i)\Phi_r(x_i)\bar{f}(x_i). \qquad (7.3.17)$$

Accordingly, if a_r denotes the corresponding coefficient calculated from
e *true* ordinates, there follows also

$$a_r - \bar{a}_r = \sum_{i=0}^{N} w(x_i)\Phi_r(x_i)E(x_i). \qquad (7.3.18)$$

his relation gives the difference between the coefficients actually
btained and those which would have been obtained if no observational
rrors (or round-off errors) were present.

If the assumption is made that $f(x)$ is actually a member of the set S_n
all functions expressible as linear combinations of $\phi_0, \ldots, \phi_n$, then
(x) is truly specified by the constants $a_0, \ldots, a_n$, and the difference
$_r - \bar{a}_r$ is the true error in the calculated value of the rth constant.
hat is, we then have $f(x) - \bar{y}(x) \equiv \Sigma(a_r - \bar{a}_r)\phi_r(x)$.

Generally, only bounds on the observational errors $E(x_i)$, or estimated
iean values of their squares over a *set* of observations, are available in
ractice. In the latter case, the weights $w(x_0), \ldots, w(x_N)$ are fre-
uently so chosen that the mean values of $w(x_0)E^2(x_0), \ldots, w(x_N)E^2(x_N)$
re (approximately) equal. Under this assumption, we may first obtain
rom (7.3.18) the relation

$$a_r - \bar{a}_r)^2 = [w(x_0)\Phi_r^2(x_0)][w(x_0)E^2(x_0)] + \cdots$$
$$+ [w(x_N)\Phi_r^2(x_N)][w(x_N)E^2(x_N)] + \cdots, \qquad (7.3.19)$$

vhere the omitted terms at the end involve products of the form
$(x_i)E(x_j)$ where $i \neq j$. If both sides of this equation are averaged over

many observations, if the mean of the product $E(x_i)E(x_j)$ is assumed to be zero when $i \neq j$, and if the common mean value of $w(x_0)E^2(x_0)$, $\ldots$ $w(x_N)E^2(x_N)$ is denoted by $(wE^2)_m$, there then follows

$$(a_r - \bar{a}_r)_m^2 = (wE^2)_m \sum_{i=0}^{N} w(x_i)\Phi_r^2(x_i). \qquad (7.3.20)$$

This result can be put into a more convenient form. For this purpose we notice first that if $\bar{f}(x_i)$ is identified with $\phi_s(x_i)$ in (7.3.9), where $0 \leq s \leq n$, there follows $\bar{a}_r = \delta_{rs}$, where $\delta_{rj} = 1$ when $r = j$ and 0 otherwise. Thus we deduce from (7.3.17) that

$$\sum_{i=0}^{N} w(x_i)\Phi_r(x_i)\phi_s(x_i) = \delta_{rs}, \qquad (7.3.21)$$

so that reference to (7.3.16) gives

$$\begin{aligned}
\sum_{i=0}^{N} w(x_i)[\Phi_r(x_i)]^2 &= \sum_{i=0}^{N} w(x_i)\Phi_r(x_i)\left[\sum_{k=0}^{n} \tilde{C}_{rk}\phi_k(x_i) \right] \\
&= \sum_{k=0}^{n}\left[\sum_{i=0}^{N} w(x_i)\Phi_r(x_i)\phi_k(x_i) \right] \tilde{C}_{rk} \\
&= \sum_{k=0}^{n} \delta_{rk}\tilde{C}_{rk} = \tilde{C}_{rr}. \qquad (7.3.22)
\end{aligned}$$

Thus (7.3.20) can be written in the form

$$(a_r - \bar{a}_r)_m^2 = \frac{C_{rr}}{D}(wE^2)_m, \qquad (7.3.23)$$

where C_{rr} is the cofactor of c_{rr} in the array of (7.3.14), and D is the determinant of that array. Here the subscript m again indicates the formation of the mean over a set of observations.

It may happen that no explicit information with respect to the errors $E(x_i)$ is available, but that the assumption that $[w(x_i)E^2(x_i)]_m$ is independent of i is to be retained, together with the assumption that the true function can be fitted exactly at the $N + 1$ points involved. In this case, it is possible to obtain an estimate of $(wE^2)_m$ in terms of the *calculable* residuals $\bar{R}(x_0)$, $\ldots$, $\bar{R}(x_N)$, such that

$$\bar{R}(x_i) \equiv \bar{f}(x_i) - \bar{y}(x_i) = \bar{f}(x_i) - \sum_{k=0}^{n} \bar{a}_k\phi_k(x_i) \qquad (i = 0, \ldots, N).$$

$$(7.3.24)$$

For this purpose, we notice first that, since $E(x_i) = f(x_i) - \bar{f}(x_i)$, we have also

$$f(x_i) - \bar{y}(x_i) = E(x_i) + \bar{R}(x_i). \qquad (7.3.25)$$

From (7.3.10) and (7.3.24), there follows

$$E(x_i) + \bar{R}(x_i) = \sum_{k=0}^{n} (a_k - \bar{a}_k)\phi_k(x_i) \qquad (7.3.26)$$

or, after using (7.3.18),

$$E(x_i) + \bar{R}(x_i) = \sum_{k=0}^{n} \phi_k(x_i) \sum_{\nu=0}^{N} w(x_\nu)\Phi_k(x_\nu)E(x_\nu). \qquad (7.3.27)$$

If we multiply both members of (7.3.26) by $w(x_i)\bar{R}(x_i)$ and sum over i, making use of the fact that $\Sigma w(x_i)\phi_k(x_i)\bar{R}(x_i) = 0$, in accordance with (7.2.8), there follows

$$\sum_{i=0}^{N} w(x_i)E(x_i)\bar{R}(x_i) = -\sum_{i=0}^{N} w(x_i)\bar{R}^2(x_i). \qquad (7.3.28)$$

Also, by multiplying both members of (7.3.27) by $w(x_i)E(x_i)$, summing over i, and making use of (7.3.28), there follows

$$\sum_{i=0}^{N} w(x_i)[f(x_i) - \bar{y}(x_i)]^2 = \sum_{i=0}^{N} w(x_i)E^2(x_i) - \sum_{i=0}^{N} w(x_i)\bar{R}^2(x_i)$$

$$= \sum_{k=0}^{n} \sum_{i=0}^{N} \sum_{\nu=0}^{N} w(x_i)\phi_k(x_i)\Phi_k(x_\nu)w(x_\nu)E(x_i)E(x_\nu). \qquad (7.3.29)$$

If we now average the equal members of (7.3.29) over a set of observations, and again assume that $[E(x_i)E(x_j)]_m = 0$ when $i \neq j$ and $[w(x_i)E^2(x_i)]_m = (wE^2)_m$ for $i = 0, \ldots, N$, only the terms for which $\nu = i$ will remain in the right-hand member, and there follows

$$\sum_{i=0}^{N} [w(x_i)[f(x_i) - \bar{y}(x_i)]^2]_m = (N+1)(wE^2)_m - \sum_{i=0}^{N} [w(x_i)\bar{R}^2(x_i)]_m$$

$$= \sum_{k=0}^{n} \Big[\sum_{i=0}^{N} w(x_i)\phi_k(x_i)\Phi_k(x_i) \Big] (wE^2)_m = (n+1)(wE^2)_m, \qquad (7.3.30)$$

since the sum in brackets in the second right-hand member is *unity* by (7.3.21). Thus there follows

$$(wE^2)_m = \frac{1}{N-n} \sum_{i=0}^{N} [w(x_i)\bar{R}^2(x_i)]_m. \qquad (7.3.31)$$

Since only the residuals which correspond to the single set of given ordinates are available (in general), the best known approximation to the mean values of $\bar{R}^2(x_i)$ consists in the set of *calculated* values. Thus we deduce the formula

$$(wE^2)_m \approx \frac{1}{N-n} \sum_{i=0}^{N} w(x_i)\,\bar{R}^2(x_i) = \frac{\sum_{i=0}^{N} w(x_i)}{N-n}\,\bar{\epsilon}_{\text{RMS}}^2, \qquad (7.3.32)$$

where the last form follows from the notation of (7.2.15).

It is convenient to summarize the preceding results in the case when $w(x) \equiv 1$, which is of most common occurence. Here $\bar{\epsilon}_{\text{RMS}}^2$ is the mean value of the squares of the $N+1$ residuals $\bar{R}(x_i) = \bar{f}(x_i) - \bar{y}(x_i)$, so that

$$\bar{\epsilon}_{\text{RMS}} = \sqrt{\frac{\Sigma[\bar{R}(x_i)]^2}{N+1}} \qquad (7.3.33)$$

measures the RMS deviation between the observed function and its calculated approximation over the $N+1$ points involved. Equation (7.3.32) affords the *estimate*

$$E_{\text{RMS}} \approx \sqrt{\frac{N+1}{N-n}}\,\bar{\epsilon}_{\text{RMS}} = \sqrt{\frac{\Sigma[\bar{R}(x_i)]^2}{N-n}} \qquad (7.3.34)$$

for the RMS deviation between the true function and the observed function over those points, and the combination of (7.3.23) and (7.3.32) gives

$$(\delta a_r)_{\text{RMS}} \approx \sqrt{\frac{C_{rr}}{D}}\,E_{\text{RMS}} \approx \sqrt{\frac{C_{rr}}{D}}\,\sqrt{\frac{\Sigma[\bar{R}(x_i)]^2}{N-n}} \qquad (7.3.35)$$

as an estimate of the RMS error in the rth calculated coefficient $\bar{a}_r$. In each case, $N+1$ denotes the number of points employed and $n+1$ the number of independent coordinate functions. Both (7.3.34) and (7.3.35) are essentially based on the assumption that the true function can be expressed in the form $\Sigma a_k \phi_k(x)$, for *some* choice of the a's, and are to be used in the more general case with a corresponding degree of caution. The estimate (7.3.34) is properly meaningless when $N = n$, since then all the data are needed to determine the *approximation*, and no data remain for the estimation of the error.

If the given data in the preceding example are empirical, the figure $\bar{\epsilon}_{\text{RMS}} \doteq 0.042$ thus represents the RMS deviation between the observed function and the "smoothed function" over the five relevant points. Since also $C_{00} = 30$, $C_{11} = 5$, and $D = 50$ in (7.3.7), (7.3.35) gives

$$(\delta a_0)_{\text{RMS}} \approx 0.8 E_{\text{RMS}}, \qquad (\delta a_1)_{\text{RMS}} \approx 0.3 E_{\text{RMS}},$$

where E_{RMS} is the RMS value of the observational errors, under the

ssumption that the true function is linear. Also, if use is made of
7.3.34), with $n = 1$ and $N = 4$, we obtain the estimate

$$E_{\text{RMS}} \approx \sqrt{\tfrac{5}{3}}\,(0.042) \doteq 0.055,$$

nder the same assumption. Accordingly, the RMS errors in a_0 and a_1
hen may be estimated as about 0.044 and 0.016, respectively. On the
ther hand, if an *independent* estimate of the RMS value of the observa-
ional errors were available, a comparison of that estimate with the
stimate obtained here would serve to indicate the validity of the assump-
ion that the true function is indeed linear.

The solution of the normal equations, and the evaluation of the relevant
leterminant and cofactors, can be conveniently effected by the use of
procedures described in §§10.4 and 10.5.

The same methods are used more generally in dealing with sets of
inear equations, in which there are more equations than unknowns,
whether or not they arise from a problem (7.3.1) in "curve fitting."
n general, the original set is inconsistent, and does not possess a solution.
The normal equations then correspond to the result of minimizing the
weighted or unweighted) squared deviations between the right- and left-
land members of those equations. If the squared deviation associated
with the kth equation is to be weighted by w_k, the same end result can be
obtained alternatively by multiplying both sides of that equation by
$\sqrt{w_k}$ and using a *unit* weight in forming the normal equations. In this
connection, it should be noticed, for example, that the equations $x = 2.3$
and $5x = 11.5$ are *not* equivalent, if the right-hand members are known
only to be correct to the places given, since the first assertion is equivalent
to $2.25 < x < 2.35$ and the second to $2.29 < x < 2.31$.

In this more general case, the coefficients of the left-hand members of
the original equations, as well as the right-hand members, may be subject
to error. Here, if the normal equations are again represented by (7.3.9),
and if ϵ_{RMS} represents the RMS error of each of the right-hand members
of the original equations, whereas η_{RMS} denotes the RMS error of each
coefficient in the original set, the estimate (7.3.35) is to be replaced by

$$(\delta a_r)_{\text{RMS}} \approx \sqrt{\frac{C_{rr}}{D}}\,\sqrt{\epsilon_{\text{RMS}}^2 + (a_0^2 + a_1^2 + \cdots + a_n^2)\eta_{\text{RMS}}^2}, \quad (7.3.36)$$

when $w(x) \equiv 1$, under the assumption that all errors are small, random,
and independent, and that the RMS errors in the coefficients of the
original equations are all equal.

7.4. Orthogonal Polynomials. We consider next the case when a
least-squares approximation is to be effected over the *interval* (a,b), and
we attempt first to construct a set of polynomials $\phi_0(x)$, $\phi_1(x)$, ...

$\phi_r(x)$, . . . such that each member is orthogonal to all others in the set over (a,b), relative to a specified weighting function $w(x)$ which is *non negative* over that interval. It is convenient to ask that $\phi_r(x)$ be a polynomial of degree r. The problem then will be solved, in particular, if we obtain a polynomial $\phi_r(x)$ which is orthogonal over (a,b) to *all* polynomials of degree inferior to r.

Thus we require a polynomial $\phi_r(x)$, of degree r, such that

$$\int_a^b w(x)\phi_r(x)q_{r-1}(x)\ dx = 0, \qquad (7.4.1)$$

where w is specified and where q_{r-1} is an *arbitrary* polynomial of degree $r - 1$ or less. In order to express this requirement in a more useful form, we integrate by parts r times, making use of the fact that $q_{r-1}^{(r)} \equiv 0$. For this purpose, we first introduce the notation

$$w(x)\phi_r(x) \equiv \frac{d^r U_r(x)}{dx^r}, \qquad (7.4.2)$$

so that (7.4.1) becomes

$$\int_a^b U_r^{(r)}(x)q_{r-1}(x)\ dx = 0$$

or, after r integrations by parts,

$$[U_r^{(r-1)}q_{r-1} - U_r^{(r-2)}q_{r-1}' + U_r^{(r-3)}q_{r-1}'' - \cdots + (-1)^{r-1}U_r q_{r-1}^{(r-1)}]_a^b = 0. \qquad (7.4.3)$$

The requirement that the function $\phi_r(x)$ defined by (7.4.2),

$$\phi_r(x) = \frac{1}{w(x)}\frac{d^r U_r(x)}{dx^r}, \qquad (7.4.4)$$

be a polynomial of degree r implies that $U_r(x)$ must satisfy the differential equation

$$\frac{d^{r+1}}{dx^{r+1}}\left[\frac{1}{w(x)}\frac{d^r U_r(x)}{dx^r}\right] = 0 \qquad (7.4.5)$$

in (a,b), whereas the requirement that (7.4.3) be satisfied for *any* values of $q_{r-1}(a)$, $q_{r-1}(b)$, $q_{r-1}'(a)$, $q_{r-1}'(b)$, and so forth, leads to the $2r$ boundary conditions

$$U_r(a) = U_r'(a) = U_r''(a) = \cdots = U_r^{(r-1)}(a) = 0, \qquad (7.4.6)$$
$$U_r(b) = U_r'(b) = U_r''(b) = \cdots = U_r^{(r-1)}(b) = 0. \qquad (7.4.7)$$

Thus if, for each integer r, a solution of (7.4.5) which satisfies (7.4.6) and (7.4.7) can be obtained, the rth member of the required set of functions is given by (7.4.4). From the homogeneity of these conditions, it follows that each such solution will contain an arbitrary multiplicative constant. It is known (see Szego [220]) that the problem thus formulated does indeed possess a solution, even when a and/or b is infinite, under the ssumptions that $w(x) \geqq 0$ in (a,b) and that $\int_a^b x^k w(x) \, dx$ exists for all onnegative integral values of k.

In accordance with the results of the preceding section 7.2, the coefficients in the expression

$$y(x) = \sum_{r=0}^n a_r \phi_r(x) \tag{7.4.8}$$

re then determined by the requirement

$$\int_a^b w(x)[f(x) - y(x)]^2 \, dx = \min \tag{7.4.9}$$

1 the form

$$a_r = \frac{\int_a^b wf\phi_r \, dx}{\int_a^b w\phi_r^2 \, dx} \equiv \frac{\int_a^b wf\phi_r \, dx}{\gamma_r}, \tag{7.4.10}$$

where the numerator depends upon f, whereas the denominator γ_r is ndependent of f and can be calculated once and for all.

The calculation of γ_r is facilitated by the following considerations. If ve write

$$\phi_r(x) = A_{r0} + A_{r1}x + \cdots + A_r x^r, \tag{7.4.11}$$

so that A_{rk} is the coefficient of x^k in $\phi_r(x)$ and $A_r \equiv A_{rr}$ is its *leading* coefficient, there follows

$$\begin{aligned} \gamma_r &= \int_a^b w(x)\phi_r(x)\phi_r(x) \, dx \\ &\equiv \int_a^b w(x)\phi_r(x)[A_{r0} + A_{r1}x + \cdots + A_r x^r] \, dx, \end{aligned}$$

and hence, if we recall the relations

$$\int_a^b w(x)\phi_r(x)x^i \, dx = 0 \qquad (i = 0, 1, \ldots, r - 1), \tag{7.4.12}$$

which are equivalent to (7.4.1), we may deduce that

$$\gamma_r = A_r \int_a^b x^r w(x)\phi_r(x) \, dx = A_r \int_a^b x^r U_r^{(r)}(x) \, dx.$$

By integrating by parts r times, and making use of (7.4.6) and (7.4.7), this relation takes the convenient form

$$\gamma_r \equiv \int_a^b w(x)\phi_r^2(x) \, dx = (-1)^r r! A_r \int_a^b U_r(x) \, dx, \tag{7.4.13}$$

where A_r is the coefficient of x^r in $\phi_r(x)$.

Principally for later reference (§8.4), it is shown next that *if $w(x) does not change sign in (a,b), the polynomial $\phi_r(x)$ possesses r distinct real zeros,*

all of which lie in the interval (a,b). In order to establish this fact, w
notice first that, since $\int_a^b w\phi_r\phi_0\,dx = A_0 \int_a^b w\phi_r\,dx = 0$ when $r \geq 1$, an
$w(x)$ is of constant sign, $\phi_r(x)$ must change sign at least *once* in (a,b) whe
$r \geq 1$.   Now let those real zeros of $\phi_r(x)$ which are of *odd* multiplicity
and which lie in (a,b), be denoted by $c_1, c_2, \ldots, c_m$ and *assume* tha
$m < r$.   Then the product

$$(x - c_1)(x - c_2) \cdots (x - c_m)\phi_r(x)$$

does not change sign in (a,b).   But, since $m < r$, the coefficient of $\phi_r(x)$
is a polynomial of degree less than r, and hence, by (7.4.1), we must hav

$$\int_a^b w(x)[(x - c_1)(x - c_2) \cdots (x - c_m)]\phi_r(x)\,dx = 0.$$

However, since $w(x)$ does not change sign in (a,b), the integrand therefor
has the same property, and a contradiction follows.   Hence there mus
follow $m = r$, and since the total multiplicity of *all* zeros is equal to
all roots must be real and distinct and must lie in (a,b), as was to be showr
   It is useful to notice that the problem specified by (7.4.8) and (7.4.9
can be generalized in the following way.   It may happen that $f(x)$ clearl
cannot be satisfactorily approximated over (a,b) by a polynomial of lov
degree, but that a certain function $v(x)$ is known such that the rati
$f(x)/v(x)$ *can* be so approximated.   Thus, if we determine the coefficient
of the relation

$$y(x) = v(x) \sum_{r=0}^n b_r\phi_r(x) \tag{7.4.14}$$

in such a way that

$$\int_a^b w(x) \left[\frac{f(x)}{v(x)} - \sum_{r=0}^n b_r\phi_r(x) \right]^2 dx = \min, \tag{7.4.15}$$

the orthogonality of the ϕ's relative to w leads to the result

$$b_r = \frac{1}{\gamma_r} \int_a^b \frac{w}{v} f\phi_r\,dx. \tag{7.4.16}$$

   It is seen that (7.4.15) is equivalent to the result of minimizing th
squared error $(f - y)^2$ with the weighting function w/v^2.   The choic
$w(x) = v(x)$ is a frequently useful one.
   Several examples of such approximations are considered in the followin
sections.
   7.5. Legendre Approximation.   For least-squares approximation ove
an interval of finite length, it is convenient to suppose that a linear chang

in variables has transformed that interval into the interval $(-1,1)$. We consider here the case when the weighting function is unity,

$$w(x) = 1. \tag{7.5.1}$$

The differential equation (7.4.5) then becomes

$$\frac{d^{2r+1}U_r}{dx^{2r+1}} = 0, \tag{7.5.2}$$

and the boundary conditions (7.4.6) and (7.4.7) take the form

$$U_r(\pm 1) = U_r'(\pm 1) = \cdots = U_r^{(r-1)}(\pm 1) = 0, \tag{7.5.3}$$

from which there follows (analytically or by inspection)

$$U_r = C_r(x^2 - 1)^r, \tag{7.5.4}$$

where C_r is an arbitrary constant. Hence, from (7.4.4), it follows that the rth relevant orthogonal polynomial is of the form

$$\phi_r(x) = C_r \frac{d^r}{dx^r} (x^2 - 1)^r. \tag{7.5.5}$$

With $C_r = 1/(2^r r!)$, the polynomial so obtained is known as the rth *Legendre polynomial* and is usually denoted by $P_r(x)$,

$$P_r(x) = \frac{1}{2^r r!} \frac{d^r}{dx^r} (x^2 - 1)^r. \tag{7.5.6}$$

From the preceding derivation, it follows that

$$\int_{-1}^1 P_r(x)P_s(x)\, dx = 0 \qquad (r \neq s), \tag{7.5.7}$$

where r and s are any nonnegative integers. The value assigned to C_r is such that $P_r(1) = 1$, and it is true also that $|P_r(x)| \leq 1$ when $|x| \leq 1$.

The first six of these polynomials may be obtained in the forms

$$P_0(x) = 1, \quad P_1(x) = x, \quad P_2(x) = \tfrac{1}{2}(3x^2 - 1),$$
$$P_3(x) = \tfrac{1}{2}(5x^3 - 3x), \quad P_4(x) = \tfrac{1}{8}(35x^4 - 30x^2 + 3), \tag{7.5.8}$$
$$P_5(x) = \tfrac{1}{8}(63x^5 - 70x^3 + 15x),$$

and additional ones can be determined from the recurrence formula†

$$P_{r+1}(x) = \frac{2r + 1}{r + 1} xP_r(x) - \frac{r}{r + 1} P_{r-1}(x). \tag{7.5.9}$$

It may be noted that the polynomials of even and odd degrees are even and odd functions of x, respectively.

† For a derivation of this formula, and of other similar formulas to be listed without derivation in the remainder of this chapter, see Szego [220].

In order to evaluate the factor (7.4.13), we notice first that (7.5.6) gives

$$P_r(x) = \frac{1}{2^r r!} \frac{d^r}{dx^r} (x^{2r} - rx^{2r-2} + \cdots) = \frac{(2r)!}{2^r (r!)^2} x^r - \cdots,$$

so that

$$A_r = \frac{(2r)!}{2^r (r!)^2}.$$

Hence (7.4.13) gives

$$\gamma_r \equiv \int_{-1}^{1} P_r^2(x) \, dx = \frac{(2r)!}{2^r r!} \frac{1}{2^r r!} \int_{-1}^{1} (1 - x^2)^r \, dx$$

$$= \frac{(2r)!}{2^{2r}(r!)^2} \frac{2^{2r+1}(r!)^2}{(2r + 1)!} = \frac{2}{2r + 1}. \tag{7.5.10}$$

Thus the nth-degree least-squares polynomial approximation to $f(x)$ over $(-1,1)$, relevant to a constant weighting function, is defined by

$$y(x) = \sum_{r=0}^{n} a_r P_r(x) \qquad (-1 < x < 1), \tag{7.5.11}$$

where

$$a_r = \frac{2r + 1}{2} \int_{-1}^{1} f(x) P_r(x) \, dx. \tag{7.5.12}$$

It has the property that, of all polynomials $y_n(x)$ of degree n or less, the integrated squared error

$$\int_{-1}^{1} [f(x) - y_n(x)]^2 \, dx$$

is least when $y_n(x)$ is identified with the polynomial defined by (7.5.11). In virtue of (7.2.14), that minimum error is given by

$$\int_{-1}^{1} f^2 \, dx - \sum_{r=0}^{n} \frac{2a_r^2}{2r + 1}.$$

In accordance with (7.4.14) to (7.4.16), it follows also that the least-squares approximation to $f(x)$ of the form

$$y(x) = v(x) \sum_{r=0}^{n} b_r P_r(x) \qquad (-1 < x < 1), \tag{7.5.13}$$

relevant to the weighting function $1/[v(x)]^2$, where $v(x)$ is a specified function, is that for which

$$b_r = \frac{2r + 1}{2} \int_{-1}^{1} \frac{f(x)}{v(x)} P_r(x) \, dx. \tag{7.5.14}$$

7.6. Laguerre Approximation. For least-squares polynomial approximation in a semi-infinite interval, it is convenient to first transform that

nterval into the interval $(0, \infty)$ by a translation of the origin. A frequently used approximation makes use of a weighting function of the form

$$w(x) = e^{-\alpha x}, \qquad (7.6.1)$$

vhere α is a positive constant, taken to be sufficiently large to ensure the
existence of the integral of the squared error over the semi-infinite interval (when this is possible).

From the results of §7.4, the relevant orthogonal polynomials are such
that

$$\phi_r(x) = e^{\alpha x} \frac{d^r U_r}{dx^r}, \qquad (7.6.2)$$

vhere

$$\frac{d^{r+1}}{dx^{r+1}} \left[e^{\alpha x} \frac{d^r U_r}{dx^r} \right] = 0 \qquad (7.6.3)$$

and where $\quad U_r(0) = U_r'(0) = \cdots = U_r^{(r-1)}(0) = 0 \qquad (7.6.4)$
and $\quad\quad U_r(\infty) = U_r'(\infty) = \cdots = U_r^{(r-1)}(\infty) = 0. \qquad (7.6.5)$

The general solution of (7.6.3) is readily found to be

$$U_r = e^{-\alpha x}(c_0 + c_1 x + \cdots + c_r x^r) + d_0 + d_1 x + \cdots + d_{r-1} x^{r-1},$$

vhere the c's and d's are arbitrary constants. The conditions (7.6.5)
require that all d's vanish, and (7.6.4) gives $c_0 = c_1 = \cdots = c_{r-1} = 0$,
so that there follows

$$U_r(x) = C_r x^r e^{-\alpha x}, \qquad (7.6.6)$$

and hence $\quad\quad \phi_r(x) = C_r e^{\alpha x} \dfrac{d^r}{dx^r} (x^r e^{-\alpha x}). \qquad (7.6.7)$

With $C_r = 1$ and $\alpha = 1$, this polynomial is called the rth *Laguerre polynomial*, and is usually denoted by $L_r(x)$,

$$L_r(x) = e^x \frac{d^r}{dx^r} (x^r e^{-x}). \qquad (7.6.8)$$

It follows that, again taking $C_r = 1$, the polynomial (7.6.7) can be
expressed in the form

$$\phi_r(x) = L_r(\alpha x), \qquad (7.6.9)$$

and that we have the orthogonality property

$$\int_0^{\infty} e^{-\alpha x} L_r(\alpha x) L_s(\alpha x) \, dx = 0 \qquad (r \neq s), \qquad (7.6.10)$$

when r and s are nonnegative integers.

The first six of the Laguerre polynomials can be obtained in the form

$$L_0(x) = 1, \quad L_1(x) = 1 - x, \quad L_2(x) = 2 - 4x + x^2,$$
$$L_3(x) = 6 - 18x + 9x^2 - x^3, \quad L_4(x) = 24 - 96x + 72x^2 - 16x^3 + x^4,$$
$$L_5(x) = 120 - 600x + 600x^2 - 200x^3 + 25x^4 - x^5, \qquad (7.6.11)$$

and additional ones can be determined from the recurrence formula

$$L_{r+1}(x) = (1 + 2r - x)L_r(x) - r^2L_{r-1}(x).   \qquad (7.6.12$$

The value assigned to C_r is such that the coefficient of x^r in $L_r(\alpha x)$ i $(-\alpha)^r$. Hence, from (7.4.13), there follows

$$\gamma_r \equiv \int_0^\infty e^{-\alpha x}L_r^2(\alpha x) \, dx = \alpha^r r! \int_0^\infty x^r e^{-\alpha x} \, dx = \frac{1}{\alpha} (r!)^2.   \quad (7.6.13$$

Thus the nth-degree least-squares polynomial approximation to $f(x$ in $(0, \infty)$, relevant to the weighting function $w(x) = e^{-\alpha x}$, is defined by

$$y(x) = \sum_{r=0}^{n} a_r L_r(\alpha x)   \qquad (0 < x < \infty),   \qquad (7.6.14$$

where
$$a_r = \frac{\alpha}{(r!)^2} \int_0^\infty e^{-\alpha x}f(x)L_r(\alpha x) \, dx.   \qquad (7.6.15$$

It has the property that, of all polynomials $y_n(x)$ of degree n or less, the integrated weighted squared error

$$\int_0^\infty e^{-\alpha x}[f(x) - y_n(x)]^2 \, dx$$

is least when $y_n(x)$ is identified with the right-hand member of (7.6.14) In order for this integral to *exist*, it is generally necessary that $|f(x)|$ grow less rapidly than $e^{\alpha x/2}$ as $x \to \infty$.

Another type of approximation employing Laguerre polynomials is obtained if we require the coefficients in the relation

$$y(x) = e^{-\alpha x} \sum_{r=0}^{n} b_r L_r(\alpha x)   \qquad (0 < x < \infty)   \qquad (7.6.16$$

such that

$$\int_0^\infty e^{\alpha x}[f(x) - y(x)]^2 \, dx \equiv \int_0^\infty e^{\alpha x} \left[f(x) - e^{-\alpha x} \sum_{k=0}^{n} b_k L_k(\alpha x) \right]^2 dx = \min.$$

$$(7.6.17$$

This is a special case of the problem specified by (7.4.14) to (7.4.16) in which $v(x) = w(x)$, and the coefficients are thus obtained in the form

$$b_r = \frac{\alpha}{(r!)^2} \int_0^\infty f(x)L_r(\alpha x) \, dx.   \qquad (7.6.18$$

In order that the integrals in (7.6.17) exist, it is generally necessary that $f(x)$ tend to zero more rapidly than $e^{-\alpha x/2}$ as $x \to \infty$.

7.7. Hermite Approximation. Over the doubly infinite interval $(-\infty < x < \infty)$, a frequently used weighting function is of the form

$$w(x) = e^{-\alpha^2 x^2}. \tag{7.7.1}$$

In this case the relevant orthogonal polynomials are defined by

$$\phi_r(x) = e^{\alpha^2 x^2} \frac{d^r U_r}{dx^r}, \tag{7.7.2}$$

where U_r satisfies the equation

$$\frac{d^{r+1}}{dx^{r+1}} \left[e^{\alpha^2 x^2} \frac{d^r U_r}{dx^r} \right] = 0 \tag{7.7.3}$$

and where U_r and its first $r - 1$ derivatives are to tend to zero as $x \to \pm \infty$.

Since the function

$$U_r(x) = C_r e^{-\alpha^2 x^2} \tag{7.7.4}$$

has the property that its rth derivative is the product of itself and a polynomial of degree r, it satisfies these conditions, and there follows

$$\phi_r(x) = C_r e^{\alpha^2 x^2} \frac{d^r}{dx^r} (e^{-\alpha^2 x^2}). \tag{7.7.5}$$

The *Hermite polynomial* of degree r is usually defined by taking $C_r = (-1)^r$ and, in addition, either $\alpha^2 = 1$ or $\alpha^2 = \frac{1}{2}$ in (7.7.5). Both definitions are used in the literature. We adopt the former one and write

$$H_r(x) = (-1)^r e^{x^2} \frac{d^r}{dx^r} (e^{-x^2}), \tag{7.7.6}$$

so that, with the choice $C_r = (-\alpha)^{-r}$, (7.7.5) becomes†

$$\phi_r(x) = H_r(\alpha x) = (-\alpha)^{-r} e^{\alpha^2 x^2} \frac{d^r}{dx^r} (e^{-\alpha^2 x^2}). \tag{7.7.7}$$

Thus these polynomials possess the orthogonality property

$$\int_{-\infty}^{\infty} e^{-\alpha^2 x^2} H_r(\alpha x) H_s(\alpha x) \, dx = 0 \qquad (r \neq s), \tag{7.7.8}$$

when r and s are nonnegative integers. The first six of the polynomials defined by (7.7.6) are obtained in the form

$$H_0(x) = 1, \quad H_1(x) = 2x, \quad H_2(x) = 4x^2 - 2,$$
$$H_3(x) = 8x^3 - 12x, \quad H_4(x) = 16x^4 - 48x^2 + 12, \tag{7.7.9}$$
$$H_5(x) = 32x^5 - 160x^3 + 120x,$$

† With the definition $H_r(x) = (-1)^r e^{x^2/2} d^r(e^{-x^2/2})/dx^r$, and the choice

$$C_r = (-1)^r 2^{-r/2} \alpha^{-r},$$

there would follow $\phi_r(x) = H_r(\sqrt{2} \, \alpha x)$.

and additional ones can be determined from the recurrence formula

$$H_{r+1}(x) = 2xH_r(x) - 2rH_{r-1}(x). \qquad (7.7.10)$$

With $A_r = (2\alpha)^r$ and $U_r = (-1/\alpha)^r \exp(-\alpha^2 x^2)$, Eq. (7.4.13) gives

$$\gamma_r \equiv \int_{-\infty}^{\infty} e^{-\alpha^2 x^2} H_r^2(\alpha x)\, dx = 2^r r! \int_{-\infty}^{\infty} e^{-\alpha^2 x^2}\, dx = \frac{2^r r!}{\alpha}\sqrt{\pi}. \qquad (7.7.11)$$

Thus the nth-degree least-squares polynomial approximation to $f(x)$ over $(-\infty, +\infty)$, relevant to the weighting function $w(x) = e^{-\alpha^2 x^2}$, is defined by

$$y(x) = \sum_{r=0}^{n} a_r H_r(\alpha x) \qquad (-\infty < x < \infty), \qquad (7.7.12)$$

where

$$a_r = \frac{\alpha}{2^r r! \sqrt{\pi}} \int_{-\infty}^{\infty} e^{-\alpha^2 x^2} H_r(\alpha x) f(x)\, dx. \qquad (7.7.13)$$

It has the property that, of all polynomials $y_n(x)$ of degree n or less, the integrated squared error

$$\int_{-\infty}^{\infty} e^{-\alpha^2 x^2} [f(x) - y_n(x)]^2\, dx$$

is least when $y_n(x)$ is identified with the right-hand member of (7.7.12). It must be assumed that the behavior of $f(x)$ is such that this integral exists.

It should be noticed that, since the weighting function $e^{-\alpha^2 x^2}$ becomes small very rapidly as x increases in magnitude, the least-squares criterion here requires that the magnitude of the deviation $f(x) - y(x)$ be small when x is small, but tolerates large values of that deviation when x is large in magnitude. A similar remark applies somewhat less strongly to the approximation of the preceding section. Thus, such approximations should not be used unless this situation is an acceptable one.

Another type of approximation, of particular importance in the theory of statistics, is obtained if we require the coefficients in the relation

$$y(x) = e^{-\alpha^2 x^2} \sum_{r=0}^{n} b_r H_r(\alpha x) \qquad (-\infty < x < \infty) \qquad (7.7.14)$$

such that

$$\int_{-\infty}^{\infty} e^{\alpha^2 x^2} [f(x) - y(x)]^2\, dx$$

$$\equiv \int_{-\infty}^{\infty} e^{\alpha^2 x^2} \left[f(x) - e^{-\alpha^2 x^2} \sum_{k=0}^{n} b_k H_k(\alpha x) \right]^2 dx = \min. \qquad (7.7.15)$$

The conditions governing the b's are obtained directly, or by reference to

(7.4.14) to (7.4.16), with $v(x) = w(x)$, in the form

$$b_r = \frac{\alpha}{2^r r! \sqrt{\pi}} \int_{-\infty}^{\infty} f(x) H_r(\alpha x) \, dx, \qquad (7.7.16)$$

assuming that the behavior of $f(x)$, for large values of $|x|$, is such that the integrals involved exist. In particular, the approximation (7.7.14) is often used in situations when $f(x)$ vanishes for all values of $|x|$ which exceed a certain value.

If the ith *moment* of $f(x)$ is defined as

$$m_i = \int_{-\infty}^{\infty} x^i f(x) \, dx, \qquad (7.7.17)$$

and use is made of the explicit forms of (7.7.9), we find that the leading coefficients in (7.7.14) are expressible in the forms

$$b_0 = \frac{\alpha}{\sqrt{\pi}} m_0, \qquad b_1 = \frac{\alpha^2}{\sqrt{\pi}} m_1, \qquad b_2 = \frac{\alpha}{4\sqrt{\pi}} (2\alpha^2 m_2 - m_0), \quad (7.7.18)$$

and that the remaining b's can be similarly expressed in terms of the moments.

7.8. Chebyshev Approximation. In cases when errors near the ends of an interval (a,b) are of particular importance, a weighting function which is of the form $1/\sqrt{(x-a)(b-x)}$ is often useful. It is supposed again that a linear change in variables has transformed the given interval into the interval $(-1,1)$, so that the weighting function becomes

$$w(x) = \frac{1}{\sqrt{1-x^2}}. \qquad (7.8.1)$$

In order to obtain the relevant orthogonal polynomials in this case, it is convenient to start with the basic condition (7.4.1), rather than with its consequences. Thus we require a polynomial $\phi_r(x)$, of degree r in x, such that

$$\int_{-1}^{1} \frac{\phi_r(x) q_{r-1}(x)}{\sqrt{1-x^2}} \, dx = 0, \qquad (7.8.2)$$

where $q_{r-1}(x)$ is an arbitrary polynomial of degree $r-1$ or less in x. If we introduce the change in variables

$$x = \cos\theta, \qquad (7.8.3)$$

this requirement becomes

$$\int_0^{\pi} \phi_r(\cos\theta) q_{r-1}(\cos\theta) \, d\theta = 0. \qquad (7.8.4)$$

Now, since $\cos k\theta$ is expressible as a polynomial of degree k in $\cos\theta$ and since, conversely, any polynomial of degree k in $\cos\theta$ can be expressed as a linear combination of 1, $\cos \theta$, $\cos 2\theta$, . . . , $\cos k\theta$, it follows that (7.8.4) will be satisfied if and only if

$$\int_0^\pi \phi_r(\cos \theta) \cos k\theta \, d\theta = 0 \qquad (k = 0, 1, \ldots, r - 1). \quad (7.8.5)$$

It is easily verified that the function

$$\phi_r(\cos \theta) = C_r \cos r\theta \qquad (7.8.6)$$

has this property. Hence, returning to the variable x by using (7.8.3), we verify that the functions

$$\phi_r(x) = C_r \cos (r \cos^{-1} x) \qquad (7.8.7)$$

are the required orthogonal polynomials. With $C_r = 1$, these polynomials are known as *Chebyshev polynomials*,† often denoted by $T_r(x)$, so that we may write

$$\phi_r(x) = T_r(x) = \cos (r \cos^{-1} x). \qquad (7.8.8)$$

Thus, these polynomials possess the orthogonality property

$$\int_{-1}^1 \frac{T_r(x) T_s(x)}{\sqrt{1 - x^2}} \, dx = 0 \qquad (r \neq s), \qquad (7.8.9)$$

when r and s are nonnegative integers. The first six of these polynomials are obtained in the form

$$\begin{aligned}
T_0(x) &= 1, \qquad T_1(x) = x, \qquad T_2(x) = 2x^2 - 1, \\
T_3(x) &= 4x^3 - 3x, \qquad T_4(x) = 8x^4 - 8x^2 + 1, \\
&\quad T_5(x) = 16x^5 - 20x^3 + 5x,
\end{aligned} \qquad (7.8.10)$$

and additional ones may be determined from the recurrence formula

$$T_{r+1}(x) = 2x T_r(x) - T_{r-1}(x). \qquad (7.8.11)$$

In order to evaluate the factor

$$\gamma_r = \int_{-1}^1 \frac{T_r^2(x)}{\sqrt{1 - x^2}} \, dx, \qquad (7.8.12)$$

we again write $x = \cos \theta$ and $T_r(x) = \cos r\theta$, so that there follows directly

$$\gamma_r = \int_0^\pi \cos^2 r\theta \, d\theta = \begin{cases} \pi & (r = 0), \\ \dfrac{\pi}{2} & (r \neq 0). \end{cases} \qquad (7.8.13)$$

Thus the nth-degree least-squares polynomial approximation to $f(x)$ in

† The name of Chebyshev (or Tschebycheff) is associated with various sets of polynomials in the literature (see also §§7.11 and 8.13).

$(-1,1)$, relevant to the weighting function $w(x) = 1/\sqrt{1 - x^2}$, is defined by

$$y(x) = \sum_{r=0}^{n} a_r T_r(x) \qquad (-1 < x < 1), \qquad (7.8.14)$$

where

$$a_0 = \frac{1}{\pi} \int_{-1}^{1} \frac{f(x)}{\sqrt{1 - x^2}} \, dx, \qquad a_r = \frac{2}{\pi} \int_{-1}^{1} \frac{f(x) T_r(x)}{\sqrt{1 - x^2}} \, dx \qquad (r \neq 0).$$

$$(7.8.15)$$

It has the property that, of all polynomials of degree n or less, the integrated weighted squared error

$$\int_{-1}^{1} \frac{1}{\sqrt{1 - x^2}} [f(x) - y_n(x)]^2 \, dx$$

is least when $y_n(x)$ is identified with the right-hand member of (7.8.14).

On the other hand, if we wish to approximate $f(x)$ by the product of $1/\sqrt{1 - x^2}$ and a polynomial, over $(-1,1)$, with the weighting function $\sqrt{1 - x^2}$, we are to determine the coefficients in the relation

$$y(x) = \frac{1}{\sqrt{1 - x^2}} \sum_{r=0}^{n} b_r T_r(x) \qquad (-1 < x < 1) \qquad (7.8.16)$$

such that

$$\int_{-1}^{1} \sqrt{1 - x^2} \, [f(x) - y(x)]^2 \, dx$$

$$\equiv \int_{-1}^{1} \sqrt{1 - x^2} \left[f(x) - \frac{1}{\sqrt{1 - x^2}} \sum_{k=0}^{n} b_k T_k(x) \right]^2 \, dx = \min.$$

The conditions determining the b's are obtained in the form

$$\int_{-1}^{1} T_r(x) \left[f(x) - \frac{1}{\sqrt{1 - x^2}} \sum_{k=0}^{n} b_k T_k(x) \right] dx = 0,$$

and the use of (7.8.9) and (7.8.13), or of (7.4.14) to (7.4.16), yields the determination

$$b_0 = \frac{1}{\pi} \int_{-1}^{1} f(x) \, dx, \qquad b_r = \frac{2}{\pi} \int_{-1}^{1} f(x) T_r(x) \, dx \qquad (r \neq 0). \quad (7.8.17)$$

A great variety of other types of least-squares polynomial approximation can be formulated in terms of other weighting functions. In particular, for the weighting function

$$w(x) = (1 - x)^\alpha (1 + x)^\beta \qquad (\alpha > -1, \beta > -1), \qquad (7.8.18)$$

over $(-1,1)$, which reduces to the Legendre case when $\alpha = \beta = 0$ and to the Chebyshev case when $\alpha = \beta = -\frac{1}{2}$, the rth orthogonal polynomial is readily found to be of the form

$$\phi_r(x) = C_r (1 - x)^{-\alpha} (1 + x)^{-\beta} \frac{d^r}{dx^r} [(1 - x)^{\alpha+r} (1 + x)^{\beta+r}], \quad (7.8.19)$$

which may be identified with the rth *Jacobi polynomial* when C_r is suitably specified (see §8.9).

In particular, the factor C_r for $T_r(x)$ is given by $(-2)^r r!/(2r)!$, so that (7.8.8) can also be written in the form

$$T_r(x) = \frac{(-2)^r r!}{(2r)!} (1 - x^2)^{\frac{1}{2}} \frac{d^r}{dx^r} (1 - x^2)^{r-\frac{1}{2}}. \qquad (7.8.20)$$

Analogous polynomials $S_r(x)$, which are associated with the weighting function $w(x) = (1 - x^2)^{\frac{1}{2}}$, and which can be expressed in the form

$$S_r(x) = \frac{\sin [(r + 1) \cos^{-1} x]}{\sin (\cos^{-1} x)} = \frac{(-2)^r (r + 1)!}{(2r + 1)!} (1 - x^2)^{-\frac{1}{2}} \frac{d^r}{dx^r} (1 - x^2)^{r+\frac{1}{2}},$$
$$(7.8.21)$$

are considered in Prob. 31.

For the weighting function

$$w(x) = x^\beta e^{-\alpha x} \qquad (\beta > -1, \alpha > 0), \qquad (7.8.22)$$

over $(0, \infty)$, there follows

$$\phi_r(x) = C_r x^{-\beta} e^{\alpha x} \frac{d^r}{dx^r} (x^{\beta+r} e^{-\alpha x}), \qquad (7.8.23)$$

and the resultant polynomials are frequently called *Sonine polynomials* or *generalized Laguerre polynomials* (for additional information see Szego [220]).

Before proceeding to a corresponding treatment of the case when *discrete* data are involved, it is desirable to establish certain analogies between integration and summation, and to obtain certain special properties of the *binomial coefficient functions* and related functions, which play the same roles in summation and differencing as do the functions $1, x, \ldots, x^n$ in integration and differentiation.

7.9. Factorial Power Functions and Summation Formulas. The product $s(s - 1) \cdots (s - n + 1)$, where n is a positive integer, is often called the *factorial nth power* of s, and the notation

$$s^{(n)} = s(s - 1) \cdots (s - n + 1) \qquad (7.9.1)$$

is frequently used. It is related to the *binomial coefficient function* by the equation

$$\binom{s}{n} = \frac{s^{(n)}}{n!}. \tag{7.9.2}$$

In the more general case when n need not be a positive integer, (7.9.1) is generalized by the definition

$$s^{(n)} = \frac{\Gamma(s+1)}{\Gamma(s-n+1)}, \tag{7.9.3}$$

in accordance with which there follows, in particular,

$$s^{(0)} = 1 \tag{7.9.4}$$

and $\qquad s^{(n)} = 0 \qquad$ when $n - s$ is a positive integer. $\qquad$ (7.9.5)

In order to establish the usefulness of the notation (7.9.1) or (7.9.3), we notice that, from (7.9.3), there follows

$$\Delta_1 s^{(n)} = \frac{\Gamma(s+2)}{\Gamma(s-n+2)} - \frac{\Gamma(s+1)}{\Gamma(s-n+1)} = \left(\frac{s+1}{s-n+1} - 1\right)\frac{\Gamma(s+1)}{\Gamma(s-n+1)}$$

$$= n\frac{\Gamma(s+1)}{(s-n+1)\Gamma(s-n+1)} = n\frac{\Gamma(s+1)}{\Gamma(s-n+2)}$$

or $\qquad\qquad\qquad\qquad \Delta_1 s^{(n)} = n s^{(n-1)}, \tag{7.9.6}$

where Δ_1 denotes the forward-difference operator with unit spacing, and where use is made of the fundamental property of the gamma function,[†]

$$\Gamma(u+1) = u\Gamma(u). \tag{7.9.7}$$

Thus the factorial power $s^{(n)}$ is related to the operator Δ_1 just as the ordinary power x^n is related to the operator $\mathbf{D} \equiv d/dx$. In this connection, it is of interest to notice that Newton's forward-difference formula (4.3.5) can be written in the form

$$f_s = f_0 + \frac{\Delta f_0}{1!}s^{(1)} + \frac{\Delta^2 f_0}{2!}s^{(2)} + \cdots + \frac{\Delta^n f_0}{n!}s^{(n)} + \frac{f^{(n+1)}(\xi)}{(n+1)!}s^{(n+1)} \tag{7.9.8}$$

and is seen to be completely analogous to the Maclaurin series, with a remainder, expressed in the form

$$f(x) = f(0) + \frac{f'(0)}{1!}x + \frac{f''(0)}{2!}x^2 + \cdots + \frac{f^{(n)}(0)}{n!}x^n + \frac{f^{(n+1)}(\xi)}{(n+1)!}x^{n+1}.$$

The combination of (7.9.2) and (7.9.6) leads to the relation

$$\Delta_1 \binom{s}{n} \equiv \binom{s+1}{n} - \binom{s}{n} = \frac{n s^{(n-1)}}{n!} = \frac{s^{(n-1)}}{(n-1)!},$$

[†] It is often convenient to write $u!$ as an abbreviation for $\Gamma(u+1)$, even though u is not a positive integer.

and hence to the corresponding useful property

$$\Delta_1 \binom{s}{n} \equiv \binom{s+1}{n} - \binom{s}{n} = \binom{s}{n-1}, \tag{7.9.9}$$

of the binomial coefficient functions.

We recall next that, from the telescoping of terms in the expansion

$$\sum_{s=M}^{N} \Delta_1 f_s = (f_{M+1} - f_M) + (f_{M+2} - f_{M+1})$$
$$+ \cdots + (f_N - f_{N-1}) + (f_{N+1} - f_N),$$

it follows that

$$\sum_{s=M}^{N} \Delta_1 f_s = f_{N+1} - f_M \equiv f_s \Big|_M^{N+1}. \tag{7.9.10}$$

This general relation is seen to be analogous to the relation

$$\int_a^b f'(x)\, dx = f(b) - f(a) = f(x) \Big|_a^b,$$

but careful notice should be taken of the fact that the limits on the right in (7.9.10) are not the same as those on the left. Thus, in particular, we may deduce from (7.9.10) and (7.9.6) the summation formula

$$\sum_{s=M}^{N} s^{(n)} = \frac{s^{(n+1)}}{n+1} \Big|_M^{N+1} \qquad (n \neq -1), \tag{7.9.11}$$

which clearly corresponds to the integral formula

$$\int_a^b x^n\, dx = \frac{x^{n+1}}{n+1} \Big|_a^b \qquad (n \neq -1).$$

Since (7.9.8) permits any polynomial in s to be expressed as a linear combination of factorial powers of s, (7.9.11) then serves to effect the summation of that polynomial. In illustration, in order to express the sum

$$S_n \equiv 1 \cdot 3 + 2 \cdot 4 + \cdots + n(n+2)$$

in closed form, we could first obtain the relation

$$s^2 + 2s = 0 + 3s^{(1)} + s^{(2)},$$

by use of undetermined coefficients or by using (7.9.8), and then make the calculation

$$S_n = \sum_{s=1}^{n} [3s^{(1)} + s^{(2)}] = [\tfrac{3}{2} s^{(2)} + \tfrac{1}{3} s^{(3)}]_1^{n+1}$$
$$= \tfrac{3}{2}(n+1)n + \tfrac{1}{3}(n+1)n(n-1) = \tfrac{1}{6}n(n+1)(7+2n).$$

The summation could also be effected by making appropriate use of (5.8.4) or of the Euler-Maclaurin sum formula (5.8.12).

There exist a large number of useful identities involving either factorial power functions or, correspondingly, binomial coefficient functions. In particular, the relation

$$s^{(n)}(s - n)^{(k)} = s^{(n+k)}, \tag{7.9.12}$$

which follows immediately from the fact that the left-hand member is given by

$$[s(s - 1) \cdots (s - n + 1)][(s - n)(s - n - 1) \cdots (s - n - k + 1)],$$

is of frequent use.

From the definition (7.9.2), we obtain the property

$$\binom{s}{n} = \binom{s}{s - n}. \tag{7.9.13}$$

Also, from the fact that

$$(1 + x)^n = \sum_{k=0}^{n} \binom{n}{k} x^k, \tag{7.9.14}$$

when n is a nonnegative integer, we deduce in particular that

$$\sum_{k=0}^{n} \binom{n}{k} = 2^n \tag{7.9.15}$$

and

$$\sum_{k=0}^{n} (-1)^k \binom{n}{k} = 0, \tag{7.9.16}$$

by setting $x = 1$ and $x = -1$, respectively.

Many other important relations are obtainable from the identity

$$\binom{m + p}{n} = \sum_{k=0}^{n} \binom{p}{k}\binom{m}{n - k} = \sum_{k=0}^{n} \binom{p}{n - k}\binom{m}{k}, \tag{7.9.17}$$

when n is a nonnegative integer. In order to establish this relation, we multiply together the series expansions of $(1 + x)^p$ and $(1 + x)^m$, noticing that those series terminate when p and m are nonnegative integers and are absolutely convergent infinite series when $|x| < 1$ otherwise, to obtain the results

$$(1 + x)^{m+p} = \left[\sum_{j=0}^{\infty} \binom{m}{j} x^j \right] \left[\sum_{k=0}^{\infty} \binom{p}{k} x^k \right] = \sum_{j=0}^{\infty} \sum_{k=0}^{\infty} \binom{p}{k}\binom{m}{j} x^{k+j}$$

$$= \sum_{n=0}^{\infty} \left[\sum_{k=0}^{n} \binom{p}{k}\binom{m}{n - k} \right] x^n \qquad (|x| < 1).$$

But since also

$$(1 + x)^{m+p} = \sum_{n=0}^{\infty} \binom{m + p}{n} x^n \qquad (|x| < 1),$$

and since the coefficient of x^n must be the same in these two forms, the first form of the desired result (7.9.17) follows. The second form results from interchanging p and m. As a special case, we may take $m = p = n$ in (7.9.17) and use (7.9.13) to obtain the result

$$\sum_{k=0}^{n} \binom{n}{k}^2 = \binom{2n}{n}. \tag{7.9.18}$$

We may notice next that

$$\binom{-p}{q} = \frac{(-p)(-p - 1) \cdots (-p - q + 1)}{q!}$$

$$= (-1)^q \frac{(p + q - 1)(p + q - 2) \cdots p}{q!},$$

and hence

$$\binom{-p}{q} = (-1)^q \binom{p + q - 1}{q}, \tag{7.9.19}$$

when q is a nonnegative integer. Hence we deduce from (7.9.17) and (7.9.19) the further relations

$$\binom{m - p}{n} = \sum_{k=0}^{n} (-1)^k \binom{p + k - 1}{k} \binom{m}{n - k}$$

$$= \sum_{k=0}^{n} (-1)^{n+k} \binom{p + n - k - 1}{n - k} \binom{m}{k}. \tag{7.9.20}$$

All these formulas can be expressed alternatively in terms of factorial power functions, by making use of (7.9.2).

Finally, a general formula which will be needed in the sequel is the sum analogy to integration by parts. In order to derive the desired formula, we notice first that

$$\Delta_1 u_s v_s = u_{s+1} v_{s+1} - u_s v_s \equiv v_{s+1}(u_{s+1} - u_s) + u_s(v_{s+1} - v_s)$$
$$= u_s \, \Delta_1 v_s + v_{s+1} \, \Delta_1 u_s.$$

Hence, by transposition, and use of (7.9.10), we deduce the formula for *summation by parts* in the form

$$\sum_{s=M}^{N} u_s \, \Delta_1 v_s = u_s v_s \Big|_M^{N+1} - \sum_{s=M}^{N} v_{s+1} \, \Delta_1 u_s. \tag{7.9.21}$$

Also, by replacing u_s by v_s and v_s by u_{s-1}, and transposing terms, we deduce the alternative form

$$\sum_{s=M}^{N} u_s \, \Delta_1 v_s = u_{s-1} v_s \Big|_M^{N+1} - \sum_{s=M}^{N} v_s \, \Delta_1 u_{s-1}. \qquad (7.9.22)$$

7.10. Polynomials Orthogonal over Discrete Ranges. For least-squares approximation over a discrete range R, it is convenient to make use of a set of polynomials which are mutually orthogonal under *summation* over R, with respect to a specified weighting function. We suppose that $N + 1$ points are to be employed in the approximation, with uniform separation h, and that the extreme points are at the ends of the interval (a,b), where $b - a = Nh$. If we then write

$$x = a + sh, \qquad (7.10.1)$$

the variable s takes on the values $s = 0, 1, 2, \ldots, N$ at those points, and we seek a set of polynomials $\phi_0(s,N)$, $\phi_1(s,N)$, $\ldots$, $\phi_N(s,N)$ such that ϕ_r is of degree r in s, and such that

$$\sum_{s=0}^{N} w(s) \phi_r(s,N) q_{r-1}(s) = 0, \qquad (7.10.2)$$

where $w(s)$ is a specified weighting function, assumed to be nonnegative in R, and where $q_{r-1}(s)$ is an *arbitrary* polynomial of degree $r - 1$ or less in R.

The procedure is analogous to that employed in §7.4. We first set

$$w(s) \phi_r(s,N) = \Delta_1^r U_r(s,N), \qquad (7.10.3)$$

so that (7.10.2) becomes

$$\sum_{s=0}^{N} [\Delta_1^r U_r(s,N)] q_{r-1}(s) = 0, \qquad (7.10.4)$$

and sum by parts r times, noticing that $\Delta_1^r q_{r-1}(s) \equiv 0$, to transform (7.10.4) to the relation

$$[\{\Delta_1^{r-1} U_r(s)\} q_{r-1}(s) - \{\Delta_1^{r-2} U_r(s + 1)\} \, \Delta_1 q_{r-1}(s) + \cdots$$
$$+ (-1)^{r-1} \{U_r(s + r - 1)\} \, \Delta_1^{r-1} q_{r-1}(s)]_{s=0}^{s=N+1} = 0. \qquad (7.10.5)$$

Since we require that ϕ_r be a polynomial of degree r, it follows from (7.10.3) that U_r must satisfy the *difference equation*

$$\Delta_1^{r+1} \left[\frac{1}{w(s)} \Delta_1^r U_r(s,N) \right] = 0 \qquad (7.10.6)$$

in R and, because of the arbitrariness of $q_{r-1}(s)$, $\Delta_1 q_{r-1}(s)$, and so forth, when $s = 0$ and $s = N + 1$, that $U_r(s + r - 1, N)$, $\Delta_1 U_r(s + r - 2, N)$, . . . , and $\Delta_1^{r-1} U_r(s,N)$ must vanish when $s = 0$ and when $s = N + 1$. It is easily seen that these requirements are equivalent to the $2r$ conditions

$$U_r(0,N) = U_r(1,N) = U_r(2,N) = \cdots = U_r(r - 1, N) = 0 \quad (7.10.7)$$

and

$$U_r(N + 1, N) = U_r(N + 2, N) = U_r(N + 3, N)$$
$$= \cdots = U_r(N + r, N) = 0. \quad (7.10.8)$$

Once U_r has been determined, necessarily with an arbitrary multiplicative constant, there follows, from (7.10.3),

$$\phi_r(s,N) = \frac{1}{w(s)} \Delta_1^r U_r(s,N). \quad (7.10.9)$$

In consequence of the results of §7.2, the coefficients in the relation

$$y(s) = \sum_{r=0}^{n} a_r \phi_r(s,N) \quad (7.10.10)$$

are then determined, by the requirement

$$\sum_{s=0}^{N} w(s) \left[f(s) - \sum_{r=0}^{n} a_r \phi_r(s,N) \right]^2 = \min, \quad (7.10.11)$$

in the form

$$a_r = \frac{1}{\gamma_r(N)} \sum_{s=0}^{N} w(s) f(s) \phi_r(s,N), \quad (7.10.12)$$

where

$$\gamma_r(N) = \sum_{s=0}^{N} w(s) \phi_r^2(s,N). \quad (7.10.13)$$

7.11. Gram Approximation. We restrict attention here to the case when $w(s) \equiv 1$. Equation (7.10.6) then requires merely that $U_r(s,N)$ be a polynomial in s of degree $2r$ and, since (7.10.7) and (7.10.8) determine its $2r$ zeros, there follows immediately

$$U_r(s,N) = C_{rN}[s(s - 1) \cdots (s - r + 1)][(s - N - 1)(s - N - 2)$$
$$\cdots (s - N - r)]$$

or

$$U_r(s,N) = C_{rN} s^{(r)} (s - N - 1)^{(r)}, \quad (7.11.1)$$

where C_{rN} is an arbitrary constant. Hence we have also

$$\phi_r(s,N) = C_{rN} \Delta_1^r [s^{(r)} (s - N - 1)^{(r)}]. \quad (7.11.2)$$

In order to express this result in a more explicit form, we first expand $(s - N - 1)^{(r)}$ in terms of factorial powers of $(s - r)$, then use (7.9.12) to express (7.11.1) in terms of factorial powers of s, and, finally, make use of (7.9.6). Thus, if we make use of the second form of (7.9.20), we obtain

$$(s - N - 1)^{(r)} = r!\left(\frac{(s - r) - (N + 1 - r)}{r}\right)$$

$$= (-1)^r r! \sum_{k=0}^{r} (-1)^k \binom{N - k}{r - k}\binom{s - r}{k} \quad (7.11.3)$$

and hence, in virtue of (7.11.1) and (7.9.12),

$$U_r(s,N) = (-1)^r r! C_{rN} \sum_{k=0}^{r} \frac{(-1)^k}{k!}\binom{N - k}{r - k} s^{(k+r)}. \quad (7.11.4)$$

Thus, by making use of (7.9.6), we obtain the result

$$\phi_r(s,N) = (-1)^r r! C_{rN} \sum_{k=0}^{r} (-1)^k \frac{(r + k)^{(r)}}{k!}\binom{N - k}{r - k} s^{(k)}, \quad (7.11.5)$$

which can be transformed easily to the more convenient form

$$\phi_r(s,N) = c_{rN} \sum_{k=0}^{r} (-1)^k \frac{(r + k)^{(2k)}}{(k!)^2} \frac{s^{(k)}}{N^{(k)}}, \quad (7.11.6)$$

where c_{rN} has been written for the arbitrary constant $(-1)^r r! N^{(r)} C_{rN}$. The expanded form appears as follows:

$$\phi_r(s,N) = c_{rN}\left[1 - \frac{r(r + 1)}{(1!)^2}\frac{s}{N} + \frac{(r - 1)r(r + 1)(r + 2)}{(2!)^2}\frac{s(s - 1)}{N(N - 1)}\right.$$
$$\left. - \frac{(r - 2)(r - 1)r(r + 1)(r + 2)(r + 3)}{(3!)^2}\frac{s(s - 1)(s - 2)}{N(N - 1)(N - 2)} + \cdots\right].$$
$$(7.11.7)$$

In most applications of least-squares methods, it is convenient to make use of an *odd* number of ordinates, so that N is *even*, and to write

$$N = 2M.$$

In such cases, it is also convenient to make the change of variables

$$s = M + t, \quad (7.11.8)$$

so that t represents distance from the *mid-point* of the range R in units of the spacing h (see Fig. 7.1) and takes on the values $0, \pm 1, \pm 2, \ldots,$ $\pm M$ at the $2M + 1$ points of R.

If also we choose

$$c_{rN} = (-1)^r \tag{7.11.9}$$

and write $p_r(t,2M) \equiv \phi_r(s,2M)$, the polynomials of degrees zero through

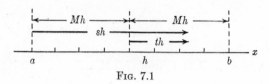

FIG. 7.1

five can be expressed explicitly as follows:

$$p_0(t,2M) = 1,$$

$$p_1(t,2M) = \frac{t}{M},$$

$$p_2(t,2M) = \frac{3t^2 - M(M + 1)}{M(2M - 1)},$$

$$p_3(t,2M) = \frac{5t^3 - (3M^2 + 3M - 1)t}{M(M - 1)(2M - 1)}, \tag{7.11.10}$$

$$p_4(t,2M) = \frac{35t^4 - 5(6M^2 + 6M - 5)t^2 + 3M(M^2 - 1)(M + 2)}{2M(M - 1)(2M - 1)(2M - 3)},$$

$$p_5(t,2M) =$$
$$\frac{63t^5 - 35(2M^2 + 2M - 3)t^3 + (15M^4 + 30M^3 - 35M^2 - 50M + 12)t}{2M(M - 1)(M - 2)(2M - 1)(2M - 3)}.$$

These polynomials thus possess the orthogonality property

$$\sum_{t=-M}^{M} p_i(t,2M)p_j(t,2M) = 0 \qquad (i \neq j) \tag{7.11.11}$$

and are usually known as *Gram polynomials* (or as *Chebyshev polynomials*, although the latter name is usually reserved for either the polynomials considered in §7.8 or those to be considered in §8.13). It may be seen that the rth polynomial is an even function of t when r is even, and an odd function of t when r is odd. Also, each polynomial takes on the value *unity* when $t = M$. Further, if t is replaced by Mx and M is then increased without limit, it can be verified that $p_r(t,2M)$ tends to the rth Legendre polynomial $P_r(x)$,

$$\lim_{M \to \infty} p_r(Mx,2M) = P_r(x).$$

In accordance with the results of the preceding section, the nth-degree least-squares polynomial approximation to $f(t)$ over the $(2M + 1)$-point range $t = -M, -M + 1, \ldots, -1, 0, 1, \ldots, M - 1, M$ is given by

$$y(t) = \sum_{r=0}^{n} a_r p_r(t,2M) \tag{7.11.12}$$

where

$$a_r = \frac{1}{\gamma_r} \sum_{t=-M}^{M} f(t) p_r(t,2M), \tag{7.11.13}$$

and where

$$\gamma_r = \sum_{t=-M}^{M} p_r^2(t,2M). \tag{7.11.14}$$

As in the earlier developments, the factors γ_r are independent of the function $f(t)$ which is to be approximated and can be calculated once and for all (see Prob. 42).

It should be noted that various conventions are adopted in the literature with regard to the value assigned to the arbitrary multiplicative constant c_{rN} in (7.11.7) in the general case. In particular, that constant is sometimes so defined that the coefficient of s^r in $\phi_r(s,N)$ is unity. Another common choice is that for which the values taken on when $s = 0$, $1, \ldots, N$ are *integers* without a common factor, so that tabulation is simplified. When $N + 1$ points are used, the sum of the squares of the $N + 1$ tabular values of the rth-degree polynomial corresponding to the normalization (7.11.9) used here is found to be

$$\frac{(N + r + 1)!(N - r)!}{(2r + 1)(N!)^2}$$

(see Prob. 42), whereas (7.11.7) shows that the coefficient of s^r is

$$\frac{(2r)!(N - r)!}{(r!)^2 N!}.$$

These results permit tabulations relevant to other normalizations to be interpreted in terms of the one used here.

7.12. Example. Five-point Least-squares Approximation. In order to illustrate the method of using the preceding results, we consider here the case in which only five ordinates are used, so that $M = 2$. The relevant orthogonal polynomials of degrees zero through four are then obtained from (7.11.10) in the forms

$$p_0(t) = 1, \quad p_1(t) = \tfrac{1}{2}t, \quad p_2(t) = \tfrac{1}{2}(t^2 - 2),$$
$$p_3(t) = \tfrac{1}{6}(5t^3 - 17t), \quad p_4(t) = \tfrac{1}{12}(35t^4 - 155t^2 + 72), \tag{7.12.1}$$

if we write $p_r(t)$ for $p_r(t,4)$.

We may notice that $p_5(t)$, as defined by (7.11.10), is nonexistent when $M = 2$. This situation corresponds to the fact that the use of polynomials of degrees zero through five over five points would not lead to a determinate problem, since infinitely many fifth-degree polynomials would fit the data *exactly* at those points. Further, the use of polynomials of degrees zero through four over five points truly would not be a "least-squares" procedure, since it necessarily would lead to the fourth-degree polynomial which fits the data exactly. Thus $p_4(t)$ is not needed when five points are used unless an exact fit at those points is desired, in which case the use of methods given in earlier chapters is usually to be preferred.

Values of the polynomials at the five relevant points are easily determined and may be tabulated as follows:

TABLE 7.1

t	p_0	p_1	p_2	p_3	f
-2	1	-1	1	-1	f_{-2}
-1	1	-0.5	-0.5	2	f_{-1}
0	1	0	-1	0	f_0
1	1	0.5	-0.5	-2	f_1
2	1	1	1	1	f_2
$\gamma_r =$	5	2.5	3.5	10	

According to (7.11.12) to (7.11.14), the coefficient a_r of each $p_r(t)$ used in the approximation is obtained by multiplying each entry in its column by the corresponding entry in the column of values of $f(t)$, summing, and dividing the result by γ_r, which is listed at the foot of the p_r column. Once the a's are calculated, the least-squares polynomial $y(t)$ can be obtained *explicitly* by forming the corresponding combination of the polynomials listed in (7.12.1). If only the value of $y(t)$ at a tabular point is required, this explicit form of $y(t)$ is not needed, since the required value is obtained by merely multiplying the tabulated value of each p_r for that t by a_r, and summing the results.

In illustration, suppose that we are provided with the empirical data

x	0.0	0.2	0.4	0.6	0.8
$F(x)$	1.10	1.78	2.74	4.12	5.69

together with some assurance that the observed values are in error by no more than a few units in the last place given, and that the true function is "smooth." In order to obtain least-squares polynomial approximations by use of Table 7.1, we then set $x = 0.4 + 0.2t$, or $t = 5x - 2$, and write $F(0.4 + 0.2t) = f(t)$. Calculation then gives

$$a_0 \doteq 3.086, \qquad a_1 \doteq 2.304, \qquad a_2 \doteq 0.314, \qquad a_3 \doteq -0.009,$$

so that least-squares approximations of degrees one, two, and three are obtained by retaining two, three, or four terms in the relation

$$f(t) \approx 3.086 p_0(t) + 2.304 p_1(t) + 0.314 p_2(t) - 0.009 p_3(t).$$

The corresponding "smoothed" values at the tabular points may be obtained, from Table 7.1, as follows:

t	-2	-1	0	1	2
f	1.10	1.78	2.74	4.12	5.69
y_3	1.105	1.759	2.772	4.099	5.695
y_2	1.096	1.777	2.772	4.081	5.704
y_1	0.782	1.934	3.086	4.238	5.390

The RMS value of the five deviations from the observed values is found to be 0.0198 for the third-degree approximation, 0.0235 for the second-degree approximation, and 0.264 for the linear approximation. The use of (7.3.34) then leads to corresponding estimates of 0.0443, 0.0372, and 0.341, respectively, for the RMS error in the observed values. Clearly, only the first two of these estimates are in accord with the given information.

If the smallest of these estimates is accepted as the most appropriate one, we may conclude that the additional smoothing afforded by the use of a parabolic approximation, in place of a cubic, probably represents a further removal of "noise" rather than a departure from the unknown true function.

If additional values of the least-squares polynomial are desired, they may be obtained conveniently by interpolation. However, if the *equation* of the parabolic approximation is required, it may be written down in the form

$$y = 3.086 p_0(t) + 2.304 p_1(t) + 0.314 p_2(t)$$
$$= 2.772 + 1.152t + 0.157t^2$$

and reduced, if so desired, to the form

$$y = 1.096 + 2.620x + 3.925x^2.$$

In particular, this result supplies the approximations 2.62, 5.76, and 8.90 to the *slope* of the unknown function at $x = 0.0, 0.4$, and 0.8, respectively, whereas the third-degree approximation would yield the values 2.30, 5.89, and 8.58. On the other hand, the result of differentiating the fourth-degree *interpolation* polynomial, which takes on the five observed values exactly, would give the respective values 3.40, 5.89, and 7.48.

By expressing the a's explicitly in terms of the observed values, we may obtain formulas which express the smoothed values directly in terms of the observed ones. Thus, corresponding to the *third*-degree least-squares approximation over five points, we obtain the formula

$$y_0 = a_0 - a_2$$
$$= \tfrac{1}{5}(f_{-2} + f_{-1} + f_0 + f_1 + f_2) - \tfrac{2}{7}(f_{-2} - \tfrac{1}{2}f_{-1} - f_0 - \tfrac{1}{2}f_1 + f_2)$$

or
$$y_0 = \tfrac{1}{35}(-3f_{-2} + 12f_{-1} + 17f_0 + 12f_1 - 3f_2), \qquad (7.12.2)$$

for the smoothed value at the mid-point $t = 0$, and the formulas

$$\begin{aligned}
y_{-2} &= \tfrac{1}{70}(69f_{-2} + 4f_{-1} - 6f_0 + 4f_1 - f_2),\\
y_{-1} &= \tfrac{1}{35}(2f_{-2} + 27f_{-1} + 12f_0 - 8f_1 + 2f_2),\\
y_1 &= \tfrac{1}{35}(2f_{-2} - 8f_{-1} + 12f_0 + 27f_1 + 2f_2),\\
y_2 &= \tfrac{1}{70}(-f_{-2} + 4f_{-1} - 6f_0 + 4f_1 + 69f_2),
\end{aligned} \qquad (7.12.3)$$

are obtained in a similar way. It is of interest to notice that these formulas can also be expressed in the simple forms

$$y_{-2} = f_{-2} - \tfrac{1}{70}\delta^4 f_0, \qquad y_{-1} = f_{-1} + \tfrac{2}{35}\delta^4 f_0, \qquad y_0 = f_0 - \tfrac{3}{35}\delta^4 f_0, \qquad (7.12.4)$$
$$y_1 = f_1 + \tfrac{2}{35}\delta^4 f_0, \qquad y_2 = f_2 - \tfrac{1}{70}\delta^4 f_0.$$

The simplicity of these last forms is due to the fact that the degree of the least-squares polynomial is exactly *one* less than the degree of the polynomial which would be uniquely determined by the five data. In the cases when this difference exceeds unity, the formulas are less simply expressed in terms of differences, particularly for off-center points, as will be seen.

Explicit formulas which avoid the necessity of effecting the summations may also be obtained by first resolving the relations (7.12.1) in the forms

$$1 = p_0(t), \qquad t = 2p_1(t), \qquad t^2 = 2p_0(t) + 2p_2(t),$$
$$t^3 = \tfrac{1}{5}[34p_1(t) + 6p_3(t)], \qquad t^4 = \tfrac{1}{35}[238p_0(t) + 310p_2(t) + 12p_4(t)]. \qquad (7.12.5)$$

Now the interpolation polynomial (of degree four) which agrees *exactly* with $f(t)$ when $t = 0, \pm 1$, and ± 2 can be expressed in the Stirling form (§4.5)

$$f_0 + (\mu\delta f_0)t + (\tfrac{1}{2}\delta^2 f_0)t^2 + (\tfrac{1}{6}\mu\delta^3 f_0)(t^3 - t) + (\tfrac{1}{24}\delta^4 f_0)(t^4 - t^2), \qquad (7.12.6)$$

and hence, by introducing (7.12.5) into (7.12.6), we obtain the relation

$$f(t) = (f_0 + \delta^2 f_0 + \tfrac{1}{6}\delta^4 f_0)p_0(t) + (2\mu\delta f_0 + \tfrac{4}{5}\mu\delta^3 f_0)p_1(t)$$
$$+ (\delta^2 f_0 + \tfrac{2}{7}\delta^4 f_0)p_2(t) + (\tfrac{1}{5}\mu\delta^3 f_0)p_3(t) + (\tfrac{1}{70}\delta^4 f_0)p_4(t), \qquad (7.12.7)$$

when t is restricted to the values $0, \pm 1$, and ± 2. For other values of t, the right-hand member represents the fourth-degree interpolation polynomial which coincides with $f(t)$ at those five points. The associated error $E(t)$ can be expressed in the familiar form

$$E(t) = \frac{1}{5!} t(t^2 - 1)(t^2 - 4)f^v(\xi) \qquad (|\xi| < 2),$$

when $f^v(t)$ exists and is continuous for $-2 \leq t \leq 2$.

Since the right-hand member of (7.12.7) is accordingly the polynomial which would be afforded by fourth-degree least squares, relative to the five points involved, and since the *coefficients* of the p's are independent of the number of p's retained, it follows that the *third*-degree least-squares polynomial relative to those points is then obtained by deleting the term involving $p_4(t)$. In particular, when attention is restricted to the five points themselves, the resultant formula can be expressed in the form

$$y(t) = f(t) - (\tfrac{1}{70}\delta^4 f_0)p_4(t) \qquad (t = 0, \pm 1, \pm 2), \qquad (7.12.8)$$

in accordance with (7.12.4). Similarly, the first-degree least-squares polynomial relevant to five points may be obtained by retaining only $p_0(t)$ and $p_1(t)$ in the right-hand member of (7.12.7).

The methods of this section are readily generalized to cases in which more than five points are used in the least-squares calculation.

7.13. Smoothing Formulas. In place of approximating $f(t)$ by a single least-squares polynomial of degree n over the entire range of an extensive tabulation, it is frequently desirable to replace each tabulated value by the value taken on by a least-squares polynomial of degree n relevant to a subrange of $2M + 1$ points centered, if possible, at the point for which the entry is to be modified. Thus, except for points near the ends of the range of tabulation, each smoothed value is obtained from a distinct least-squares polynomial. In this section we list certain sets of smoothing formulas which are obtainable for this purpose by the methods of the preceding section.

For *first-degree* least-squares approximation relevant to *three points*, the formulas are of the form

$$\begin{aligned}
y_{-1} &= \tfrac{1}{6}(5f_{-1} + 2f_0 - f_1) \equiv f_{-1} - \tfrac{1}{6}\delta^2 f_0, \\
y_0 &= \tfrac{1}{3}(f_{-1} + f_0 + f_1) \equiv f_0 + \tfrac{1}{3}\delta^2 f_0, \\
y_1 &= \tfrac{1}{6}(-f_{-1} + 2f_0 + 5f_1) \equiv f_1 - \tfrac{1}{6}\delta^2 f_0,
\end{aligned} \qquad (7.13.1)$$

whereas the formulas relevant to *five points* are

$$\begin{aligned}
y_{-2} &= \tfrac{1}{5}(3f_{-2} + 2f_{-1} + f_0 - f_2), \\
y_{-1} &= \tfrac{1}{10}(4f_{-2} + 3f_{-1} + 2f_0 + f_1), \\
y_0 &= \tfrac{1}{5}(f_{-2} + f_{-1} + f_0 + f_1 + f_2),
\end{aligned} \qquad (7.13.2)$$

. . . .

where the omitted formulas, for y_1 and y_2, are obtained from the formulas for y_{-1} and y_{-2} by reversing the numbering of the ordinates. Thus, for example, if first-degree five-point least squares were to be used, the central formula would be used for all values except the first two and the last two, for which the off-center formulas would be used.

The formulas for *third-degree five-point* least squares were obtained in the preceding section and are listed again, for convenient reference, in the forms

$$
\begin{aligned}
y_{-2} &= \tfrac{1}{70}(69f_{-2} + 4f_{-1} - 6f_0 + 4f_1 - f_2) \equiv f_{-2} - \tfrac{1}{70}\delta^4 f_0, \\
y_{-1} &= \tfrac{1}{35}(2f_{-2} + 27f_{-1} + 12f_0 - 8f_1 + 2f_2) \equiv f_{-1} + \tfrac{2}{35}\delta^4 f_0, \\
y_0 &= \tfrac{1}{35}(-3f_{-2} + 12f_{-1} + 17f_0 + 12f_1 - 3f_2) \equiv f_0 - \tfrac{3}{35}\delta^4 f_0,
\end{aligned} \tag{7.13.3}
$$

whereas the corresponding *seven-point* formulas are

$$
\begin{aligned}
y_{-3} &= \tfrac{1}{42}(39f_{-3} + 8f_{-2} - 4f_{-1} - 4f_0 + f_1 + 4f_2 - 2f_3), \\
y_{-2} &= \tfrac{1}{42}(8f_{-3} + 19f_{-2} + 16f_{-1} + 6f_0 - 4f_1 - 7f_2 + 4f_3), \\
y_{-1} &= \tfrac{1}{42}(-4f_{-3} + 16f_{-2} + 19f_{-1} + 12f_0 + 2f_1 - 4f_2 + f_3), \\
y_0 &= \tfrac{1}{21}(-2f_{-3} + 3f_{-2} + 6f_{-1} + 7f_0 + 6f_1 + 3f_2 - 2f_3),
\end{aligned} \tag{7.13.4}
$$

Finally, the *fifth-degree seven-point* least-squares formulas may be listed as follows:

$$
\begin{aligned}
y_{-3} &= \tfrac{1}{924}(923f_{-3} + 6f_{-2} - 15f_{-1} + 20f_0 - 15f_1 + 6f_2 - f_3) \\
&\qquad\qquad\qquad\qquad\qquad\qquad\qquad\qquad \equiv f_{-3} - \tfrac{1}{924}\delta^6 f_0, \\
y_{-2} &= \tfrac{1}{154}(f_{-3} + 148f_{-2} + 15f_{-1} - 20f_0 + 15f_1 - 6f_2 + f_3) \\
&\qquad\qquad\qquad\qquad\qquad\qquad\qquad\qquad \equiv f_{-2} + \tfrac{1}{154}\delta^6 f_0, \\
y_{-1} &= \tfrac{1}{308}(-5f_{-3} + 30f_{-2} + 233f_{-1} + 100f_0 - 75f_1 + 30f_2 - 5f_3) \\
&\qquad\qquad\qquad\qquad\qquad\qquad\qquad\qquad \equiv f_{-1} - \tfrac{5}{308}\delta^6 f_0, \\
y_0 &= \tfrac{1}{231}(5f_{-3} - 30f_{-2} + 75f_{-1} + 131f_0 + 75f_1 - 30f_2 + 5f_3) \\
&\qquad\qquad\qquad\qquad\qquad\qquad\qquad\qquad \equiv f_0 + \tfrac{5}{231}\delta^6 f_0,
\end{aligned}
$$

$$\tag{7.13.5}$$

The use of an nth-degree least-squares polynomial relevant to $2M + 1$ points essentially assumes that the true function can be approximated by some nth-degree polynomial over each subrange of $2M + 1$ points, but it admits the possibility that no single nth-degree polynomial may be satisfactory over the entire range. The amount of smoothing *increases* with the number of *points* used in the smoothing formula and *decreases* with increasing values of the *degree* n.

It is often desirable and convenient to employ a smoothing technique involving a relatively small number of points, so that the relevant formulas are of simple form, and to iterate the process as many times as appears to be desirable. The degree n is chosen to be as small as pos-

sible, in consistency with the assumption that differences of the *true*
function, of order higher than n, are small. If such a process were
iterated indefinitely, the sequence of smoothed functions would tend to
the least-squares polynomial of degree n relevant to the *entire* range of
tabulated values. The computer can and generally must rely upon his
judgment with regard to the stage at which the iteration is to be terminated, so that most of the "noise" is eliminated but essential characteristics of the function are not appreciably modified. The choice of n is
often dictated by the fact that the first n differences of the observed function f are fairly regular, whereas the $(n + 1)$th differences fluctuate
erratically and have a mean value near zero.

As an illustration, we consider the data listed in the second column of
the following table.

TABLE 7.2†

x	$f(x)$	5-point once	5-point twice	Spencer	W. and R.
0	431	402	405		419
1	409	423	422		422
2	429	444	439		435
3	422	459	456		454
4	530	469	472		473
5	505	483	485		487
6	459	504	499		496
7	499	510	516		508
8	526	527	536		526
9	563	554	557		550
10	587	584	585	582	578
11	595	612	616	614	610
12	647	649	650	648	646
13	669	683	684	682	685
14	746	720	720	716	724
15	760	756	752	749	758
16	778	792	784		787
17	828	810	815		812
18	846	841	847		837
19	836	876	880		868
20	916	914	922		910
21	956	960	966		961
22	1014	1019	1012		1016
23	1076	1061	1060		1069
24	1134	1106	1107		1112
25	1124	1152	1154		1141

† These data were taken from Spencer [215] and have been analyzed in various ways
by Whittaker and Robinson [20], and others.

A plot of the given data suggests that, whereas the true function is
almost certainly not linear, it can be fairly approximated by a linear

function over any subrange of, say, three or five points. The smoothe‹ data given by the first-degree five-point formulas of (7.13.2) are listed i‹ the third column of the table. Each smoothed value except the tw‹ values at each end of the tabulation is obtained very simply as the aver‹ age of the five values centered at the point considered. Off-center for‹

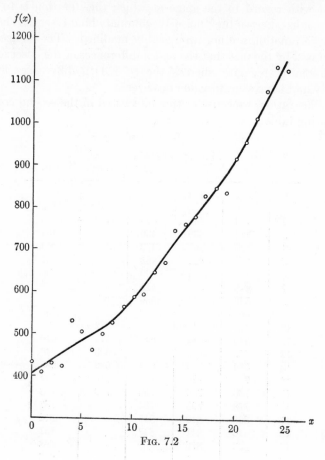

FIG. 7.2

mulas are used for those points. A second application of this process leads to the values listed in the fourth column and is represented by a continuous curve in Fig. 7.2. A quantitative estimate of the degree of smoothing is afforded by the fact that the means of the absolute values of the second and third differences of the given data are 41 and 75, respectively, whereas the corresponding means for the results of the second smoothing are 2.1 and 2.6, respectively. At the same time, it appears that the characteristic trend of the data is preserved in the smoothing.

The results of applying the first-degree three-point formulas of (7.13.1) *three* times are found to be quite similar to the results of using the five-point formulas twice, in the present example.

In the fifth column of the table are listed the results obtained by Spencer, by use of an elaborate 21-point formula which yields smoothed values only at points which are more than 10 intervals away from the ends.

The sixth column of the table lists results obtained by Whittaker and Robinson, by use of another elaborate 21-point formula combined with an appreciable amount of auxiliary calculation relevant to the smoothing of the first and last 10 entries. Whereas the smoothed values generally do not differ appreciably from those obtained (much more simply) in the fourth column, the advantage in smoothness actually belongs to the results of the simpler method, in the sense that the mean absolute second and third differences relevant to the data of the sixth column are found to be 5.2 and 3.4, respectively, as compared with 2.1 and 2.6 for the data of the fourth column.

It should be emphasized, however, that the smallness of certain mean absolute differences cannot *in itself* be taken as an indication of a satisfactory smoothing. By repeating the smoothing which led to column three indefinitely often, we would eventually be led to a "smoothed curve" which is represented by a *straight line* over the entire range, and hence for which *all* differences of order greater than one would *vanish*. This linear approximation would be obtained *directly* by use of first-degree 26-point formulas.

It is, of course, conceivable that the deviation from linearity of the smoothed curve is *still* predominantly "noise" and that a much more drastic smoothing is indeed called for. It is at this point that the judgment of the computer (or the weight of additional evidence) must be brought into play.

As a further example, a plot of the data

x	0	1	2	3	4	5	6	7	8
$f(x)$	54	145	227	359	401	342	259	112	65

(see Fig. 7.3) suggests that the true function can be approximated by a third-degree polynomial over each subrange of five points. The use of the formulas of (7.13.3) yields the smoothed values

x	0	1	2	3	4	5	6	7	8
$y(x)$	57	134	244	348	393	352	242	124	62

which are plotted and joined by a continuous curve in Fig. 7.3.

Whereas it is possible to determine a set of orthogonal polynomials over a discrete range relative to a specified weighting function w (an important special case is treated in §9.5) and to derive corresponding smoothing formulas, a more convenient procedure which tends to accomplish about the same purpose, when w does not vary excessively, consists in applying the preceding smoothing formulas to the product wf and then

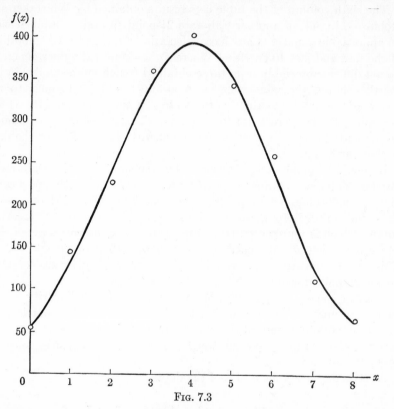

Fig. 7.3

dividing the result by w. More generally, the function f may be first transformed in an appropriate way to a new function g, and the new function g may be smoothed, after which the inverse transformation may be applied to the smoothed function. In particular, in the case of the last preceding example, the graph of the function $f(x)$ (Fig. 7.3) indicates a resemblance to a function of the form $\exp [-(Ax^2 + Bx + C)]$ and suggests that the smoothing be applied to $\log f(x)$, rather than to $f(x)$ itself.

Finally, it may be pointed out that the *central* smoothing formulas can be obtained rather simply without explicitly determining the least-squares polynomials involved. In this connection, we notice that the orthogonal polynomials $p_r(t, 2M)$ defined in §7.11 vanish at $t = 0$ when is odd.   Hence, if n is *even*, the central smoothing formula corresponding to a least-squares polynomial of degree n will be identical with the formula corresponding to that of degree $n + 1$.

For $n = 0$ or $n = 1$, there follows merely $y_0 = a_0$ and hence, since $p_0(t, 2M) = 1$,

$$y_0 = \frac{1}{2M + 1} \sum_{r = -M}^{M} f_r. \qquad (7.13.6)$$

Thus, as in the special cases of (7.13.1) and (7.13.2), each smoothed value of f_0 is the average of the $2M + 1$ values centered about f_0.

For $n = 2$ or $n = 3$, reference to (7.11.10) gives

$$y_0 = a_0 + a_2 p_2(0, 2M) = a_0 - \frac{M + 1}{2M - 1} a_2 \qquad (7.13.7)$$

where

$$a_0 = \frac{1}{2M + 1} \sum_{r = -M}^{M} f_r \qquad (7.13.8)$$

and

$$a_2 = \frac{1}{\gamma_2} \frac{1}{M(2M - 1)} \sum_{r = -M}^{M} [3r^2 - M(M + 1)] f_r, \qquad (7.13.9)$$

with

$$\gamma_2 = \sum_{r = -M}^{M} p_2^2(r, 2M). \qquad (7.13.10)$$

The calculation of γ_2 can be effected by the summation technique outlined in §7.9 [following (7.9.11)], in the form

$$\gamma_2 = \frac{(2M + 1)(2M + 2)(2M + 3)}{10M(2M - 1)}, \qquad (7.13.11)$$

and the insertion of (7.13.8), (7.13.9), and (7.13.11) into (7.13.7) leads immediately to the required formula

$$y_0 = \frac{3}{(4M^2 - 1)(2M + 3)} \sum_{r = -M}^{M} [(3M^2 + 3M - 1) - 5r^2] f_r, \qquad (7.13.12)$$

which specializes to the central formulas of (7.13.3) and (7.13.4) when $M = 2$ and $M = 3$, respectively.

A similar analysis leads to the central smoothing formula

$$y_0 = \frac{15}{4(4M^2 - 1)(4M^2 - 9)(2M + 5)} \sum_{r = -M}^{M} [(15M^4 + 30M^3 - 35M^2$$
$$- 50M + 12) - 35(2M^2 + 2M - 3)r^2 + 63r^4] f_r, \qquad (7.13.13)$$

relevant to *fourth*- or *fifth-degree* least-square approximation using $2M +$ points, which specializes to the central formula of (7.13.5) when $M = 3.$

As was pointed out earlier, the central smoothing formulas alone are generally useful only for smoothing values at points at least M interval distant from the ends of the range of tabulation. However, they can be used throughout the entire range in the special cases when the true function is known to vanish outside the range of tabulation and to tend to zero smoothly as the ends of the range are approached from the interior so that the zero values at exterior points can be used in smoothing values at interior points near the ends.

7.14. Supplementary References. For comprehensive treatments of orthogonal polynomials, see Jackson [124] and Szego [220]. See also the bibliography of Shohat, Hille, and Walsh [212]. Least-squares techniques, and associated error analyses, are considered by Aitken [24], Birge and Weinberg [42], Lewis [133], Guest [99, 100], and Hayes and Vickers [108]. See also texts such as Fisher [78], Scarborough [17], and Whittaker and Robinson [20]. The orthogonal (Gram) polynomials relative to a unit weighting function over a discrete set of points are tabulated by Anderson and Houseman [243] and by De Lury [248]. For additional smoothing techniques, see Spencer [215], Rhodes [194], Whittaker and Robinson [20], Wolfenden [239], Sard [206], Doodson [70], Lanczos [131], Schoenberg [209], and Wiener [236].

PROBLEMS

Section 7.2

1. Show that the functions $\phi_0(x) = 1$ and $\phi_1(x) = x$ are orthogonal under integration over $(-1,1)$, and obtain the linear least-squares approximation $y_1(x)$ to a given function $f(x)$ over $(-1,1)$,

$$f(x) \approx y_1(x) \equiv a_0 + a_1x \qquad (-1 \leq x \leq 1),$$

for which

$$\int_{-1}^{1} (f - y_1)^2 \, dx = \min,$$

in the form

$$y_1(x) = \tfrac{1}{2} \int_{-1}^{1} (1 + 3xt)f(t) \, dt.$$

Show also that the corresponding RMS error in $(-1,1)$ is given by

$$\left[\tfrac{1}{2} \int_{-1}^{1} f^2 \, dx - a_0^2 - \tfrac{1}{3}a_1^2\right]^{\frac{1}{2}}.$$

2. Show that the functions $\phi_0(x) = 1$ and $\phi_1(x) = x$ are orthogonal under summation over the abscissas $x_0 = -1$, $x_1 = 0$, and $x_2 = 1$, and obtain the linear least

† The central formulas (7.13.12) and (7.13.13) are written out explicitly for $M \leq 10$ in Whittaker and Robinson [20].

quares approximation $y_2(x)$ to a given function $f(x)$ over $(-1,1)$,

$$f(x) \approx y_2(x) \equiv A_0 + A_1 x \qquad (-1 \leq x \leq 1),$$

or which

$$\sum_{k=0}^{2} [f(x_k) - y_2(x_k)]^2 = \min,$$

n the form

$$y_2(x) = \tfrac{1}{6}[(2 - 3x)f(-1) + 2f(0) + (2 + 3x)f(1)].$$

Show also that the corresponding RMS error over the three relevant points is given by

$$\left[\tfrac{1}{3} \sum_{k=0}^{2} [f(x_k)]^2 - A_0^2 - \tfrac{2}{3} A_1^2 \right]^{\frac{1}{2}}.$$

3. If $y_1(x)$ is the linear approximation to $f(x)$ obtained in Prob. 1, and if $f''(x)$ is continuous in $(-1,1)$, show that

$$f(x) - y_1(x) = \int_{-1}^{1} g_1(x,s) f''(s) \, ds,$$

where

$$g_1(x,s) = (x - s)_+ - \tfrac{1}{2} \int_{-1}^{1} (t - s)_+ (1 + 3xt) \, dt$$

$$= \begin{cases} -\tfrac{1}{4}(1 + s)^2(1 - 2x + sx) & (s \leq x), \\ -\tfrac{1}{4}(1 - s)^2(1 + 2x + sx) & (s \geq x). \end{cases}$$

Show also that $g_1(x,s)$ is of constant sign for x and s in $(-1,1)$ if and only if $|x| \leq \tfrac{1}{3}$ or $|x| = 1$, and establish the relation

$$f(x) = y_1(x) - \tfrac{1}{6}(1 - 3x^2)f''(\xi) \qquad (|x| \leq \tfrac{1}{3} \text{ or } |x| = 1),$$

where $-1 < \xi < 1$, showing, in particular, that

$$(-1) - y_1(-1) = \tfrac{1}{3}f''(\xi_1), \quad f(0) - y_1(0) = -\tfrac{1}{6}f''(\xi_2), \quad f(1) - y_1(1) = \tfrac{1}{3}f''(\xi_3).$$

4. If $y_2(x)$ is the linear approximation to $f(x)$ obtained in Prob. 2, and if $f''(x)$ is continuous in $(-1,1)$, show that

$$f(x) - y_2(x) = \int_{-1}^{1} g_2(x,s) f''(s) \, ds,$$

where

$$g_2(x,s) = (x - s)_+ - \tfrac{1}{3}(-s)_+ - \tfrac{1}{6}(1 - s)(2 + 3x).$$

Show also that $g_2(x,s)$ is of constant sign for x and s in $(-1,1)$ if and only if $|x| \leq \tfrac{2}{3}$ or $|x| = 1$, and establish the relation

$$f(x) - y_2(x) = -\tfrac{1}{6}(2 - 3x^2)f''(\xi) \qquad (|x| \leq \tfrac{2}{3} \text{ or } |x| = 1),$$

where $-1 < \xi < 1$.

5. If $y_3(x)$ is the second-degree polynomial which agrees exactly with $f(x)$ when $x = -1$, 0, and 1, and if $y_2(x)$ is the linear approximation of Prob. 2, show that

$$y_2(x) = y_3(x) + \tfrac{1}{6}(2 - 3x^2) \, \delta^2 f(0),$$

where δ is the central-difference operator with unit spacing. In particular, show that

$$f(-1) - y_2(-1) = -\tfrac{1}{2}[f(0) - y_2(0)] = f(1) - y_2(1) = \tfrac{1}{6}\delta^2 f(0),$$

that the RMS error over the three points $x = -1$, 0, and 1 is

$$\frac{1}{2\sqrt{2}} |\delta^2 f(0)|,$$

and that $\qquad\qquad y_2(x) = f(x) + \tfrac{1}{6}(2 - 3x^2)f''(x),$

for all values of x, if $f(x)$ is a polynomial of degree two or less.

Section 7.3

6. If the right-hand member of the rth normal equation associated with (7.3.4) denoted by v_r $(r = 0, 1, \ldots, n)$, show that the weighted sum of the squares of the $N + 1$ residuals is given by

$$\sum_{i=0}^{N} w(x_i)[f(x_i)]^2 - \sum_{r=0}^{n} a_r v_r,$$

and use this relation to calculate that sum for the numerical example of §7.3.

7. Suppose that the following empirical data are available:

x	1.36	1.49	1.73	1.81	1.95	2.16	2.28	2.48
$\bar{f}(x)$	14.094	15.069	16.844	17.378	18.435	19.949	20.963	22.495

Determine least-squares polynomial approximations $y_1(x)$ and $y_2(x)$ of degrees one and two, respectively, weighting all data equally, and calculate the RMS value of the eight residuals in both cases.

8. Obtain estimated values of the RMS deviation between the unknown true function $f(x)$ and the observed function $\bar{f}(x)$ in Prob. 7, based on the approximations $y_1(x)$ and $y_2(x)$, and also determine the approximate RMS errors in the calculated coefficients involved in those approximations. Would either (or both) of the approximations be acceptable if it were known, independently, that the RMS value of the observational errors is about 0.04?

Section 7.4

9. With the notation of §7.4, show that

$$a_r = \frac{1}{r!A_r} \frac{\displaystyle\int_a^b U_r(x)f^{(r)}(x)\,dx}{\displaystyle\int_a^b U_r(x)\,dx}$$

if $f^{(r)} \equiv d^r f/dx^r$ exists everywhere in (a,b) and is continuous.

10. If $w(x) = (x - a)^\alpha(b - x)^\beta$, verify that

$$U_r(x) = C_r(x - a)^{r+\alpha}(b - x)^{r+\beta}$$

satisfies the conditions of §7.4, when C_r is a constant, if $\alpha > -1$ and $\beta > -1$.

11. If $w(x) = x$ and $(a,b) = (0,1)$, show that the rth orthogonal polynomial is given by

$$\phi_r(x) = C_r x^{-1} \frac{d^r}{dx^r} [x^{r+1}(1 - x)^r],$$

and that the arbitrary normalization $\phi_r(0) = 1$ requires that

$$C_r = \frac{1}{(r+1)!}.$$

Determine the polynomials of degrees zero through four, and prove that

$$A_r = (-1)^r \frac{(2r+1)!}{[(r+1)!]^2}, \qquad \gamma_r = \frac{1}{2(r+1)^3},$$

in consequence of the relation

$$\int_0^1 x^{p-1}(1-x)^{q-1} \, dx = \frac{\Gamma(p)\Gamma(q)}{\Gamma(p+q)}.$$

12. Use the results of Prob. 11 to show that the nth-degree least-squares polynomial approximation to $f(x)$ over $(0,1)$, relevant to the weighting function $w(x) = x$, is defined by

$$y(x) = \sum_{r=0}^n a_r \phi_r(x),$$

where

$$a_r = 2(r+1)^3 \int_0^1 x f(x)\phi_r(x) \, dx,$$

and where $\phi_r(x)$ is defined in Prob. 11. In particular, show that the linear approximation is of the form

$$y(x) = 6 \int_0^1 [(3t - 4t^2) - 2(2t - 3t^2)x]f(t) \, dt.$$

Section 7.5

13. By expanding $(x^2 - 1)^r$ in descending powers of x^2, and appropriately differentiating term by term, show that (7.5.6) implies the relation

$$P_r(x) = \sum_{k=0}^r (-1)^k \frac{(2r - 2k)!}{2^r k!(r-k)!(r-2k)!} x^{r-2k}$$

where the series terminates when $k = r/2$ if r is even and when $k = (r-1)/2$ if r is odd.

14. Show that the coefficient of $P_r(x)$ in (7.5.11) can be expressed in the form

$$a_r = \frac{2r+1}{2^{r+1}r!} \int_{-1}^1 (1 - x^2)^r f^{(r)}(x) \, dx$$

if $f^{(r)}(x)$ exists everywhere in $(-1,1)$ and is continuous.

15. Show that the leading terms in the Legendre expansion of $f(x) = \cos(\pi x/2)$ over $(-1,1)$ are of the form

$$\cos\frac{\pi x}{2} = \frac{2}{\pi}P_0(x) - \frac{10}{\pi^3}(12 - \pi^2)P_2(x) + \frac{18}{\pi^5}(\pi^4 - 180\pi^2 + 1680)P_4(x) - \cdots .$$

16. Compare numerically the approximations to $f(x) = \cos(\pi x/2)$ afforded by the least-squares polynomials of degrees two and four, obtained in Prob. 15, with the approximating polynomials of corresponding degrees afforded by truncated power series and by fitting $f(x)$ exactly at three and at five equally spaced points in $(-1,1)$.

17. If $f(x) = [(x + 1)/2]^{\frac{1}{2}}$, show that the coefficient of $P_r(x)$ in the Legendre expansion of $f(x)$ in $(-1,1)$ is given by

$$a_r = \frac{2r + 1}{2^{r+1}r!} \int_{-1}^{1} (1 - x^2)^r \frac{d^r}{dx^r} \left(\frac{x + 1}{2}\right)^{\frac{1}{2}} dx = \frac{2r + 1}{r!} \int_{0}^{1} s^r (1 - s)^r \frac{d^r s^{\frac{1}{2}}}{ds^r} ds$$

$$= (-1)^{r+1} \frac{2}{(2r - 1)(2r + 3)},$$

so that

$$\left(\frac{x + 1}{2}\right)^{\frac{1}{2}} = \frac{2}{3} P_0(x) + \frac{2}{1 \cdot 5} P_1(x) - \frac{2}{3 \cdot 7} P_2(x) + \frac{2}{5 \cdot 9} P_3(x) - \cdots \qquad (|x| < 1).$$

18. Assuming the results of Prob. 17, compare the least-squares polynomial approximations to $f(x) = [(x + 1)/2]^{\frac{1}{2}}$ of degrees two and four over $(-1,1)$ with the corresponding results of truncating power series and with the polynomials of degrees two and four which agree with $f(x)$ at three and at five equally spaced points in $(-1,1)$.

19. Obtain the expansion

$$|x| = \tfrac{1}{2} P_0(x) + \tfrac{5}{8} P_2(x) - \tfrac{3}{16} P_4(x) + \tfrac{13}{128} P_6(x) - \cdots \qquad (|x| < 1),$$

and compare the approximations of degrees two and four with the corresponding polynomial approximations which agree exactly with $f(x)$ at three and at five equally spaced points in $(-1,1)$.

Section 7.6

20. By using Leibnitz' formula (3.3.11), show that (7.6.8) implies the relation

$$L_r(x) = \sum_{k=0}^{r} \frac{(-1)^k}{(r - k)!} \left(\frac{r!}{k!}\right)^2 x^k \equiv r! \sum_{k=0}^{r} (-1)^k \binom{r}{k} \frac{x^k}{k!}.$$

21. Show that (7.6.15) can be expressed in the form

$$a_r = \frac{(-1)^r \alpha}{(r!)^2} \int_{0}^{\infty} x^r e^{-\alpha x} f^{(r)}(x) \, dx$$

if $f^{(r)}(x)$ exists for all $x \geqq 0$ and is continuous, and if $f(x)$ and its first r derivatives are dominated by $x^{-r-2} e^{\alpha x}$ as $x \to \infty$. Show also that

$$a_r = \frac{(-1)^r c^r \alpha}{r!(\alpha - c)^{r+1}} \qquad (\alpha > c)$$

when $f(x) = e^{cx}$, and that

$$a_r = \frac{(-1)^r [\Gamma(s + 1)]^2}{\alpha^s (r!)^2 \Gamma(s - r + 1)} \qquad (s > -1)$$

when $f(x) = x^s$.

22. If $f(x) = [1 - (x/N)]^N$ when $0 \leqq x \leqq N$ and $f(x) = 0$ when $x \geqq N$, obtain the leading terms of the expansion (7.6.16), with $\alpha = 1$, in the form

$$f(x) = \frac{N}{N + 1} e^{-x} \left[1 + \frac{2}{N + 2} L_1(x) - \frac{N - 6}{2(N + 2)(N + 3)} L_2(x) + \cdots \right] \qquad (x > 0).$$

23. Show that the requirement that the best linear approximation to $e^{\alpha x} f(x)$ is s constant, in the sense of (7.6.17), determines α in the form

$$\alpha = \frac{\int_0^\infty f(x) \, dx}{\int_0^\infty x f(x) \, dx}.$$

In particular, show that the most appropriate choice of α for Prob. 22 (in this sense) is $(N + 2)/N$.

Section 7.7

24. Obtain from (7.7.6) the relations

$$\frac{d}{dx} H_r(x) = 2r H_{r-1}(x),$$

$$\frac{d}{dx}\left[e^{-x^2} \frac{d}{dx} H_r(x) \right] = -2r e^{-x^2} H_r(x)$$

and deduce also that $H_r(x)$ satisfies the differential equation

$$H_r'' - 2x H_r' + 2r H_r = 0.$$

25. Use the first relation of Prob. 24, with the relation $H_0(x) = 1$, to show that the coefficient of x^r in $H_r(x)$ is 2^r. Also, by writing

$$H_r(x) = \sum_{k=0}^\infty a_k x^{r-2k}$$

in the differential equation of Prob. 24, show that

$$a_{k+1} = -\frac{(r - 2k)(r - 2k - 1)}{4(k + 1)} a_k,$$

and deduce that

$$H_r(x) = (2x)^r - \frac{r(r - 1)}{1!} (2x)^{r-2} + \frac{r(r - 1)(r - 2)(r - 3)}{2!} (2x)^{r-4} - \cdots,$$

where the series terminates with a multiple of x when r is odd and with a constant when r is even.

26. Show that (7.7.13) can be written in the form

$$a_r = \frac{\alpha^{1-r}}{2^r r! \sqrt{\pi}} \int_{-\infty}^\infty e^{-\alpha 2 x^2} f^{(r)}(x) \, dx$$

if $f^{(r)}(x)$ exists and is continuous for all x, and if $f(x)$ and its first r derivatives are dominated by $x^{-2} e^{\alpha^2 x^2}$ as $x \to \pm \infty$.

27. By taking $f(x) = e^{2cx}$ and $\alpha = 1$ in the result of Prob. 26, obtain the expansion

$$e^{2cx-c^2} = \sum_{k=0}^\infty \frac{c^k}{k!} H_k(x).$$

28. If $f(x) = 1 - |x|$ when $|x| \leq 1$ and $f(x) = 0$ when $|x| \geq 1$, obtain the expansion

$$f(x) = \frac{\alpha}{\sqrt{\pi}} e^{-\alpha^2 x^2} \left[H_0(\alpha x) - \frac{3 - \alpha^2}{12} H_2(\alpha x) + \frac{45 - 30\alpha^2 + 4\alpha^4}{1440} H_4(\alpha x) + \cdots \right]$$

and show that, if α is chosen such that the coefficient of H_2 vanishes, there follows

$$f(x) = \sqrt{\frac{3}{\pi}}\, e^{-3x^2} [H_0(\sqrt{3}\,x) - \tfrac{1}{160}H_4(\sqrt{3}\,x) + \cdots].$$

29. If the origin is chosen such that $m_1 = 0$, and if α^2 is then taken to be $m_0/(2m_2)$ with the notation of (7.7.17), show that the expansion (7.7.14) becomes

$$f(x) = \frac{\alpha}{\sqrt{\pi}}\, e^{-\alpha^2 x^2}\left[\, m_0 + \frac{\alpha(2\alpha^2 m_3 - 3m_1)}{12}\, H_3(\alpha x) + \frac{(4a^4 m_4 - 12\alpha^2 m_2 + 3)}{96}\, H_4(\alpha x)\right.$$
$$\left. + \cdots\right.$$

Section 7.8

30. Obtain the expansion

$$|x| = \frac{4}{\pi}\left[\tfrac{1}{2}T_0(x) + \tfrac{1}{3}T_2(x) - \cdots + (-1)^{k+1}\frac{1}{4k^2 - 1}\, T_{2k}(x) + \cdots\right],$$

when $|x| < 1$, and compare the approximations of degrees two and four with those obtained in Prob. 19.

31. Show that the function $S_r(x)$ defined by the relation

$$S_r(x) = \frac{1}{r+1}\, T'_{r+1}(x)$$

is a polynomial of degree r, expressible in the form

$$S_r(x) = \frac{1}{\sqrt{1-x^2}}\sin\,[(r+1)\cos^{-1}x] = \frac{\sin\,(r+1)\theta}{\sin\theta} \qquad (\theta = \cos^{-1}x),$$

that the polynomials $S_0(x),\ S_1(x),\ \ldots,\ S_r(x),\ \ldots$ are orthogonal over $(-1,1)$ relative to the weighting function $w(x) = \sqrt{1-x^2}$, that $A_r = 2^r$ and $\gamma_r = \pi/2$, and that the coefficients in the approximation

$$f(x) \approx y(x) = \sum_{r=0}^{n} a_r S_r(x) \qquad (|x| < 1)$$

are given by

$$a_r = \frac{2}{\pi}\int_{-1}^{1}\sqrt{1-x^2}\, f(x)S_r(x)\, dx$$

when the requirement

$$\int_{-1}^{1}\sqrt{1-x^2}\,[f(x) - y(x)]^2\, dx = \min$$

is imposed.

32. Using the notation of Prob. 31, obtain the expansion

$$|x| = \frac{4}{\pi}\left[\tfrac{1}{3}S_0(x) + \tfrac{1}{5}S_2(x) - \cdots + (-1)^{k+1}\frac{1}{(2k-1)(2k+3)}\, S_{2k}(x) + \cdots\right],$$

and compare the approximations of degrees two and four with those considered in Prob. 30.

Section 7.9

33. Express the following sums in closed forms:

(a) $1 \cdot 2 + 2 \cdot 3 + \cdots + n(n+1) \equiv \sum_{s=2}^{n+1} s^{(2)}.$

(b) $1 \cdot 2 \cdot 3 + 2 \cdot 3 \cdot 4 + \cdots + n(n+1)(n+2).$

(c) $1 \cdot 2 + 4 \cdot 5 + 7 \cdot 8 + \cdots + (3n-2)(3n-1).$

34. Express the following sums in closed forms, and determine the limit of each as $n \to \infty$:

(a) $\dfrac{1}{1 \cdot 2} + \dfrac{1}{2 \cdot 3} + \cdots + \dfrac{1}{n(n+1)} \equiv \sum_{s=0}^{n-1} s^{(-2)}.$

(b) $\dfrac{1}{1 \cdot 2 \cdot 3} + \dfrac{1}{2 \cdot 3 \cdot 4} + \cdots + \dfrac{1}{n(n+1)(n+2)}.$

(c) $\dfrac{1}{1 \cdot 2 \cdot 3} + \dfrac{3}{2 \cdot 3 \cdot 4} + \dfrac{5}{3 \cdot 4 \cdot 5} + \cdots + \dfrac{2n-1}{n(n+1)(n+2)}.$

35. Show that

$$(-m)^{(n)} = (-1)^n (m+n-1)^{(n)}$$

when n is a positive integer.

36. Show that

$$\binom{m}{n}\binom{m+p}{p} = \binom{n+p}{n}\binom{m+p}{n+p}.$$

37. If m is a positive integer, show that

$$\binom{s}{m} = \sum_{k=0}^{m} \binom{n}{m-k}\binom{s-n}{k},$$

and hence that

$$s^{(m)} = \sum_{k=0}^{m} \frac{m!}{k!}\binom{n}{m-k}(s-n)^{(k)},$$

and deduce the relation

$$s^{(m)} s^{(n)} = \sum_{k=0}^{m} \frac{m!}{k!}\binom{n}{m-k} s^{(n+k)}.$$

38. Show that

$$\sum_{s=M}^{N} s\,\Delta_1^2 u_s = [s\,\Delta_1 u_s - u_{s+1}]_M^{N+1}$$

and use this formula to obtain the result

$$\sum_{s=0}^{N} s a^s = \frac{1}{(a-1)^2}[Na^{N+2} - (N+1)a^{N+1} + a] \qquad (a \neq 1),$$

by taking $u_s = a^s/(a-1)^2$ or otherwise.

39. Show that

$$\sum_{s=M}^{N} u_s \, \Delta_1^r v_s = [u_s \, \Delta_1^{r-1} v_s - (\Delta_1 u_s)(\Delta_1^{r-2} v_{s+1}) + (\Delta_1^2 u_s)(\Delta_1^{r-3} v_{s+2}) - \cdots$$

$$+ (-1)^{r-1}(\Delta_1^{r-1} u_s) v_{s+r-1}]_M^{N+1} + (-1)^r \sum_{s=M}^{N} (\Delta_1^r u_s) v_{s+r}$$

and also that

$$\sum_{s=M}^{N} u_s \, \Delta_1^r v_s = [u_{s-1} \, \Delta_1^{r-1} v_s - (\Delta_1 u_{s-2})(\Delta_1^{r-2} v_s) + (\Delta_1^2 u_{s-3})(\Delta_1^{r-3} v_s) - \cdots$$

$$+ (-1)^{r-1}(\Delta_1^{r-1} u_{s-r}) v_s]_M^{N+1} + (-1)^r \sum_{s=M}^{N} (\Delta_1^r u_{s-r}) v_s.$$

Section 7.10

40. Show that (7.10.13) can be written in the form

$$\gamma_r(N) = (-1)^r r! A_r \sum_{s=0}^{N} U_r(s + r, N),$$

where A_r is the coefficient of s^r in $\phi_r(s,N)$.

41. Prove that, if $w(s) \geq 0$ for $s = 0, 1, \ldots, N$, then the polynomial $\phi_r(s,N)$ possesses r real zeros in the interval $0 < s < N$.

Section 7.11

42. With the notation of Prob. 40, show that, when (7.11.9) is imposed on (7.11.6), there follows

$$\gamma_r(N) \equiv \sum_{s=0}^{N} [\phi_r(s,N)]^2 = \frac{(-1)^r (2r)!}{[r! N^{(r)}]^2} \sum_{s=0}^{N} (s + r)^{(r)}(s + r - N - 1)^{(r)}.$$

By making use of appropriate summations by parts, show further that

$$\gamma_r(N) = \frac{1}{[N^{(r)}]^2} \sum_{s=0}^{N} (s + r)^{(2r)}$$

and deduce the closed form

$$\gamma_r(N) = \frac{1}{2r + 1} \frac{(N + r + 1)^{(r+1)}}{N^{(r)}}.$$

43. Use the results of Prob. 42 and of Eqs. (7.11.10) to express the leading terms of (7.11.12) in the form

$$y(t) = \frac{1}{2M + 1} \sum_{k=-M}^{M} f(k) + \frac{3t}{M(M + 1)(2M + 1)} \sum_{k=-M}^{M} k f(k)$$

$$+ \frac{15t^2 - 5M(M + 1)}{M(M + 1)(2M - 1)(2M + 1)(2M + 3)} \sum_{k=-M}^{M} [3k^2 - M(M + 1)]f(k) + \cdots.$$

Section 7.12

44. Prepare a table analogous to Table 7.1 in the case $M = 3$, when seven points are employed in the least-squares approximation, including only the orthogonal polynomials of degrees five and less.

45. By using the table prepared in Prob. 44, obtain least-squares polynomial approximations of degrees one through five to $f(t) \equiv F(2x - 3)$ for $|t| \leq 3$ from the following approximate data, calculate the respective smoothed values at the tabular points, and determine which approximation is probably most appropriate if the data are empirical, with errors having an estimated RMS value of about 0.07:

x	0.0	0.5	1.0	1.5	2.0	2.5	3.0
$F(x)$	15.564	18.059	20.548	23.554	26.348	29.498	32.830

46. Use the results of Prob. 45 to obtain approximate values of the following quantities from the smoothed data:

$$F(0.1), \ F(1.8), \ F'(1.0), \ F'(1.3), \ \int_0^3 F(x) \, dx, \ \int_{1.2}^{2.3} F(x) \, dx.$$

47. Obtain a formula analogous to (7.12.8) for fifth-degree seven-point least-squares approximation.

Section 7.13

48. Use (7.13.4) and (7.13.5) to obtain smoothed values of the data given in Prob. 45, corresponding to third-degree and fifth-degree least squares, and verify that the results agree with those obtained in Prob. 45.

49. The following data represent estimated world route mileages of scheduled air services in the years given, in units of 1000 miles. Calculate smoothed values, using both first- and third-degree five-point formulas, and plot the two smoothed curves together with points representing the given data.

1919	3.2	1926	48.5	1933	200.3
1920	9.7	1927	54.7	1934	223.1
1921	12.4	1928	90.7	1935	278.2
1922	16.0	1929	125.8	1936	305.2
1923	16.1	1930	156.8	1937	333.5
1924	20.3	1931	185.1	1938	349.1
1925	34.0	1932	190.2		

Also use the two sets of smoothed data to obtain estimates of the annual rate of increase of mileage, at the end of the tabulation, to be used for long-range and short-range predictions.

CHAPTER 8

GAUSSIAN QUADRATURE AND RELATED TOPICS

8.1. Introduction. The formulas given in Chaps. 3 and 5, for the purpose of numerical integration (with or without differences), each involve sets of ordinates which correspond to *equally spaced* abscissas. As might be expected, corresponding formulas which are generally capable of supplying comparable accuracy with fewer (about half as many) ordinates can be obtained by determining the *optimal* distribution of the abscissas, rather than prescribing them in an arbitrary way. It is found that the abscissas so determined are generally specified by irrational numbers and that the same is usually true of the weights by which the corresponding ordinates are to be multiplied.

As a specific, but typical, example, which may be helpful in motivating some remarks with regard to such formulas, the five-point Newton-Cotes formula (3.5.13), of closed type, is of the form

$$\int_{-1}^{1} f(x)\,dx = \tfrac{1}{45}[7f(-1) + 32f(-\tfrac{1}{2}) + 12f(0) + 32f(\tfrac{1}{2}) + 7f(1)]$$
$$- \frac{f^{\mathrm{vi}}(\xi)}{15120}, \quad (8.1.1)$$

when related to the interval $(-1,1)$, whereas the Legendre-Gauss three-point formula, to be derived in §8.5, is of the form

$$\int_{-1}^{1} f(x)\,dx = \frac{1}{9}\left[5f\left(-\frac{\sqrt{15}}{5}\right) + 8f(0) + 5f\left(\frac{\sqrt{15}}{5}\right)\right] + \frac{f^{\mathrm{vi}}(\eta)}{15750}, \quad (8.1.2)$$

where ξ and η both lie somewhere in $(-1,1)$.

A comparison of the two error terms shows that the second formula, which requires the values of only three ordinates, may generally be expected to afford about the same accuracy as the first, which requires five ordinates, when the error terms are neglected. Also, since the weights are positive in both formulas, the error in the result, due to possible errors in the *ordinates*, cannot exceed (but may equal) twice the maximum of those errors in both cases. Moreover, if *random* errors in the ordinates are considered, the corresponding RMS errors in the approximations afforded by the first and second formulas are found to be given by about 0.48 and about 0.68 times the RMS ordinate error, respectively.

Thus the apparent advantage of the second formula consists in the fact that, aside from the central ordinate, which is needed in both, it involves only half as many ordinates as the first.   However, unless $f(x)$ is a polynomial (in which case the formulas are not needed) the required ordinates are generally to be obtained by reference to a table of values of $f(x)$.   It is then often argued that, since two of the abscissas in (8.1.2) are irrational, interpolation involving *at least* two tabulated ordinates will be required for the determination of each of the two off-center ordinates, so that at least five ordinates will truly be involved in the use of (8.1.2). Thus, the apparent advantage is lost, and even reversed, since (8.1.1) involves the five ordinates needed in a simple and specific form.

For this reason, and also because of the fact that the *weights* in most Gaussian formulas are also irrational (the present case is an exception), so that, in place of multiplying each ordinate by an integer, one must multiply it by a number with at least as many significant digits as are required in the final result, relatively little practical use has been made of such formulas.

This situation is indeed unfortunate, since the second reason given, while an important one when calculations are necessarily effected by hand, slide rule, or use of tables of logarithms, is clearly of no significance when a computing device with even the relatively limited efficiency of a modern desk calculator is available, and the argument supplying the first reason is (rather obviously) generally fallacious.   Specifically, it assumes that the ordinates denoted as $f(-1)$, $f(-\frac{1}{2})$, and so forth, are known or can be found directly in tables, without the need of interpolation, and is valid only then.

It is true that available tables of many functions, such as e^{-x^2} and $J_0(x)$, for example, include these arguments, and these are typical of the functions which most frequently appear in textbooks dealing with numerical integration.   But practical problems tend to deal instead with functions such as $e^{-\alpha x^2/L^2}$ and $J_0(\alpha x/L)$ over the interval $(-L,L)$ and, correspondingly, with $e^{-\alpha x^2}$ and $J_0(\alpha x)$ over the normalized interval $(-1,1)$, where α is a function of certain physical quantities and is most unlikely to have an integral (or rational) value.   Thus, in practical situations, it is probable that *each* of the ordinates appearing in either of the forms (8.1.1) and (8.1.2) will have to be determined by interpolation (or by direct calculation), and the interpolation for $J_0(\alpha\sqrt{15}/5)$ would be more difficult than that for $J_0(\alpha/2)$ *only* in that the determination of the numerical argument of the interpolate in the former case would involve a multiplication of *two* n-digit numbers.   The necessary accuracy of the interpolation would be no higher in one case than in the other.

Further, it may be noted that, when use is made of a large-scale digital computer, and when $f(x)$ is defined analytically, values of the integrand usually are not obtained by interpolation in tables in any case, but are generated directly by "subroutines" incorporated in the program. Here, since the machine does not distinguish between rational and irrational arguments, the approximate evaluation of $f(\sqrt{15}/5)$ is in no way more complicated than that of $f(1/2)$.

Thus, formulas such as (8.1.2) are indeed advantageous when the determination of ordinates needed for the conventional formulas would involve either *direct calculation, physical measurement,* or *interpolation* and when the use of a "high-precision" formula is appropriate (see §3.7), and they are beginning to receive the attention they deserve.†

The developments of this chapter relate these formulas to a method of "osculating interpolation," associated with the name of Hermite, which is treated in §8.2, and to an associated quadrature formula (§8.3). Several of the classical quadrature formulas of the Gaussian type, in which no abscissas are arbitrarily preassigned, are considered, together with their error terms, in the subsequent sections, which depend upon certain results from Chap. 7. The following section (§8.10) deals with the modifications necessary when certain of the abscissas are preassigned, and the results are illustrated in the next two sections. Section 8.13 deals with a special class of quadrature formulas in which the weights, rather than the abscissas, are preassigned, and §8.14 with algebraic methods for deriving quadrature formulas, of the type considered in this chapter, without making use of properties of orthogonal polynomials.

8.2. Hermite Interpolation. The interpolation formulas so far considered make use only of a certain number of values (approximate or exact) of the function to be approximated. Except in the case of the least-squares formulas of the preceding chapter, the interpolation polynomial $y(x)$ has been defined as that polynomial of lowest degree which agrees with the approximated function $f(x)$ at a certain discrete set of points.

In certain cases, values of both $f(x)$ and its derivative $f'(x)$ are available, say, at m points.‡ We next derive an interpolation formula which

---

† Perhaps because of the fact that they are particularly useful when the integrand is defined analytically, they are usually called *quadrature formulas,* whereas formulas of the usual type are usually called *integration formulas.* There is no basic distinction between the terms.

‡ In the preceding chapters, integration formulas were obtained by integrating the interpolation polynomial of degree n which agrees with the integrand at $n + 1$ points, so that the principal emphasis was on the degree n of that interpolation polynomial, and it was convenient to number the relevant $n + 1$ abscissas from 0 to n. On the other hand, the derivations of the integration formulas which are to be treated in the present chapter are based on certain properties of the polynomial whose *zeros* are the

utilizes these $2m$ data and, in the remainder of this chapter, show that the result leads to useful formulas for numerical integration which do *not* depend upon knowledge of values of $f'(x)$.

Before proceeding to these matters, however, it is desirable to review the Lagrangian interpolation formula treated in Chap. 3 and to write it in a slightly modified form. If the values of $f(x)$ are known at the m points $x = x_1, x_2, \ldots, x_m$, the auxiliary functions

$$\pi(x) = (x - x_1)(x - x_2) \cdots (x - x_m) \qquad (8.2.1)$$

and

$$\begin{aligned} l_i(x) &= \frac{\pi(x)}{(x - x_i)\pi'(x_i)} \\ &\equiv \frac{(x - x_1) \cdots (x - x_{i-1})(x - x_{i+1}) \cdots (x - x_m)}{(x_i - x_1) \cdots (x_i - x_{i-1})(x_i - x_{i+1}) \cdots (x_i - x_m)} \\ &\qquad\qquad\qquad\qquad (i = 1, 2, \ldots, m) \quad (8.2.2) \end{aligned}$$

are first defined, with the properties

$$\pi(x_j) = 0, \qquad\qquad\qquad (8.2.3)$$

and

$$l_i(x_j) = \delta_{ij}, \qquad\qquad\qquad (8.2.4)$$

where δ_{ij} is the Kronecker delta (zero when $i \neq j$ and unity when $i = j$). With these notations, the polynomial of degree $m - 1$ which takes on the values $f(x_1), f(x_2), \ldots,$ and $f(x_m)$ is expressible in the form

$$y(x) = \sum_{k=1}^{m} l_k(x) f(x_k). \qquad\qquad (8.2.5)$$

Also, if $f^{(m)}(x)$ is continuous in the interval I limited by the largest and smallest of the $m + 1$ numbers $x_1, x_2, \ldots, x_m$, and x, the error

$$E(x) = f(x) - y(x)$$

is expressible in the form

$$E(x) = \frac{f^{(m)}(\xi)}{m!} \pi(x), \qquad\qquad (8.2.6)$$

where ξ is somewhere in I.

Now suppose that values of both $f(x)$ and $f'(x)$ are known for $x_1, \ldots,$ x_m. Since a polynomial of degree $2m - 1$ is specified by $2m$ parameters, it is plausible that one such polynomial $y(x)$ can be determined in such a way that $y(x)$ and $f(x)$ possess the same value and the same derivative at each of these m points. We next attempt to determine such a polyno-

---

abscissas of the points involved in the integration formula. It is thus more convenient to use a new symbol, say m, to represent the degree of *that* polynomial, and hence also to represent the *number of ordinates* employed, and to number the ordinates from 1 to m.

mial by assuming that it is expressible in the form

$$y(x) = \sum_{k=1}^{m} h_k(x)f(x_k) + \sum_{k=1}^{m} \bar{h}_k(x)f'(x_k), \qquad (8.2.7)$$

where $h_i(x)$ and $\bar{h}_i(x)$ $(i = 1, 2, \ldots, m)$ are polynomials of maximum degree $2m - 1$, to be determined.

The requirement that $y(x_j) = f(x_j)$ clearly will be satisfied if

$$h_i(x_j) = \delta_{ij}, \qquad \bar{h}_i(x_j) = 0, \qquad (8.2.8)$$

whereas the requirement $y'(x_j) = f'(x_j)$ will be satisfied if

$$h_i'(x_j) = 0, \qquad \bar{h}_i'(x_j) = \delta_{ij}, \qquad (8.2.9)$$

for $1 \leq i \leq m$ and $1 \leq j \leq m$. Now, since $l_i(x)$ is a polynomial of degree $m - 1$ which satisfies (8.2.4), the function $[l_i(x)]^2$ is a polynomial of degree $2m - 2$ which satisfies (8.2.4) and whose derivative vanishes at x_j when $i \neq j$. Hence, since $h_i(x)$ and $\bar{h}_i(x)$ are polynomials of degree $2m - 1$, there must follow

$$h_i(x) = r_i(x)[l_i(x)]^2, \qquad \bar{h}_i(x) = s_i(x)[l_i(x)]^2, \qquad (8.2.10)$$

where $r_i(x)$ and $s_i(x)$ are *linear* functions of x, in order that the first condition of (8.2.9) and the second condition of (8.2.8) be satisfied. The other two conditions then give

$$r_i(x_i) = 1, \qquad r_i'(x_i) + 2l_i'(x_i) = 0 \qquad (8.2.11)$$

and

$$s_i(x_i) = 0, \qquad s_i'(x_i) = 1, \qquad (8.2.12)$$

from which there follows

$$r_i(x) = 1 - 2l_i'(x_i)(x - x_i), \qquad s_i(x) = x - x_i. \qquad (8.2.13)$$

Hence, by combining (8.2.7), (8.2.10), and (8.2.13), we obtain the desired polynomial in the form

$$y(x) = \sum_{k=1}^{m} h_k(x)f(x_k) + \sum_{k=1}^{m} \bar{h}_k(x)f'(x_k), \qquad (8.2.14)$$

where

$$h_i(x) = [1 - 2l_i'(x_i)(x - x_i)][l_i(x)]^2 \qquad (8.2.15)$$

and

$$\bar{h}_i(x) = (x - x_i)[l_i(x)]^2. \qquad (8.2.16)$$

This result is known as *Hermite's interpolation formula* or, frequently, as the formula for *osculating interpolation* (for a more general formula, which also uses values of higher derivatives of $f(x)$, see Fort [82]).

An expression for the error $E(x) = f(x) - y(x)$ can be obtained by a method similar to that used in §2.6. Thus we notice that both $E(x)$ and $[\pi(x)]^2$ vanish *together with their first derivatives* at each of the m points

$x = x_1, \ldots, x_m$. We then form a linear combination of these functions,

$$F(x) = f(x) - y(x) - K[\pi(x)]^2, \qquad (8.2.17)$$

which therefore has the same properties, and determine K in such a way that $F(x)$ also vanishes at an arbitrarily chosen additional point $x = \bar{x}$.

Now let $\bar{I}$ represent the closed interval limited by the smallest and largest of the numbers $x_1, x_2, \ldots, x_m$, and $\bar{x}$. Since $F(x)$ vanishes at these $m + 1$ distinct points, $F'(x)$ must vanish at at least m intermediate points inside $\bar{I}$. But since $F'(x)$ also vanishes at the m points $x_1, \ldots, x_m$, it vanishes at least $2m$ times in $\bar{I}$. Thus $F''(x)$ vanishes at least $2m - 1$ times *inside* $\bar{I}$, $F'''(x)$ at least $2m - 2$ times, $\ldots$, and hence, finally, $F^{(2m)}(x)$ vanishes at least *once* inside $\bar{I}$, assuming the continuity of the derivatives considered. Let one such point be $\bar{\xi}$. Then, recalling that $y(x)$ is a polynomial of degree $2m - 1$, and hence that $y^{(2m)}(x) \equiv 0$, we obtain from (8.2.17) the result

$$0 = F^{(2m)}(\bar{\xi}) = f^{(2m)}(\bar{\xi}) - K \cdot (2m)!$$

or

$$K = \frac{f^{(2m)}(\bar{\xi})}{(2m)!}.$$

Thus, since $F(\bar{x}) = 0$, there follows

$$E(\bar{x}) \equiv f(\bar{x}) - y(\bar{x}) = \frac{f^{(2m)}(\bar{\xi})}{(2m)!} [\pi(\bar{x})]^2,$$

where $\bar{\xi}$ is somewhere in $\bar{I}$. Since both sides of this relation vanish when $\bar{x}$ is identified with one of the points x_i, the relation is true also for such values of $\bar{x}$, and hence for *any* $\bar{x}$. Hence, by suppressing the bars, we deduce that the error associated with approximating $f(x)$ by the right-hand member of (8.2.14) is of the form

$$E(x) = \frac{f^{(2m)}(\xi)}{(2m)!} [\pi(x)]^2, \qquad (8.2.18)$$

where ξ is somewhere in the interval I. In particular, we may deduce easily that the polynomial (8.2.14) is the *only* one having the desired properties.

Thus the Hermite m-point formula yields exact results when $f(x)$ is identified with any polynomial of degree not exceeding $2m - 1$.

8.3. Hermite Quadrature. From the Hermite interpolation formula we may deduce the formula

$$\int_a^b w(x)f(x)\, dx = \sum_{k=1}^m H_k f(x_k) + \sum_{k=1}^m \bar{H}_k f'(x_k) + E, \qquad (8.3.1)$$

with the weighting coefficients defined by the equations

$$H_i = \int_a^b w(x)h_i(x)\, dx = \int_a^b w(x)[1 - 2l_i'(x_i)(x - x_i)][l_i(x)]^2\, dx \quad (8.3.2)$$

and $$\bar{H}_i = \int_a^b w(x)\bar{h}_i(x)\, dx = \int_a^b w(x)(x - x_i)[l_i(x)]^2\, dx, \quad (8.3.3)$$

and with the error expressible in the form

$$E = \int_a^b w(x)E(x)\, dx = \frac{1}{(2m)!} \int_a^b f^{(2m)}(\xi)w(x)[\pi(x)]^2\, dx, \quad (8.3.4)$$

where $a < \xi < b$ if the points $x_1, x_2, \ldots, x_m$ lie in that interval. The result of neglecting the error term is called the *Hermite quadrature formula.*

If the *weighting function* $w(x)$ is nonnegative in (a,b),

$$w(x) \geqq 0, \quad (8.3.5)$$

as will be assumed throughout this chapter, the coefficient of $f^{(2m)}(\xi)$ in the integrand of (8.3.4) is nonnegative. Hence the second law of the mean may be invoked to permit (8.3.4) to be written in the more convenient form

$$E = \frac{f^{(2m)}(\eta)}{(2m)!} \int_a^b w(x)[\pi(x)]^2\, dx. \quad (8.3.6)$$

These results may be compared with the result which corresponds to Lagrangian interpolation employing m points, which can be expressed in the form

$$\int_a^b w(x)f(x)\, dx = \sum_{k=1}^m W_k f(x_k) + E, \quad (8.3.7)$$

where $$W_i = \int_a^b w(x)l_i(x)\, dx \quad (8.3.8)$$

and $$E = \frac{1}{m!} \int_a^b f^{(m)}(\xi)w(x)\pi(x)\, dx. \quad (8.3.9)$$

Since $\pi(x)$ changes sign at each of the points $x_1, \ldots, x_m$, the law of the mean cannot be applied directly to (8.3.9) to produce a form analogous to (8.3.6).

If a quadrature formula yields exact results when $f(x)$ is an arbitrary polynomial of degree r or less, but fails to give exact results for at least one polynomial of degree $r + 1$, it is said to possess a *degree of precision* equal to r (see §5.11). From the linearity of the process, it follows that this situation exists if and only if exact results are afforded for 1, x, x^2, $\ldots$, x^r, but not for x^{r+1}.

From (8.3.6) we see that the degree of precision of the Hermite m-point formula is exactly $2m - 1$. It follows also from (8.3.9) that the degree of precision of the Lagrangian quadrature formula, based on m points, is at least $m - 1$. Furthermore, if we take $f(x) = [\pi(x)]^2$, we see that all terms in the sum involved in (8.3.7) *vanish*, and hence, for this function, the Lagrangian formula would give

$$\int_a^b w(x)[\pi(x)]^2 \, dx = 0.$$

Under the assumption (8.3.5), this situation is impossible. Hence, since $[\pi(x)]^2$ is a polynomial of degree $2m$, it follows that the degree of precision of the Lagrangian m-point formula cannot *exceed* $2m - 1$. Unless further information concerning the choice of the points $x_1, \ldots, x_m$ is available, no more specific statement can be made. However, it is shown in the following section that there exists a class of formulas of the simple Lagrangian type (8.3.7) which actually have the maximum degree of precision $2m - 1$.

8.4. Gaussian Quadrature. An inspection of (8.3.1) shows that, if the points $x_1, \ldots, x_m$ can be chosen in such a way that the weighting coefficients $\bar{H}_k$ associated with the derivative terms vanish, then the Hermite formula will reduce to a formula of the simple type (8.3.7) while retaining the degree of precision $2m - 1$. With the notation of (8.2.1) and (8.2.2), the definition (8.3.3) can be expressed in the equivalent form

$$\bar{H}_i = \frac{1}{\pi'(x_i)} \int_a^b w(x)\pi(x)l_i(x) \, dx, \tag{8.4.1}$$

where, as before,

$$\pi(x) = (x - x_1)(x - x_2) \cdots (x - x_m), \tag{8.4.2}$$

so that $x_1, \ldots, x_m$ are the m zeros of $\pi(x)$.

Thus $\bar{H}_i$ will vanish for $1 \leq i \leq m$, and the degree of precision $2m - 1$ will be preserved, if $\pi(x)$ is *orthogonal* to $l_1(x), \ldots, l_m(x)$ over (a,b), relative to the weighting function $w(x)$. Since each $l_i(x)$ is a polynomial of degree $m - 1$, in virtue of (8.2.2), a *sufficient* condition is that $\pi(x)$ be orthogonal to *all* polynomials of degree inferior to m over (a,b), relative to $w(x)$.

This condition is also *necessary*. To see this, assume that

$$\bar{H}_i = 0 \qquad (1 \leq i \leq m), \tag{8.4.3}$$

and that the formula has a degree of precision $2m - 1$. Let $f(x)$ be a polynomial, of degree $2m - 1$ or less, expressed in the special form

$$f(x) = \pi(x)u_{m-1}(x), \tag{8.4.4}$$

where $u_{m-1}(x)$ is an arbitrary polynomial of degree $m - 1$ or less. Then, since $\pi(x_i) = 0$ for $1 \leq i \leq m$, there follows $f(x_i) = 0$, and hence, for this polynomial, (8.3.1) becomes

$$\int_a^b w(x)f(x)\ dx \equiv \int_a^b w(x)\pi(x)u_{m-1}(x)\ dx = 0, \tag{8.4.5}$$

as was to be shown, since $\bar{H}_i = 0$ by assumption and $E = 0$ by virtue of the fact that here $f^{(2m)}(x) \equiv 0$.

Hence we deduce that *if and only if the polynomial $\pi(x)$, of degree m, is orthogonal to all polynomials of inferior degree over (a,b), relative to $w(x)$, the Hermite quadrature formula reduces to the formula*

$$\int_a^b w(x)f(x)\ dx = \sum_{k=1}^m H_k f(x_k) + E, \tag{8.4.6}$$

where
$$E = \frac{f^{(2m)}(\eta)}{(2m)!} \int_a^b w(x)[\pi(x)]^2\ dx, \tag{8.4.7}$$

and where the m abscissas $x_1, \ldots, x_m$ are the zeros of $\pi(x)$.

A formula of this type is usually called a *Gaussian quadrature formula*, although it appears that only the case in which $w(x) = 1$ was explicitly considered by Gauss.

Since (8.4.6) is a special case of both (8.3.1) and (8.3.7), the weighting coefficients H_i and W_i given by (8.3.2) and (8.3.8) must be equal in this case. Thus we may write

$$H_i = \int_a^b w(x)[l_i(x)]^2\ dx = \int_a^b w(x)l_i(x)\ dx = W_i, \tag{8.4.8}$$

the first form being obtained from (8.3.2) by writing that formula in the form

$$H_i = \int_a^b w(x)[l_i(x)]^2\ dx - 2l_i'(x_i)\bar{H}_i \tag{8.4.9}$$

and recalling that here $\bar{H}_i = 0$.

The polynomial $\pi(x)$ is precisely that numerical multiple of the polynomial $\phi_m(x)$, specified by Eqs. (7.4.4) to (7.4.7), for which the coefficient of the leading power of x is unity. Thus, as was shown in §7.4, its m zeros are indeed real and distinct and are all located inside the interval (a,b). The interval need not be of finite length, so long as $w(x) \geq 0$ and the integral $\int_a^b x^k w(x)\ dx$ exists for all nonnegative integral values of k.

It is of particular importance to notice that, in virtue of the first form of (8.4.8), *the weighting coefficients in a Gaussian quadrature formula are all positive.*

With the notation of §7.4, the error (8.4.7) can be expressed in the form

$$E = \frac{\gamma_m}{A_m^2} \frac{f^{(2m)}(\eta)}{(2m)!}, \tag{8.4.10}$$

where γ_m is the normalizing factor corresponding to $\phi_m(x)$ and is defined by (7.4.13), and where A_m is the coefficient of x^m in $\phi_m(x)$.†

In order to determine explicitly the weights H_i defined by (8.4.8), we first establish certain important additional properties of the relevant orthogonal polynomials $\phi_k(x)$.

We first notice that

$$\phi_{k+1}(x) - \frac{A_{k+1}}{A_k} x\phi_k(x)$$

is a polynomial of maximum degree k. Hence, if we write

$$a_k \equiv \frac{A_{k+1}}{A_k}, \tag{8.4.11}$$

it follows that $\phi_{k+1}(x) - a_k x\phi_k(x)$ can be expressed as a linear combination of $\phi_0(x)$, $\phi_1(x)$, . . . , $\phi_k(x)$, in the form

$$\phi_{k+1}(x) - a_k x\phi_k(x) = b_k\phi_k(x) + c_k\phi_{k-1}(x) + \cdots , \tag{8.4.12}$$

for some constant values of b_k, c_k, ... But, since $x\phi_0(x)$, $x\phi_1(x)$, ... , and $x\phi_{k-2}(x)$ are polynomials of degree inferior to k, the two terms in the left-hand member of (8.4.12) are both orthogonal to ϕ_0, ϕ_1, . . . , ϕ_{k-2} over (a,b), relative to $w(x)$. Hence the same statement applies to the right-hand member, so that the omitted terms in (8.4.12) vanish, and we deduce that $\phi_k(x)$ satisfies a *recurrence formula* of the form

$$\phi_{k+1}(x) = (a_k x + b_k)\phi_k(x) + c_k\phi_{k-1}(x), \tag{8.4.13}$$

where a_k is defined by (8.4.11), and b_k and c_k are certain other constants. Equations (7.5.9), (7.6.12), and (7.7.10) serve as illustrations of this fact. In order that (8.4.13) also hold when $k = 0$, the convention $\phi_{-1}(x) \equiv 0$ may be adopted.

If we multiply the equal members of (8.4.13) successively by $w\phi_{k+1}$, $w\phi_k$, and $w\phi_{k-1}$, and integrate each resultant equation over (a,b), we obtain the additional relations

$$\gamma_{k+1} = a_k \int_a^b xw(x)\phi_k(x)\phi_{k+1}(x) \, dx,$$

$$0 = a_k \int_a^b xw(x)[\phi_k(x)]^2 \, dx + b_k\gamma_k,$$

$$0 = a_k \int_a^b xw(x)\phi_{k-1}(x)\phi_k(x) \, dx + c_k\gamma_{k-1}.$$

† Whereas $\phi_m(x)$ could always be so defined that either γ_m or A_m is unity, this choice usually does not lead to a standard (tabulated) form. Hence, the formulas are given without such a restriction.

If k is replaced by $k - 1$ in the first equation, the result can be used to eliminate the unknown integral from the third equation and to establish the relation

$$c_k = - \frac{a_k \gamma_k}{a_{k-1} \gamma_{k-1}}. \tag{8.4.14}$$

Hence (8.4.13) can be rewritten in the form

$$x \frac{\phi_k(x)}{\gamma_k} = \frac{\phi_{k+1}(x)}{a_k \gamma_k} + \frac{\phi_{k-1}(x)}{a_{k-1} \gamma_{k-1}} - \frac{b_k \phi_k(x)}{a_k \gamma_k}. \tag{8.4.15}$$

Next, if both members of (8.4.15) are multiplied by $\phi_k(y)$, where y is an arbitrary parameter, and the result of interchanging x and y in the result is subtracted from that result, the constant b_k is eliminated, and the more symmetrical relation

$$(x - y) \frac{\phi_k(x) \phi_k(y)}{\gamma_k} = \frac{\phi_{k+1}(x) \phi_k(y) - \phi_k(x) \phi_{k+1}(y)}{a_k \gamma_k}$$
$$- \frac{\phi_k(x) \phi_{k-1}(y) - \phi_{k-1}(x) \phi_k(y)}{a_{k-1} \gamma_{k-1}} \tag{8.4.16}$$

is obtained. The result of summing the equal members from $k = 0$ to $k = m$ and taking advantage of the "telescoping" of terms on the right, is then the important relation

$$\sum_{k=0}^{m} \frac{\phi_k(x) \phi_k(y)}{\gamma_k} = \frac{\phi_{m+1}(x) \phi_m(y) - \phi_m(x) \phi_{m+1}(y)}{a_m \gamma_m (x - y)}, \tag{8.4.17}$$

known as the *Christoffel-Darboux identity.*

Now, if we notice that

$$\phi_m(x) = A_m \pi(x), \tag{3.4.18}$$

and identify y with x_i, where x_i is a zero of $\pi(x)$, so that $\phi_m(x_i) = 0$, Eq. (8.4.17) specializes to the form

$$\frac{\phi_{m+1}(x_i)}{a_m \gamma_m} \frac{\phi_m(x)}{x - x_i} = - \sum_{k=0}^{m} \frac{\phi_k(x) \phi_k(x_i)}{\gamma_k}. \tag{3.4.19}$$

The result of multiplying the equal members of (8.4.19) by $w(x) \phi_0(x)$, integrating the results over (a,b), and making use of the orthogonality of the polynomials, relative to $w(x)$, is then

$$\frac{\phi_{m+1}(x_i)}{a_m \gamma_m} \int_a^b w(x) \frac{\phi_0(x) \phi_m(x)}{x - x_i} \, dx = - \phi_0(x_i)$$

or, since $\phi_0(x)$ is a constant,

$$\int_a^b w(x) \frac{\phi_m(x)}{x - x_i} dx = - \frac{a_m \gamma_m}{\phi_{m+1}(x_i)}. \qquad (8.4.20)$$

Finally, since

$$l_i(x) = \frac{\pi(x)}{\pi'(x_i)(x - x_i)} = \frac{\phi_m(x)}{\phi_m'(x_i)(x - x_i)}, \qquad (8.4.21)$$

reference to the second form of (8.4.8) leads to the desired result

$$H_i = \frac{1}{\phi_m'(x_i)} \int_a^b w(x) \frac{\phi_m(x)}{x - x_i} dx = - \frac{A_{m+1}\gamma_m}{A_m \phi_m'(x_i) \phi_{m+1}(x_i)}. \qquad (8.4.22)$$

Alternatively, since (8.4.13) and (8.4.14) give

$$\phi_{m+1}(x_i) = - \frac{A_{m+1} A_{m-1}}{A_m^2} \frac{\gamma_m}{\gamma_{m-1}} \phi_{m-1}(x_i),$$

this result may be expressed in the equivalent form

$$H_i = \frac{A_m \gamma_{m-1}}{A_{m-1} \phi_m'(x_i) \phi_{m-1}(x_i)}. \qquad (8.4.23)$$

Many other useful results can be deduced from the identity (8.4.17). In particular, by considering the limiting form of that relation as $y \to x$, we obtain the equation

$$\sum_{k=0}^m \frac{[\phi_k(x)]^2}{\gamma_k} = \frac{A_m}{A_{m+1}\gamma_m} [\phi_{m+1}'(x)\phi_m(x) - \phi_m'(x)\phi_{m+1}(x)], \qquad (8.4.24)$$

and the result of setting $x = x_i$, where x_i is a zero of $\phi_m(x)$, is the curious relationship

$$\sum_{k=0}^m \frac{[\phi_k(x_i)]^2}{\gamma_k} = - \frac{A_m \phi_m'(x_i)\phi_{m+1}(x_i)}{A_{m+1}\gamma_m} = \frac{1}{H_i}. \qquad (8.4.25)$$

8.5. Legendre-Gauss Quadrature. In the case when a constant weighting function is to be used over a finite interval, it is convenient to suppose that a suitable change of variables has transformed that interval into the interval $(-1,1)$. From the results of §7.5, we then have

$$\pi(x) = \frac{1}{A_m} P_m(x), \qquad (8.5.1)$$

where $P_m(x)$ is the mth Legendre polynomial, and where

$$A_m = \frac{(2m)!}{2^m(m!)^2}. \qquad (8.5.2)$$

With the additional result

$$\gamma_m = \frac{2}{2m+1},$$ (3.5.3)

Eqs. (8.4.6), (8.4.22) or (8.4.23), and (8.4.10) reduce to the quadrature formula

$$\int_{-1}^{1} f(x) \, dx = \sum_{k=1}^{m} H_k f(x_k) + E,$$ (8.5.4)

where x_i is the ith zero of $P_m(x)$, and where

$$H_i = -\frac{2}{(m+1)P_{m+1}(x_i)P'_m(x_i)} = \frac{2}{mP_{m-1}(x_i)P'_m(x_i)}$$ (8.5.5)

and

$$E = \frac{2^{2m+1}(m!)^4}{(2m+1)[(2m)!]^3} f^{(2m)}(\xi).$$ (8.5.6)

From the known relation†

$$(1 - x^2)P'_m(x) = mxP_m(x) + mP_{m-1}(x)$$

$$= (m+1)xP_m(x) - (m+1)P_{m+1}(x),$$ (8.5.7)

there follows also

$$(1 - x_i^2)P'_m(x_i) = mP_{m-1}(x_i) = -(m+1)P_{m+1}(x_i),$$

so that (8.5.5) can also be expressed in the forms

$$H_i = \frac{2}{(1 - x_i^2)[P'_m(x_i)]^2} = \frac{2(1 - x_i^2)}{(m+1)^2[P_{m+1}(x_i)]^2}.$$ (8.5.8)

In illustration, when $m = 3$, there follows

$$\pi(x) = \tfrac{2}{5}P_3(x) = x(x^2 - \tfrac{3}{5}),$$

and hence

$$x_1 = -\frac{\sqrt{15}}{5}, \qquad x_2 = 0, \qquad x_3 = \frac{\sqrt{15}}{5}$$

and

$$H_1 = \tfrac{5}{9}, \qquad H_2 = \tfrac{8}{9}, \qquad H_3 = \tfrac{5}{9}.$$

Thus

$$\int_{-1}^{1} f(x) \, dx = \frac{1}{9}\left[5f\left(-\frac{\sqrt{15}}{5}\right) + 8f(0) + 5f\left(\frac{\sqrt{15}}{5}\right) \right] + \frac{f^{vi}(\xi)}{15750},$$ (8.5.9)

where $|\xi| < 1$.

† For derivations of (8.5.7), and of other similar differential recurrence formulas listed in this chapter, see Szegö [220].

The abscissas and weights corresponding to formulas for which $2 \leqq m \leqq 5$ are listed, to six digits, in Table 8.1. More elaborate tabulations are listed in the references.

TABLE 8.1

m	Abscissas	Weights
2	± 0.577350	1
3	0	$\frac{8}{9}$
	± 0.774597	$\frac{5}{9}$
4	± 0.339981	0.652145
	± 0.861136	0.347855
5	0	0.568889
	± 0.538469	0.478629
	± 0.906180	0.236927

8.6. Laguerre-Gauss Quadrature. In the case when the weighting function

$$w(x) = e^{-x} \tag{8.6.1}$$

is used over the semi-infinite interval $(0, \infty)$, the results of §7.6 give

$$\pi(x) = \frac{1}{A_m} L_m(x), \tag{8.6.2}$$

where $L_m(x)$ is the mth Laguerre polynomial, and where

$$A_m = (-1)^m. \tag{8.6.3}$$

In addition, there follows

$$\gamma_m = (m!)^2, \tag{8.6.4}$$

and hence the formulas of §8.4 become

$$\int_0^\infty e^{-x} f(x)\, dx = \sum_{k=1}^m H_k f(x_k) + E, \tag{8.6.5}$$

where x_i is the ith zero of $L_m(x)$,† and where

$$H_i = \frac{(m!)^2}{L_m'(x_i) L_{m+1}(x_i)} = -\frac{[(m-1)!]^2}{L_m'(x_i) L_{m-1}(x_i)} \tag{8.6.6}$$

and

$$E = \frac{(m!)^2}{(2m)!} f^{(2m)}(\xi), \tag{8.6.7}$$

where $0 < \xi < \infty$. From the relation

$$xL_m'(x) = mL_m(x) - m^2 L_{m-1}(x) = (x - m - 1)L_m(x) + L_{m+1}(x), \tag{8.6.8}$$

there follows also

$$x_i L_m'(x_i) = -m^2 L_{m-1}(x_i) = L_{m+1}(x_i),$$

† The more general case in which e^{-x} is replaced by $e^{-\alpha x}$ in (8.6.5) is clearly reduced to the present case by a simple change of variables.

so that (8.6.6) can also be expressed in the forms

$$H_i = \frac{(m!)^2}{x_i[L'_m(x_i)]^2} = \frac{(m!)^2 x_i}{[L_{m+1}(x_i)]^2}. \tag{8.6.9}$$

In illustration, when $m = 2$, there follows

$$\pi(x) = L_2(x) = x^2 - 4x + 2,$$

and hence

$$x_1 = 2 - \sqrt{2}, \qquad x_2 = 2 + \sqrt{2}$$

and

$$H_1 = \frac{2 + \sqrt{2}}{4}, \qquad H_2 = \frac{2 - \sqrt{2}}{4}.$$

Thus

$$\int_0^\infty e^{-x} f(x)\, dx = \tfrac{1}{4}[(2 + \sqrt{2})f(2 - \sqrt{2}) + (2 - \sqrt{2})f(2 + \sqrt{2})]$$
$$+ \frac{f^{iv}(\xi)}{6} \tag{8.6.10}$$

where $0 < \xi < \infty$ or, more generally,

$$\int_0^\infty e^{-\alpha x} f(x)\, dx = \frac{1}{4\alpha}\left[(2 + \sqrt{2})f\left(\frac{2 - \sqrt{2}}{\alpha}\right) + (2 - \sqrt{2})f\left(\frac{2 + \sqrt{2}}{\alpha}\right) \right]$$
$$+ \frac{f^{iv}(\xi)}{6\alpha^5}. \tag{8.6.11}$$

The abscissas and weights corresponding to formulas for which $2 \leqq m \leqq 5$ are listed, to six digits, in Table 8.2.   Other tabulations are listed in the references.

TABLE 8.2

m	Abscissas	Weights
2	0.585786	0.853553
	3.414214	0.146447
3	0.415775	0.711093
	2.294280	0.278518
	6.289945	0.0103893
4	0.322548	0.603154
	1.745761	0.357419
	4.536620	0.0388879
	9.395071	0.000539295
5	0.263560	0.521756
	1.413403	0.398667
	3.596426	0.0759424
	7.085810	0.00361176
	12.640801	0.0000233700

When the weighting function (8.6.1) is generalized to the function

$$w(x) = x^\beta e^{-x} \qquad (\beta > -1), \tag{8.6.12}$$

it is easily found, by the methods of §7.6, that

$$\pi(x) = \frac{1}{A_m} L_m^\beta(x), \tag{8.6.13}$$

where $L_m^\beta(x)$ is the generalized Laguerre polynomial of degree m,

$$L_m^\beta(x) = e^x x^{-\beta} \frac{d^m}{dx^m} (e^{-x} x^{\beta+m}), \tag{8.6.14}$$

and that

$$A_m = (-1)^m, \qquad \gamma_m = m! \int_0^\infty x^{\beta+m} e^{-x} \, dx = m! \Gamma(m + \beta + 1). \tag{8.6.15}$$

It can also be shown that the differential recurrence formula

$$xL_m^{\beta\prime}(x) = mL_m^\beta(x) - m(m + \beta)L_{m-1}^\beta(x) = (x - m - \beta - 1)L_m^\beta + L_{m+1}^\beta \tag{8.6.16}$$

is satisfied.

From these results, the corresponding quadrature formula is readily derived in the form

$$\int_0^\infty x^\beta e^{-x} f(x) \, dx = \sum_{k=1}^m H_k f(x_k) + E, \tag{8.6.17}$$

where x_i is the ith zero of $L_m^\beta(x)$, and where

$$H_i = \frac{m! \Gamma(m + \beta + 1)}{x_i [L_m^{\beta\prime}(x_i)]^2} = \frac{m! \Gamma(m + \beta + 1) x_i}{[L_{m+1}^\beta(x_i)]^2} \tag{8.6.18}$$

and

$$E = \frac{m! \Gamma(m + \beta + 1)}{(2m)!} f^{(2m)}(\xi). \tag{8.6.19}$$

A brief table of abscissas and weights $(m, \beta = 2,3,4)$ has been given by Burnett [52].

8.7. Hermite-Gauss Quadrature. In the case when the weighting function

$$w(x) = e^{-x^2} \tag{8.7.1}$$

is used over the interval $(-\infty, \infty)$, the results of §7.7 give

$$\pi(x) = \frac{1}{A_m} H_m(x), \tag{8.7.2}$$

where $H_m(x)$ is the mth Hermite polynomial, and where

$$A_m = 2^m. \tag{8.7.3}$$

In addition, there follows

$$\gamma_m = \sqrt{\pi}\, 2^m m!,$$ (8.7.4)

so that the appropriate Gaussian formula is of the form

$$\int_{-\infty}^{\infty} e^{-x^2} f(x)\, dx = \sum_{k=1}^{m} H_k f(x_k) + E,$$ (8.7.5)

where x_i is the ith zero of $H_m(x)$, and where

$$H_i = -\frac{2^{m+1} m!\, \sqrt{\pi}}{H'_m(x_i) H_{m+1}(x_i)} = \frac{2^m (m-1)!\, \sqrt{\pi}}{H'_m(x_i) H_{m-1}(x_i)}$$ (8.7.6)

and

$$E = \frac{m!\, \sqrt{\pi}}{2^m (2m)!}\, f^{(2m)}(\xi),$$ (8.7.7)

for some ξ. From the relation

$$H'_m(x) = 2m H_{m-1}(x) = 2x H_m(x) - H_{m+1}(x),$$ (8.7.8)

there follows also

$$H'_m(x_i) = 2m H_{m-1}(x_i) = -H_{m+1}(x_i),$$

so that (8.7.6) can also be expressed in the forms

$$H_i = \frac{2^{m+1} m!\, \sqrt{\pi}}{[H'_m(x_i)]^2} = \frac{2^{m+1} m!\, \sqrt{\pi}}{[H_{m+1}(x_i)]^2}.$$ (8.7.9)

In illustration, when $m = 3$, there follows

$$\pi(x) = \tfrac{1}{8} H_3(x) = x(x^2 - \tfrac{3}{2}),$$

and hence

$$x_1 = -\frac{\sqrt{6}}{2}, \qquad x_2 = 0, \qquad x_3 = \frac{\sqrt{6}}{2}$$

and

$$H_1 = \frac{\sqrt{\pi}}{6}, \qquad H_2 = \frac{2\sqrt{\pi}}{3}, \qquad H_3 = \frac{\sqrt{\pi}}{6}.$$

Thus

$$\int_{-\infty}^{\infty} e^{-x^2} f(x)\, dx = \frac{\sqrt{\pi}}{6}\left[f\left(-\frac{\sqrt{6}}{2}\right) + 4f(0) + f\left(\frac{\sqrt{6}}{2}\right) \right] + \frac{\sqrt{\pi}\, f^{\mathrm{vi}}(\xi)}{960}$$ (8.7.10)

or, more generally,

$$\int_{-\infty}^{\infty} e^{-\alpha^2 x^2} f(x)\, dx = \frac{\sqrt{\pi}}{6\alpha}\left[f\left(-\frac{\sqrt{6}}{2\alpha}\right) + 4f(0) + f\left(\frac{\sqrt{6}}{2\alpha}\right) \right] + \frac{\sqrt{\pi}\, f^{\mathrm{vi}}(\xi)}{960\alpha^7}.$$ (8.7.11)

The abscissas and weights corresponding to formulas for which $2 \leqq m \leqq 5$ are listed, to six digits, in Table 8.3. More extensive tabulations are listed in the references.

TABLE 8.3

m	Abscissas	Weights
2	± 0.707107	0.886227
3	0	1.181636
	± 1.224745	0.295409
4	± 0.524648	0.804914
	± 1.650680	0.0813128
5	0	0.945309
	± 0.958572	0.393619
	± 2.020183	0.0199532

It should be noticed that no restrictions are imposed on ξ in the error formula (8.7.7), other than that it be real. (Similarly, in the error formula of the preceding section, it is known only that ξ is real and positive.) Thus, in those cases when $f^{(2m)}(x)$ varies greatly in magnitude when m is large, as x takes on all real values, the imprecision associated with the use of (8.7.7) is correspondingly great.

For example, if $f(x) = 1/(1 + x^2)$, it is easily seen from the Maclaurin expansion of $f(x)$ that $f^{(2m)}(x) = (2m)!$ when $x = 0$, so that, in the evaluation of the integral

$$\int_{-\infty}^{\infty} e^{-x^2} \frac{dx}{1 + x^2} = 1.34329 \cdots$$

by m-point Hermite quadrature, the error formula (8.7.7) would admit the possibility of an error as large as $\sqrt{\pi}\, m!/2^m$, if the appropriate (but unknown) value of ξ_m were near zero. If this were indeed the case, the error would increase rapidly with m, when $m > 2$. However, it has been pointed out by Rosser [197] that the errors corresponding to the use of 2, 10, and 16 points are about 0.16, 0.0016, and 0.00016, respectively. Thus the error truly decreases with increasing m, so that ξ_m must increase rapidly in magnitude as m increases, at least for $m \leq 16$, but the rate of convergence is extremely slow. Similar slow convergence (or divergence) may be expected, more generally, whenever $f(x)$ possesses singularities, in the finite part of the complex plane, which are fairly near the real axis (compare §3.7).

In this connection, it may be noticed that, in view of the appropriate generalization of (5.11.34), the truncation error in the general Gaussian quadrature formula (8.4.6) can be expressed in the form

$$E = \int_a^b w(x)[\pi(x)]^2 f[x_1,x_1,x_2,x_2, \ldots ,x_m,x_m,x]\, dx$$

$$= f[x_1,x_1,x_2,x_2, \ldots ,x_m,x_m,\xi_1] \int_a^b w(x)[\pi(x)]^2\, dx$$

$$= \frac{\gamma_m}{A_m^2} f[x_1,x_1,x_2,x_2, \ldots ,x_m,x_m,\xi_1], \qquad (8.7.12)$$

with the notation used in (8.4.10), where $a < \xi_1 < b$. This form reduces to (8.4.10) when the divided difference is replaced by $f^{(2m)}(\xi_2)/(2m)!$, where $a < \xi_2 < b$. Since ξ_1 and ξ_2 generally cannot be estimated, one generally must replace either the divided difference or the derivative by its maximum absolute value for all ξ in (a,b), to obtain an *upper bound* on $|E|$, and it may happen that the bound obtained from (8.7.12) is much less conservative than that obtained from (8.4.10).

In illustration, if $f(x) = 1/(x + a)$, there follows

$$f[x_1,x_1, \ldots ,x_m,x_m,\xi_1] = \frac{1}{[(a + x_1) \cdots (a + x_m)]^2(a + \xi_1)}$$

and

$$\frac{f^{(2m)}(\xi_2)}{(2m)!} = \frac{1}{(a + \xi_2)^{2m+1}}.$$

Thus, for example, if five-point Laguerre-Gauss quadrature were to be used to approximate the integral

$$\int_0^\infty \frac{e^{-x}}{x + 1} \, dx,$$

the truncation-error terms corresponding to the use of (8.7.12) and (8.6.7) would be of the forms

$$\frac{(120)^2}{(2.39 \times 10^6)(1 + \xi_1)} \doteq \frac{0.0060}{1 + \xi_1} \quad \text{and} \quad \frac{1.44 \times 10^4}{(1 + \xi_2)^{11}},$$

respectively, where the abscissas are taken from Table 8.2 and where ξ_1 and ξ_2 are known only to be positive. Accordingly, the use of (8.7.12) here permits the determination of an error bound which is smaller than that obtainable from (8.6.7) in a ratio of about 2.4×10^6. The actual truncation error rounds to 0.0013.

Whereas this case is a rather extreme one, still, when $f(x)$ is such that an upper bound on the magnitude of the relevant divided difference can be obtained practically, the use of (8.7.12) is usually preferable to that of (8.4.10).

8.8. Chebyshev-Gauss Quadrature. For the weighting function

$$w(x) = \frac{1}{\sqrt{1 - x^2}}, \tag{8.8.1}$$

over the interval $(-1,1)$, the results of §7.8 give

$$\pi(x) = \frac{1}{A_m} T_m(x), \tag{8.8.2}$$

where $T_m(x)$ is the mth Chebyshev polynomial. With the additional results

$$A_m = 2^{m-1}, \qquad \gamma_m = \frac{\pi}{2}, \tag{8.8.3}$$

the relevant Gaussian formula is obtained in the form

$$\int_{-1}^{1} \frac{f(x)}{\sqrt{1 - x^2}} dx = \sum_{k=1}^{m} H_k f(x_k) + E, \qquad (8.8.4)$$

where x_i is the ith zero of $T_m(x)$, and where

$$H_i = -\frac{\pi}{T'_m(x_i) T_{m+1}(x_i)} \qquad (8.8.5)$$

and

$$E = \frac{2\pi}{2^{2m}(2m)!} f^{(2m)}(\xi), \qquad (8.8.6)$$

where $|\xi| < 1$.

Since

$$T_m(x) = \cos(m \cos^{-1} x), \qquad (8.8.7)$$

the abscissas are obtainable in the explicit form

$$x_i = \cos\left[\frac{(2i - 1)\pi}{2m}\right] \qquad (i = 1, 2, \ldots, m). \qquad (8.8.8)$$

Also, direct calculation shows that

$$T'_m(x_i) = \frac{(-1)^{i+1}m}{\sin \alpha_i}, \qquad T_{m+1}(x_i) = (-1)^i \sin \alpha_i, \qquad (8.8.9)$$

where

$$\alpha_i = \frac{2i - 1}{2m} \pi, \qquad (8.8.10)$$

and hence (8.8.5) reduces to the remarkably simple form

$$H_i = \frac{\pi}{m}. \qquad (8.8.11)$$

Thus *the weights in* (8.8.4) *are all equal.*

The formula (8.8.4) hence can be written in the explicit form

$$\int_{-1}^{1} \frac{f(x)}{\sqrt{1 - x^2}} dx = \frac{\pi}{m} \sum_{k=1}^{m} f\left(\cos \frac{2k - 1}{2m} \pi\right) + \frac{2\pi}{2^{2m}(2m)!} f^{(2m)}(\xi), \qquad (8.8.12)$$

where $|\xi| < 1$.

8.9. Jacobi-Gauss Quadrature. Most of the other Gaussian quadrature formulas which have been investigated in the literature correspond to the use of a specialization of the weighting function

$$w(x) = (1 - x)^\alpha (1 + x)^\beta \qquad (\alpha > -1, \beta > -1), \qquad (8.9.1)$$

over the interval $(-1,1)$, or to the result of transforming this problem to the interval $(0,1)$. The special cases $\alpha = \beta = 0$ and $\alpha = \beta = -\frac{1}{2}$ have been considered in §§8.5 and 8.8.

In the general case, we may take $\pi(x)$ as the appropriate multiple of the polynomial

$$
\phi_m(x) = C_m (1 - x)^{-\alpha}(1 + x)^{-\beta} \frac{d^m}{dx^m}\left[(1 - x)^{\alpha+m}(1 + x)^{\beta+m}\right]
$$

$$
= (-1)^m C_m 2^m m! \sum_{k=0}^{m} \binom{m + \alpha + \beta + k}{k}\binom{m + \alpha}{m - k}\left(\frac{x - 1}{2}\right)^k
$$

$$
\equiv C_m V_m(x) \tag{8.9.2}
$$

which, as was noted in §7.8, reduces with a certain (not universally agreed upon) choice of C_m to the mth Jacobi polynomial.†

The coefficient of x^m is found to be

$$
A_m = (-1)^m \frac{\Gamma(2m + \alpha + \beta + 1)}{\Gamma(m + \alpha + \beta + 1)} C_m, \tag{8.9.3}
$$

whereas the normalizing factor is obtained, from (7.4.13), in the form

$$
\gamma_m = C_m^2 m! \frac{\Gamma(2m + \alpha + \beta + 1)}{\Gamma(m + \alpha + \beta + 1)}\int_{-1}^{1}(1 - x)^{\alpha+m}(1 + x)^{\beta+m}\,dx
$$

$$
= C_m^2 m! \frac{\Gamma(2m + \alpha + \beta + 1)}{\Gamma(m + \alpha + \beta + 1)}\frac{\Gamma(m + \alpha + 1)\Gamma(m + \beta + 1)}{\Gamma(2m + \alpha + \beta + 2)}2^{2m+\alpha+\beta+1}
$$

$$
= C_m^2 \frac{2^{2m+\alpha+\beta+1}m!}{2m + \alpha + \beta + 1}\frac{\Gamma(m + \alpha + 1)\Gamma(m + \beta + 1)}{\Gamma(m + \alpha + \beta + 1)}, \tag{8.9.4}
$$

where use was made of the formula

$$
\int_{-1}^{1}(1 - x)^p (1 + x)^q\,dx = 2^{p+q+1}\frac{\Gamma(p + 1)\Gamma(q + 1)}{\Gamma(p + q + 2)}
$$
$$
(p > -1, q > -1). \tag{8.9.5}
$$

The results (8.9.2) to (8.9.4) reduce to (8.5.1) to (8.5.3) when $\alpha = \beta = 0$ with the choice $C_m = (-1)^m/(2^m m!)$, corresponding to $\phi_m(x) = P_m(x)$, and to (8.8.2) and (8.8.3) when $\alpha = \beta = -\frac{1}{2}$ with the special choice $C_m = (-2)^m m!/(2m)!$, corresponding to $\phi_m(x) = T_m(x)$.

Thus we obtain the quadrature formula

$$
\int_{-1}^{1}(1 - x)^\alpha (1 + x)^\beta f(x)\,dx = \sum_{k=1}^{m} H_k f(x_k) + E, \tag{8.9.6}
$$

where x_i is the ith zero of $V_m(x)$, and where, from (8.4.22) or (8.4.23) and (8.4.10),

$$
H_i = \frac{2m + \alpha + \beta + 2}{m + \alpha + \beta + 1}\frac{\Gamma(m + \alpha + 1)\Gamma(m + \beta + 1)}{\Gamma(m + \alpha + \beta + 1)}\frac{2^{2m+\alpha+\beta+1}m!}{V_m'(x_i)V_{m+1}(x_i)} \tag{8.9.7}
$$

† See Szegö [220]. The choice made in that reference is $C_m = (-1)^m/(2^m m!)$.

and

$$E = \frac{\Gamma(m + \alpha + 1)\Gamma(m + \beta + 1)\Gamma(m + \alpha + \beta + 1)}{(2m + \alpha + \beta + 1)[\Gamma(2m + \alpha + \beta + 1)]^2} \frac{2^{2m+\alpha+\beta+1}m!}{(2m)!} f^{(2m)}(\xi),$$
$$(8.9.8)$$

where $|\xi| < 1$. Integration based on (8.9.6) is often known as *Mehler quadrature*.

It is possible to establish the relation (see Szegö [220])

$$(2m + \alpha + \beta + 2)(1 - x^2)V'_m(x) = (m + \alpha + \beta + 1)[(2m + \alpha + \beta + 2)x + (\alpha - \beta)]V_m(x) + (m + \alpha + \beta + 1)V_{m+1}(x), \quad (8.9.9)$$

from which there follows

$$V_{m+1}(x_i) = \frac{2m + \alpha + \beta + 2}{m + \alpha + \beta + 1}(1 - x_i^2)V'_m(x_i),$$

so that (8.9.7) can also be written in the somewhat simpler form

$$H_i = \frac{\Gamma(m + \alpha + 1)\Gamma(m + \beta + 1)}{\Gamma(m + \alpha + \beta + 1)} \frac{2^{2m+\alpha+\beta+1}m!}{(1 - x_i^2)[V'_m(x_i)]^2}. \quad (8.9.10)$$

As an example, we consider the weighting function

$$w(x) = 1 - x^2, \quad (8.9.11)$$

in which case (8.9.2) gives

$$V_m(x) = (1 - x^2)^{-1}\frac{d^m}{dx^m}(1 - x^2)^{m+1}.$$

By making use of the relationship

$$\frac{d^{r-k}(x^2 - 1)^r}{dx^{r-k}} = 2^r r! \frac{(r - k)!}{(r + k)!}(x^2 - 1)^k \frac{d^k P_r(x)}{dx^k}, \quad (8.9.12)$$

this result can be written in the form

$$V_m(x) = \frac{(-1)^m 2^{m+1}m!}{m + 2}\frac{dP_{m+1}(x)}{dx}.$$

Hence there follows

$$\int_{-1}^{1}(1 - x^2)f(x)\,dx = \sum_{k=1}^{m} H_k f(x_k) + E, \quad (8.9.13)$$

where x_i is the ith zero of $P'_{m+1}(x)$, and where, from (8.9.10) and (8.9.8),

$$H_i = \frac{2(m + 1)(m + 2)}{(1 - x_i^2)[P''_{m+1}(x_i)]^2} \quad (8.9.14)$$

and

$$E = \frac{m!(m + 2)!}{(2m)!}\left[\frac{(m + 1)!}{(2m + 2)!}\right]^2 \frac{2^{2m+3}}{2m + 3} f^{(2m)}(\xi). \quad (8.9.15)$$

Since $P_{m+1}(x)$ satisfies the differential equation

$$(1 - x^2)P''_{m+1}(x) - 2xP'_{m+1}(x) + (m + 1)(m + 2)P_{m+1}(x) = 0,$$

there follows

$$(1 - x_i^2)P''_{m+1}(x_i) = -(m + 1)(m + 2)P_{m+1}(x_i)$$

when $P'_{m+1}(x_i) = 0$, so that (8.9.14) can also be expressed in the form

$$H_i = \frac{2(1 - x_i^2)}{(m + 1)(m + 2)[P_{m+1}(x_i)]^2}. \tag{8.9.16}$$

By making use of the Stirling approximation (3.7.5) to the factorial, and of the fact that $\Gamma(m + k + 1) \equiv (m + k)! \sim m^k m!$ as $m \to \infty$, when k is fixed, we find from (8.9.8) that

$$E \sim \frac{\pi}{2^{2m+\alpha+\beta}} \frac{f^{(2m)}(\zeta)}{(2m)!} \tag{8.9.17}$$

when m is large, in the general case of (8.9.6). This result holds, in particular, in the special cases $\alpha = \beta = 0$ (Legendre-Gauss), $\alpha = \beta = -\frac{1}{2}$ (Chebyshev-Gauss), and $\alpha = \beta = 1$ (8.9.13).

Thus, if $f(x)$ possesses singularities in the finite part of the complex x plane, and if the singularity nearest ξ is at a distance R_ξ from ξ, so that $f^{(2m)}(\xi)$ is generally of the order of magnitude of $(2m)!/R_\xi^{2m}$ when m is large, the magnitude of the error is generally of the order $\pi/(2R_\xi)^{2m}$. Accordingly, if there exists a singularity at distance less than $\frac{1}{2}$ from the segment $(-1,1)$ of the real axis of a complex x plane, the sequence of approximations afforded by increasing values of m may be slowly convergent, or divergent, as in the case of the Newton-Cotes formulas (§3.7). In the Hermite-Gauss quadrature, the error in this case is of the order $\sqrt{\pi}\, m!/(\sqrt{2}\, R_\xi)^{2m}$, while it is of the order $(m!)^2/R_\xi^{2m}$ in the Laguerre-Gauss case. Whereas such errors would increase rapidly with increasing m if R_ξ remained bounded, in both these situations the permissible range of ξ, and hence of R_ξ, is infinite, so that the relevant value of R_ξ may itself increase rapidly in magnitude as m increases, as was noted in §8.7.

8.10. Formulas with Assigned Abscissas. In some applications it is desirable to *prescribe* one or more of the m abscissas to be involved in a quadrature formula. In particular, whereas none of the true Gaussian formulas involves the values of $f(x)$ at the *ends* of the interval, it is sometimes important that one or both of these end values be used. It may be expected that, for each *arbitrarily* prescribed abscissa, the degree of precision generally will be reduced by unity below the maximum value of

$m - 1$. In particular, if *all* abscissas were prescribed at random, the maximum degree of precision would generally be reduced to $m - 1$. Clearly, exceptions occur when the abscissas are preassigned in special ways.

Whereas the Gaussian formulas were derived in §8.4 from the Hermite formulas, by requiring that the m weights $\bar{H}_i$ vanish, a somewhat different approach (which could also have been used in the Gaussian case) is desirable here.

We recall first that the Lagrangian quadrature formula

$$\int_a^b w(x)f(x)\,dx = \sum_{k=1}^{m} W_k f(x_k) + E, \qquad (8.10.1)$$

where
$$\pi(x) = (x - x_1)(x - x_2)\cdots(x - x_m) \qquad (8.10.2)$$

and
$$W_k = \int_a^b w(x)l_i(x)\,dx \equiv \frac{1}{\pi'(x_i)}\int_a^b w(x)\frac{\pi(x)}{x - x_i}\,dx, \qquad (8.10.3)$$

always has a degree of precision of *at least* $m - 1$. Now any function $f(x)$ can be expressed as the sum

$$f(x) = p_{m-1}(x) + \pi(x)f[x_1,x_2,\ \ldots\ ,x_m,x], \qquad (8.10.4)$$

where $p_{m-1}(x)$ is the polynomial, of degree $m - 1$ or less, agreeing with $f(x)$ at the m points $x_1,\ \ldots\ ,\ x_m$, and where $f[x_1,\ \ldots\ ,x_m,x]$ is the mth divided difference of $f(x)$, relative to $x_1,\ \ldots\ ,\ x_m$, defined in Chap. 2. Hence $f(x)$ can be replaced by that sum in (8.10.1). But since the result of replacing $f(x)$ by $p_{m-1}(x)$ will vanish, and since $\pi(x_i) = 0$, we thus obtain the expression

$$E = \int_a^b w(x)\pi(x)f[x_1,\ \ldots\ ,x_m,x]\,dx, \qquad (8.10.5)$$

for the error E in (8.10.1)†

If $f(x)$ is a polynomial of degree $m + r$, its divided difference of order m is a polynomial of degree r, and conversely. Hence we deduce from (8.10.5) that *the quadrature formula* (8.10.1) *has a degree of precision of at least $m + r - 1$ if and only if the polynomial $\pi(x)$, whose m zeros are the abscissas, is orthogonal, relative to $w(x)$, to all polynomials of degree less than r.*

When $r = m$, this result reduces to the result of §8.4 and serves to specify the *Gaussian* quadrature formulas, which were also derivable as special Hermite formulas for which $\bar{H}_i = 0$, and for which also $H_i = W_i$.

Now suppose that $m - r$ of the m abscissas are preassigned, leaving the r "free" abscissas $x_1, x_2,\ \ldots\ ,\ x_r$ to be determined so that the degree

† This result is equivalent to (5.11.34). The derivation is repeated here, for completeness, in the modified notation of the present chapter.

of precision will be maximized. If we write

$$\pi(x) = [(x - x_1) \cdots (x - x_r)][(x - x_{r+1}) \cdots (x - x_m)] \equiv \bar\pi(x)v(x),$$

$$(8.10.6)$$

where
$$\bar\pi(x) = (x - x_1)(x - x_2) \cdots (x - x_r) \qquad (8.10.7)$$

is a polynomial of degree r whose r zeros are the *free* abscissas, which are to be determined, and where

$$v(x) = (x - x_{r+1})(x - x_{r+2}) \cdots (x - x_m) \qquad (8.10.8)$$

is a *known* polynomial, of degree $m - r$, whose zeros are the *preassigned* abscissas, the condition

$$\int_a^b w(x)\pi(x)u_{r-1}(x)\,dx = 0, \qquad (8.10.9)$$

where $u_{r-1}(x)$ is an *arbitrary* polynomial of degree $r - 1$ or less, takes the form

$$\int_a^b [w(x)v(x)]\bar\pi(x)u_{r-1}(x)\,dx = 0. \qquad (8.10.10)$$

Thus we may consider $\bar\pi(x)$ as the appropriate multiple of the rth member of a set of polynomials $\phi_0(x)$, $\phi_1(x)$, . . . , $\phi_r(x)$, . . . , of degrees $0, 1, \ldots, r, \ldots$, respectively, which are orthogonal over (a,b) relative to the *modified weighting function*

$$\bar w(x) = w(x)v(x), \qquad (8.10.11)$$

and the methods of §7.4 are again available for its determination. However, if $v(x)$ changes sign in (a,b), the *modified* weighting function $\bar w(x)$ will have the same property. Thus there is then no assurance that the zeros of $\phi_r(x)$ will be *real* or, if so, that they will lie inside (a,b).

In the important cases for which only one or both of the *end points* $x = a$ and $x = b$ are taken as preassigned abscissas, so that $v(x)$ is given by $x - a, x - b$, or $(x - a)(x - b)$, this difficulty does not arise since then $v(x)$ is of fixed sign in (a,b). Attention will be restricted to these cases in what follows.

In order to evaluate the weights W_i, we write $\bar\pi(x) = \phi_r(x)/A_r$, to take into account the fact that the polynomial $\phi_r(x)$ which is most conveniently employed may not have unity as its highest coefficient, and notice that then

$$\pi(x) = \frac{1}{A_r} v(x)\phi_r(x),$$

where $v(x)$ is defined by (8.10.8). Equation (8.10.3) then becomes

$$W_i = \frac{1}{\{[v(x)\phi_r(x)]'\}_{x=x_i}} \int_a^b w(x) \frac{v(x)\phi_r(x)}{x - x_i}\,dx, \qquad (8.10.12)$$

and is, of course, independent of A_r. For $i = 1, 2, \ldots, r$ the abscissa c_i is a zero of $\phi_r(x)$. Hence there follows

$$W_i = \frac{1}{v(x_i)\phi_r'(x_i)} \int_a^b w(x)v(x) \frac{\phi_r(x)}{x - x_i} \, dx, \qquad (8.10.13)$$

or $i = 1, 2, \ldots, r$, and a comparison of this form with (8.4.22), with n replaced by r and $w(x)$ by $\bar{w}(x)$, leads to the desired result

$$W_i = - \frac{A_{r+1}\bar{\gamma}_r}{A_r v(x_i)\phi_r'(x_i)\phi_{r+1}(x_i)} \qquad (i = 1, 2, \ldots, r), \quad (8.10.14)$$

where A_r is the coefficient of x^r in $\phi_r(x)$, and where

$$\bar{\gamma}_r = \int_a^b \bar{w}(x)[\phi_r(x)]^2 \, dx \equiv \int_a^b w(x)v(x)[\phi_r(x)]^2 \, dx. \quad (8.10.15)$$

Equation (8.10.14) determines all weights except those corresponding to the preassigned abscissas.

In the case when only the abscissa $x = a$ is preassigned, so that $v(x) = x - a$, the corresponding weight is expressed by (8.10.12) in the form

$$W = \frac{1}{\phi_r(a)} \int_a^b w(x)\phi_r(x) \, dx \qquad (x_i = a), \qquad (8.10.16)$$

whereas when only $x = b$ is fixed, so that $v(x) = x - b$, there follows

$$W = \frac{1}{\phi_r(b)} \int_a^b w(x)\phi_r(x) \, dx \qquad (x_i = b). \qquad (8.10.17)$$

In the case when both $x = a$ and $x = b$ are fixed, so that

$$v(x) = (x - a)(x - b),$$

there follows

$$W = \frac{1}{(b - a)\phi_r(a)} \int_a^b (b - x)w(x)\phi_r(x) \, dx \qquad (x_i = a) \qquad (8.10.18)$$

and $$W = \frac{1}{(b - a)\phi_r(b)} \int_a^b (x - a)w(x)\phi_r(x) \, dx \qquad (x_i = b). \qquad (8.10.19)$$

Alternatively, the weights corresponding to the prescribed end ordinate or ordinates can be determined in terms of the remaining weights by use of one or both of the relations

$$\sum_{k=1}^m W_k = \int_a^b w(x) \, dx, \qquad \sum_{k=1}^m x_k W_k = \int_a^b xw(x) \, dx, \quad (8.10.20)$$

which require that the error in (8.10.1) vanish when $f(x) = 1$ and when $f(x) = x$, respectively.

The special cases in which $w(x)$ is constant are treated in the two following sections.

In the general case, it is possible to show that the relevant quadrature formula can be obtained by replacing $f(x)$ in the integrand by the polynomial of degree $m + r - 1$ which agrees with $f(x)$ when $x = x_1, \ldots x_m$ and whose derivative agrees with $f'(x)$ at the unassigned points $x = x_1, \ldots, x_r$. Thus the error can be expressed in the form

$$E = \int_a^b w(x)[(x - x_1) \cdots (x - x_r)]^2(x - x_{r+1}) \cdots (x - x_m)$$
$$\cdot f[x_1,x_1, \ldots ,x_r,x_r,x_{r+1}, \ldots ,x_m,x] \, dx. \quad (8.10.21)$$

In particular, if $w(x) \geqq 0$ in (a,b), if no assigned abscissas lie *inside* (a,b), and if $f^{(m+r)}(x)$ is continuous, there follows also

$$E = \frac{f^{(m+r)}(\xi)}{(m + r)!} \int_a^b w(x)[(x - x_1) \cdots (x - x_r)]^2(x - x_{r+1})$$
$$\cdots (x - x_m) \, dx$$
$$= \frac{f^{(m+r)}(\xi)}{(m + r)!} \int_a^b \bar{w}(x)[\bar{\pi}(x)]^2 \, dx$$
$$= \frac{\bar{\gamma}_r}{A_r^2} \frac{f^{(m+r)}(\xi)}{(m + r)!}, \quad (8.10.22)$$

where ξ lies between the largest and smallest of $x_1, \ldots, x_m$, a, and b.

8.11. Radau Quadrature. In the case of a finite interval, with a unit weighting function, when one end of the interval is assigned as an abscissa, it is again convenient to suppose that the interval has been transformed to $(-1,1)$, with $x = -1$ as the fixed abscissa, by an appropriate change in variables. We then have

$$v(x) = x + 1 \quad (8.11.1)$$
and
$$\pi(x) = (x + 1)\bar{\pi}(x), \quad (8.11.2)$$

where $\bar{\pi}(x)$ is a multiple of the rth member of a set of orthogonal polynomials $\phi_0(x), \phi_1(x), \ldots, \phi_r(x), \ldots$, which has the property

$$\int_{-1}^1 (x + 1)\phi_r(x)u_{r-1}(x) \, dx = 0, \quad (8.11.3)$$

where $u_{r-1}(x)$ is an arbitrary polynomial of degree $r - 1$ or less.

If we follow the procedure of §7.4, by writing

$$(x + 1)\phi_r(x) = \frac{d^r}{dx^r} U_r(x)$$

and integrating the left-hand member of (8.11.3) by parts r times, we find that $U_r(x)$ must satisfy the equation

$$\frac{d^{r+1}}{dx^{r+1}} \left[\frac{1}{x+1} \frac{d^r}{dx^r} U_r \right] = 0$$

and the requirements that U_r, U_r', . . . , $U_r^{(r-1)}$ vanish when $x = \pm 1$, and hence that U_r must be of the form

$$U_r = C_r(x+1)(x^2-1)^r.$$

Thus it follows finally that

$$\phi_r(x) = \frac{C_r}{x+1} \frac{d^r}{dx^r} [(x+1)(x^2-1)^r], \qquad (8.11.4)$$

which can be expressed in the form

$$\phi_r(x) = \frac{C_r}{x+1} \left[(x+1) \frac{d^r}{dx^r} (x^2-1)^r + r \frac{d^{r-1}}{dx^{r-1}} (x^2-1)^r \right]$$

or, by making use of the relationship (8.9.12), in the form

$$\phi_r(x) = 2^r r! C_r \left[P_r(x) + \frac{x-1}{r+1} P_r'(x) \right]. \qquad (8.11.5)$$

It is convenient to take

$$C_r = \frac{1}{2^r r!}. \qquad (8.11.6)$$

Then, noticing that here $r = m - 1$, since only one abscissa is pre-assigned, we conclude that the $m - 1$ free abscissas are the zeros of

$$\phi_{m-1}(x) = \frac{1}{2^{m-1}(m-1)!} \frac{1}{x+1} \frac{d^{m-1}}{dx^{m-1}} [(x+1)^m(x-1)^{m-1}]$$

$$= P_{m-1}(x) + \frac{x-1}{m} P_{m-1}'(x) = \frac{P_{m-1}(x) + P_m(x)}{1+x}, \qquad (8.11.7)$$

where the last form follows from the recurrence formula (8.5.7). The leading coefficient is found to be

$$A_{m-1} = \frac{(2m-1)!}{2^{m-1}m[(m-1)!]^2}. \qquad (8.11.8)$$

With this result, we notice next that

$$\bar{\gamma}_{m-1} = \int_{-1}^{1} (1+x)\phi_{m-1}(x)\phi_{m-1}(x)\, dx$$

$$= A_{m-1} \int_{-1}^{1} x^{m-1}(1+x)\phi_{m-1}(x)\, dx$$

$$= \frac{A_{m-1}}{2^{m-1}(m-1)!} \int_{-1}^{1} x^{m-1} \frac{d^{m-1}}{dx^{m-1}} [(1+x)(x^2-1)^{m-1}]\, dx,$$

and an $(m - 1)$-fold integration by parts, followed by the use of $(8.9.5)$, leads to the simple result

$$\bar{\gamma}_{m-1} = \frac{2}{m}. \tag{8.11.9}$$

Thus, by introducing $(8.11.8)$ and $(8.11.9)$ into $(8.10.14)$, we obtain the weights

$$W_i = - \frac{2(2m + 1)}{m(m + 1)} \frac{1}{(1 + x_i)\phi'_{m-1}(x_i)\phi_m(x_i)} \qquad (x_i \neq -1), \tag{8.11.10}$$

corresponding to the $m - 1$ free abscissas. By making appropriate use of the formula $(8.5.7)$, together with the fact that $\phi_{m-1}(x_i) = 0$ implies

$$P_{m-1}(x_i) = \frac{1 - x_i}{m} P'_{m-1}(x_i) = -P_m(x_i),$$

we find, after some manipulation, that

$$\phi'_{m-1}(x_i) = \frac{2m}{1 - x_i^2} P_{m-1}(x_i), \qquad \phi_m(x_i) = - \frac{2m + 1}{m + 1} P_{m-1}(x_i),$$

so that $(8.11.10)$ reduces to

$$W_i = \frac{1}{m^2} \frac{1 - x_i}{[P_{m-1}(x_i)]^2} = \frac{1}{1 - x_i} \frac{1}{[P'_{m-1}(x_i)]^2} \qquad (x_i \neq -1). \tag{8.11.11}$$

The weight corresponding to the abscissa $x = -1$ follows from $(8.10.16)$ in the form

$$W = \frac{1}{\phi_{m-1}(-1)} \int_{-1}^{1} \phi_{m-1}(x) \, dx \qquad (x_i = -1). \tag{8.11.12}$$

We obtain first

$$\int_{-1}^{1} \phi_{m-1}(x) \, dx = \int_{-1}^{1} \left[P_{m-1}(x) + \frac{x - 1}{m} P'_{m-1}(x) \right] dx$$

or, after integrating the second member by parts and noticing that the first member integrates to zero (when $m > 1$),

$$\int_{-1}^{1} \phi_{m-1}(x) \, dx = \frac{2}{m} P_{m-1}(-1) = \frac{(-1)^{m-1} 2}{m},$$

since $P_{m-1}(-1) = (-1)^{m-1}$. By making use of the additional fact that $P'_{m-1}(-1) = (-1)^m m(m - 1)/2$, we obtain also

$$\phi_{m-1}(-1) = (-1)^{m-1} m, \tag{8.11.13}$$

and hence $(8.11.12)$ becomes

$$W = \frac{2}{m^2} \qquad (x_i = -1). \tag{8.11.14}$$

Thus, in summary, we have obtained the quadrature formula

$$\int_{-1}^{1} f(x) \, dx = \frac{2}{m^2} f(-1) + \sum_{k=1}^{m-1} W_k f(x_k) + E, \qquad (8.11.15)$$

where x_i is the ith zero of the polynomial (8.11.7), and where the weights are defined by (8.11.10) and are *positive*. This formula is one of several attributed to *Radau*.

In order to obtain an expression for the error E, we first specialize (8.10.5) to the form

$$E = \int_{-1}^{1} \pi(x) f[x_1, \ldots, x_m, x] \, dx, \qquad (8.11.16)$$

appropriate to the present case. We have also

$$\pi(x) = (x + 1)\bar{\pi}(x) = \frac{x + 1}{A_{m-1}} \, \phi_{m-1}(x) = \frac{1}{A_{m-1}} \frac{d^{m-1} U(x)}{dx^{m-1}}, \qquad (8.11.17)$$

where

$$U(x) \equiv U_{m-1}(x) = \frac{1}{2^{m-1}(m-1)!} (x + 1)^m (x - 1)^{m-1}. \qquad (8.11.18)$$

Thus (8.11.16) becomes

$$E = \frac{1}{A_{m-1}} \int_{-1}^{1} \frac{d^{m-1} U}{dx^{m-1}} f[x_1, \ldots, x_m, x] \, dx. \qquad (8.11.19)$$

If we integrate by parts $m - 1$ times, making use of the fact that U, U', $\ldots$, $U^{(m-2)}$ all vanish when $x = \pm 1$, and of the fact that

$$\frac{d^{m-1}}{dx^{m-1}} f[x_1, \ldots, x_m, x] = \frac{(m-1)!}{(2m-1)!} f^{(2m-1)}(\eta), \qquad (8.11.20)$$

in accordance with (5.11.36), where $|\eta| < 1$, there follows

$$E = \frac{(-1)^{m-1}(m-1)!}{(2m-1)! A_{m-1}} \int_{-1}^{1} U(x) f^{(2m-1)}(\eta) \, dx. \qquad (8.11.21)$$

Now, since $U(x)$ does not change sign in $(-1,1)$, the second law of the mean can be applied, to give

$$\begin{aligned}
E &= \frac{(-1)^{m-1}(m-1)! f^{(2m-1)}(\xi)}{(2m-1)! A_{m-1}} \int_{-1}^{1} U(x) \, dx \\
&= \frac{(m-1)!}{(2m-1)!} \cdot \frac{2^{m-1} m[(m-1)!]^2}{(2m-1)!} \cdot \frac{1}{2^{m-1}(m-1)!} f^{(2m-1)}(\xi) \\
&\qquad \cdot \int_{-1}^{1} (x + 1)^m (x - 1)^{m-1} \, dx
\end{aligned}$$

or finally, after using (8.9.5),

$$E = \frac{2^{2m-1}m[(m-1)!]^4}{[(2m-1)!]^3} f^{(2m-1)}(\xi) \qquad (|\xi| < 1), \qquad (8.11.22)$$

in accordance with (8.10.22).

The first six of the polynomials (8.11.7) are found to be of the form

$$\phi_0(x) = 1, \qquad \phi_1(x) = \tfrac{1}{2}(3x - 1), \qquad \phi_2(x) = \tfrac{1}{2}(5x^2 - 2x - 1),$$
$$\phi_3(x) = \tfrac{1}{8}(35x^3 - 15x^2 - 15x + 3),$$
$$\phi_4(x) = \tfrac{1}{40}(315x^4 - 140x^3 - 210x^2 + 60x + 15), \qquad (8.11.23)$$
$$\phi_5(x) = \tfrac{1}{16}(231x^5 - 105x^4 - 210x^3 + 70x^2 + 35x - 5),$$

and additional ones can be obtained from the recurrence formula

$$\phi_{r+1}(x) = \frac{1}{(r+2)(2r+1)} \{[(2r+1)(2r+3)x - 1]\phi_r(x)$$
$$- r(2r+3)\phi_{r-1}(x)\}, \qquad (8.11.24)$$

or by reference to (8.11.7).

TABLE 8.4

m	Abscissas	Weights
2	-1	$\tfrac{1}{2}$
	$\tfrac{1}{3}$	$\tfrac{3}{2}$
3	-1	0.222222
	-0.289898	1.024972
	0.689898	0.752806
4	-1	0.125000
	-0.575319	0.657689
	0.181066	0.776387
	0.822824	0.440925
5	-1	0.080000
	-0.720480	0.446207
	-0.167181	0.623653
	0.446314	0.562712
	0.885792	0.287427

In the simplest nontrivial case, $m = 2$, there follows $x_1 = \tfrac{1}{3}$. The weight W_1 is found to be $\tfrac{3}{2}$, and the weight relative to $x = -1$ to be $\tfrac{1}{2}$. Thus, the best two-point formula with $x = -1$ preassigned is of the form

$$\int_{-1}^1 f(x)\, dx = \tfrac{1}{2}f(-1) + \tfrac{3}{2}f(\tfrac{1}{3}) + \tfrac{2}{27}f'''(\xi) \qquad (|\xi| < 1). \quad (8.11.25)$$

By setting $x = 2t - 1$, and writing $f(2t - 1) = F(t)$, we may rewrite this formula in the form

$$\int_0^1 F(t)\,dt = \tfrac{1}{4}F(0) + \tfrac{3}{4}F(\tfrac{2}{3}) + \tfrac{1}{216}F'''(\eta) \qquad (0 < \eta < 1), \quad (8.11.26)$$

and similar forms can be obtained in the other cases.

The abscissas and weights corresponding to formulas for which $2 \leqq m \leqq 5$ are listed, to six digits, in Table 8.4.

8.12. Lobatto Quadrature. In the case when both ends of the interval $(-1,1)$ are preassigned as abscissas, the weighting function being unity, the derivation is quite similar to that of the preceding section.

Thus, with

$$v(x) = x^2 - 1, \qquad (8.12.1)$$

it is found that

$$\phi_r(x) = \frac{C_r}{x^2 - 1}\frac{d^r}{dx^r}(x^2 - 1)^{r+1}, \qquad (8.12.2)$$

and that, in accordance with (8.9.12), if we set

$$C_r = \frac{r+2}{2^{r+1}r!}, \qquad (8.12.3)$$

this result is of the form $\phi_r(x) = P'_{r+1}(x)$. Hence, since here $r = m - 2$, the free abscissas are the zeros of the polynomial

$$\phi_{m-2}(x) = P'_{m-1}(x) = \frac{m}{2^{m-1}(m-2)!}\frac{1}{x^2-1}\frac{d^{m-2}}{dx^{m-2}}(x^2-1)^{m-1}. \quad (8.12.4)$$

The additional results

$$A_{m-2} = \frac{(2m-2)!}{2^{m-1}(m-1)!(m-2)!} \qquad (8.12.5)$$

and

$$\bar{\gamma}_{m-2} = -\frac{2m(m-1)}{2m-1}, \qquad (8.12.6)$$

the negative sign in (8.12.6) being a consequence of the fact that here $v(x)$ is negative in $(-1,1)$, are obtained by methods similar to those of the preceding section. Next the weights corresponding to the *free* abscissas are obtained in the form

$$W_i = -\frac{2m}{(1-x_i^2)P''_{m-1}(x_i)P'_m(x_i)} \qquad (x_i \neq \pm 1),$$

which can be rewritten more conveniently as

$$W_i = \frac{2}{m(m-1)[P_{m-1}(x_i)]^2} \qquad (x_i \neq \pm 1). \qquad (8.12.7)$$

The weights corresponding to the fixed abscissas $x = \pm 1$ are found to be equal and to have the value

$$W = \frac{P_{m-1}(1)}{P'_{m-1}(1)} = -\frac{P_{m-1}(-1)}{P'_{m-1}(-1)} = \frac{2}{m(m-1)} \qquad (x_i = \pm 1), \quad (8.12.8)$$

which is the same as that given by the right-hand member of (8.12.7) when $x_i = \pm 1$.

The corresponding quadrature formula,

$$\int_{-1}^{1} f(x)\, dx = \frac{2}{m(m-1)} [f(1) + f(-1)] + \sum_{k=1}^{m-2} W_k f(x_k) + E, \quad (8.12.9)$$

where x_i is the ith zero of $P'_{m-1}(x)$, and W_i is given by (8.12.7) and is *positive*, is known as *Lobatto's quadrature formula*.

In order to obtain an expression for the error E, we may notice that here

$$\pi(x) = \frac{1}{A_{m-2}} \frac{d^{m-2}U}{dx^{m-2}} \quad \text{where } U = \frac{m}{2^{m-1}(m-2)!} (x^2 - 1)^{m-1}, \quad (8.12.10)$$

and hence, from (8.10.5), we have

$$E = \frac{1}{A_{m-2}} \int_{-1}^{1} \frac{d^{m-2}U}{dx^{m-2}} f[x_1, \ldots, x_m, x]\, dx$$

$$= \frac{(-1)^{m-2}(m-2)!}{(2m-2)! A_{m-2}} \int_{-1}^{1} U(x) f^{(2m-2)}(\eta)\, dx$$

$$= \frac{(-1)^{m-2}(m-2)! f^{(2m-2)}(\xi)}{(2m-2)! A_{m-2}} \int_{-1}^{1} U(x)\, dx$$

or, finally,

$$E = - \frac{m(m-1)^3 2^{2m-1}[(m-2)!]^4}{(2m-1)[(2m-2)!]^3} f^{(2m-2)}(\xi) \qquad (|\xi| < 1), \quad (8.12.11)$$

in accordance with (8.10.22), by arguments completely analogous to those used in deducing (8.11.22).

In the simplest nontrivial case, $m = 3$, the free abscissa is found from the equation $P'_2(x) \equiv 3x = 0$ to be $x = 0$, as would be expected from the symmetry. The corresponding weight is found to be $\frac{4}{3}$, whereas the weights corresponding to $x = \pm 1$ are each $\frac{1}{3}$. Hence, as also might have been anticipated, the Lobatto formula reduces in this simple case to *Simpson's rule*.

The abscissas and weights corresponding to formulas for which $3 \leq m \leq 6$ are listed, to six digits, in Table 8.5. More elaborate tabulations are listed in the references.

When the Lobatto formula is applied to a function $f(x)$ which *vanishes* at both ends of the interval of integration, so that only $r \equiv m - 2$ ordinates are actually involved in the calculation, the degree of precision is $2m - 3 = 2r + 1$. Similarly, when the Radau formula is applied to an integrand which vanishes at the lower limit, so that $r \equiv m - 1$ ordinates are used, the degree of precision is $2m - 2 = 2r$. Thus, in such cases, a higher effective degree of precision is attained than that afforded

TABLE 8.5

m	Abscissas	Weights
3	0	$\frac{4}{3}$
	± 1	$\frac{1}{3}$
4	± 0.447214	$\frac{5}{6}$
	± 1	$\frac{1}{6}$
5	0	$\frac{32}{45}$
	± 0.654654	$\frac{49}{90}$
	± 1	$\frac{1}{10}$
6	± 0.285232	0.554858
	± 0.765055	0.378475
	± 1	0.066667

by the formulas of Gaussian type, in which the use of r ordinates leads to a degree of precision of $2r - 1$.

8.13. Chebyshev Quadrature. By imposing various restrictions on the abscissas and/or weights in a formula of the type (8.10.1), various classes of quadrature formulas may be obtained in addition to those so far considered. In this connection, it may be noticed that, if the abscissas are required to be *equally spaced*, the Newton-Cotes formulas of Chap. 3 are obtained when $w(x) = 1$. In this case, m abscissas are fixed and the degree of precision may be expected to be reduced from $2m - 1$ to $m - 1$. However, as was seen in Chap. 3, when m is *odd*, so that the *mid-point* of the interval is one of the abscissas, the degree of precision is increased to m.†

Another important class of formulas, associated with the name of Chebyshev, is that in which all the *weights* are made equal. This situation is desirable, not only for convenience, but also in order that the effects of errors in the ordinates will be minimized. Here the common weight and the m abscissas are "free," and it may be expected that a formula with a degree of precision of at least m may be determinable. However, this expectation is not always to be realized.

We suppose again that the original interval has been transformed into $(-1,1)$, so that the desired formula is of the form

$$\int_{-1}^{1} w(x)f(x)\,dx = W \sum_{k=1}^{m} f(x_k) + E[f(x)], \qquad (8.13.1)$$

where W is the common weight. It may be noticed first that the weight W cannot be assigned, if the degree of precision is to be positive, but is

† It should be recalled that m here corresponds to $n + 1$ in Chap. 3.

determined by the requirement that $E = 0$ when $f(x) = 1$, in the form

$$W = \frac{\lambda}{m} \qquad \text{where } \lambda = \int_{-1}^{1} w(x) \, dx. \qquad (8.13.2)$$

Now we *assume* that a set of m abscissas x_i exists in $(-1,1)$ such that the degree of precision is indeed at least m, and, as before, we write

$$\pi(x) = (x - x_1)(x - x_2) \cdots (x - x_m). \qquad (8.13.3)$$

Then, following the derivation of Chebyshev, we identify $f(x)$ in particular with the special function

$$f(x) = \frac{1}{u - x} \qquad (u > 1), \qquad (8.13.4)$$

in which case (8.13.1) becomes

$$\int_{-1}^{1} w(x) \, \frac{dx}{u - x} = \frac{\lambda}{m} \sum_{k=1}^{m} \frac{1}{u - x_k} + E\left[\frac{1}{u - x}\right]. \qquad (8.13.5)$$

The reason for choosing the special function $1/(u - x)$ is now seen if we notice that, since

$$\log \pi(u) = \sum_{k=1}^{m} \log (u - x_k),$$

the finite sum in (8.13.5) can be expressed as

$$\frac{d}{du} \log \pi(u),$$

and hence that equation becomes

$$\int_{-1}^{1} w(x) \, \frac{dx}{u - x} = \frac{\lambda}{m} \frac{d}{du} [\log \pi(u)] + E\left[\frac{1}{u - x}\right] \qquad (8.13.6)$$

or, after an integration with respect to u,

$$\int_{-1}^{1} w(x) \log (u - x) \, dx = \text{const} + \frac{\lambda}{m} \log \pi(u) - Q(u), \qquad (8.13.7)$$

where
$$Q(u) = \int_{u}^{\infty} E \, du. \qquad (8.13.8)$$

Equation (8.13.7) can be resolved in the form

$$\pi(u) = C_m \exp \left[\frac{m}{\lambda} \int_{-1}^{1} w(x) \log (u - x) \, dx + \frac{m}{\lambda} Q(u)\right],$$

or, equivalently, in the form

$$\pi(u) = C_m u^m \exp\left[\frac{m}{\lambda} \int_{-1}^{1} w(x) \log\left(1 - \frac{x}{u}\right) dx\right] \exp\left[\frac{m}{\lambda} Q(u)\right]. \quad (8.13.9)$$

Now the error term in (8.13.6) is expressible in the form

$$E\left[\frac{1}{u - x}\right] = \int_{-1}^{1} G(s) \frac{d^{m+1}}{ds^{m+1}}\left(\frac{1}{u - s}\right) ds$$

$$= (m + 1)! \int_{-1}^{1} G(s) \frac{ds}{(u - s)^{m+2}}, \quad (8.13.10)$$

where $G(s)$ is the influence function defined by the relation

$$m!G(s) = \int_{s}^{1} w(x)(x - s)^m \, dx - \frac{\lambda}{m} \sum_{x_k \geq s} (x_k - s)^m, \quad (8.13.11)$$

in accordance with (5.11.15) and (5.11.16). Accordingly, there follows

$$Q(u) = \int_{u}^{\infty} E \, du = m! \int_{-1}^{1} G(s) \frac{ds}{(u - s)^{m+1}}. \quad (8.13.12)$$

For present purposes, it is not necessary to evaluate this expression explicitly. However, it is important to notice that it can be expanded in the form

$$Q(u) = m! \frac{1}{u^{m+1}} \int_{-1}^{1} G(s)\left[1 + (m + 1)\frac{s}{u} + \frac{(m + 1)(m + 2)}{2!}\frac{s^2}{u^2}\right.$$
$$\left. + \cdots\right] ds$$

$$= \frac{g_0}{u^{m+1}} + \frac{g_1}{u^{m+2}} + \cdots, \quad (8.13.13)$$

since $u > 1$, where the coefficient g_k is a certain multiple of $\int_{-1}^{1} s^k G(s) \, ds$.

Similarly, we see that

$$\int_{-1}^{1} w(x) \log\left(1 - \frac{x}{u}\right) dx = -\int_{-1}^{1} w(x)\left(\frac{x}{u} + \frac{x^2}{2u^2} + \cdots\right) dx$$

$$= -\frac{c_1}{u} - \frac{c_2}{2u^2} - \cdots, \quad (8.13.14)$$

when $u > 1$, where

$$c_k = \int_{-1}^{1} x^k w(x) \, dx. \quad (8.13.15)$$

Hence (8.13.9) can be expanded in the form

$$\pi(u) = C_m u^m \exp\left[-\frac{m}{\lambda}\left(\frac{c_1}{u} + \frac{c_2}{2u^2} + \cdots\right)\right]$$

$$\cdot \exp\left[\frac{m}{\lambda}\left(\frac{g_0}{u^{m+1}} + \frac{g_1}{u^{m+2}} + \cdots\right)\right]$$

$$= C_m u^m \left(1 - \frac{m}{\lambda}\frac{c_1}{u} + \cdots\right)\left(1 + \frac{m}{\lambda}\frac{g_0}{u^{m+1}} + \cdots\right), \qquad (8.13.16)$$

where the two relevant power series in u^{-1} converge when $u > 1$. But, since $\pi(u)$ is a *polynomial* of degree m, the *product* of the two series will *terminate* before the term containing u^{-m-1}. Thus the terms in the second series, after the leading term, therefore do not enter into the determination of the terms which will remain in the product, but serve only to bring about the cancellation of all terms involving u^{-m-1}, u^{-m-2}, and so forth. Hence the second series can be disregarded, and the desired polynomial can be obtained by merely *terminating* the first series with the term involving u^{-m}. Also, since the coefficient of u^m in $\pi(u)$ is to be unity, we must take $C_m = 1$.

It thus follows that *if $\pi(x)$ exists such that (8.13.1) has a degree of precision of at least m, then $\pi(x)$ is defined by the expansion*

$$\exp\left[\frac{m}{\lambda}\int_{-1}^{1} w(t)\log(x-t)\,dt\right] \equiv x^m \exp\left[\frac{m}{\lambda}\int_{-1}^{1} w(t)\log\left(1 - \frac{t}{x}\right)dt\right]$$

$$\equiv x^m \exp\left[-\frac{m}{\lambda}\left(\frac{c_1}{x} + \frac{c_2}{2x^2} + \cdots\right)\right] \equiv x^m - \frac{mc_1}{\lambda}x^{m-1} - \cdots,$$

$$(8.13.17)$$

where the last series is to be terminated with the last term having a nonnegative exponent.

In the special case when

$$w(x) = 1, \qquad (8.13.18)$$

and hence also

$$\lambda = 2, \qquad W = \frac{2}{m}, \qquad (8.13.19)$$

the first four terms of the expansion of

$$x^m \exp\left[\frac{m}{2}\int_{-1}^{1}\log\left(1 - \frac{t}{x}\right)dt\right]$$

$$= x^m \exp\left[-m\left(\frac{1}{6x^2} + \frac{1}{20x^4} + \frac{1}{42x^6} + \cdots\right)\right]$$

are found to be

$$\pi(x) = x^m - \frac{m}{6}x^{m-2} + \frac{m}{360}(5m - 18)x^{m-4}$$

$$- \frac{m}{45360}(35m^2 - 378m + 1080)x^{m-6} + \cdots, \qquad (8.13.20)$$

where the series is to be terminated with the first term if $m = 0$ or 1, with the second if $m = 2$ or 3, and so forth. If the mth such polynomial is denoted here by $G_m(x)$, the first six such polynomials are thus obtained as follows:

$$G_0(x) = 1, \qquad G_1(x) = x, \qquad G_2(x) = \tfrac{1}{3}(3x^2 - 1),$$
$$G_3(x) = \tfrac{1}{2}(2x^3 - x), \qquad G_4(x) = \tfrac{1}{45}(45x^4 - 30x^2 + 1), \qquad (8.13.21)$$
$$G_5(x) = \tfrac{1}{72}(72x^5 - 60x^3 + 7x).$$

It is seen that the polynomials of even and odd degrees are even and odd functions of x, respectively, so that their zeros are symmetrically placed about $x = 0$.

It has been found that the zeros of the polynomials $G_1(x)$, $G_2(x)$, . . . , $G_7(x)$ and $G_9(x)$ are all real, that they lie inside the interval $(-1,1)$, and that the quadrature formula (8.13.1), with abscissas identified with a set of such zeros, accordingly does indeed have a degree of precision equal to or greater than the number of abscissas, when $w(x) = 1$. However, *six of the zeros of $G_8(x)$ are complex, and each $G_m(x)$ for $m \geqq 10$ possesses at least one pair of complex zeros* (see Bernstein [36]). Thus, when $w(x) = 1$, the quadrature formula is useful only when $m \leqq 7$ and $m = 9$.

The abscissas corresponding to the formula

$$\int_{-1}^{1} f(x)\, dx = \frac{2}{m} \sum_{k=1}^{m} f(x_k) + E, \qquad (8.13.22)$$

for all relevant values of m, are listed to six digits in Table 8.6.

TABLE 8.6

m	Abscissas	m	Abscissas
2	± 0.577350	7	0
			± 0.323912
3	0		± 0.529657
	± 0.707107		± 0.883862
4	± 0.187592	9	0
	± 0.794654		± 0.167906
			± 0.528762
5	0		± 0.601019
	± 0.374541		± 0.911589
	± 0.832497		
6	± 0.266635		
	± 0.422519		
	± 0.866247		

Whereas the appropriate error term in each case can be expressed in the form

$$E = \int_{-1}^{1} G(s) f^{(m+1)}(s)\, ds, \qquad (8.13.23)$$

where $G(s)$ is defined by (8.13.11), with $w(x) = 1$, recourse to the third method of §5.11 leads more simply to the desired results. For this purpose, we may notice first that, since the coefficient of x^m in $G_m(x)$ is unity, there follows $w(x)\pi(x) = G_m(x)$. Further, by integrating the expressions given in (8.13.21), and determining the constant of integration in each case such that the integral vanishes at one (and hence both) of the limits ± 1, there follows

$$G_1(x) = [\tfrac{1}{2}(x^2 - 1)]', \quad G_2(x) = [\tfrac{1}{3}(x^3 - x)]' = [\tfrac{1}{12}(x^2 - 1)^2]'',$$
$$G_3(x) = [\tfrac{1}{4}x^2(x^2 - 1)]', \quad G_4(x) = [\tfrac{1}{45}(9x^5 - 10x^3 + x)]' \qquad (8.13.24)$$
$$= [\tfrac{1}{90}(x^2 - 1)^2(1 + 3x^2)]'',$$
$$G_5(x) = [\tfrac{1}{144}(x^2 - 1)(24x^4 - 6x^2 + 1)]',$$

and so forth. Thus, when m is *odd*, there follows $G_m(x) = V'_m(x)$, where V_m vanishes at the ends of the interval $(-1,1)$ and is of constant sign inside that interval, whereas, when m is *even*, there follows $G_m(x) = V''_m(x)$, where V_m and V'_m vanish at the ends of the interval and V_m is of constant sign in the interior.

It follows from (5.11.38), with $n + 1 = m$, that the error E_m associated with an m-point formula is given by

$$E_m = \begin{cases} c_m \dfrac{f^{(m+1)}(\xi)}{(m + 1)!} & (m \text{ odd}), \\[2mm] c_m \dfrac{f^{(m+2)}(\xi)}{(m + 2)!} & (m \text{ even}), \end{cases} \qquad (8.13.25)$$

where $\quad c_m = \begin{cases} -\displaystyle\int_{-1}^{1} V_m(x)\,dx = \int_{-1}^{1} xG_m(x)\,dx & (m \text{ odd}), \\[2mm] 2\displaystyle\int_{-1}^{1} V_m(x)\,dx = \int_{-1}^{1} x^2G_m(x)\,dx & (m \text{ even}). \end{cases} \qquad (8.13.26)$

The first six of these values are found to be $c_1 = \tfrac{2}{3}$, $c_2 = \tfrac{8}{45}$, $c_3 = \tfrac{1}{15}$, $c_4 = \tfrac{32}{945}$, $c_5 = \tfrac{13}{756}$, $c_6 = \tfrac{16}{1575}$.

In the case $m = 2$, formula (8.13.22) reduces to the Legendre-Gauss two-point formula. It may be noticed that the degree of precision is m when m is odd, but is $m + 1$ when m is even. More generally, whenever $w(x)$ is an even function of x, it is apparent from the symmetry that both members of (8.13.1) will vanish when $f(x)$ is any polynomial of odd degree (or any odd function of x). Hence, in such cases, if m is even and if the degree of precision is at least m, then it is also at least $m + 1$.†

The Chebyshev-Gauss formula of §8.8, with $w(x) = (1 - x^2)^{-\frac{1}{2}}$, is a particularly notable member of the general class of formulas considered

---

† The difference between this situation and that relevant to Newton-Cotes quadrature is a consequence of the fact that there the *minimum* degree of precision is $m - 1$, where m ordinates are used. Thus an increase of (at least) one degree occurs if $m - 1$ is even, and hence m is *odd*.

in this section, since in that case it was seen that *the degree of precision attains its maximum value* $2m - 1$, in spite of the fact that the weights are equal. It can be rederived here by noticing that (8.13.2) gives $\lambda = \pi$, and hence $W = \pi/m$, in accordance with (8.8.11). Equation (8.13.17) then gives

$$\exp\left[\frac{m}{\lambda}\int_{-1}^{1} w(t)\log(x - t)\,dt\right] = \exp\left[\frac{m}{\pi}\int_{-1}^{1} \frac{\log(x - t)}{\sqrt{1 - t^2}}\,dt\right]$$

$$= \exp\left[m\log\left(\frac{x + \sqrt{x^2 - 1}}{2}\right)\right] = \left(\frac{x + \sqrt{x^2 - 1}}{2}\right)^m$$

$$= \frac{x^m}{2^m}\left(1 + \sqrt{1 - \frac{1}{x^2}}\right)^m = x^m\left(1 - \frac{1}{4x^2} + \cdots\right)^m$$

$$= x^m - \frac{m}{4}x^{m-2} + \cdots,$$

when $x > 1$, and the *polynomial part* of the last indicated expansion can be shown to be identical with the expanded form of

$$2^{1-m}T_m(x) = 2^{1-m}\cos(m\cos^{-1}x).$$

8.14. Algebraic Derivations. Any specific one of the quadrature formulas considered in this chapter can be obtained directly by purely algebraic methods, without the use of properties of orthogonal functions. In cases in which the weighting function is given empirically, or in which only a single specific formula is desired, such methods are often to be preferred. For this reason, they are discussed briefly in this section.

We suppose here that the formula is to be of the form

$$\int_{a}^{b} w(x)f(x)\,dx = \sum_{k=1}^{m} W_k f(x_k) + E, \qquad (8.14.1)$$

where $w(x) \geqq 0$ in (a,b), and that the abscissas and weights are to be chosen in such a way that the degree of precision is *at least* $m - 1$, so that $E = 0$ at least when $f(x) = x^r$ $(r = 0, 1, \ldots, m - 1)$. If we define the rth *moment* M_r, associated with $w(x)$ over (a,b), by the equation

$$\int_{a}^{b} x^r w(x)\,dx = M_r \qquad (r = 0, 1, 2, \ldots), \qquad (8.14.2)$$

the requirement that the degree of precision of (8.14.1) be at least N is represented by the $N + 1$ conditions

$$\sum_{k=1}^{m} W_k x_k^r = M_r \qquad (r = 0, 1, \ldots, N). \qquad (8.14.3)$$

Whereas these equations are linear in the m weights W_i, they are non-linear in the m abscissas x_i, and the purpose of this section is to indicate in what way the difficulties associated with this nonlinearity can be minimized.

The procedures to be used, in those situations in which no conditions are imposed on the *weights*, may be easily generalized from the simple case in which $m = 2$. Hence, in order to simplify the notation, we consider that case specifically, but describe the procedures in general terms.

The *simplest case*, clearly, is that in which the m abscissas are pre-assigned. Then, unless they are chosen in a special way, we can require only that the degree of precision N be at least $m - 1$. When $m = 2$, the two conditions to be satisfied are then

$$\begin{aligned} W_1 + W_2 &= M_0, \\ W_1 x_1 + W_2 x_2 &= M_1. \end{aligned} \tag{8.14.4}$$

Since the abscissas are assigned, we have m simultaneous *linear* equations in the m unknown weights, and it can be shown that these equations always possess a unique solution.

On the other extreme, we have the *Gaussian case*, in which no constraints are imposed and in which the degree of precision is to be $2m - 1$. In the case $m = 2$, the four conditions to be satisfied are then of the form

$$\begin{aligned} W_1 + W_2 &= M_0, \\ W_1 x_1 + W_2 x_2 &= M_1, \\ W_1 x_1^2 + W_2 x_2^2 &= M_2, \\ W_1 x_1^3 + W_2 x_2^3 &= M_3, \end{aligned} \tag{8.14.5}$$

representing four equations in the four unknown quantities x_1, x_2, W_1, and W_2. In order to solve these equations, we let x_1 and x_2 be the zeros of $\pi(x)$,

$$\pi(x) = (x - x_1)(x - x_2) \equiv x^2 + \alpha_1 x + \alpha_2, \tag{8.14.6}$$

and attempt first to determine the *coefficients* α_1 and α_2. If we multiply the third equation of (8.14.5) by 1, the second by α_1, and the first by α_2, and add the results, making use of the fact that

$$x_1^2 + \alpha_1 x_1 + \alpha_2 = 0, \qquad x_2^2 + \alpha_1 x_2 + \alpha_2 = 0,$$

we obtain the condition

$$M_2 + M_1 \alpha_1 + M_0 \alpha_2 = 0. \tag{8.14.7}$$

Similarly, from the fourth, third, and second equations we obtain the requirement

$$M_3 + M_2 \alpha_1 + M_1 \alpha_2 = 0. \tag{8.14.8}$$

The last two equations are *linear* in α_1 and α_2. If $M_1^2 \neq M_0 M_2$, they possess a unique solution. The abscissas x_1 and x_2 are then determined as the roots of the algebraic equation $\pi(x) = 0$, and the weights W_1 and W_2 are finally determined from any two (say the first two) equations of (8.14.5).

The generalization is obvious, since, in the general case, $\pi(x)$ will be specified by m α's and the $2m$ equations replacing (8.14.5) will provide m sets of $m + 1$ successive equations, from each of which a *linear* equation in the α's may be obtained by the same general procedure as that which led to (8.14.7). These equations will (generally) determine the α's, after which the abscissas are obtained as the roots of $\pi(x) = 0$ and, finally, the first m of the basic equations determine the weights.

In the *intermediate cases*, in which, say, $m - r$ of the m abscissas are preassigned, we can hope only for a degree of precision $m + r - 1$ (unless those abscissas are assigned in a special way), and hence there will be $m + r$ basic equations replacing (8.14.5). If we again let $\pi(x)$ denote the product $(x - x_1)(x - x_2) \cdots (x - x_m)$, involving the fixed abscissas as well as the free ones, then $\pi(x)$ will again be specified by m α's. From the $m + r$ basic equations, we can proceed as in the derivation of (8.14.7) r times, and hence can obtain r linear equations in the α's. The $m - r$ additional linear equations needed for the determination of the m α's then follow from the requirements that the $m - r$ fixed abscissas satisfy the equation $\pi(x) = 0$.

Thus, in the case $m = 2$, $r = 1$, the three basic equations are

$$\begin{aligned} W_1 + W_2 &= M_0, \\ W_1 x_1 + W_2 x_2 &= M_1, \\ W_1 x_1^2 + W_2 x_2^2 &= M_2. \end{aligned} \qquad (8.14.9)$$

Under the assumption that x_1 and x_2 satisfy the equation

$$x^2 + \alpha_1 x + \alpha_2 = 0, \qquad (8.14.10)$$

we again obtain (8.14.7). By combining this condition with the requirement that the preassigned value x_1 satisfy (8.14.10), we deduce that α_1 and α_2 are determined uniquely by the two linear equations

$$\begin{aligned} M_2 + M_1 \alpha_1 + M_0 \alpha_2 &= 0, \\ x_1^2 + x_1 \alpha_1 + \alpha_2 &= 0, \end{aligned} \qquad (8.14.11)$$

under the assumption that $M_0 x_1 \neq M_1$.

There is no guarantee, in this case, that the zeros of $\pi(x)$ will be real and distinct or, if so, that they will lie in (a,b). However, if a quadrature formula of the type sought exists, it can be obtained by the method outlined.

As a simple illustrative example, we suppose that a quadrature formula is required to be of the form

$$\int_0^1 x^{\frac{1}{2}}f(x)\,dx = W_1f(x_1) + W_2f(1) + E, \qquad (8.14.12)$$

where $x_2 = 1$ is preassigned. The expected degree of precision is then two, corresponding to the fact that three free parameters x_1, W_1, and W_2 are available. We first calculate the relevant moments,

$$M_r = \int_0^1 x^{(2r+1)/2}\,dx = \frac{2}{2r+3} \qquad (r = 0, 1, 2),$$

after which the three basic conditions (8.14.9) become

$$W_1 + W_2 = \tfrac{2}{3}, \qquad W_1x_1 + W_2 = \tfrac{2}{5}, \qquad W_1x_1^2 + W_2 = \tfrac{2}{7}. \quad (8.14.13)$$

By writing $\pi(x) = (x - x_1)(x - 1) = x^2 + \alpha_1 x + \alpha_2$, we deduce from (8.14.11) that α_1 and α_2 must satisfy the equations

$$\tfrac{2}{7} + \tfrac{2}{5}\alpha_1 + \tfrac{2}{3}\alpha_2 = 0,$$
$$1 + \alpha_1 + \alpha_2 = 0,$$

and obtain $\alpha_1 = -\tfrac{10}{7}$, $\alpha_2 = \tfrac{3}{7}$, and hence $\pi(x) = (7x^2 - 10x + 3)/7$. Thus there follows

$$x_1 = \tfrac{3}{7}, \qquad x_2 = 1. \qquad (8.14.14)$$

With these results, the first two equations of (8.14.13) give

$$W_1 = \tfrac{7}{15}, \qquad W_2 = \tfrac{1}{5}. \qquad (8.14.15)$$

Thus (8.14.12) becomes

$$\int_0^1 x^{\frac{1}{2}}f(x)\,dx = \tfrac{7}{15}f(\tfrac{3}{7}) + \tfrac{1}{5}f(1) + E. \qquad (8.14.16)$$

We verify that $E = 0$ for $f(x) = 1$, x, and x^2, and find that $E \neq 0$ when $f(x) = x^3$. Hence $N = 2$.

In order to obtain an expression for the error term E, we may make use of one of the methods of §5.11. In particular, the influence function (5.11.16) is readily determined in the form

$$G(s) = \begin{cases} -\tfrac{8}{105}s^{\frac{7}{2}} & (0 \leqq s \leqq \tfrac{3}{7}), \\ -\tfrac{1}{210}(16s^{\frac{7}{2}} - 49s^2 + 42s - 9) & (\tfrac{3}{7} \leqq s \leqq 1), \end{cases} \qquad (8.14.17)$$

and is found to be negative throughout the interior of the interval $(0,1)$. Thus the formula (5.11.31) can be used, to give

$$E = \frac{f'''(\xi)}{3!}\left[\int_0^1 x^{\frac{1}{2}}\,dx - \tfrac{7}{15}(\tfrac{3}{7})^3 - \tfrac{1}{5}(1)^3\right] = -\tfrac{16}{6615}f'''(\xi), \qquad (8.14.18)$$

where $0 < \xi < 1$.

The same result can be obtained somewhat more easily by use of the third method described in §5.11. For we find that

$$w(x)\pi(x) = \frac{d}{dx}\left[\tfrac{2}{7}x^{\frac{3}{2}}(x-1)^2\right],$$

where the constant of integration is determined so that the content of the brackets vanishes when $x = 0$. Since it vanishes also when $x = 1$, and is positive for all intermediate values of x, we may make use of (5.11.38), with $n + 1 \equiv m = 2$, $r = 1$, and $V = \tfrac{2}{7}x^{\frac{3}{2}}(x - 1)^2$, to deduce that

$$E = -\frac{f'''(\xi)}{6}\int_0^1 \tfrac{2}{7}x^{\frac{3}{2}}(x-1)^2\, dx = -\tfrac{16}{6615}f'''(\xi),$$

as before.

Finally, in the general case of *Chebyshev quadrature*, in which all the weights are to be equal, the formula is of the form

$$\int_a^b w(x)f(x)\, dx = W\sum_{k=1}^m f(x_k) + E, \qquad (8.14.19)$$

and the $m + 1$ conditions requiring that the degree of precision be at least m are of the form

$$
\begin{aligned}
x_1^0 + x_2^0 + x_3^0 + \cdots + x_m^0 &= \bar{M}_0,\\
x_1 + x_2 + x_3 + \cdots + x_m &= \bar{M}_1,\\
x_1^2 + x_2^2 + x_3^2 + \cdots + x_m^2 &= \bar{M}_2, \qquad (8.14.20)\\
&\cdots\cdots\cdots\cdots\cdots\cdots\\
x_1^m + x_2^m + x_3^m + \cdots + x_m^m &= \bar{M}_m,
\end{aligned}
$$

where we have written

$$\bar{M}_r = \frac{1}{W}M_r = \frac{1}{W}\int_a^b x^r w(x)\, dx. \qquad (8.14.21)$$

From the first equation, there follows immediately $\bar{M}_0 = m$, and hence

$$W = \frac{1}{m}\int_a^b w(x)\, dx = \frac{1}{m}M_0. \qquad (8.14.22)$$

Under the *assumption* that the problem possesses a (real) solution,† we again write

$$
\begin{aligned}
\pi(x) &= (x - x_1)(x - x_2)\cdots(x - x_m)\\
&\equiv x^m + \alpha_1 x^{m-1} + \alpha_2 x^{m-2} + \cdots + \alpha_{m-1}x + \alpha_m, \qquad (8.14.23)
\end{aligned}
$$

and attempt to determine the m coefficients $\alpha_1, \ldots, \alpha_m$.

† As was pointed out in §8.13, this assumption is not always valid.

First, by multiplying the first equation in (8.14.20) by α_m, the second by α_{m-1}, . . . , the next-to-last by α_1, and the last by 1, adding the results, and using the fact that each x_i satisfies $\pi(x) = 0$, we obtain one linear equation relating the α's in the form

$$\bar{M}_m + \bar{M}_{m-1}\alpha_1 + \bar{M}_{m-2}\alpha_2 + \cdots + \bar{M}_1\alpha_{m-1} + m\alpha_m = 0. \quad (8.14.24)$$

In order to obtain $m - 1$ complementary relations, we require certain results from the theory of so-called *symmetric functions*. We recall that the coefficients in (8.14.23) are related to the zeros of $\pi(x)$ by the equations

$$\begin{aligned}
x_1 + x_2 + x_3 + \cdots + x_m &= -\alpha_1, \\
x_1x_2 + x_1x_3 + \cdots + x_{m-1}x_m &= \alpha_2, \\
x_1x_2x_3 + x_1x_2x_4 + \cdots + x_{m-2}x_{m-1}x_m &= -\alpha_3, \\
\cdots \cdots \cdots \cdots \cdots \cdots \cdots \cdots \\
x_1x_2 \cdots x_m &= (-1)^m\alpha_m,
\end{aligned} \quad (8.14.25)$$

where the left-hand member of the rth equation is the sum of all products of r of the roots and is known as the rth *elementary symmetric function* of $x_1, x_2, \ldots, x_m$. The left-hand members of (8.14.20) are also symmetric functions of the zeros, since they are unchanged when any two of the symbols $x_1, \ldots, x_m$ are interchanged, and it is known that the rth member of either set can be expressed as a polynomial function of the first r members of the other set.

In particular, we have immediately

$$\alpha_1 = -\bar{M}_1, \quad (8.14.26)$$

and it is easily seen that

$$\alpha_2 = \tfrac{1}{2}(\bar{M}_1^2 - \bar{M}_2) = -\tfrac{1}{2}(\bar{M}_1\alpha_1 + \bar{M}_2). \quad (8.14.27)$$

These relations, as well as that of (8.14.24), are special cases of the general recurrence formula

$$r\alpha_r + \bar{M}_1\alpha_{r-1} + \bar{M}_2\alpha_{r-2} + \cdots + \bar{M}_{r-1}\alpha_1 + \bar{M}_r = 0 \quad (r = 1, 2, \ldots), \quad (8.14.28)$$

which permits the expression of each of the α's in terms of the *reduced moments* $\bar{M}_1, \bar{M}_2, \ldots$, and $\bar{M}_m$. The required abscissas are then the roots of the equation

$$x^m + \alpha_1 x^{m-1} + \alpha_2 x^{m-2} + \cdots + \alpha_{m-1}x + \alpha_m = 0, \quad (8.14.29)$$

if those roots are real and distinct. Otherwise, the desired formula does not exist.

In illustration, in order to determine the Chebyshev abscissas for the quadrature formula

$$\int_{-1}^{1} (1 - x^2)f(x)\, dx = W[f(x_1) + f(x_2) + f(x_3)] + E, \quad (8.14.30)$$

we first calculate the common weight,

$$W = \tfrac{1}{3} \int_{-1}^{1} (1 - x^2)\, dx = \tfrac{4}{9},$$

and then the relevant reduced moments,

$$\bar{M}_1 = \tfrac{9}{4} \int_{-1}^{1} x(1 - x^2)\, dx = 0, \qquad \bar{M}_2 = \tfrac{9}{4} \int_{-1}^{1} x^2(1 - x^2)\, dx = \tfrac{3}{5},$$

$$\bar{M}_3 = \tfrac{9}{4} \int_{-1}^{1} x^3(1 - x^2)\, dx = 0.$$

Next, from (8.14.28) with $r = 1, 2,$ and 3, there follows

$$\alpha_1 = -\bar{M}_1 = 0, \qquad \alpha_2 = \tfrac{1}{2}(-\bar{M}_1\alpha_1 - \bar{M}_2) = -\tfrac{3}{10},$$

$$\alpha_3 = \tfrac{1}{3}(-\bar{M}_1\alpha_2 - \bar{M}_2\alpha_1 - \bar{M}_3) = 0.$$

Hence, the required abscissas are obtained as the roots of the equation $x^3 - \tfrac{3}{10}x = 0$, in the form

$$x_1 = -\sqrt{\tfrac{3}{10}}, \qquad x_2 = 0, \qquad x_3 = \sqrt{\tfrac{3}{10}}, \qquad (8.14.31)$$

so that the desired formula is

$$\int_{-1}^{1} (1 - x^2)f(x)\, dx = \tfrac{4}{9}[f(-\sqrt{\tfrac{3}{10}}) + f(0) + f(\sqrt{\tfrac{3}{10}})] + E. \quad (8.14.32)$$

It is easily verified that $E = 0$ when $f(x) = 1, x, x^2,$ and x^3, but that $E \neq 0$ when $f(x) = x^4$, so that the degree of precision is $N = 3$.

An expression for the error term is obtained most readily by use of the third method of §5.11. Thus, we find that

$$\int_{-1}^{x} w(t)\pi(t)\, dt = \int_{-1}^{x} (t^3 - \tfrac{3}{10}t)(1 - t^2)\, dt$$

$$= -\tfrac{1}{120}(20x^6 - 39x^4 + 18x^2 + 1)$$

$$= -\tfrac{1}{120}(x^2 - 1)^2(20x^2 + 1),$$

so that $w(x)\pi(x) = V'(x)$, where $V(x) = -\tfrac{1}{120}(x^2 - 1)^2(20x^2 + 1)$. Since $V(x)$ vanishes at both ends of the interval of integration and is of constant sign inside that interval, use may be made of (5.11.38), with $n + 1 \equiv m = 3$ and $r = 1$, to give

$$E = -\frac{f^{\mathrm{iv}}(\xi)}{4!} \int_{-1}^{1} V(x)\, dx$$

or

$$E = \tfrac{1}{700}f^{\mathrm{iv}}(\xi), \qquad (8.14.33)$$

where $|\xi| < 1$. The same result can be obtained, somewhat more laboriously, by use of the appropriate influence function (5.11.16). A check is afforded by an application of the formula to $f(x) = x^4$.

8.15. Supplementary References. Classical references include Mehler [146], Chebyshev [54], and Radau [184, 185, 186]. For more recent contributions, see Shohat and Winston [211], Winston [238], Bernstein [36], Burnett [52], and Greenwood and Danford [96]. The relationship between Gaussian quadrature and osculating (Hermite) quadrature is pointed out by Fort [82]. Salzer [271] presents a table of coefficients for osculating quadrature. Rosser [197] warns of dangers in indiscriminate use of Hermite-Gauss quadrature. For the use of Gaussian quadrature in the numerical solution of *integral equations*, see Reiz [192], Nyström [169], and Scarborough [17]. Gaussian abscissas and weights are given by Lowan, Davids, and Levensen [252] for the Legendre case; by Greenwood and Miller [250], Kopal [251], and Salzer, Zucker, and Capuano [272] for the Hermite case; in [274] for the Laguerre case; by Radau [185] for the Lobatto case; and by Salzer [267] for the Chebyshev case. Salzer [266, 267] gives tables facilitating error detection in the Chebyshev and Hermite cases. For examples of the algebraic derivation of quadrature formulas of Gaussian type, see Beard [33].

PROBLEMS

Section 8.2

1. Obtain the formula

$$f_s = (1 + 2s)(1 - s)^2 f_0 + (3 - 2s)s^2 f_1 + s(1 - s)^2 h f_0' - s^2(1 - s)h f_1'$$
$$+ \frac{h^4}{4!} f^{\mathrm{iv}}(\xi)s^2(1 - s)^2,$$

where $f_s \equiv f(x_0 + hs)$ and $x_0 < \xi < x_0 + h$, if $0 \leqq s \leqq 1$, and deduce the special formula

$$f_{\frac{1}{2}} = \tfrac{1}{2}(f_0 + f_1) + \frac{h}{8}(f_0' - f_1') + \frac{h^4}{384} f^{\mathrm{iv}}(\xi).$$

2. Obtain the formula

$$f_s = \tfrac{1}{4}(4 + 3s)s^2(1 - s)^2 f_{-1} + (1 - s^2)^2 f_0 + \tfrac{1}{4}(4 - 3s)s^2(1 + s)^2 f_1$$
$$+ \tfrac{1}{4}(1 + s)s^2(1 - s)^2 h f_{-1}' + s(1 - s^2)^2 h f_0' - \tfrac{1}{4}(1 - s)s^2(1 + s)^2 h f_1'$$
$$+ \frac{h^6}{6!} f^{\mathrm{vi}}(\xi)s^2(1 - s^2)^2,$$

where $f_s \equiv f(x_0 + hs)$ and $x_0 - h < \xi < x_0 + h$, if $|s| \leqq 1$, and deduce the special formula

$$f_{\frac{1}{2}} = \tfrac{1}{128}(11f_{-1} + 72f_0 + 45f_1) + \frac{3h}{128}(f_{-1}' + 12f_0' - 3f_1') + \frac{h^6}{5120} f^{\mathrm{vi}}(\xi),$$

together with a corresponding formula for $f_{-\frac{1}{2}}$.

3. From the following tabular values of the function

$$\mathrm{Si}(x) = \int_0^x \frac{\sin t}{t}\, dt,$$

determine approximate values of $\mathrm{Si}(2.5)$ and $\mathrm{Si}(3.5)$ by use of the formulas of Probs. 1 and 2:

x	2.0	3.0	4.0
$\mathrm{Si}(x)$	1.605	1.849	1.758

Section 8.3

4. From the results of Prob. 1, deduce the formulas

$$\int_{x_0}^{x_1} f(x)\,dx = \frac{h}{2}\,(f_0 + f_1) + \frac{h^2}{12}\,(f_0' - f_1') + \frac{h^5}{720}\,f^{\mathrm{iv}}(\xi)$$

and

$$\int_{x_0}^{x_1} (x - x_0)f(x)\,dx = \frac{h^2}{20}\,(3f_0 + 7f_1) + \frac{h^3}{60}\,(2f_0' - 3f_1') + \frac{h^6}{1440}\,f^{\mathrm{iv}}(\xi)$$

where $h = x_1 - x_0$ and $x_0 < \xi < x_1$ in each formula.

5. From the results of Prob. 2, deduce the formula

$$\int_{x_{-1}}^{x_1} f(x)\,dx = \frac{h}{15}\,(7f_{-1} + 16f_0 + 7f_1) + \frac{h^2}{15}\,(f_{-1}' - f_1') + \frac{h^i}{4725}\,f^{\mathrm{vi}}(\xi),$$

where $x_1 = x_0 + h = x_{-1} + 2h$ and $x_{-1} < \xi < x_1$.

6. Use the data given in Prob. 3, and the first formula of Prob. 4, to obtain approximate values of the integral $\int_a^b \mathrm{Si}(x)\,dx$ for $(a,b) = (2,3)$ and $(3,4)$, and compare the sum with the result given by the formula of Prob. 5.

Section 8.4

7. If B_r is the coefficient of x^{r-1} in $\phi_r(x)$, show that the coefficient b_k in the recurrence formula (8.4.13) is given by

$$b_k = a_k \left(\frac{B_{k+1}}{A_{k+1}} - \frac{B_k}{A_k} \right),$$

so that (8.4.13) can be written in the form

$$\phi_{k+1}(x) = \frac{A_{k+1}}{A_k} \left[x + \left(\frac{B_{k+1}}{A_{k+1}} - \frac{B_k}{A_k} \right) \right] \phi_k(x) - \frac{A_{k+1}A_{k-1}}{A_k^2}\,\frac{\gamma_k}{\gamma_{k-1}}\,\phi_{k-1}(x).$$

8. If $y_n(x)$ is the least-squares polynomial approximation of degree n to $f(x)$ over (a,b), relative to the weighting function $w(x)$, and if $\phi_r(x)$ is the rth relevant orthogonal polynomial, use the Christoffel-Darboux identity to show that

$$y_n(x) = \frac{1}{a_n \gamma_n} \int_a^b \frac{w(t)f(t)}{x - t}\,[\phi_{n+1}(x)\phi_n(t) - \phi_n(x)\phi_{n+1}(t)]\,dt.$$

9. If $(a,b) = (0,1)$ and $w(x) = x$, show that the abscissas in (8.4.6) are the zeros of the polynomial

$$\phi_m(x) = \frac{1}{(m+1)!}\,x^{-1}\,\frac{d^m}{dx^m}\,[x^{m+1}(1 - x)^m],$$

that the ith weight is given by

$$H_i = -\frac{2m + 1}{m^2(m + 1)^2 \phi_m'(x_i)\phi_{m-1}(x_i)},$$

and that the error term is of the form

$$E = \frac{m + 1}{2(2m + 1)^2}\,\frac{(m!)^4}{[(2m)!]^3}\,f^{(2m)}(\xi).$$

In particular, obtain the formulas

$$\int_0^1 xf(x)\,dx = \tfrac{1}{2}f(\tfrac{2}{3}) + \tfrac{1}{72}f''(\xi)$$

and $$\int_0^1 xf(x)\,dx = \frac{9 - \sqrt{6}}{36} f\left(\frac{6 - \sqrt{6}}{10}\right) + \frac{9 + \sqrt{6}}{36} f\left(\frac{6 + \sqrt{6}}{10}\right) + \tfrac{1}{14400}f^{iv}(\xi).$$

Section 8.5

10. After making an appropriate linear change of variables, determine approximate values of the integral

$$\int_2^8 \frac{dx}{x}$$

by use of Gaussian formulas involving two, three, four, and five ordinates, and compare the approximations with those afforded by corresponding Newton-Cotes formulas. In each case, obtain an upper bound on the error analytically and verify that it is conservative.

11. Proceed as in Prob. 10 with the integral

$$\int_0^{\pi/2} \sin x\,dx.$$

12. Proceed as in Prob. 10 with the integral

$$\int_0^\pi \sin x\,dx.$$

13. If $f(x)$ can be represented by a power series near $x = \xi$, and if $|f^{(k)}(\xi)|$ is of the order of magnitude of $k!/R^k$ when k is large, so that $R = R(\xi)$ is the radius of convergence of that series, show that the error term (8.5.6) is of the order of magnitude of $\pi/(2R)^{2m}$ when m is large.

14. Obtain approximations to the integral

$$\int_{-4}^4 \frac{dx}{1 + x^2},$$

using Gaussian quadratures with two, three, four, and five points, and compare the results with the true value (see also §3.7).

Section 8.6

15. Determine approximate values of the integral

$$\int_0^\infty e^{-x} \sin x\,dx$$

by use of Laguerre-Gauss quadratures employing two, three, four, and five ordinates. In each case, obtain an upper bound on the error and verify that it is conservative.

16. Proceed as in Prob. 15 with the integral

$$\int_0^\infty \frac{e^{-x}}{x + 4}\,dx \doteq 0.206346.$$

17. Proceed as in Prob. 15 with respect to the integral

$$\int_0^\infty \frac{x^{\frac{1}{2}}}{x + 4} e^{-x}\,dx \doteq 0.16776,$$

omitting the analytical determination of error bounds.

18. Derive the results of (8.6.17) to (8.6.19), and obtain the special formula

$$\int_0^\infty x^\beta e^{-x} f(x)\,dx = \frac{\Gamma(1+\beta)}{2(2+\beta)}\, [(2+\beta - \sqrt{2+\beta})f(2+\beta + \sqrt{2+\beta})$$
$$+ (2+\beta + \sqrt{2+\beta})f(2+\beta - \sqrt{2+\beta})] + \frac{\Gamma(3+\beta)}{12}\, f^{iv}(\xi),$$

where $\beta > -1$ and $\xi > 0$, in the case when $m = 2$. Also use the two-point formula to approximate the integral in Prob. 17, and compare the result with that afforded by the two-point Laguerre-Gauss formula.

Section 8.7

19. Determine approximate values of the integral

$$\int_{-\infty}^\infty e^{-x^2} \cos x\,dx = \sqrt{\pi}\, e^{-1/4}$$

by use of Hermite-Gauss quadratures employing two, three, four, and five ordinates. In each case, obtain an upper bound on the error and verify that it is conservative.

20. Transform the integral of Prob. 17 to the form

$$\int_{-\infty}^\infty \frac{t^2}{t^2 + 4}\, e^{-t^2}\,dt$$

and determine approximate values by use of Hermite-Gauss quadratures employing two, three, four, and five ordinates. Also compare the results with the corresponding results in Prob. 17.

21. From the following tabulated rounded values of $J_0(x)$, together with the fact that $J_0(-x) = J_0(x)$, determine approximate values of the integral

$$\int_{-\infty}^\infty e^{-x^2} J_0(x)\,dx \doteq 1.570301$$

by use of Hermite-Gauss quadrature employing two, three, four, and five ordinates:

x	0.0	0.5	1.0	1.5	2.0	2.5
$J_0(x)$	1.000000	0.938470	0.765198	0.511828	0.223891	−0.048384

Section 8.8

22. Determine approximate values of the integral

$$\int_{-1}^1 \frac{\cos x}{\sqrt{1 - x^2}}\,dx = \pi J_0(1) \doteq 2.40394$$

by use of Chebyshev-Gauss quadratures employing two, three, four, and five ordinates. In each case, obtain an upper bound on the error and verify that it is conservative.

23. Determine approximate values of the integral

$$\int_{-1}^1 \frac{dx}{\sqrt{(1 - x^2)(16 - x^2)}} \doteq 0.794121$$

by use of Chebyshev-Gauss quadratures employing two, three, four, and five ordinates.

24. Use the results of Prob. 31 of Chap. 7 to deduce the quadrature formula

$$\int_{-1}^{1} \sqrt{1 - x^2}\, f(x)\, dx = \frac{\pi}{m+1} \sum_{k=1}^{m} \sin^2\left(\frac{k\pi}{m+1}\right) f\left(\cos \frac{k\pi}{m+1}\right)$$

$$+ \frac{\pi}{2^{2m+1}} \frac{f^{(2m)}(\xi)}{(2m)!} \qquad (|\xi| < 1).$$

25. Proceed as in Prob. 22, using the formula of Prob. 24 to deal with the integral

$$\int_{-1}^{1} \sqrt{1 - x^2} \cos x\, dx \doteq 1.38246.$$

Section 8.9

26. Determine, to six decimal places, the abscissas and weights in a formula

$$\int_{-1}^{1} (1 + x)^{\frac{1}{2}} f(x)\, dx = H_1 f(x_1) + H_2 f(x_2) + E,$$

with degree of precision equal to three, and obtain an expression for the error in terms of f^{iv}. Also transform the results into a formula of the form

$$\int_{0}^{1} x^{\frac{1}{2}} F(x)\, dx = H_1' F(x_1') + H_2' F(x_2') + E'.$$

27. By making appropriate use of (8.9.12), obtain the quadrature formula

$$\int_{-1}^{1} (1 - x^2)^n f(x)\, dx = \sum_{k=1}^{m} H_k f(x_k) + E,$$

when n is a nonnegative integer, with x_i the ith zero of the polynomial

$$\phi_m(x) = P^{(n)}_{m+n}(x) \equiv \frac{d^n}{dx^n} P_{m+n}(x),$$

and with

$$H_i = \frac{2(m + 2n)!}{m!(1 - x_i^2)[P^{(n+1)}_{m+n}(x_i)]^2}$$

and

$$E = \frac{m!(m + 2n)!}{(2m)!} \left[\frac{(m + n)!}{(2m + 2n)!}\right]^2 \frac{2^{2m+2n+1}}{2m + 2n + 1} f^{(2m)}(\xi) \qquad (|\xi| < 1).$$

Section 8.10

28. Suppose that a quadrature formula of the form

$$\int_{0}^{\infty} e^{-x} f(x)\, dx = W_1 f(0) + \sum_{k=2}^{m} W_k f(x_k) + E$$

is required, with the abscissa $x_1 = 0$ assigned. Show that the $m - 1$ free abscissas should then be zeros of the polynomial $\phi_{m-1}(x)$, where

$$\phi_r(x) = C_r x^{-1} e^x \frac{d^r}{dx^r} [x^{r+1} e^{-x}]$$

$$= C_r x^{-1} e^x \left[x \frac{d^r}{dx^r} (x^r e^{-x}) + r \frac{d^{r-1}}{dx^{r-1}} (x^r e^{-x})\right],$$

if the degree of precision is to be maximized. Verify the relation

$$\frac{d^{r-1}}{dx^{r-1}}(x^r e^{-x}) = -\frac{x}{r} e^{-x} \frac{d}{dx} L_r(x),$$

and hence, by taking $C_r = 1$, deduce that the free abscissas must be zeros of

$$\phi_{m-1}(x) = L_{m-1}(x) - L'_{m-1}(x),$$

where the prime denotes differentiation.

29. For the set of polynomials $\phi_r(x)$ obtained in Prob. 28, show that

$$A_r = (-1)^r, \qquad \bar{\gamma}_r = r!(r+1)!,$$

and hence deduce that the weights associated with the free abscissas are given by

$$W_i = \frac{(m-1)!m!}{x_i \phi'_{m-1}(x_i)\phi_m(x_i)} \qquad (i \neq 1).$$

Show also that

$$W_1 = \frac{-1}{\phi_{m-1}(0)} \int_0^\infty \frac{d}{dx}[e^{-x}L_{m-1}(x)]\,dx = \frac{1}{m}.$$

30. Show that the error term in the formula of Prob. 28 can be obtained by the following steps:

$$\begin{aligned}
E &= (-1)^{m-1}\int_0^\infty e^{-x}x\phi_{m-1}(x)f[x_1, \ldots, x_m, x]\,dx \\
&= (-1)^{m-1}\int_0^\infty f[x_1, \ldots, x_m, x]\frac{d^{m-1}}{dx^{m-1}}(x^m e^{-x})\,dx \\
&= \int_0^\infty \left\{\frac{d^{m-1}}{dx^{m-1}}f[x_1, \ldots, x_m, x]\right\}x^m e^{-x}\,dx \\
&= \frac{(m-1)!}{(2m-1)!}f^{(2m-1)}(\xi)\int_0^\infty x^m e^{-x}\,dx \qquad \text{[see (5.11.36)]} \\
&= \frac{(m-1)!m!}{(2m-1)!}f^{(2m-1)}(\xi) \qquad (\xi > 0).
\end{aligned}$$

31. Show that the results of Probs. 28 to 30 reduce to the formulas

$$\int_0^\infty e^{-x}f(x)\,dx = \tfrac{1}{2}[f(0) + f(2)] + \tfrac{1}{3}f'''(\xi)$$

and

$$\int_0^\infty e^{-x}f(x)\,dx = \tfrac{1}{3}f(0) + \tfrac{1}{6}[(2 + \sqrt{3})f(3 - \sqrt{3}) + (2 - \sqrt{3})f(3 + \sqrt{3})] + \tfrac{1}{10}f^v(\xi)$$

when $m = 2$ and 3, where $\xi > 0$ in both cases.

32. Use the second formula of Prob. 31 to approximate the integral

$$\int_0^\infty e^{-x}\sin x\,dx,$$

and compare the result with that of using two (nonzero) ordinates in Prob. 15.

Section 8.11

33. Obtain approximate values of the integral

$$\int_0^{\pi/2}\sin x\,dx$$

by use of Radau quadratures employing two, three, four, and five ordinates, taking the vanishing ordinate as the assigned one. Also compare the results with corresponding ones (employing one, two, three, and four *nonvanishing* ordinates) in Prob. 11.

34. Proceed as in Prob. 33 with the integral

$$\int_0^1 x \cos x \, dx$$

and compare the results when $m = 2$ and 3 with those given by the two explicit formulas of Prob. 9 (in which x is to be considered as a weighting function).

Section 8.12

35. Obtain approximate values of the integral

$$\int_0^\pi \sin x \, dx$$

by use of Lobatto quadratures employing three, four, five, and six ordinates. Also compare the results with corresponding ones (employing one, two, three, and four *nonvanishing* ordinates) in Prob. 12.

36. Proceed as in Prob. 35 with the integral

$$\int_{-1}^1 (1 - x^2) \cos x \, dx,$$

and compare the results when $m = 3$ and 4 with corresponding ones obtained by using (8.9.13) and employing like numbers (one and two) of nonvanishing ordinates.

37. Derive the formula

$$\int_{-1}^1 \frac{f(x)}{\sqrt{1 - x^2}} \, dx = \frac{\pi}{m} \left[\tfrac{1}{2}f(-1) + \tfrac{1}{2}f(1) + \sum_{k=1}^{m-1} f\left(\cos \frac{k\pi}{m}\right) \right] - \frac{2\pi}{2^{2m}(2m)!} f^{(2m)}(\xi),$$

making use of Prob. 31 of Chap. 7 and of Eq. (7.8.21), and noticing that $m + 1$ ordinates are employed. [Show that the error term can be expressed in the form

$$E = \int_{-1}^1 \frac{1}{\sqrt{1 - x^2}} \pi(x) f[-1, x_1, \ldots, x_{m-1}, 1, x] \, dx$$

where $\pi(x) = 2^{-m+1}(x^2 - 1)S_{m-1}(x)$ and where $x_k = \cos (k\pi/m)$.]

Section 8.13

38. Rework Prob. 10 by use of Chebyshev quadratures employing two, three, four, and five ordinates, and compare the results with the results of that problem.

39. Suppose that independent errors $\epsilon_1, \epsilon_2, \ldots, \epsilon_m$ are associated with the m ordinates used in a Chebyshev quadrature over $(-1,1)$, and that each of these errors is distributed about a zero mean with RMS deviation not exceeding ϵ_{RMS}. If R is the corresponding error in the approximate integral, show that

$$|R|_{max} \leqq 2|\epsilon|_{max}, \qquad R_{RMS} \leqq \frac{2}{\sqrt{m}} \epsilon_{RMS}.$$

Show also that the first relation holds for Legendre-Gauss quadrature while the factor $2/\sqrt{m}$ in the second relation is increased by only about 5 per cent when $m = 3, 4,$ and

5 (the same is true for $m = 6$, 7, and 9), but that somewhat larger increases in this factor occur when corresponding Newton-Cotes formulas are used over $(-1,1)$. Also determine the values of this factor associated with the trapezoidal and parabolic rules when $m = 3, 5, 7$, and 9.

40. Verify that the interval $(-1,1)$ can be replaced by (a,b) in (8.13.1) and (8.13.17), when $(a,b) \neq (-\infty, \infty)$, and, in the *Laguerre-Chebyshev* case when $(a,b) = (0, \infty)$ and $w(x) = e^{-x}$, show that the m relevant abscissas are to be the zeros of the polynomial part of the formal expansion

$$x^m \exp\left[-m\left(\frac{1}{x} + \frac{1!}{x^2} + \frac{2!}{x^3} + \frac{3!}{x^4} + \cdots \right)\right]$$

$$= x^m - mx^{m-1} + \frac{m}{2}(m-2)x^{m-2} - \frac{m}{6}(m^2 - 6m + 12)x^{m-3}$$

$$+ \frac{m}{24}(m^3 - 12m^2 + 60m - 144)x^{m-4} + \cdots,$$

if those zeros are real. Show further that, when $m = 2$, the quadrature formula is identical with the first formula of Prob. 31, and also that two of the abscissas are complex when $m = 3$, so that no three-point formula of the required type can exist. [The same has been shown to be true for all m such that $3 \leq m \leq 10$ (see Salzer [203]).]

41. Assuming the validity of (8.13.17) with $(-1,1)$ replaced by $(-\infty, \infty)$ in the *Hermite-Chebyshev* case when also $w(x) = e^{-x^2}$ (a modified derivation is necessary), show that the relevant abscissas are to be the zeros of the polynomial part of the formal expansion

$$x^m \exp\left[-m\left(\frac{1}{4x^2} + \frac{3}{16x^4} + \cdots \right)\right] = x^m - \frac{m}{4}x^{m-2} + \frac{m}{32}(m-6)x^{m-4} - \cdots,$$

that the zeros are real when $m = 2$ and $m = 3$, but that two of the zeros are complex when $m = 4$ and $m = 5$. [The presence of complex zeros has been established for all m such that $4 \leq m \leq 10$ (see Salzer [203]).]

42. Show that the two-point formula of Prob. 41 is identical with the Hermite-Gauss two-point formula, and that the three-point formula is of the form

$$\int_{-\infty}^{\infty} e^{-x^2} f(x) \, dx = \frac{\sqrt{\pi}}{3}\left[f\left(-\frac{\sqrt{3}}{2}\right) + f(0) + f\left(\frac{\sqrt{3}}{2}\right)\right] + E.$$

Show also that the error term can be expressed in the form

$$E = \int_{-\infty}^{\infty} e^{-x^2}(x^3 - \tfrac{3}{4}x)f[x_1,x_2,x_3,x] \, dx$$

and transformed by integration by parts to give

$$E = \tfrac{1}{2}\int_{-\infty}^{\infty} e^{-x^2}(x^2 + \tfrac{1}{4})f[x_1,x_2,x_3,x,x] \, dx$$

$$= \frac{\sqrt{\pi}}{64} f^{\mathrm{iv}}(\xi),$$

for some value of ξ.

Section 8.14

43. Determine algebraically the unknown abscissas and/or weights for the formula

$$\int_{-1}^{1} f(x) \, dx = \sum_{k=1}^{3} W_k f(x_k) + E,$$

subject to the requirement that the degree of precision be as high as possible in consistency with each of the following sets of constraints, and determine the degree of precision in each case:

(a) $x_1 = -\frac{1}{2}$, $x_2 = 0$, $x_3 = \frac{1}{2}$.

(b) No constraints.

(c) $W_1 = W_2 = W_3$.

(d) $x_1 = -1$.

44. Suppose that the abscissas $x_1 = -1$ and $x_2 = \alpha$ are assigned, and that the quadrature formula

$$\int_{-1}^{1} f(x)\,dx = W_1 f(-1) + W_2 f(\alpha) + W_3 f(x_3) + E \qquad (-1 < \alpha \leqq 1)$$

is to possess a degree of precision of at least three. Determine x_3 and the three weights as functions of α, by algebraic methods, showing, in particular, that no such formula exists if $\alpha = \frac{1}{3}$, that x_3 is outside $(-1,1)$ for all other α such that $0 < \alpha < \frac{1}{2}$, and that the ordinate at $x = -1$ is not involved if $\alpha = \pm 1/\sqrt{3}$.

45. Show that the two-point Gaussian quadrature formula of the form

$$\int_{0}^{\pi} f(x) \sin nx\,dx = W_1 f(x_1) + W_2 f(x_2) + E,$$

where n is a nonnegative integer, is such that

$$x_1 = \frac{\pi}{2} - \sqrt{\left(\frac{\pi}{2}\right)^2 - \frac{6}{n^2}}, \qquad x_2 = \frac{\pi}{2} + \sqrt{\left(\frac{\pi}{2}\right)^2 - \frac{6}{n^2}},$$

$$W_1 = -W_2 = \frac{\pi}{n\sqrt{\pi^2 - 24/n^2}}$$

when n is *even*, and such that

$$x_1 = \frac{\pi}{2} - \sqrt{\left(\frac{\pi}{2}\right)^2 - \frac{2}{n^2}}, \qquad x_2 = \frac{\pi}{2} + \sqrt{\left(\frac{\pi}{2}\right)^2 - \frac{2}{n^2}},$$

$$W_1 = W_2 = \frac{1}{n},$$

when n is *odd*. Show also that the degree of precision is four when n is even and three when n is odd.

46. Show that the error term in the quadrature formula of Prob. 45 can be expressed in the form

$$E = \int_{0}^{\pi} f[x_1,x_2,x]\pi(x) \sin nx\,dx = \frac{1}{2}\int_{0}^{\pi} f''(\eta)\pi(x) \sin nx\,dx \qquad (0 < \eta < \pi),$$

where $\pi(x) = x^2 - \pi x + 6n^{-2}$ when n is even and $\pi(x) = x^2 - \pi x + 2n^{-2}$ when n is odd, and that, when $n = 1$, this expression can be transformed to

$$E = \frac{1}{24}f^{iv}(\xi) \int_{0}^{\pi} x^2\pi(x) \sin x\,dx = \frac{10 - \pi^2}{6}f^{iv}(\xi) \qquad (0 < \xi < \pi).$$

[Notice that here $w(x) \equiv \sin nx$ changes sign inside the range of integration when $n > 1$.]

47. Derive the Gaussian integration formulas

$$\int_0^1 f(x) \log x \, dx = -f(\tfrac{1}{4}) + E$$

and

$$\int_0^1 f(x) \log x \, dx = -W_1 f(x_1) - W_2 f(x_2) + E,$$

where

$$x_1 = \frac{15 - \sqrt{106}}{42} \doteq 0.112009, \qquad x_2 = \frac{15 + \sqrt{106}}{42} \doteq 0.602277$$

and

$$W_1 = \frac{212 + 9\sqrt{106}}{424} \doteq 0.718539, \qquad W_2 = \frac{212 - 9\sqrt{106}}{424} \doteq 0.281461.$$

48. Show that the error terms associated with the two formulas of Prob. 47 are of the forms

$$E = \int_0^1 (x - \tfrac{1}{4})^2 f[\tfrac{1}{4}, \tfrac{1}{4}, x] \log x \, dx = -\tfrac{7}{288} f''(\xi)$$

and

$$E = \int_0^1 (x^2 - \tfrac{5}{7}x + \tfrac{17}{252})^2 f[x_1, x_1, x_2, x_2, x] \log x \, dx = -\tfrac{647}{5443200} f^{iv}(\xi)$$

$$\doteq -0.00012 f^{iv}(\xi),$$

respectively, where $0 < \xi < 1$ in each case.

CHAPTER 9

APPROXIMATIONS OF VARIOUS TYPES

9.1. Introduction. Whereas polynomials are usually the most convenient coordinate functions for the approximation of a continuous function (or for least-squares approximation of a function which is continuous except for finite "jumps") when the desired interval of approximation is finite, they are well adapted to the approximation of *periodic* functions only over relatively short ranges. When $f(x)$ is periodic and is to be approximated over one or more complete periods, it is desirable to make use of periodic coordinate functions, having the same period as $f(x)$, in constructing its approximation. The most convenient set of such functions (which, indeed, satisfies all the requirements of §1.2 when f is also continuous) is the composite set of all sines and cosines which possess that period. While formulas analogous to Lagrange's formula exist for the determination of such an approximation, they are seldom used, and resort is usually had to least-squares methods. The relevant analysis, due originally to Fourier and often known as *harmonic analysis*, is presented and illustrated for continuous ranges in §9.2 and for discrete ranges in §9.3.

When empirical data correspond to a simple decay or growth process, or to a combination of such processes, and an approximation is desired for a semi-infinite range of the independent variable (frequently representing time), real exponential functions are appropriate coordinate functions. On the other hand, when the superposition of two or more simple or damped harmonics, of unknown periods, is to be analyzed, complex exponential functions are appropriate. Prony's method of curve fitting, which includes both these cases, is presented in §9.4 and is specialized to the second case in §9.5.

Methods of *optimum* polynomial interpolation, based on preselected abscissas, are considered in §§9.6 and 9.7, and the Lanczos method of improving the efficiency of a given polynomial approximation is described in §9.8.

A natural generalization of polynomial approximation consists in approximation by *ratios* of polynomials, that is, by rational functions.

Such approximations are expressed conveniently in terms of continued fractions and are treated in the concluding sections of this chapter (§§9.9 to 9.12).

9.2. Fourier Approximation: Continuous Range. We suppose here that the function $f(x)$ to be approximated is a *periodic* function, of known period, and that the scale of units has been so adjusted that the period is 2π, so that

$$f(x + 2\pi) = f(x). \qquad (9.2.1)$$

A particularly convenient class of coordinate functions is represented by the set

$$1, \cos x, \cos 2x, \ldots, \cos rx, \ldots,$$
$$\sin x, \sin 2x, \ldots, \sin rx, \ldots,$$

each member of which is of period 2π. This set has the useful property that the *product* of any two members is expressible as a linear combination of two members. Also, the *derivative* of each member is also a member, and the same is true of the *integral* of each member except the constant.

But the principal source of convenience is the verifiable fact that the set is *orthogonal* over any period interval, say the interval $(-\pi,\pi)$, so that

$$\int_{-\pi}^{\pi} \sin jx \sin kx \, dx = 0 \qquad (j \neq k),$$
$$\int_{-\pi}^{\pi} \cos jx \cos kx \, dx = 0 \qquad (j \neq k), \qquad (9.2.2)$$
$$\int_{-\pi}^{\pi} \sin jx \cos kx \, dx = 0,$$

when j and k are nonnegative integers. Clearly, negative integers need not be considered.

Suppose, then, that we require an approximation of the form

$$f(x) \approx a_0 + \sum_{k=1}^{n} (a_k \cos kx + b_k \sin kx), \qquad (9.2.3)$$

where the coefficients are to be determined in such a way that the integrated squared error is least. From the periodicity of $f(x)$ and of the sine and cosine harmonics, it follows that attention may be restricted to one period interval, say the interval $(-\pi,\pi)$. Thus the requirement

$$\int_{-\pi}^{\pi} [f(x) - a_0 - \sum_{k=1}^{n} (a_k \cos kx + b_k \sin kx)]^2 \, dx = \min \quad (9.2.4)$$

leads to the conditions

$$\int_{-\pi}^{\pi} \left[f(x) - a_0 - \sum_{k=1}^{n} (a_k \cos kx + b_k \sin kx) \right] dx = 0,$$

$$\int_{-\pi}^{\pi} \cos rx \left[f(x) - a_0 - \sum_{k=1}^{n} (a_k \cos kx + b_k \sin kx) \right] dx = 0$$

$$(r = 1, 2, \ldots, n),$$

$$\int_{-\pi}^{\pi} \sin rx \left[f(x) - a_0 - \sum_{k=1}^{n} (a_k \cos kx + b_k \sin kx) \right] dx = 0$$

$$(r = 1, 2, \ldots, n),$$

(9.2.5)

when the partial derivatives of the left-hand member of (9.2.4) with respect to a_0, a_r, and b_r are equated to zero. Reference to the relations (9.2.2), and to the relations

$$\int_{-\pi}^{\pi} dx = 2\pi, \qquad \int_{-\pi}^{\pi} \cos^2 kx \, dx = \int_{-\pi}^{\pi} \sin^2 kx \, dx = \pi \qquad (k \neq 0),$$

(9.2.6)

then leads to the determinations

$$a_0 = \frac{1}{2\pi} \int_{-\pi}^{\pi} f(x) \, dx, \qquad a_k = \frac{1}{\pi} \int_{-\pi}^{\pi} f(x) \cos kx \, dx \qquad (k \neq 0),$$

$$b_k = \frac{1}{\pi} \int_{-\pi}^{\pi} f(x) \sin kx \, dx.$$

(9.2.7)

If $f(x)$ is an *even* function, so that $f(-x) = f(x)$, it is seen that $b_k = 0$, so that (9.2.3) then reduces to

$$f(x) \approx a_0 + \sum_{k=1}^{n} a_k \cos kx$$

(9.2.8)

where

$$a_0 = \frac{1}{2\pi} \int_{-\pi}^{\pi} f(x) \, dx = \frac{1}{\pi} \int_{0}^{\pi} f(x) \, dx,$$

$$a_k = \frac{1}{\pi} \int_{-\pi}^{\pi} f(x) \cos kx \, dx = \frac{2}{\pi} \int_{0}^{\pi} f(x) \cos kx \, dx \qquad (k \neq 0).$$

(9.2.9)

Similarly, if $f(x)$ is an *odd* function, so that $f(-x) = -f(x)$, there follows $a_0 = a_k = 0$, and (9.2.3) then becomes

$$f(x) \approx \sum_{k=1}^{n} b_k \sin kx$$

(9.2.10)

where

$$b_k = \frac{1}{\pi} \int_{-\pi}^{\pi} f(x) \sin kx \, dx = \frac{2}{\pi} \int_{0}^{\pi} f(x) \sin kx \, dx.$$

(9.2.11)

If the periodic function $f(x)$ is fairly well behaved, in particular, if only $f(x)$ is bounded and piecewise differentiable, it is known that the approximation actually tends to $f(x)$ as $n \to \infty$ for all values of x at which $f(x)$ is continuous, and that it tends to the mean value $\frac{1}{2}[f(x+) + f(x-)]$ of the right- and left-hand limits at each point of discontinuity.

It is important to notice that, as is typical of least-squares approximations by orthogonal functions, each coefficient is determined independently of all others, and its value does not depend upon the number of harmonics to be retained in the approximation.

As an example, suppose that $f(x)$ is defined over $(-\pi,\pi)$ in such a way that

$$f(x) = \begin{cases} 0 & (-\pi < x \leqq 0), \\ x & \left(0 \leqq x \leqq \dfrac{\pi}{2}\right), \\ \dfrac{\pi}{2} & \left(\dfrac{\pi}{2} \leqq x < \pi\right), \end{cases} \qquad (9.2.12)$$

and is defined elsewhere by the requirement that it be periodic, with period 2π (see Fig. 9.1). Since $f(x)$ is neither even nor odd, the presence

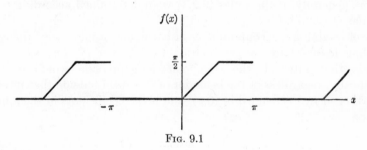

$f(x)$

$\dfrac{\pi}{2}$

$-\pi$ $\qquad$ π $\qquad$ x

FIG. 9.1

of both sine and cosine harmonics may be anticipated. Equations (9.2.7) give

$$a_0 = \frac{1}{2\pi}\left[\int_{-\pi}^{0} 0 \, dx + \int_{0}^{\pi/2} x \, dx + \int_{\pi/2}^{\pi} \frac{\pi}{2} \, dx\right] = \frac{3\pi}{16},$$

$$a_k = \frac{1}{\pi}\left[\int_{-\pi}^{0} 0 \cos kx \, dx + \int_{0}^{\pi/2} x \cos kx \, dx + \int_{\pi/2}^{\pi} \frac{\pi}{2} \cos kx \, dx\right]$$

$$= -\frac{1}{\pi k^2}\left(1 - \cos \frac{k\pi}{2}\right) \qquad (k \neq 0),$$

$$b_k = \frac{1}{\pi}\left[\int_{-\pi}^{0} 0 \sin kx \, dx + \int_{0}^{\pi/2} x \sin kx \, dx + \int_{\pi/2}^{\pi} \frac{\pi}{2} \sin kx \, dx\right]$$

$$= \frac{1}{\pi k^2}\left(\sin \frac{k\pi}{2} - \frac{k\pi}{2} \cos k\pi\right).$$

Thus there follows

$$f(x) = \frac{3\pi}{16} - \frac{1}{\pi}\cos x - \frac{1}{2\pi}\cos 2x - \frac{1}{9\pi}\cos 3x - \cdots$$

$$+ \frac{2 + \pi}{2\pi}\sin x - \frac{1}{4}\sin 2x + \frac{3\pi - 2}{9\pi}\sin 3x - \cdots. \quad (9.2.13)$$

If the best least-squares approximation to $f(x)$ involving only harmonics through the second were required, it would be obtained, by suppressing all higher harmonics in (9.2.13), in the form $f(x) \approx 0.589 - 0.318\cos x - 0.159\cos 2x + 0.818\sin x - 0.250\sin 2x$ if (say) the coefficients were rounded to three places.

Because of the discontinuities in $f(x)$, a rather large number of terms would be needed, in this particular case, to afford a good approximation to $f(x)$, particularly near the discontinuities. However, there are in fact many practical situations in which only the coefficients of certain harmonics of low order are required and in which the degree of approximation afforded by a given number of harmonics is not of great interest.

It is clear that if $f(x)$ were *not* periodic, but were defined by (9.2.12) in the interval $(-\pi,\pi)$, the expansion (9.2.13) would still be valid *inside that interval*, regardless of the behavior of $f(x)$ elsewhere.

More generally, if the series (9.2.3) were determined according to the formulas of (9.2.7), for *any* function $f(x)$ for which the integrals exist, the result of retaining a certain number of harmonics would afford the corresponding least-squares approximation to $f(x)$ *over the interval* $(-\pi,\pi)$. Outside that interval, the trigonometric expression would continue periodically, regardless of the behavior of $f(x)$ itself outside that interval.

Further, if $f(x)$ is defined in $(0,\pi)$, and if the coefficients in the approximation

$$f(x) \approx a_0 + \sum_{k=1}^{n} a_k \cos kx \qquad (0 < x < \pi) \qquad (9.2.14)$$

are determined by the equations

$$a_0 = \frac{1}{\pi}\int_0^\pi f(x)\,dx, \qquad a_k = \frac{2}{\pi}\int_0^\pi f(x)\cos kx\,dx \qquad (k = 1, 2, \ldots, n),$$

$$(9.2.15)$$

the result will represent the least-squares cosine-harmonic approximation to $f(x)$ over $(0,\pi)$. Similarly, the least-squares sine-harmonic approximation over that half range is given by

$$f(x) \approx \sum_{k=1}^{n} b_k \sin kx \qquad (0 < x < \pi), \qquad (9.2.16)$$

where

$$b_k = \frac{2}{\pi}\int_0^\pi f(x)\sin kx\,dx. \qquad (9.2.17)$$

These results are immediate consequences of the verifiable orthogonality relations

$$\int_0^\pi \sin jx \sin kx \, dx = \begin{cases} 0 & (j \neq k), \\ \dfrac{\pi}{2} & (j = k \neq 0), \end{cases} \tag{9.2.18}$$

$$\int_0^\pi \cos jx \cos kx \, dx = \begin{cases} 0 & (j \neq k), \\ \dfrac{\pi}{2} & (j = k \neq 0), \\ \pi & (j = k = 0), \end{cases} \tag{9.2.19}$$

where j and k are nonnegative integers. These relations can also be deduced directly from (9.2.2).

9.3. Fourier Approximation : Discrete Range. We suppose again that $f(x)$ is of period 2π, but that its values are known only at a discrete set of equally spaced points in a period interval, say at the $2N + 1$ points

$$-\pi, \, -\frac{(N-1)\pi}{N}, \, \cdots, \, -\frac{\pi}{N}, 0, \frac{\pi}{N}, \, \cdots, \, \frac{(N-1)\pi}{N}, \, \pi,$$

of the interval $(-\pi,\pi)$. Since $f(-\pi) = f(\pi)$, from the assumed periodicity,[†] we then have $2N$ *independent* data, which may be expected to serve to determine the coefficients of $2N$ terms of an approximation of the form (9.2.3).

If we denote the rth abscissa as

$$x_r = r\frac{\pi}{N} \quad (r = -N+1, -N+2, \ldots, -1, 0, 1, \ldots, N-1, N),$$
$$\tag{9.3.1}$$

so that the $2N$ independent values $f_r \equiv f(x_r)$ are prescribed, we may verify that only the $2N$ functions

$$1, \cos x, \cos 2x, \ldots, \cos Nx; \sin x, \sin 2x, \ldots, \sin (N-1)x$$

of the set considered in the preceding section are independent over the domain comprising this set of abscissas, for the function $\sin Nx$ *vanishes* at each of these points, and each of the functions $\cos (N+1)x, \ldots$ and $\sin (N+1)x, \ldots$ takes on the same values at points in the set as does one of the $2N$ functions listed above. For example, since $\sin Nx_r = 0$, we have

$$\cos (N+1)x_r = \cos Nx_r \cos x_r = (-1)^r \cos x_r = \cos (N-1)x_r.$$

It is possible to show that this set of functions is orthogonal under *summation* over the set (9.3.1) (see Probs. 7 and 8), so that, with the

---

[†] If $f(x)$ is *discontinuous* at the ends of the period interval $(-\pi,\pi)$, or undefined outside that interval, the mean value $[f(\pi-) + f(\pi+)]/2 = [f(\pi-) + f(-\pi+)]/2$ is to be assigned to $f(x)$ at both end points.

notation of (9.3.1),

$$\sum_{r=-N+1}^{N} \sin jx_r \sin kx_r = 0 \qquad (j \neq k),$$

$$\sum_{r=-N+1}^{N} \cos jx_r \cos kx_r = 0 \qquad (j \neq k), \tag{9.3.2}$$

$$\sum_{r=-N+1}^{N} \sin jx_r \cos kx_r = 0,$$

when j and k are integers between 0 and N, inclusive, in analogy to (9.2.2). Furthermore, in the excluded cases for which $j = k$, the results

$$\sum_{r=-N+1}^{N} \sin^2 kx_r = \sum_{r=-N+1}^{N} \cos^2 kx_r = N \qquad (k \neq 0, N),$$

$$\sum_{r=-N+1}^{N} 1 = 2N, \qquad \sum_{r=-N+1}^{N} \cos^2 Nx_r = 2N \tag{9.3.3}$$

can be established, in analogy to (9.2.6).

If now an approximation is assumed in the form

$$f(x) \approx A_0 + \sum_{k=1}^{n} (A_k \cos kx + B_k \sin kx), \tag{9.3.4}$$

where $n \leq N$, and if the least-squares criterion

$$\sum_{r=-N+1}^{N} \left[f(x_r) - A_0 - \sum_{k=1}^{n} (A_k \cos kx_r + B_k \sin kx_r) \right]^2 = \min \tag{9.3.5}$$

is adopted, a derivation completely analogous to that leading from (9.2.4) to (9.2.7), making use of (9.3.2) and (9.3.3), yields the determinations

$$A_0 = \frac{1}{2N} \sum_{r=-N+1}^{N} f(x_r), \qquad A_k = \frac{1}{N} \sum_{r=-N+1}^{N} f(x_r) \cos kx_r \qquad (k \neq 0, N),$$

$$\tag{9.3.6}$$

$$A_N = \frac{1}{2N} \sum_{r=-N+1}^{N} f(x_r) \cos Nx_r, \qquad B_k = \frac{1}{N} \sum_{r=-N+1}^{N} f(x_r) \sin kx_r.$$

Thus the coefficients in (9.3.4) are easily obtained by summation, and the calculation of each coefficient is again independent of the calculation of the others, and is independent of n, so long as $n \leqq N$. When $n = N$, the least-squares criterion becomes equivalent to the requirement that the two members of (9.3.4) agree exactly at the $2N$ points specified by (9.3.1).

The formulas (9.3.6) can be written in the more symmetrical forms

$$A_0 = \frac{1}{2N} [\tfrac{1}{2}f_{-N} + f_{-N+1} + \cdots + f_{-1} + f_0 + f_1 + \cdots + f_{N-1} + \tfrac{1}{2}f_N],$$

$$A_k = \frac{1}{N} [\tfrac{1}{2}f_{-N} \cos kx_{-N} + f_{-N+1} \cos kx_{-N+1} + \cdots + f_{-1} \cos kx_{-1}$$
$$+ f_0 \cos kx_0 + f_1 \cos kx_1 + \cdots + f_{N-1} \cos kx_{N-1}$$
$$+ \tfrac{1}{2}f_N \cos kx_N] \qquad (k \neq 0, N),$$

$$A_N = \frac{1}{2N} [\tfrac{1}{2}f_{-N} \cos Nx_{-N} + f_{-N+1} \cos Nx_{-N+1} + \cdots \qquad (9.3.7)$$
$$+ f_{-1} \cos Nx_{-1} + f_0 \cos Nx_0 + f_1 \cos Nx_1 + \cdots$$
$$+ f_{N-1} \cos Nx_{N-1} + \tfrac{1}{2}f_N \cos Nx_N],$$

$$B_k = \frac{1}{N} [\tfrac{1}{2}f_{-N} \sin kx_{-N} + f_{-N+1} \sin kx_{-N+1} + \cdots$$
$$+ f_{-1} \sin kx_{-1} + f_0 \sin kx_0 + f_1 \sin kx_1 + \cdots$$
$$+ f_{N-1} \sin kx_{N-1} + \tfrac{1}{2}f_N \sin kx_N],$$

in view of the relations $f_{-N} = f_N$.

If we notice that the spacing h is given by

$$h = \frac{\pi}{N}, \qquad (9.3.8)$$

we may observe the curious fact that Eqs. (9.3.7) are identical with the results of using the *trapezoidal rule* to approximate the right-hand members of (9.2.7), when $k < N$.†

For the purpose of numerical calculation, it is convenient to resolve $f(x)$ into its *even* and *odd* components, by introducing the auxiliary functions

$$F(x) = \tfrac{1}{2}[f(x) + f(-x)], \qquad G(x) = \tfrac{1}{2}[f(x) - f(-x)], \qquad (9.3.9)$$

so that
$$f(x) = F(x) + G(x). \qquad (9.3.10)$$

If we recall that $x_{-r} = -x_r$, and that $x_0 = 0$, we find that Eqs. (9.3.6) or

---

† In this connection, it is interesting to recall that the Euler-Maclaurin sum formula, written in the form (5.9.1), reduces to the trapezoidal rule for *any* periodic function, with period equal to the length of the range of integration. That is, the "correction terms" in that formula all vanish in any such case. This fact obviously does not indicate that the trapezoidal rule is "exact" for periodic functions, since the error term (5.8.14) remains, but may indeed serve to illustrate the dangers associated with lack of proper regard for the error term in such formulas.

(9.3.7) may be reduced to the forms

$$A_0 = \frac{1}{N} \left(\tfrac{1}{2}F_0 + F_1 + F_2 + \cdots + F_{N-1} + \tfrac{1}{2}F_N \right),$$

$$A_k = \frac{2}{N} \left(\tfrac{1}{2}F_0 + F_1 \cos kx_1 + F_2 \cos kx_2 + \cdots \right.$$
$$\left. + F_{N-1} \cos kx_{N-1} + \tfrac{1}{2}F_N \cos kx_N \right) \qquad (k \neq 0, N),$$

$$A_N = \frac{1}{N} \left(\tfrac{1}{2}F_0 - F_1 + F_2 - \cdots + (-1)^{N-1}F_{N-1} + (-1)^N \tfrac{1}{2}F_N \right), \qquad (9.3.11)$$

$$B_k = \frac{2}{N} \left(G_1 \sin kx_1 + G_2 \sin kx_2 + \cdots + G_{N-1} \sin kx_{N-1} \right).$$

In order to illustrate the use of these formulas, we consider the case $N = 6$, corresponding to the use of 12 independent ordinates. The tabular forms which follow are then appropriate (although further systematization is clearly possible):

TABLE 9.1a

x	Data	$\cos x$	$\cos 2x$	$\cos 3x$	$\cos 4x$	$\cos 5x$	$\cos 6x$
0	$\tfrac{1}{2}f_0 = \tfrac{1}{2}F_0$	1	1	1	1	1	1
$\dfrac{\pi}{6}$	$\tfrac{1}{2}(f_1 + f_{-1}) = F_1$	$\tfrac{1}{2}\sqrt{3}$	$\tfrac{1}{2}$	0	$-\tfrac{1}{2}$	$-\tfrac{1}{2}\sqrt{3}$	-1
$\dfrac{\pi}{3}$	$\tfrac{1}{2}(f_2 + f_{-2}) = F_2$	$\tfrac{1}{2}$	$-\tfrac{1}{2}$	-1	$-\tfrac{1}{2}$	$\tfrac{1}{2}$	1
$\dfrac{\pi}{2}$	$\tfrac{1}{2}(f_3 + f_{-3}) = F_3$	0	-1	0	1	0	-1
$\dfrac{2\pi}{3}$	$\tfrac{1}{2}(f_4 + f_{-4}) = F_4$	$-\tfrac{1}{2}$	$-\tfrac{1}{2}$	1	$-\tfrac{1}{2}$	$-\tfrac{1}{2}$	1
$\dfrac{5\pi}{6}$	$\tfrac{1}{2}(f_5 + f_{-5}) = F_5$	$-\tfrac{1}{2}\sqrt{3}$	$\tfrac{1}{2}$	0	$-\tfrac{1}{2}$	$\tfrac{1}{2}\sqrt{3}$	-1
π	$\tfrac{1}{2}f_6 = \tfrac{1}{2}F_6$	-1	1	-1	1	-1	1
	$6A_0$	$3A_1$	$3A_2$	$3A_3$	$3A_4$	$3A_5$	$6A_6$

In Table 9.1a, the sum of the entries in the data column is $6A_0$, whereas the sum of products of corresponding entries in the data column and the column headed $\cos kx$ is $3A_k$ or $6A_6$. Similarly, the sum of products of corresponding entries in the data column of Table 9.1b and the column headed $\sin kx$ is $3B_k$.

In illustration, for the empirical data

θ	$0°$	$30°$	$60°$	$90°$	$120°$	$150°$	$180°$	$210°$	$240°$	$270°$	$300°$	$330°$	$360°$
f	1.21	1.32	1.46	1.40	1.34	1.18	1.07	1.01	1.05	1.10	1.14	1.17	1.21
x	0	$\dfrac{\pi}{6}$	$\dfrac{\pi}{3}$	$\dfrac{\pi}{2}$	$\dfrac{2\pi}{3}$	$\dfrac{5\pi}{6}$	π	$-\dfrac{5\pi}{6}$	$-\dfrac{2\pi}{3}$	$-\dfrac{\pi}{2}$	$-\dfrac{\pi}{3}$	$-\dfrac{\pi}{6}$	2π

TABLE 9.1b

x	Data	$\sin x$	$\sin 2x$	$\sin 3x$	$\sin 4x$	$\sin 5x$
$\dfrac{\pi}{6}$	$\tfrac{1}{2}(f_1 - f_{-1}) = G_1$	$\tfrac{1}{2}$	$\tfrac{1}{2}\sqrt{3}$	1	$\tfrac{1}{2}\sqrt{3}$	$\tfrac{1}{2}$
$\dfrac{\pi}{3}$	$\tfrac{1}{2}(f_2 - f_{-2}) = G_2$	$\tfrac{1}{2}\sqrt{3}$	$\tfrac{1}{2}\sqrt{3}$	0	$-\tfrac{1}{2}\sqrt{3}$	$-\tfrac{1}{2}\sqrt{3}$
$\dfrac{\pi}{2}$	$\tfrac{1}{2}(f_3 - f_{-3}) = G_3$	1	0	-1	0	1
$\dfrac{2\pi}{3}$	$\tfrac{1}{2}(f_4 - f_{-4}) = G_4$	$\tfrac{1}{2}\sqrt{3}$	$-\tfrac{1}{2}\sqrt{3}$	0	$\tfrac{1}{2}\sqrt{3}$	$-\tfrac{1}{2}\sqrt{3}$
$\dfrac{5\pi}{6}$	$\tfrac{1}{2}(f_5 - f_{-5}) = G_5$	$\tfrac{1}{2}$	$-\tfrac{1}{2}\sqrt{3}$	1	$-\tfrac{1}{2}\sqrt{3}$	$\tfrac{1}{2}$
		$3B_1$	$3B_2$	$3B_3$	$3B_4$	$3B_5$

the entries in the respective data columns of Tables 9.1a, b are

0.605	
1.245	0.075
1.300	0.160
1.250	0.150
1.195	0.145
1.095	0.085
0.535	

and calculation gives

$$A_0 = 1.204, \quad A_1 = 0.084, \quad A_2 = -0.062, \quad A_3 = -0.012,$$
$$A_4 = -0.009, \quad B_1 = 0.165, \quad B_2 = 0.001, \quad B_3 = 0.003, \quad B_4 = -0.007,$$

for the coefficients of harmonics through the fourth.

In order to obtain a seven-point cosine-series approximation to a function $F(x)$ over the half range $0 < x < \pi$, through harmonics of order not exceeding six, use would be made of Table 9.1a only, whereas for a five-point sine-series approximation to $G(x)$ over the same half range, through harmonics of order not exceeding five, only Table 9.1b would be used. In any case, if all the *available* harmonics are retained, the resultant approximation takes on the prescribed value at each of the points employed in the calculation. Retention of a smaller number of harmonics leads to the appropriate *least-squares* approximation relevant to that set of points.†

Tables corresponding to those given here, but employing larger sets of data and further systematized in various ways, may be found in the

† For the *cosine* approximation, the result corresponds to the use of one-half weights with respect to the errors at 0 and N (see Prob. 9).

literature (see Whittaker and Robinson [20] and Willers [21]).   A related procedure is described in §9.7.

9.4. Exponential Approximation.   In certain cases it is desired to determine an approximation of the form

$$f(x) \approx C_1 e^{a_1 x} + C_2 e^{a_2 x} + \cdots + C_n e^{a_n x} \qquad (9.4.1)$$

or, equivalently, of the form

$$f(x) \approx C_1 \mu_1^x + C_2 \mu_2^x + \cdots + C_n \mu_n^x, \qquad (9.4.2)$$
where
$$\mu_k = e^{a_k}. \qquad (9.4.3)$$

It is somewhat more convenient here to work with the second form (9.4.2).   We suppose that a linear change of variables has been introduced, in advance, in such a way that values of $f(x)$ (exact or empirical) are specified at the N equally spaced points $x = 0, 1, 2, \ldots, N - 1$.

If (9.4.1) were to be an equality for these values of x, the equations

$$
\begin{aligned}
C_1 + C_2 + \cdots + C_n &= f_0, \\
C_1 \mu_1 + C_2 \mu_2 + \cdots + C_n \mu_n &= f_1, \\
C_1 \mu_1^2 + C_2 \mu_2^2 + \cdots + C_n \mu_n^2 &= f_2, \\
&\cdots\cdots\cdots\cdots\cdots \\
C_1 \mu_1^{N-1} + C_2 \mu_2^{N-1} + \cdots + C_n \mu_n^{N-1} &= f_{N-1}
\end{aligned}
\qquad (9.4.4)
$$

would necessarily be satisfied, and the approximation (9.4.2) may be based on the result of satisfying these equations as nearly as possible. If the constants $\mu_1, \ldots, \mu_n$ were known (or preassigned), this set would comprise N linear equations in the n unknowns $C_1, \ldots, C_n$ and could be solved exactly if $N = n$ or approximately, by the least-squares method of §7.3, if $N > n$.

However, if the μ's are also to be determined, at least $2n$ equations are needed, and the difficulty consists in the fact that the equations are *nonlinear* in the μ's.   This difficulty can be minimized by a method, similar to methods used in §8.14, next to be described.

Let $\mu_1, \ldots, \mu_n$ be the roots of the algebraic equation

$$\mu^n - \alpha_1 \mu^{n-1} - \alpha_2 \mu^{n-2} - \cdots - \alpha_{n-1}\mu - \alpha_n = 0, \qquad (9.4.5)$$

so that the left-hand member of (9.4.5) is identified with the product $(\mu - \mu_1)(\mu - \mu_2) \cdots (\mu - \mu_n)$.   In order to determine the coefficients $\alpha_1, \ldots, \alpha_n$, we multiply the first equation in (9.4.4) by α_n, the second equation by $\alpha_{n-1}, \ldots$, the nth equation by α_1, and the $(n + 1)$th equation by -1, and add the results.   If use is made of the fact that each μ satisfies (9.4.5), the result is seen to be of the form

$$f_n - \alpha_1 f_{n-1} - \cdots - \alpha_n f_0 = 0.$$

A set of $N - n - 1$ additional equations of similar type is obtained in the same way by starting instead successively with the second, third, . . . , $(N - n)$th equations. In this way we find that (9.4.4) and (9.4.5) imply the $N - n$ *linear* equations

$$f_{n-1}\alpha_1 + f_{n-2}\alpha_2 + \cdots + f_0\alpha_n = f_n,$$
$$f_n\alpha_1 + f_{n-1}\alpha_2 + \cdots + f_1\alpha_n = f_{n+1}, \qquad (9.4.6)$$
$$\cdots\cdots\cdots\cdots\cdots\cdots\cdots\cdots\cdots\cdots\cdots$$
$$f_{N-2}\alpha_1 + f_{N-3}\alpha_2 + \cdots + f_{N-n-1}\alpha_n = f_{N-1}.$$

Since the ordinates f_k are known, this set generally can be solved directly for the n α's if $N = 2n$, or solved approximately, by the method of least squares, if $N > 2n$.

After the α's are determined, the n μ's are found as the roots of (9.4.5). They may be real or complex. The equations (9.4.4) then become linear equations in the n C's, with known coefficients. The C's can be determined, finally, from the first n of these equations or, preferably, by applying the least-squares technique to the entire set.

Thus the nonlinearity of the system is concentrated in the single algebraic equation (9.4.5). The technique described is known as *Prony's method.*

Obvious modifications are necessary when certain of the μ's (or a's) are prescribed and the remainder are to be determined. When such constraints are imposed, and are to be satisfied *exactly*, it is essential to satisfy them (by using them to eliminate unknowns from the set of equations to be solved) *before* applying the method of least squares.

The most common situation of this sort is that in which it is known that $f(x)$ tends to a finite limit (the value of which is generally unknown) as $x \to \infty$. The approximation

$$f(x) \approx C_0 + C_1 e^{a_1 x} + \cdots + C_n e^{a_n x} \qquad (9.4.7)$$

is then appropriate, where the a's are expected to have negative real parts. Since this approximation implies that

$$\Delta f(x) \approx C_1' e^{a_1 x} + \cdots + C_n' e^{a_n x},$$

where the coefficient C_k' is an unknown constant which is simply related to the unknown C_k, the equations (9.4.6) may be modified, in this case, by replacing each f_k by the difference $\Delta f_k \equiv f_{k+1} - f_k$, after which the α's and μ's are determined as before. The equations (9.4.4) are then modified by the insertion of the unknown C_0 in each left-hand member. At least $N = 2n + 1$ independent data are needed for the determination.

If one or more of the μ's satisfying (9.4.5) are not real and positive, the corresponding values of the a's in (9.4.1) will not be real. In particular, if μ_k is real and negative, say $\mu_k = -\rho_k$, where ρ_k is positive, the term $u_k^x = (-\rho_k)^x$ is real only when x takes on the (integral) values for which data are prescribed, or values which differ from those values by integral multiples of the (unit) spacing. However, we may notice that $(-1)^x = \cos \pi x$ *for any such value of* x. Hence, if we replace $(-\rho_k)^x$ by $\rho_k^x \cos \pi x$ or, equivalently, by $e^{x \log \rho_k} \cos \pi x$, we so obtain a suitable interpolating function which is real for all real values of x.

More generally, if one value of μ is *complex*, and hence expressible in the polar form $\rho e^{i\beta}$, where ρ and β are real and ρ is *positive*, then the conjugate $\rho e^{-i\beta}$ must also be involved, since the coefficients in (9.4.5) are necessarily real. The corresponding part of (9.4.2) can then be written as

$$\rho^x(A_1 e^{i\beta x} + A_2 e^{-i\beta x})$$

where A_1 and A_2 are constants which must be conjugate complex in order that the expression be real when x is real. Hence, by writing $A_1 = (C_1 + iC_2)/2$ and $A_2 = (C_1 - iC_2)/2$, this part of the approximation can be expressed in the more convenient form

$$\rho^x(C_1 \cos \beta x + C_2 \sin \beta x) \equiv e^{x \log \rho}(C_1 \cos \beta x + C_2 \sin \beta x), \quad (9.4.8)$$

after the μ's are determined from (9.4.5) and (9.4.6), but before equations corresponding to (9.4.4) are formed and solved for the coefficients of the approximating functions.

In order to illustrate both the technique and the existence of unfavorable situations, we consider the attempt to recover the equation of the function

$$f(x) = 2.32 - 1.08e^{-x} + 1.20e^{-2x} \qquad (9.4.9)$$

from the values of that function for $x = 0$, 1, 2, 3, and 4, under the hypothesis that the numerical coefficients in (9.4.9) are exact. These values are given, to four decimal places, in the following tabulation:

x	0	1	2	3	4
$f(x)$	2.4400	2.0851	2.1958	2.2692	2.3006

If the ordinates are arbitrarily rounded to *two* decimal places, the required differences of the rounded values are found to be -0.35, 0.11, 0.07, and 0.03, and Eqs. (9.4.6), with f_r replaced by Δf_r, become

$$\begin{aligned} 0.11\alpha_1 - 0.35\alpha_2 &= 0.07, \\ 0.07\alpha_1 + 0.11\alpha_2 &= 0.03, \end{aligned} \qquad (9.4.10)$$

from which there follows $\alpha_1 = \frac{91}{183} \doteq 0.497$ and $\alpha_2 = -\frac{8}{183} \doteq -0.0437$. Equation (9.4.5) then becomes

$$183\mu^2 - 91\mu + 8 = 0$$

and yields $\mu_1 \doteq 0.383$ and $\mu_2 \doteq 0.114$, to three places. Thus the required approximation is to be of the form

$$f(x) \approx C_0 + C_1(0.383)^x + C_2(0.114)^x$$
$$= C_0 + C_1 e^{-0.96x} + C_2 e^{-2.18x}, \qquad (9.4.11)$$

after which the C's may be determined by fitting the data at three points, or by use of a least-squares procedure over the five points for which data are provided.   More nearly accurate determinations of the decay factors would have resulted from a reduction of inherent errors in the data employed, or from the result of using additional data to supply additional equations, and solving the resultant set approximately by least-squares methods.

Suppose, however, that the values $f(1) \doteq 2.0851$ and $f(2) \doteq 2.1958$ were incorrectly rounded to 2.08 and 2.19, respectively.   We notice that the round-off errors so introduced are only slightly greater than those effected by the correct rounding, and we may consider these additional errors as representative of observational errors which could result if the data were empirical.   The four relevant differences are then -0.36, 0.11, 0.08, and 0.03, and the equations replacing (9.4.10) become

$$0.11\alpha_1 - 0.36\alpha_2 = 0.08,$$
$$0.08\alpha_1 + 0.11\alpha_2 = 0.03, \qquad (9.4.12)$$

from which there follows $\alpha_1 = \frac{196}{409} \doteq 0.479$ and $\alpha_2 = -\frac{31}{409} \doteq -0.0758$. The equation which determines approximations to μ_1 and μ_2 is then $409\mu^2 - 196\mu + 31 = 0$, which yields the *complex* roots $\mu_{1,2} \doteq 0.240 \pm 0.361i$.   Since, accordingly, $\mu_{1,2} \doteq e^{-1.29 \pm 0.515i}$, the form replacing (9.4.11) here becomes

$$f(x) \approx C_0 + e^{-1.29x}(C_1 \cos 0.515x + C_2 \sin 0.515x), \qquad (9.4.13)$$

from which the C's may be determined by collocation or by least squares.

Whereas it is found that the coefficients in (9.4.11) and (9.4.13) can be determined in such a way that they *both* provide good approximations to the true function (9.4.9) for $0 \leq x \leq 4$ and, indeed, depart only slightly from $f(x)$ for all $x \geq 0$, the latter approximation is oscillatory, while the true function and the former approximation are not.   The slight additional errors introduced into the given data here lead to completely incorrect information concerning the *decay factors*.

While this example was selected deliberately to illustrate a particularly unfavorable situation, this type of "instability" is of common occurrence when it is necessary to determine the approximating *coordinate functions* themselves, in addition to the constants of combination to be associated with them.   In such cases, it is particularly desirable that an error analysis be made.

Since here the true values of μ_1 and μ_2 are $e^{-1} \doteq 0.368$ and $e^{-2} \doteq 0.135$, the true values of α_1 and α_2 are $e^{-1} + e^{-2} \doteq 0.503$ and $-e^{-3} \doteq -0.0498$. Thus, in the second calculation, errors of magnitude smaller than 0.006 in the data employed lead to errors of about 0.024 and 0.026 in the calculation of α_1 and α_2, respectively, and these errors, in turn, lead to complex approximations of the real μ_1 and μ_2. The *possibility* of appreciably larger errors than those actually encountered in the calculation of α_1 and α_2 from *either* of the sets (9.4.10) and (9.4.12), assuming the coefficients to be correct to the places given, could have been predicted by an analysis of those sets.† Once such estimates are obtained, the maximum (or RMS) values of the errors $\delta\mu_1$ and $\delta\mu_2$ in the roots of $\mu^2 - \alpha_1\mu - \alpha_2 = 0$ may be estimated, by use of the differential relation

$$(2\mu - \alpha_1)\,d\mu = \mu\,d\alpha_1 + d\alpha_2,$$

as

$$|\delta\mu_1|_{\max} \approx \frac{1 + |\mu_1|}{|\mu_2 - \mu_1|}\,|\delta\alpha|_{\max}, \qquad |\delta\mu_2|_{\max} \approx \frac{1 + |\mu_2|}{|\mu_2 - \mu_1|}\,|\delta\alpha|_{\max} \quad (9.4.14)$$

or

$$(\delta\mu_1)_{\mathrm{RMS}} \approx \frac{\sqrt{1 + \mu_1^2}}{|\mu_2 - \mu_1|}\,(\delta\alpha)_{\mathrm{RMS}}, \qquad (\delta\mu_2)_{\mathrm{RMS}} \approx \frac{\sqrt{1 + \mu_2^2}}{|\mu_2 - \mu_1|}\,(\delta\alpha)_{\mathrm{RMS}}, \quad (9.4.15)$$

with μ_1 and μ_2 replaced by their calculated values, if those calculated values are real, and if the errors are small. The reality of μ_1 and μ_2 depends upon the positivity of $\alpha_1^2 + 4\alpha_2$ and is in doubt if $|\alpha_1^2 + 4\alpha_2| < 2|2 + \alpha_1|\,|\delta\alpha|_{\max}$, when α_1 and α_2 are estimated by their calculated values. Similar considerations apply to the more involved cases in which more coordinate functions are employed.

9.5. Determination of Constituent Periodicities. It frequently happens that an empirical function $f(x)$ is known to be expressible as a linear combination of two or more periodic terms whose periods are unknown and are not necessarily commensurable, and the approximate determination of these periods from empirical data is often of considerable importance.

If m distinct periods, denoted by $2\pi/\omega_1, \ldots, 2\pi/\omega_m$, are known (or assumed) to be present, then $f(x)$ correspondingly can be assumed to be approximated by an expression of the form

$$f(x) \approx A_1 \cos \omega_1 x + B_1 \sin \omega_1 x + \cdots + A_m \cos \omega_m x + B_m \sin \omega_m x. \tag{9.5.1}$$

But such an approximation is a special case of (9.4.1), in which $n = 2m$

---

† The analysis of RMS errors relevant to the normal equations obtained in a least-squares procedure is described in §7.3 [see (7.3.36)]. For the corresponding analysis of maximum errors when least-squares methods are not used, as in the present case, see §10.6.

and in which the a's are identified respectively with $i\omega_1$, $-i\omega_1$, . . . , $i\omega_m$, and $-i\omega_m$. Thus the desired values of ω may be obtained, by Prony's method, if we set $n = 2m$ and $\mu = e^{i\omega}$ in (9.4.5) and (9.4.6), again assuming $f(x)$ to be given for $x = 0, 1, 2, . . . , N - 1$.†

Since, in this case, the roots of (9.4.5) are known (or required) to occur in reciprocal pairs $(e^{i\omega_k}, e^{-i\omega_k})$, it follows that (9.4.5) must be invariant under the substitution of $1/\mu$ for μ, so that we must have $\alpha_{2m} = -1$, $\alpha_{2m-1} = \alpha_1$, . . . , $\alpha_{m+1} = \alpha_{m-1}$. Thus, with $\mu = e^{i\omega}$, Eq. (9.4.5) becomes

$$e^{i2m\omega} - \alpha_1 e^{i(2m-1)\omega} - \cdots - \alpha_{m-1}e^{i(m+1)\omega} - \alpha_m e^{im\omega} - \alpha_{m-1}e^{i(m-1)\omega}$$
$$- \cdots - \alpha_1 e^{i\omega} + 1 = 0$$

or

$$e^{im\omega}[(e^{im\omega} + e^{-im\omega}) - \alpha_1(e^{i(m-1)\omega} + e^{-i(m-1)\omega}) - \cdots$$
$$- \alpha_{m-1}(e^{i\omega} + e^{-i\omega}) - \alpha_m] = 0$$

and hence, finally, since $e^{im\omega} \neq 0$, we find that the equation determining ω is of the form

$$2 \cos m\omega - 2\alpha_1 \cos (m - 1)\omega - \cdots - 2\alpha_{m-1}\cos \omega - \alpha_m = 0. \quad (9.5.2)$$

Since $\cos k\omega$ is expressible as a polynomial of degree k in $\cos \omega$, this equation can be expressed as an algebraic equation of degree m in $\cos \omega$. Indeed, it can be expressed in the form

$$T_m(\cos \omega) - \alpha_1 T_{m-1}(\cos \omega) - \cdots - \alpha_{m-1}T_1(\cos \omega) - \tfrac{1}{2}\alpha_m = 0,$$

in terms of the Chebyshev polynomials of §7.8.

The N equations (9.4.6), which serve to determine the coefficients $\alpha_1, . . . , \alpha_m$ in (9.5.2), reduce (again with $n = 2m$, $\alpha_{m+k} = \alpha_{m-k}$, and $\alpha_{2m} = -1$) to the forms

$$(f_1 + f_{2m-1})\alpha_1 + (f_2 + f_{2m-2})\alpha_2 + \cdots + (f_{m-1} + f_{m+1})\alpha_{m-1}$$
$$+ f_m\alpha_m = f_0 + f_{2m},$$
$$(f_2 + f_{2m})\alpha_1 + (f_3 + f_{2m-1})\alpha_2 + \cdots + (f_m + f_{m+2})\alpha_{m-1}$$
$$+ f_{m+1}\alpha_m = f_1 + f_{2m+1}, \quad (9.5.3)$$
$$\cdot \cdot \cdot \cdot \cdot \cdot \cdot \cdot \cdot \cdot \cdot \cdot \cdot \cdot \cdot \cdot \cdot \cdot \cdot \cdot \cdot$$
$$(f_{N-2m} + f_{N-2})\alpha_1 + (f_{N-2m+1} + f_{N-3})\alpha_2 + \cdots$$
$$+ (f_{N-m-2} + f_{N-m})\alpha_{m-1} + f_{N-m-1}\alpha_m = f_{N-2m-1} + f_{N-1}.$$

In accordance with the fact that the approximation (9.5.1) involves $3m$ unknown constants, we must have $N \geqq 3m$. The set (9.5.3) then comprises $N - 2m \geqq m$ equations in the m unknowns a_k.

† In the more general case, the dimensionless variable x accordingly represents displacement from a reference point in units of the actual spacing h, as in the preceding section, and the calculated periods are also to be considered as expressed in units of h.

This set is to be solved (approximately, by least-squares, if $N > 3m$) for the α's, and the ω's are then determined from (9.5.2), after which the coefficients in (9.5.1) are determined (if their values are desired) by writing down the conditions which would require (9.5.1) to be an equality for at least $2m$ of the N relevant values of x, and solving that set approximately, by the method of least-squares, if more than $2m$ conditions are used.

If, in addition, an unknown constant A_0 is present in the right-hand member of (9.5.1), Eqs. (9.5.3) are to be modified by replacing each f_k by Δf_k, and the constant A_0 will then appear only in the set of equations determining the *coefficients* in (9.5.1). Here we must have $N \geq 3m + 1$ given data.

As a simple illustration, we attempt to determine the constituent periods of the function

$$f(x) = \cos \frac{\pi x}{3} + \sin \frac{\pi x}{4}, \qquad (9.5.4)$$

assuming knowledge only of the following rounded values of that function:

x	0	1	2	3	4	5	6	7	8	9	10
$f(x)$	1.00	1.21	0.50	-0.29	-0.50	-0.21	0.00	-0.21	-0.50	-0.29	0.50

If we suppose that the vanishing of the over-all mean value of $f(x)$ is not known in advance, but that there is evidence (from physical considerations or otherwise) that the *deviation* from the mean is due to the superposition of two periodic processes, we first calculate the relevant *differences:*

x	0	1	2	3	4	5	6	7	8	9
$\Delta f(x)$	0.21	-0.71	-0.79	-0.21	0.29	0.21	-0.21	-0.29	0.21	0.79

Next, the six equations corresponding to (9.5.3) are written down,

$$
\begin{aligned}
-0.92\alpha_1 - 0.79\alpha_2 &= 0.50, \\
-0.50\alpha_1 - 0.21\alpha_2 &= -0.50, \\
0.29\alpha_2 &= -1.00, \\
0.08\alpha_1 + 0.21\alpha_2 &= -0.50, \\
-0.08\alpha_1 - 0.21\alpha_2 &= 0.50, \\
- 0.29\alpha_2 &= 1.00,
\end{aligned}
\qquad (9.5.5)
$$

and the relevant normal equations are obtained in the form

$$
\begin{aligned}
1.1092\alpha_1 + 0.8654\alpha_2 &= -0.2900, \\
0.8654\alpha_1 + 0.9246\alpha_2 &= -1.0800.
\end{aligned}
\qquad (9.5.6)
$$

The solution is found to be $\alpha_1 \doteq 2.4092$, $\alpha_2 \doteq -3.4230$, to four places, after which (9.5.2) becomes

$$2 \cos 2\omega - 4.8184 \cos \omega + 3.4230 = 0$$

or
$$4 \cos^2 \omega - 4.8184 \cos \omega + 1.4230 = 0, \qquad (9.5.7)$$

and yields the values

$$\cos \omega_1 \doteq 0.5186, \qquad \cos \omega_2 \doteq 0.6860,$$

from which the appropriate approximations to the true periods

$$P_1 = \frac{2\pi}{\omega_1} = 6, \qquad P_2 = \frac{2\pi}{\omega_2} = 8$$

are found to be

$$P_1 \approx \frac{2\pi}{1.0256} \doteq 6.12, \qquad P_2 \approx \frac{2\pi}{0.8147} \doteq 7.71. \qquad (9.5.8)$$

Hence the round-off errors introduced into the given data here correspond to errors of about 2 and 4 per cent in the calculations of P_1 and P_2, respectively. The corresponding approximation to the governing equation would then be obtained, if it were desired, by fitting the equation

$$f(x) \approx A_0 + A_1 \cos 1.026x + B_1 \sin 1.026x$$
$$+ A_2 \cos 0.815x + B_2 \sin 0.815x \qquad (9.5.9)$$

to the data by use of the least-squares procedure.

Here, and in the general case, it may be noticed that only the value of $\cos \omega_k$ is determinate. Thus, if we denote by $\bar{\omega}_k$ the admissible value of ω_k which lies between 0 and π, we can conclude only that the proper approximate value of ω_k is one of the numbers $\pm \bar{\omega}_k + 2r\pi$ ($r = 0, 1, 2, \ldots$), so that, if the true physical spacing is h, the actual approximate period is known only to be one of the numbers

$$\frac{2\pi h}{\bar{\omega}_k + 2r\pi}, \qquad \frac{2\pi h}{2\pi - \bar{\omega}_k + 2r\pi} \qquad (r = 0, 1, \ldots).$$

Of these possibilities, only those corresponding to $r = 0$ can exceed the spacing h; the first $[2\pi h/\bar{\omega}_k]$ exceeds $2h$, whereas the second $[2\pi h/(2\pi - \bar{\omega}_k)]$ lies between h and $2h$. The data employed clearly cannot be expected to determine periods smaller than the spacing with any appreciable accuracy, in general. Whether or not either of the two remaining appropriate alternatives truly represents an approximate period could be determined mathematically by investigating whether a second calculation based on a set of additional data, with a spacing incommensurable with h, also yields that alternative. In practice, the decision frequently can be based more simply on an inspection of the graph of the data or on physical considerations.

Situations in which two or more of the constituent periods are nearly equal are of frequent practical occurrence and are the most troublesome ones. In such cases it is particularly important to retain sufficiently many terms in the approximation and to use a sufficiently large set of data when the data are inexact. An interesting example of this type is treated successfully in Whittaker and Robinson [20] (§175), by a method which differs from the present one, and also in Willers [21] (§30), by a method equivalent to that given here. In that case, 600 empirical data are available for the determination of two constituent periods, and all are employed in the former treatment. Whereas the latter treatment does not use all the 595 equations which could be formed, in analogy to (9.5.5), it first makes use of a selected set of 78 equations whose formation involves the use of most of the data, and then checks the results by a recalculation using a judiciously chosen similar set of 17 equations.

9.6. Optimum Polynomial Interpolation with Selected Abscissas. It has been shown in earlier chapters that, if a function $f(x)$ is approximated by the polynomial $y(x)$ of degree n which agrees with $f(x)$ at $n + 1$ points $x_0, x_1, \ldots, x_n$, we may write

$$f(x) = y(x) + \pi(x) \frac{f^{(n+1)}(\xi)}{(n+1)!}, \qquad (9.6.1)$$

where

$$\pi(x) = (x - x_0)(x - x_1) \cdots (x - x_n), \qquad (9.6.2)$$

and where ξ lies in the interval I limited by the largest and smallest of $x_0, x_1, \ldots, x_n$, and x. We suppose here that an appropriate change of variables has reduced this interval to the interval $(-1,1)$.

Furthermore, in the preceding chapter it was seen that appropriate choices of the $n + 1$ abscissas lead to *quadrature* formulas having certain desirable characteristics. In this section we investigate briefly a related class of interpolation formulas and single out a particular formula which is related to *trigonometric* approximation in the following section.

Whereas the parameter ξ in (9.6.1) depends upon the $n + 1$ abscissas and the variable x, the nature of that dependence will depend, in turn, upon the nature of the function $f(x)$. Thus, if we desire to choose the abscissas in such a way that the error will tend to be as small as possible over $(-1,1)$, in some sense, for the set of *all* such functions having $n + 1$ continuous derivatives in $(-1,1)$, we may attempt to make $|\pi(x)|$ as small as possible, in the same sense, over that interval, recalling that the coefficient of the highest power of x in $\pi(x)$ must be *unity*, from (9.6.2).

In particular, we may require that

$$\int_{-1}^{1} w(x)[\pi(x)]^2 \, dx = \min, \qquad (9.6.3)$$

where $w(x)$ is a prescribed weighting function which is nonnegative in

$(-1,1)$.   If we notice that $\pi(x)$ is expressible in the form

$$\pi(x) = x^{n+1} + c_n x^n + \cdots + c_2 x^2 + c_1 x + c_0, \qquad (9.6.4)$$

and hence may be considered to be specified by the $n + 1$ coefficients $c_0, c_1, \ldots, c_n$, we deduce that (9.6.3) leads to the requirement that the partial derivative of the left-hand member with respect to each c_r must vanish.   Since also

$$\frac{\partial \pi(x)}{\partial c_r} = x^r \qquad (r = 0, 1, \ldots, n), \qquad (9.6.5)$$

this requirement becomes

$$2 \int_{-1}^{1} w(x) \frac{\partial \pi(x)}{\partial c_r} \pi(x) \, dx \equiv 2 \int_{-1}^{1} w(x) \pi(x) x^r \, dx = 0 \qquad (r = 0, 1, \ldots, n),$$
$$(9.6.6)$$

so that $\pi(x)$ *is to be that polynomial of degree $n + 1$, with leading coefficient unity, which is orthogonal to all polynomials of inferior degree over $(-1,1)$, relative to $w(x)$.*   The abscissas of the $n + 1$ points, at which the agreement between $f(x)$ and the polynomial approximation should be effected, are thus the zeros of that polynomial.

It is of interest to notice that, with the interpolation polynomial so determined, the integral approximation

$$\int_{-1}^{1} w(x) f(x) \, dx \approx \int_{-1}^{1} w(x) y(x) \, dx$$

is the corresponding *Gaussian quadrature* formula of Chap. 8.

Thus, in particular, if we take $w(x) = 1$, and so attempt to minimize the integral of the square of the error $E(x)$ over the interval $(-1,1)$, it follows from the results of §7.5 that the $n + 1$ abscissas should be the zeros of $P_{n+1}(x)$.   Certain such sets of abscissas are listed in Table 8.1 (§8.5).

Further, if we take $w(x) = 1/\sqrt{1 - x^2}$, and so attempt to minimize the integral of $[E(x)]^2/\sqrt{1 - x^2}$, the results of §7.8 show that the abscissas are to be the zeros of the $(n + 1)$th Chebyshev polynomial $T_{n+1}(x)$,

$$T_{n+1}(x) = \cos\left[(n + 1) \cos^{-1} x\right], \qquad (9.6.7)$$

and hence are given by

$$x_i = \cos\left(\frac{2i + 1}{n + 1} \frac{\pi}{2}\right) \qquad (i = 0, 1, \ldots, n). \qquad (9.6.8)$$

Since the coefficient of x^r in $T_r(x)$ is 2^{r-1}, it follows also that then

$$\pi(x) = 2^{-n} T_{n+1}(x). \qquad (9.6.9)$$

In addition, we may notice that the *extreme* values of $\pi(x)$ in $(-1,1)$ are then $\pm 2^{-n}$ and are taken on (with successively alternating signs) at the end points $x = \pm 1$ and at n additional interior points, each of which separates a pair of adjacent abscissas. Thus, with this choice of the abscissas, the coefficient of $f^{(n+1)}(\xi)/(n + 1)!$ in the error term of (9.6.1) oscillates with *constant* amplitude 2^{-n} as x increases from -1 to 1.

On the other hand, since the coefficient of x^r in $P_r(x)$ is $2^{-r}(2r)!/(r!)^2$, the use of the zeros of $P_{n+1}(x)$ as the abscissas corresponds to the identification

$$\pi(x) = \frac{2^{n+1}[(n + 1)!]^2}{(2n + 2)!} P_{n+1}(x). \tag{9.6.10}$$

Now the Legendre polynomial takes on the value $+1$ at $x = +1$ and the value $(-1)^{n+1}$ at $x = -1$, and $P_{n+1}(x)$ performs oscillations in $(-1,1)$ in such a way that the n successive maxima and minima separating pairs of adjacent zeros inside the interval decrease in magnitude toward the center of that interval. Thus, in particular, the maximum absolute value of $\pi(x)$ in (9.6.10), over $(-1,1)$, is given by the numerical factor in that equation, which is approximated by $2^{-n}\sqrt{\pi n/4}$ when n is large.

Hence it follows that, whereas use of the zeros of $P_{n+1}(x)$ minimizes the RMS value of $\pi(x)$ over $(-1,1)$, the use of the zeros of $T_{n+1}(x)$ leads to a value of $|\pi(x)|_{max}$ which is smaller than that corresponding to the former choice, by a factor which tends to increase in proportion to $n^{\frac{1}{2}}$ as n increases. Furthermore, the error will tend to oscillate uniformly over $(-1,1)$ in the second case, whereas it will tend to oscillate with an amplitude increasing toward the ends of the interval in the first case, on the average. Thus, if it is desirable to control the *maximum* error, rather than the RMS error, the second choice will generally be preferable to the first.

Indeed, it was discovered by Chebyshev that this choice is the *best possible* one, when the maximum-error criterion is adopted. The proof follows most easily by assuming, on the contrary, that there exists a polynomial $\bar{\pi}(x)$ of degree $n + 1$ (with leading coefficient unity) whose maximum absolute value in $(-1,1)$ is smaller than 2^{-n}. Then the difference $\bar{\pi}(x) - 2^{-n}T_{n+1}(x)$ is negative at the maxima of $T_{n+1}(x)$ and positive at its minima. Hence, since $2^{-n}T_{n+1}(x)$ takes on its extreme values $(\pm 2^{-n})$ at $n + 2$ points of $(-1,1)$, including the ends, the difference $\bar{\pi}(x) - 2^{-n}T_{n+1}(x)$ must vanish at least $n + 1$ times. But, since this difference is a polynomial of degree n or less (the common leading term x^{n+1} being removed by the subtraction), this situation is impossible, and the desired contradiction is obtained.†

---

† It should be noticed that this result applies only to the minimization of the maximum value of $|\pi(x)|$ over $(-1,1)$. For any *specific* function $f(x)$, the maximum absolute value of the *error* $\pi(x)f^{(n+1)}(\xi)/(n + 1)!$ in (9.6.1) generally will not be minimized exactly, since the maximum value of $|f^{(n+1)}(\xi)|$ generally will not be attained in correspondence with an abscissa for which $|\pi(x)|$ is greatest.

9.7. Chebyshev Interpolation. In this section, we consider in more detail the polynomial interpolation formula based on collocation at the zeros of $T_{n+1}(x)$. Since any polynomial of degree n can be expressed as a linear combination of Chebyshev polynomials of degrees zero through n, it is convenient to express the polynomial $y(x)$ which agrees with $f(x)$ when $x = x_0, x_1, \ldots, x_n$, where x_r is the rth zero of $T_{n+1}(x)$, in such a form, and so to write

$$f(x) = \sum_{k=0}^{n} C_k T_k(x) + \frac{1}{2^n(n+1)!} T_{n+1}(x)f^{(n+1)}(\xi), \qquad (9.7.1)$$

in accordance with (9.6.1), where $|\xi| < 1$ under the assumption that x is in $(-1,1)$. The C's are to be determined in such a way that the result of suppressing the error term is correct when $x = x_0, x_1, \ldots, x_n$, where

$$x_i = \cos\left(\frac{2i+1}{2n+2}\pi\right) \qquad (i = 0, 1, \ldots, n). \qquad (9.7.2)$$

Whereas the desired interpolation polynomial could be expressed in the Lagrangian form of Chap. 3, the following alternative procedure is usually more convenient for its determination.

If we introduce the change of variables

$$x = \cos\theta \qquad (0 \le \theta \le \pi), \qquad (9.7.3)$$

the requirement

$$f(x) \approx \sum_{k=0}^{n} C_k T_k(x) \qquad (-1 < x < 1) \qquad (9.7.4)$$

becomes

$$F(\theta) \approx \sum_{k=0}^{n} C_k \cos k\theta \qquad (0 < \theta < \pi), \qquad (9.7.5)$$

with the abbreviation

$$F(\theta) = f(\cos\theta). \qquad (9.7.6)$$

The C's are now to be determined in such a way that (9.7.5) is an equality when $\theta = \theta_i$, where

$$\theta_i = \cos^{-1} x_i = \frac{2i+1}{2n+2}\pi \qquad (i = 0, 1, \ldots, n). \qquad (9.7.7)$$

Thus the agreement is to occur at the *equally spaced* points $\pi/(2n+2)$, $3\pi/(2n+2), \ldots, (2n+1)\pi/(2n+2)$, which are seen to be midway between the successive points $0, \pi/(n+1), 2\pi/(n+1), \ldots, \pi$ which would have been employed in the procedure of §9.3, as the points of collocation for the determination of the C's in an approximation of the form (9.7.5).

In analogy to corresponding results of that section, it happens that $\cos j\theta$ and $\cos k\theta$ are orthogonal under summation over the $n + 1$ points defined by (9.7.7) (see Prob. 22),

$$\sum_{r=0}^{n} \cos j\theta_r \cos k\theta_r = \begin{cases} 0 & (j \neq k), \\ \dfrac{n+1}{2} & (j = k \neq 0), \\ n+1 & (j = k = 0), \end{cases} \qquad (9.7.8)$$

where j and k are nonnegative integers not exceeding n. Moreover, since the left-hand member of (9.7.8) is identical with

$$\sum_{r=0}^{n} T_j(x_r) T_k(x_r),$$

it follows that, whereas $T_0(x)$, $T_1(x)$, . . . are orthogonal under *integration* over $(-1,1)$ relative to $w(x) = 1/\sqrt{1 - x^2}$, the functions $T_0(x)$, $T_1(x)$, . . . , $T_n(x)$ are orthogonal under *summation* over the zeros of $T_{n+1}(x)$, with a *unit* weighting function.

The truth of (9.7.8) permits us to deduce immediately that the required C's are expressible in the form

$$C_0 = \frac{1}{n+1} \sum_{r=0}^{n} F(\theta_r), \qquad C_k = \frac{2}{n+1} \sum_{r=0}^{n} F(\theta_r) \cos k\theta_r \qquad (k \neq 0),$$

$$(9.7.9)$$

where θ_i is defined by (9.7.7), or, alternatively, in the form

$$C_0 = \frac{1}{n+1} \sum_{r=0}^{n} f(x_r), \qquad C_k = \frac{2}{n+1} \sum_{r=0}^{n} f(x_r) T_k(x_r) \qquad (k \neq 0),$$

$$(9.7.10)$$

where x_i is defined by (9.7.2).

Thus, for example, we may construct Table 9.2 when $n = 5$. Here use has been made of the abbreviations

$$A = \cos \frac{\pi}{12} = \tfrac{1}{2} \sqrt{2 + \sqrt{3}} \doteq 0.96593,$$

$$B = \cos \frac{5\pi}{12} = \tfrac{1}{2} \sqrt{2 - \sqrt{3}} \doteq 0.25882. \qquad (9.7.11)$$

The dual headings permit the table to be used either with the function expressed as $f(x)$ over $-1 \leq x \leq 1$, with the unequally spaced abscissas listed in the third column, or with the function expressed as $F(\theta)$ over $0 \leq \theta \leq \pi$, with the equally spaced abscissas listed in the first column.

TABLE 9.2

θ	$f(x)$	$x = T_1(x)$	$T_2(x)$	$T_3(x)$	$T_4(x)$	$T_5(x)$
	$F(\theta)$	$\cos\theta$	$\cos 2\theta$	$\cos 3\theta$	$\cos 4\theta$	$\cos 5\theta$
$\dfrac{\pi}{12}$	$F_1 = f_1$	A	$\frac{1}{2}\sqrt{3}$	$\frac{1}{2}\sqrt{2}$	$\frac{1}{2}$	B
$\dfrac{\pi}{4}$	$F_2 = f_2$	$\frac{1}{2}\sqrt{2}$	0	$-\frac{1}{2}\sqrt{2}$	-1	$-\frac{1}{2}\sqrt{2}$
$\dfrac{5\pi}{12}$	$F_3 = f_3$	B	$-\frac{1}{2}\sqrt{3}$	$-\frac{1}{2}\sqrt{2}$	$\frac{1}{2}$	A
$\dfrac{7\pi}{12}$	$F_4 = f_4$	$-B$	$-\frac{1}{2}\sqrt{3}$	$\frac{1}{2}\sqrt{2}$	$\frac{1}{2}$	$-A$
$\dfrac{3\pi}{4}$	$F_5 = f_5$	$-\frac{1}{2}\sqrt{2}$	0	$\frac{1}{2}\sqrt{2}$	-1	$\frac{1}{2}\sqrt{2}$
$\dfrac{11\pi}{12}$	$F_6 = f_6$	$-A$	$\frac{1}{2}\sqrt{3}$	$-\frac{1}{2}\sqrt{2}$	$\frac{1}{2}$	$-B$
	$6C_0$	$3C_1$	$3C_2$	$3C_3$	$3C_4$	$3C_5$

Thus, for example, the coefficient of $\cos 4\theta$ in (9.7.5) is given by

$$C_4 = \tfrac{1}{3}(\tfrac{1}{2}F_1 - F_2 + \tfrac{1}{2}F_3 + \tfrac{1}{2}F_4 - F_5 + \tfrac{1}{2}F_6),$$

whereas the coefficient of $T_4(x)$ in (9.7.4) is given by

$$C_4 = \tfrac{1}{3}(\tfrac{1}{2}f_1 - f_2 + \tfrac{1}{2}f_3 + \tfrac{1}{2}f_4 - f_5 + \tfrac{1}{2}f_6).$$

In order to obtain an exact fit at the six relevant points, all the harmonics involved are to be used. The result of retaining a smaller number of harmonics would give the corresponding *least-squares* approximation over the six points.

Once the C's are determined, the evaluation of the right-hand member of the approximation

$$f(x) \approx \sum_{k=0}^{n} C_k T_k(x) \tag{9.7.12}$$

at intermediate points is facilitated by the use of available tables of the Chebyshev polynomials [see reference [273], in which the function $2T_k(x/2)$ is tabulated instead and is denoted by $C_k(x)$].

9.8. Economization of Power Series. It was seen in §7.8 that the nth-degree least-squares polynomial approximation to a function $f(x)$ over $(-1,1)$, where the integral of the product of $1/\sqrt{1 - x^2}$ and the square of the error is to be minimized, is of the form

$$f(x) \approx y(x) = \sum_{k=0}^{n} a_k T_k(x) \qquad (|x| < 1), \qquad (9.8.1)$$

where

$$a_0 = \frac{1}{\pi} \int_{-1}^{1} \frac{f(x)}{\sqrt{1 - x^2}} \, dx, \qquad a_k = \frac{2}{\pi} \int_{-1}^{1} \frac{f(x) T_k(x)}{\sqrt{1 - x^2}} \, dx \qquad (k \geqq 1).$$

$$(9.8.2)$$

The approximation so determined generally will not be identified with that of (9.7.12), since the coefficients, determined in the one case by summation over a discrete set and in the other by integration over an interval, are generally unequal. However, the two approximations may be expected to be of similar nature, in the sense that the error associated with each will tend to oscillate with uniform amplitude over $(-1,1)$, whereas that afforded by the finite Legendre series arising from least-squares approximation with uniform weighting (§7.5) will tend to oscillate with an amplitude which increases toward the ends of that interval, on the average. Accordingly, if the smallness of the *maximum* error is to be the governing criterion, it may be expected that a satisfactory approximation may be afforded by fewer terms of the Chebyshev series than would be required for the Legendre series.

For many functions, the evaluation of the integrals occurring in (9.8.2) is not readily effected. However, if a function $f(x)$ is defined by a power series in x, for sufficiently small values of $|x|$, or if such an expansion is readily obtainable, an alternative method suggested by Lanczos (see references [129] and [273]) is often useful.

Suppose that one has the relation

$$f(x) = \sum_{k=0}^{n} A_k x^k + E_n(x), \qquad (9.8.3)$$

where it is known that

$$|E_n(x)| < \epsilon_1 \qquad (-1 \leqq x \leqq 1), \qquad (9.8.4)$$

and that ϵ_1 is smaller than the prescribed error tolerance ϵ, whereas $|A_n| + \epsilon_1$ is *not* a tolerable error, so that the last term in the approximation

$$f(x) \approx \sum_{k=0}^{n} A_k x^k \qquad (9.8.5)$$

cannot be safely neglected.

Now let the right-hand member of (9.8.5) be expanded in a series of Chebyshev polynomials. Since that member is a polynomial of degree n, the resultant series will terminate with the term involving $T_n(x)$ and hence will be of the form

$$\sum_{k=0}^{n} A_k x^k \equiv \sum_{k=0}^{n} a_k T_k(x). \tag{9.8.6}$$

From the fact that the terms of highest degree in $T_r(x)$ are given by

$$T_r(x) = 2^{r-1}\left(x^r - \frac{r}{4}x^{r-2} + \cdots\right), \tag{9.8.7}$$

it follows that the result of expressing the two members of (9.8.6) in terms of decreasing powers of x will be of the form

$$A_n x^n + A_{n-1}x^{n-1} + A_{n-2}x^{n-2} + \cdots = 2^{n-1}a_n\left(x^n - \frac{n}{4}x^{n-2} + \cdots\right)$$

$$+ 2^{n-2}a_{n-1}\left(x^{n-1} - \frac{n-1}{4}x^{n-3} + \cdots\right)$$

$$+ 2^{n-3}a_{n-2}(x^{n-2} - \cdots) + \cdots , \tag{9.8.8}$$

so that there must follow

$$a_n = 2^{-(n-1)}A_n, \qquad a_{n-1} = 2^{-(n-2)}A_{n-1},$$

$$a_{n-2} = 2^{-(n-3)}\left(A_{n-2} + \frac{n}{4}A_n\right), \qquad \cdots . \tag{9.8.9}$$

Thus, if n is sufficiently large, the coefficients of $T_n(x)$, $T_{n-1}(x)$, $\ldots$, $T_{n-m+1}(x)$ in (9.8.6) will be small relative to the respective coefficients of x^n, x^{n-1}, $\ldots$, x^{n-m+1} in (9.8.3), for some m, and it may happen that $(|a_{n-m+1}| + |a_{n-m+2}| + \cdots + |a_n|) + \epsilon_1$ is smaller than ϵ and hence is a tolerable error in the desired approximation to $f(x)$. Since $|T_r(x)| \leqq 1$ in $(-1,1)$, the last m terms in the right-hand member of (9.8.6) are then negligible, and the approximation (9.8.5) can then be replaced by

$$f(x) \approx \sum_{k=0}^{n-m} a_k T_k(x), \tag{9.8.10}$$

where $m > 0$, after which this approximation can be transformed back to an expression of the form

$$f(x) \approx \sum_{k=0}^{n-m} \bar{A}_k x^k, \tag{9.8.11}$$

if this is desirable. In this way we obtain a polynomial approximation to $f(x)$, over $(-1,1)$, involving fewer terms than would be required by a truncated power series and tending to involve the smallest possible number of polynomial terms which will supply an accuracy within the prescribed tolerance limits.†

The transformations involved are facilitated by the use of the two following sets of relations, the second set being taken from the results of §7.8, and the first set being obtained by successively inverting the members of the second set.

$$1 = T_0,$$
$$x = T_1,$$
$$x^2 = \tfrac{1}{2}(T_0 + T_2),$$
$$x^3 = \tfrac{1}{4}(3T_1 + T_3),$$
$$x^4 = \tfrac{1}{8}(3T_0 + 4T_2 + T_4),$$
$$x^5 = \tfrac{1}{16}(10T_1 + 5T_3 + T_5),$$
$$x^6 = \tfrac{1}{32}(10T_0 + 15T_2 + 6T_4 + T_6),$$
$$x^7 = \tfrac{1}{64}(35T_1 + 21T_3 + 7T_5 + T_7),$$
$$x^8 = \tfrac{1}{128}(35T_0 + 56T_2 + 28T_4 + 8T_6 + T_8),$$
$$x^9 = \tfrac{1}{256}(126T_1 + 84T_3 + 36T_5 + 9T_7 + T_9),$$

$$T_0 = 1,$$
$$T_1 = x,$$
$$T_2 = 2x^2 - 1,$$
$$T_3 = 4x^3 - 3x,$$
$$T_4 = 8x^4 - 8x^2 + 1,$$
$$T_5 = 16x^5 - 20x^3 + 5x,$$
$$T_6 = 32x^6 - 48x^4 + 18x^2 - 1,$$
$$T_7 = 64x^7 - 112x^5 + 56x^3 - 7x,$$
$$T_8 = 128x^8 - 256x^6 + 160x^4 - 32x^2 + 1,$$
$$T_9 = 256x^9 - 576x^7 + 432x^5 - 120x^3 + 9x.$$

$$(9.8.12)$$

In illustration, suppose that a polynomial approximation to e^x is required in $(-1,1)$, with a tolerance of 0.01. The truncation of a Maclaurin series gives a polynomial approximation of degree five,

$$e^x \approx 1 + x + \tfrac{1}{2}x^2 + \tfrac{1}{6}x^3 + \tfrac{1}{24}x^4 + \tfrac{1}{120}x^5 \equiv y(x), \qquad (9.8.13)$$

with an error

$$|E(x)| = \left| \frac{e^\xi}{720} x^6 \right| < \frac{e}{720} < 0.0038, \qquad (9.8.14)$$

for which the neglect of the term $x^5/120$ would admit the possibility of an error exceeding the prescribed tolerance. The use of the first set of relations in (9.8.12) transforms (9.8.13) into the equivalent form

$$y(x) = \tfrac{81}{64}T_0 + \tfrac{217}{192}T_1 + \tfrac{13}{48}T_2 + \tfrac{17}{384}T_3 + \tfrac{1}{192}T_4 + \tfrac{1}{1920}T_5, \qquad (9.8.15)$$

where $T_r \equiv T_r(x)$. Neglect of the last two terms will introduce an additional error not exceeding $\tfrac{11}{1920} < 0.0058$ for all x in $(-1,1)$. Thus, with a total error smaller in magnitude than 0.0096, we have

$$e^x \approx \tfrac{81}{64}T_0 + \tfrac{217}{192}T_1 + \tfrac{13}{48}T_2 + \tfrac{17}{384}T_3 \qquad (9.8.16)$$

or, after using the second set in (9.8.12),

$$e^x \approx \tfrac{1}{384}(382 + 383x + 208x^2 + 68x^3) \qquad (|x| \leq 1). \qquad (9.8.17)$$

† It should be noticed that, in this procedure, the error $E_n(x)$ in (9.8.3) is accepted as a *fixed* error, and an efficient approximation to $f(x) - E_n(x)$ is sought. Thus the approximation obtained is generally not the best possible one, but may be expected to differ little from it if $|E_n(x)|$ is small relative to ϵ.

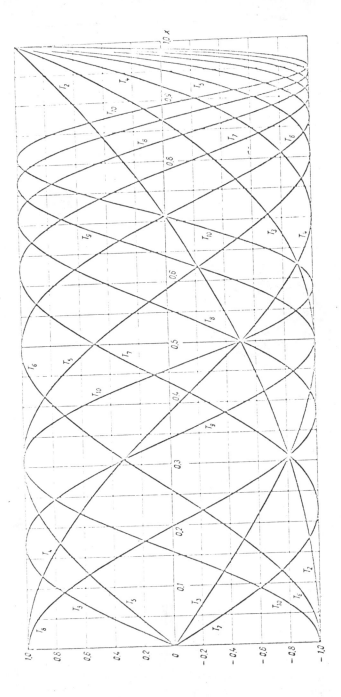

Table 9.   Chebyshev Polynomials T_2 Through T_{10} in the Interval from 0 to 1

For the purpose of comparison, it may be noted that a similar manipulation gives the form

$$y(x) = \tfrac{47}{40}P_0 + \tfrac{309}{280}P_1 + \tfrac{5}{14}P_2 + \tfrac{19}{270}P_3 + \tfrac{1}{105}P_4 + \tfrac{1}{945}P_5, \quad (9.8.18)$$

in terms of the Legendre polynomials $P_r \equiv P_r(x)$. Here only the last term could be neglected, so that a polynomial approximation of *fourth* degree would be required.

The procedure described here, called "economization of power series" by Lanczos, is useful in those situations when a minimization of the number of numerical operations is desirable. It clearly can be applied to *any* polynomial, whether that polynomial is obtained by truncating a power series or otherwise, once the interval of interest has been transformed to the interval $(-1,1)$.

9.9. Approximation by Continued Fractions. Newton's divided-difference polynomial interpolation formula (2.5.2), with an error term, can be considered as the *identity* which results from writing

$$f(x) = u_0(x) \quad (9.9.1)$$

and effecting the successive substitutions

$$u_k(x) = u_k(x_k) + (x - x_k)u_{k+1}(x) \quad (k = 0, 1, \ldots, n - 1), \quad (9.9.2)$$

with the abbreviation

$$u_k(x) = f[x_0, x_1, \ldots, x_{k-1}, x]. \quad (9.9.3)$$

Thus, for example, when $n = 3$ there follows

$$\begin{aligned}
f(x) &= u_0(x_0) + (x - x_0)\{u_1(x_1) + (x - x_1)[u_2(x_2) + (x - x_2)u_3(x)]\} \\
&= u_0(x_0) + (x - x_0)u_1(x_1) + (x - x_0)(x - x_1)u_2(x_2) + E(x) \\
&= f[x_0] + (x - x_0)f[x_0, x_1] + (x - x_0)(x - x_1)f[x_0, x_1, x_2] + E(x),
\end{aligned}$$
$$(9.9.4)$$

where

$$\begin{aligned}
E(x) &= (x - x_0)(x - x_1)(x - x_2)u_3(x) \\
&= (x - x_0)(x - x_1)(x - x_2)f[x_0, x_1, x_2, x]. \quad (9.9.5)
\end{aligned}$$

The algorithm for the calculation of the successive *divided differences* follows directly from (9.9.2) and (9.9.3), with $x = x_k$, in the form

$$f[x_0, \ldots, x_{k-2}, x_{k-1}, x_k] = \frac{f[x_0, \ldots, x_{k-2}, x_k] - f[x_0, \ldots, x_{k-2}, x_{k-1}]}{x_k - x_{k-1}}.$$
$$(9.9.6)$$

The result of *assuming* that the $(n + 1)$th divided difference $u_{n+1}(x)$ is identically zero (or that the nth divided difference is constant) is the equation of the polynomial $y(x)$, of degree n or less, which agrees with

$f(x)$ at the $n + 1$ points $x_0, x_1, \ldots, x_n$. If $u_{n+1}(x)$ *actually* vanishes identically, then $y(x) \equiv f(x)$.

A great variety of other identities can be obtained in a similar way, and interpreted similarly as approximation formulas, by making use of other sets of transformations, in place of (9.9.2). In particular, the substitution sequence

$$f(x) = v_0(x),$$

$$v_k(x) = v_k(x_k) + \frac{x - x_k}{v_{k+1}(x)} \qquad (k = 0, 1, 2, \ldots) \qquad (9.9.7)$$

leads to an interesting and useful result. We see that the first three substitutions give

$$f(x) = v_0(x) = v_0(x_0) + \frac{x - x_0}{v_1(x)} = v_0(x_0) + \cfrac{x - x_0}{v_1(x_1) + \cfrac{x - x_1}{v_2(x)}}$$

$$= v_0(x_0) + \cfrac{x - x_0}{v_1(x_1) + \cfrac{x - x_1}{v_2(x_2) + \cfrac{x - x_2}{v_3(x)}}}. \qquad (9.9.8)$$

More generally, we are thus led to the *continued-fraction* representation

$$f(x) = a_0 + \cfrac{x - x_0}{a_1 + \cfrac{x - x_1}{a_2 + \cfrac{x - x_2}{a_3 + \cdots}}} \qquad (9.9.9)$$

where $$a_k = v_k(x_k), \qquad (9.9.10)$$

and where, when the fraction is terminated after n divisions, the constant a_n is to be replaced by $a_n + (x - x_n)/v_{n+1}(x)$ in the last denominator. If we then set $x = x_k$, where $0 \leq k \leq n$, the fraction terminates before the *residual* $(x - x_n)/v_{n+1}(x)$ is introduced. Thus, since (9.9.9) is an *identity*, the result of replacing $1/v_{n+1}(x)$ by zero (that is, terminating the fraction with a_n) will give a function $r_{n+1}(x)$ which agrees with $f(x)$ at the $n + 1$ points $x_0, \ldots, x_n$, under the assumptions that the constants $a_0, \ldots, a_n$ are actually existent and that the portion of the truncated fraction inferior to $x - x_k$ does not vanish when $x = x_k$, for $k = 0, \ldots, n - 1$. The result of this termination may be called the $(n + 1)$th *convergent* (or *approximant*) of the representation, so that the *first* convergent is merely the constant $a_0 = f(x_0)$.

If we introduce the notation

$$v_k(x) = \phi_k[x_0, x_1, \ldots, x_{k-1}, x], \qquad (9.9.11)$$

so that (9.9.10) becomes

$$a_k = \phi_k[x_0,x_1, \ldots ,x_{k-1},x_k], \tag{9.9.12}$$

reference to (9.9.7) gives

$$\phi_0[x] = f(x), \qquad \phi_1[x_0,x] = \frac{x - x_0}{\phi_0[x] - \phi_0[x_0]} = \frac{x - x_0}{f(x) - f(x_0)},$$

$$\phi_2[x_0,x_1,x] = \frac{x - x_1}{\phi_1[x_0,x] - \phi_1[x_0,x_1]},$$

and, in general,

$$\phi_k[x_0,x_1, \ldots ,x_{k-1},x] = \frac{x - x_{k-1}}{\phi_{k-1}[x_0, \ldots ,x_{k-2},x] - \phi_{k-1}[x_0, \ldots ,x_{k-2},x_{k-1}]}. \tag{9.9.13}$$

Accordingly, we have also

$$\phi_k[x_0, \ldots ,x_{k-1},x_k] = \frac{x_k - x_{k-1}}{\phi_{k-1}[x_0, \ldots ,x_{k-2},x_k] - \phi_{k-1}[x_0, \ldots ,x_{k-2},x_{k-1}]}. \tag{9.9.14}$$

Thus $\phi_1[x_0,x_1]$ is the *inverted* first divided difference of $f(x)$, relative to x_0 and x_1, $\phi_2[x_0,x_1,x_2]$ is the inverted divided difference of the inverted first divided difference $\phi_1[x_0,x]$, relative to x_1 and x_2, . . . , and $\phi_k[x_0, \ldots ,x_{k-2},x_{k-1},x_k]$ is the inverted divided difference of $\phi_{k-1}[x_0, \ldots , x_{k-2},x]$, relative to x_{k-1} and x_k. For brevity, we will refer to the quantity defined by (9.9.13) as a kth *inverted difference* of $f(x)$.

Whereas the definition shows that the inverted difference $\phi_k[x_0, \ldots , x_{k-2},x_{k-1},x_k]$ is symmetrical in its *last two* arguments x_{k-1} and x_k, it is *not* generally symmetrical in its other arguments.† Thus it *must* be formed from the specific inverted differences $\phi_{k-1}[x_0, \ldots ,x_{k-2},x_{k-1}]$ and $\phi_{k-1}[x_0, \ldots ,x_{k-2},x_k]$, which possess its first $k - 1$ arguments in common. The following calculational arrangement is convenient for this purpose:

$$\begin{array}{llll}
x_0 & f(x_0) & & \\
x_1 & f(x_1) & \phi_1[x_0,x_1] & \\
x_2 & f(x_2) & \phi_1[x_0,x_2] & \phi_2[x_0,x_1,x_2] \\
x_3 & f(x_3) & \phi_1[x_0,x_3] & \phi_2[x_0,x_1,x_3] \qquad \phi_3[x_0,x_1,x_2,x_3]
\end{array}$$
. . . .

Here, for example, we have

$$\phi_2[x_0,x_1,x_3] = \frac{x_3 - x_1}{\phi_1[x_0,x_3] - \phi_1[x_0,x_1]}.$$

The *diagonal* elements thus are the desired constants $a_0, a_1, a_2, a_3, \ldots$ which appear in (9.9.9).

† A related quantity, which possesses complete symmetry, is considered in §9.12.

In illustration, for the given data

x	0	1	2	3	4	5	6
$f(x)$	2	$\frac{3}{2}$	$\frac{4}{5}$	$\frac{1}{2}$	$\frac{6}{17}$	$\frac{7}{26}$	$\frac{8}{37}$

we may number the abscissas in increasing algebraic order and, accordingly, form the array

x	f	ϕ_1	ϕ_2	ϕ_3	ϕ_4
0	2				
1	$\frac{3}{2}$	-2			
2	$\frac{4}{5}$	$-\frac{5}{3}$	3		
3	$\frac{1}{2}$	-2	∞	0	
4	$\frac{6}{17}$	$-\frac{17}{7}$	-7	$-\frac{1}{5}$	-5
5	$\frac{7}{26}$	$-\frac{26}{9}$	$-\frac{9}{2}$	$-\frac{2}{5}$	-5
6	$\frac{8}{37}$	$-\frac{37}{11}$	$-\frac{11}{3}$	$-\frac{3}{5}$	-5

for which the fourth inverted differences are equal. Thus, if we use only the first five points $x_0 = 0$, $x_1 = 1$, $x_2 = 2$, $x_3 = 3$, and $x_4 = 4$, we have $a_0 = 2$, $a_1 = -2$, $a_2 = 3$, $a_3 = 0$, and $a_4 = -5$, so that (9.9.9) becomes

$$f(x) \approx 2 + \cfrac{x}{-2 + \cfrac{x-1}{3 + \cfrac{x-2}{0 + \cfrac{x-3}{-5}}}} \equiv r_5(x), \qquad (9.9.15)$$

where the approximation would become *exact* if the last denominator -5 were replaced by the (unknown) quantity $-5 + (x - 4)/\phi_5[0,1,2,3,4,x]$. Thus $r_5(x)$ may be expected to agree with $f(x)$ at the five points employed in its determination. But since the tabular array shows that the *same* approximation would be obtained if the abscissa $x = 4$ were replaced by either $x = 5$ or $x = 6$, it may be expected that $r_5(x)$ will agree with $f(x)$ at those two points as well.

Successive reductions will convert the right-hand member of (9.9.15) to the simpler form

$$r_5(x) = \frac{2 + x}{1 + x^2}, \qquad (9.9.16)$$

if this reduction is desired, and the agreement can be verified directly. Furthermore, the respective approximating *convergents* corresponding to termination of the fraction with a_0, a_1, and a_2, and hence to collocation at one, two, and three successive points, are found to be

$$r_1(x) = 2, \qquad r_2(x) = \frac{4 - x}{2}, \qquad r_3(x) = \frac{14 - 5x}{7 - x},$$

However, since the present example is exceptional to the extent that $a_3 = 0$, the fourth convergent does not agree with $f(x)$ at the four points $x = 0, 1, 2$, and 3. Indeed, this convergent is identical with $r_2(x)$, which agrees with $f(x)$ at $x = 0, 1$, and also at $x = 3$, but does not do so at $x = 2$.

9.10. Nature of Continued-fraction Approximations. It is easily seen that the nth convergent of the continued fraction (9.9.9) is expressible in the form

$$r_n(x) = \frac{\alpha_0 + \alpha_1 x + \cdots + \alpha_p x^p}{\beta_0 + \beta_1 x + \cdots + \beta_{p-1} x^{p-1}} \qquad (n = 2p) \qquad (9.10.1a)$$

if n is *even*, and is of the form

$$r_n(x) = \frac{\alpha_0 + \alpha_1 x + \cdots + \alpha_p x^p}{\beta_0 + \beta_1 x + \cdots + \beta_p x^p} \qquad (n = 2p + 1) \qquad (9.10.1b)$$

if n is *odd*. Thus the nth convergent affords an approximation to $f(x)$ by a *ratio of polynomials*, that is, by a *rational function* of x, which generally agrees with $f(x)$ at the n points $x_0, x_1, \ldots, x_{n-1}$ if $a_{n-1} \neq 0$, and if all preceding a's are finite.

This situation is in accordance with the fact that, since the numerator and denominator of either form of (9.10.1) can be divided through by any one of the nonzero constants, the first form involves $2p$ independent parameters and the second form $2p + 1$ such parameters, so that in either case n independent constants are available for the determination of the approximation.

Given a set of n distinct points, there cannot exist more than one *irreducible* rational function† of the form (9.10.1) which takes on prescribed values at those points. The proof follows simply by first writing (9.10.1) in the form $r_n(x) = M_n(x)/N_n(x)$, where M_n and N_n are polynomials, and supposing that *another* such ratio, $\bar{M}_n(x)/\bar{N}_n(x)$, takes on the same values as does $r_n(x)$ at n distinct points. Here, in accordance with (9.10.1), the degrees of M_n and $\bar{M}_n$ cannot exceed $n/2$ when n is even or $(n - 1)/2$ when n is odd, whereas the degrees of N_n and $\bar{N}_n$ cannot exceed $(n - 2)/2$ when n is even or $(n - 1)/2$ when n is odd. It then follows that the function $M_n(x)\bar{N}(x) - \bar{M}_n(x)N_n(x)$ also vanishes at those points. But, since this function is a polynomial of degree $n - 1$ or less, it must therefore vanish identically, so that $M_n(x)\bar{N}_n(x) \equiv \bar{M}_n(x)N_n(x)$. Under the assumption that $r_n(x)$ is irreducible, M_n and N_n possess no common linear factors. Thus all linear factors of M_n must also be factors of $\bar{M}_n$, and the converse is also true since $\bar{M}_n/\bar{N}_n$ is also assumed to be irreducible. The same argument applies to N_n and $\bar{N}_n$,

† A rational function is said to be *reducible* if its numerator and denominator possess a common polynomial factor, other than a constant.

so that the respective numerators and denominators can differ only to the extent of a common constant multiplicative factor, as was to be shown.

However, there may be *no* such function. For example, if we attempt to determine directly a function of the form

$$r_4(x) = \frac{\alpha_0 + \alpha_1 x + \alpha_2 x^2}{\beta_0 + \beta_1 x}$$

which takes on the values prescribed in the preceding example at the four points $x = 0, 1, 2,$ and 3, we must solve the simultaneous equations

$$2\beta_0 = \alpha_0,$$
$$\tfrac{3}{2}(\beta_0 + \beta_1) = \alpha_0 + \alpha_1 + \alpha_2,$$
$$\tfrac{4}{5}(\beta_0 + 2\beta_1) = \alpha_0 + 2\alpha_1 + 4\alpha_2,$$
$$\tfrac{1}{2}(\beta_0 + 3\beta_1) = \alpha_0 + 3\alpha_1 + 9\alpha_2,$$

which result from clearing fractions and equating the resultant members at the four points, and we find that the general solution is given by the relations

$$\alpha_0 = 8\alpha_2, \qquad \alpha_1 = -6\alpha_2, \qquad \beta_0 = 4\alpha_2, \qquad \beta_1 = -2\alpha_2,$$

where α_2 is arbitrary. Thus the assumed form becomes

$$r_4(x) = \frac{8 - 6x + x^2}{4 - 2x} = \frac{(4 - x)(2 - x)}{2(2 - x)}$$

and is *reducible* to $r_2(x) = (4 - x)/2$, in accordance with the result obtained from (9.9.15). The original form is indeterminate at $x = 2$, whereas the reduced form does not take on the prescribed value at that point. Thus the defect of the fourth convergent of (9.9.15) is due to the nonexistence of a form of the type required at that stage, rather than to a failure of the determining process.

In the case of (9.9.15), a warning was served by the fact that $a_3 = 0$. It should be remarked, however, that the kth convergent may be defective, for the same reason as above, even though a_{k-1} does not vanish, although this situation is an unusual one. In illustration, the data

x	0	1	2	3
$f(x)$	2	1	1	0

lead to the inverted-difference array

x	f	ϕ_1	ϕ_2	ϕ_3
0	2			
1	1	-1		
2	1	-2	-1	
3	0	$-\tfrac{3}{2}$	-4	$-\tfrac{1}{3}$

in which no diagonal element vanishes. Whereas the corresponding approximation

$$f(x) \approx 2 + \cfrac{x}{-1 + \cfrac{x-1}{-1 + \cfrac{x-2}{-\cfrac{1}{3}}}} = \frac{12 - 13x + 3x^2}{6 - 4x}$$

is properly exact at the four tabular points, the third convergent of the fraction is seen to be

$$r_3(x) = 2 + \frac{x}{-1 - (x-1)} = 2 - \frac{x}{x},$$

and is undefined at the tabular point $x = 0$. It is easily verified that there exists no irreducible fraction of the form $(\alpha_0 + \alpha_1 x)/(\beta_0 + \beta_1 x)$ which takes on the first three prescribed values.

On the other hand, even though the n given data serve to determine a rational approximation of the form (9.10.1), the continued-fraction expansion will fail to exist, in the form assumed, if $a_k = \infty$ for some $k \leqq n - 1$. Thus, whereas the data

x	0	1	2	3	4	5
$f(x)$	1	1	$\frac{3}{5}$	$\frac{2}{5}$	$\frac{5}{17}$	$\frac{3}{13}$

correspond to the function

$$f(x) = \frac{1+x}{1+x^2},$$

it is seen that $\phi_1[0,1] = \infty$, so that there exists no expansion, of the form

$$f(x) = a_0 + \cfrac{x}{a_1 + \cfrac{x-1}{a_2 + \cdot}},$$

which takes on the prescribed values when $x_0 = 0$, $x_1 = 1$, and $x_2 = 2$. This difficulty can be averted here by reordering the abscissas in such a way that the equal ordinates are not consecutive. Thus, if we take $x_0 = 0, x_1 = 2, x_2 = 1, x_3 = 3$, and $x_4 = 4$, we obtain the following array:

0	1				
2	$\frac{3}{5}$	-5			
1	1	∞	0		
3	$\frac{2}{5}$	-5	∞	0	
4	$\frac{5}{17}$	$-\frac{17}{3}$	-3	-1	-1
5	$\frac{3}{13}$	$-\frac{13}{2}$	-2	-2	-1

The additional line is included to illustrate the constancy of the fourth inverted difference in the present case.

From these results we deduce the approximation

$$f(x) \approx 1 + \cfrac{x}{-5 + \cfrac{x-2}{0 + \cfrac{x-1}{0 + \cfrac{x-3}{-1}}}}$$

which properly reduces exactly to $(1 + x)/(1 + x^2)$. In this form, the successive convergents are 1, $(5 - x)/5$, 1, $(5 - x)/5$, and $(1 + x)/(1 + x^2)$. As was predicted by the presence of the zeros, the third and fourth convergents are both defective, in that the third takes on the prescribed values only at the first and third points while the fourth does so only at the first, second, and fourth points. If, for example, the abscissas are taken in the order 1, 2, 3, 4, 0, we obtain the form

$$f(x) \approx 1 + \cfrac{x-1}{-\cfrac{5}{2} + \cfrac{x-2}{-\cfrac{6}{5} + \cfrac{x-3}{\cfrac{35}{2} + \cfrac{x-4}{\cfrac{1}{5}}}}}$$

which naturally also reduces to $(1 + x)/(1 + x^2)$, but which possesses no defective convergents.

In the usual cases, the ordinates can be introduced in any order. For calculation near the beginning of a tabulation, it is usually desirable to number the abscissas in increasing algebraic order, whereas near the end of a tabulation the reverse numbering is desirable, in analogy to the Newton forward- and backward-difference polynomial interpolation formulas. Inside the tabular range it often is desirable first to introduce the abscissa nearest the abscissa of the interpolant, and then successively to introduce abscissas at increasing distance from x_0, alternately forward and backward, in analogy to the central-difference interpolation formulas. These choices tend to maximize the effective initial rate of convergence of the sequence of successive convergents in practical situations, for which the sequence generally does not terminate.

9.11. Determination of Convergents of Continued Fractions. In place of basing numerical calculations on the approximation expressed as a truncated continued fraction, or of transforming that fraction to a simple fraction by direct reduction, we may conveniently make use of certain recurrence formulas which may be derived as follows.

From the definition (9.9.7), it is easily seen that $f(x)$ is expressible as the ratio of two linear functions of any $v_k(x)$, say in the convenient form

$$f(x) = \frac{(x - x_{k-1})P_k(x) + v_k(x)M_k(x)}{(x - x_{k-1})Q_k(x) + v_k(x)N_k(x)}. \tag{9.11.1}$$

In order to determine M_k, N_k, P_k, and Q_k, we may notice that $f(x)$ is consequently also given both by the result of replacing k by $k + 1$ in (9.11.1) and also by the result of using (9.9.7) to express $v_k(x)$ in terms of $v_{k+1}(x)$ in (9.11.1), so that there must follow

$$\frac{(x - x_k)P_{k+1}(x) + v_{k+1}(x)M_{k+1}(x)}{(x - x_k)Q_{k+1}(x) + v_{k+1}(x)N_{k+1}(x)}$$
$$= \frac{(x - x_k)M_k(x) + v_{k+1}(x)[a_kM_k(x) + (x - x_{k-1})P_k(x)]}{(x - x_k)N_k(x) + v_{k+1}(x)[a_kN_k(x) + (x - x_{k-1})Q_k(x)]}. \tag{9.11.2}$$

This requirement is satisfied, for arbitrary v_{k+1}, if the desired functions satisfy the relations

$$\begin{aligned}
M_{k+1}(x) &= a_kM_k(x) + (x - x_{k-1})M_{k-1}(x), \\
N_{k+1}(x) &= a_kN_k(x) + (x - x_{k-1})N_{k-1}(x), \\
P_k(x) &= M_{k-1}(x), \\
Q_k(x) &= N_{k-1}(x),
\end{aligned} \tag{9.11.3}$$

in accordance with which M_k, N_k, P_k, and Q_k clearly will be *polynomials* in x if M_0, M_1, N_0, and N_1 are polynomials. Thus we may write (9.11.1) in the form

$$f(x) = \frac{M_k(x) + \dfrac{(x - x_{k-1})M_{k-1}(x)}{\phi_k[x_0, \ldots, x_{k-1}, x]}}{N_k(x) + \dfrac{(x - x_{k-1})N_{k-1}(x)}{\phi_k[x_0, \ldots, x_{k-1}, x]}}. \tag{9.11.4}$$

Since, when $k = 1$, this form must reduce to the form given by (9.9.7),

$$f(x) = a_0 + \frac{x - x_0}{\phi_1[x_0, x]},$$

we must have $N_0(x) = 0$, $M_1(x)/N_1(x) = a_0$, and $M_0(x)/N_1(x) = 1$. It is convenient to take $N_1(x) = 1$.

Thus M_k and N_k can be determined by the recurrence formulas

$$\begin{aligned}
M_{k+1}(x) &= a_kM_k(x) + (x - x_{k-1})M_{k-1}(x), \\
M_0(x) &= 1, \qquad M_1(x) = a_0
\end{aligned} \tag{9.11.5}$$

and

$$\begin{aligned}
N_{k+1}(x) &= a_kN_k(x) + (x - x_{k-1})N_{k-1}(x), \\
N_0(x) &= 0, \qquad N_1(x) = 1.
\end{aligned} \tag{9.11.6}$$

In particular, the kth convergent to $f(x)$ is given simply by

$$r_k(x) = \frac{M_k(x)}{N_k(x)}. \tag{9.11.7}$$

The error associated with the approximation $f(x) \approx r_k(x)$ can be estimated by use of (9.11.4) if information with regard to $\phi_k[x_0, \ldots, x_{k-1}, x]$ is available, say, in the form of sample values of the kth inverted difference formed with $x_0, \ldots$, and x_{k-1} as its first k arguments. For this purpose it is convenient to rewrite (9.11.4) in the equivalent form

$$f(x) - r_k(x) = -\frac{c_k(x)}{1 + c_k(x)}[r_k(x) - r_{k-1}(x)], \qquad (9.11.8)$$

where
$$c_k(x) = \frac{(x - x_{k-1})N_{k-1}}{\phi_k[x_0, \ldots, x_{k-1}, x]N_k}. \qquad (9.11.9)$$

When $f(x)$ is not a rational function, the sequence of convergents generally is infinite, and it may or may not tend to $f(x)$ as $n \to \infty$. However, it generally at least approaches $f(x)$ more and more closely, for any fixed value of x inside the range of the tabular values $x_0, \ldots, x_n$, as n increases up to a certain stage. The determination of successive convergents is desirable in order that the rate of "effective convergence" may be estimated.

It is useful to notice that the expansion (9.9.9) can be expressed in the alternative forms

$$f(x) = a_0 + \cfrac{x - x_0}{a_1 + \cfrac{x - x_1}{a_2 + \cfrac{x - x_2}{a_3 + \cdots}}} = a_0 + \cfrac{\dfrac{x - x_0}{a_1}}{1 + \cfrac{\dfrac{x - x_1}{a_1 a_2}}{1 + \cfrac{\dfrac{x - x_2}{a_2 a_3}}{1 + \cdots}}} \qquad (9.11.10)$$

if none of the a_i vanish. The more compact symbolic arrangement

$$f(x) = a_0 + \frac{x - x_0}{a_1} + \frac{x - x_1}{a_2} + \frac{x - x_2}{a_3} + \cdots$$

of the first form is often used.

Approximation by rational functions is often useful in the neighborhood of a point x_0 at which the true function $f(x)$ becomes *infinite*, although, in such cases, it may be preferable to apply *polynomial* interpolation to $1/f(x)$ or to $(x - x_0)^m f(x)$, where m is determined (analytically or empirically) in an appropriate way.† In illustration, the following calculation is for the purpose of interpolating for cot 0.15 ($\doteq 6.6166$) from the given three-place values.

---

† If $f(x)$ becomes *logarithmically* infinite at x_0, neither type of approximation is efficient.

x_k	f_k	ϕ_1	ϕ_2	ϕ_3	$x - x_k$	M_k	N_k	r_k
0.1	9.967				0.05	1	0	—
0.2	4.933	−0.019865			−0.05	9.967	1	9.967
0.3	3.233	−0.029700	−10.168		−0.15	−0.14799	−0.019865	7.450
0.4	2.365	−0.039463	−10.205	−2.70	−0.25	1.00641	0.15199	6.622
						−2.69511	−0.40739	6.6156

With this arrangement, the two factors in each product involved in (9.11.5) and (9.11.6) appear in the same horizontal line. Thus, for example, we have

$$M_3 = (-10.168)(-0.14799) + (-0.05)(9.967) \doteq 1.00641,$$
$$N_4 = (-2.70)(0.15199) + (-0.15)(-0.019865) \doteq -0.40739.$$

In the calculation of the successive inverted differences, about one more digit was retained in each inverted difference than would be expected to be significant if all digits retained in the two preceding entries, from which it is calculated, were correct, when account is taken of the loss of significant figures in the subtractions involved. The tabulated a's are then treated as though they were exact in the calculation of the M's and N's, so that, for example, (at least) five digits are retained in N_4, even though not more than three of its digits would be significant if the value -2.70 were correct to the places given, and only to those places.

Because of the fact that errors in the given ordinates and in the a's, M's, and N's enter into the determination of the required r's in a nonlinear way, it is difficult to estimate in advance the number of digits which should be retained in each intermediate calculation, but it is usually desirable to retain at least as many digits as are required by the preceding rule. In the present case, the tabulated value of a_3 would be modified in its third digit if additional digits were retained in the calculation of preceding divided differences, and this modification would change M_4 and N_4 in the third digit. However, the calculated value of the *ratio* $r_4 = M_4/N_4$ would be modified by only two units in its *fifth* digit. The deviation of the calculated value r_4 from the true value, by one unit in its fourth digit, is due principally to the round-off errors in the *given* data (see Prob. 42).

The fact that the value of the convergent r_4 itself is not sensitive to appreciable errors in a_3 can be seen more directly by inspection of the actual truncated continued fraction:

$$r_4(0.15) \approx 9.967 + \cfrac{0.05}{-0.019865 + \cfrac{-0.05}{-10.168 + \cfrac{-0.15}{-2.70}}}.$$

In this particular example, the near-linearity of the first inverted difference $\phi_1[0.1,x]$ suggests the use of *polynomial* extrapolation over the three available values for the determination of $\phi_1[0.1,0.15]$. The use of Newton's forward-difference formula (retaining the second difference) gives $\phi_1[0.1,0.15] \approx 0.014923$, so that there follows

$$\frac{0.15 - 0.10}{f(0.15) - 9.967} \approx 0.014923, \qquad f(0.15) \approx 6.6165,$$

and the calculation of *inverted* differences of higher order is avoided.

It can be shown (see Prob. 38) that the kth convergent of (9.11.10) can be expressed in the form

$$r_k = a_0 + \frac{x - x_0}{N_1 N_2} - \frac{(x - x_0)(x - x_1)}{N_2 N_3} + \frac{(x - x_0)(x - x_1)(x - x_2)}{N_3 N_4}$$
$$- \cdots + (-1)^k \frac{(x - x_0)(x - x_1) \cdots (x - x_{k-2})}{N_{k-1} N_k}. \qquad (9.11.11)$$

In the case of the preceding example, the kth convergent r_k is thus obtained by retaining k terms in the sum

$$9.967 - \frac{0.05}{0.019865} - \frac{0.0025}{0.0030193} - \frac{0.000375}{0.06192},$$

and successive results agree, to three decimal places, with the values obtained previously.

9.12. Thiele's Continued-fraction Expansions. Whereas the kth "inverted difference" $\phi_k[x_0, \ldots ,x_{k-2},x_{k-1},x_k]$ of a function $f(x)$ is symmetrical only in its last two arguments, it happens that the quantity

$$\rho_k[x_0, \ldots ,x_k] = \phi_k[x_0, \ldots ,x_k] + \phi_{k-2}[x_0, \ldots ,x_{k-2}]$$
$$+ \phi_{k-4}[x_0, \ldots ,x_{k-4}] + \cdots \qquad (9.12.1)$$

is symmetrical in all its $k + 1$ arguments. Here the last term on the right is $\phi_0[x_0]$ if k is even, and is $\phi_1[x_0,x_1]$ if k is odd. This quantity is often known as a kth *reciprocal difference* of $f(x)$.

In particular, we have

$$\rho_0[x_0] = \phi_0[x_0] = f(x_0),$$
$$\rho_1[x_0,x_1] = \phi_1[x_0, x_1] = \frac{x_1 - x_0}{f(x_1) - f(x_0)}, \qquad (9.12.2)$$

and calculation shows that

$$\rho_2[x_0,x_1,x_2] = \phi_0[x_0] + \phi_2[x_0,x_1,x_2]$$
$$= \frac{x_0 f_0(f_1 - f_2) + x_1 f_1(f_2 - f_0) + x_2 f_2(f_0 - f_1)}{x_0(f_1 - f_2) + x_1(f_2 - f_0) + x_2(f_0 - f_1)}, \qquad (9.12.3)$$

in which cases the symmetry is apparent. While an *inductive* generalization is possible, the following argument is somewhat more simple. It is easily verified that, when use is made of (9.11.5) and (9.11.6), the nth convergent of (9.9.9) is given by (9.10.1a) when $n = 2p$, with $\alpha_p = 1$ and $\beta_{p-1} = \rho_{2p-1}[x_0, \ldots, x_{2p-1}]$, and by (9.10.1b) when $n = 2p + 1$, with $\alpha_p = \rho_{2p}[x_0, \ldots, x_{2p}]$ and $\beta_p = 1$. Thus it follows that ρ_{2p} is the ratio of the "leading" coefficients in the numerator and denominator of the rational function of form (9.10.1b) which agrees with $f(x)$ at the $2p + 1$ points $x_0, \ldots, x_{2p}$, whereas ρ_{2p-1} is the reciprocal of that ratio for the rational function of form (9.10.1a) which agrees with $f(x)$ at the $2p$ points $x_0, \ldots, x_{2p-1}$. These ratios are clearly independent of any *ordering* of the points involved.

Since (9.12.1) implies that

$$\rho_k[x_0, \ldots, x_k] - \rho_{k-2}[x_0, \ldots, x_{k-2}] = \phi_k[x_0, \ldots, x_k], \quad (9.12.4)$$

reference to (9.9.13) shows that the successive reciprocal differences may be obtained by use of the recurrence formula

$$\rho_k[x_0, \ldots, x_{k-2}, x_{k-1}, x_k] =$$
$$\frac{x_k - x_{k-1}}{\rho_{k-1}[x_0, \ldots, x_{k-2}, x_k] - \rho_{k-1}[x_0, \ldots, x_{k-2}, x_{k-1}]} + \rho_{k-2}[x_0, \ldots, x_{k-2}].$$
$$(9.12.5)$$

While this formula is less simply applied than (9.9.13), the symmetry of the kth reciprocal difference permits its calculation from *any* two $(k - 1)$th reciprocal differences having $k - 1$ of its arguments in common, together with the $(k - 2)$th reciprocal difference formed with those arguments.

Thus, in particular, a *reciprocal-difference table* may be constructed in the convenient form

$$
\begin{array}{llllll}
x_0 & f(x_0) & & & & \\
 & & \rho_1[x_0,x_1] & & & \\
x_1 & f(x_1) & & \rho_2[x_0,x_1,x_2] & & \\
 & & \rho_1[x_1,x_2] & & \rho_3[x_0,x_1,x_2,x_3] \\
x_2 & f(x_2) & & \rho_2[x_1,x_2,x_3] & & \\
 & & \rho_1[x_2,x_3] & & & \\
x_3 & f(x_3) & & & &
\end{array}
$$

From this table we may determine the coefficients in (9.9.9) by combining (9.9.12) and (9.12.4) (this procedure is due to Thiele [19]), so that

$$a_0 = f(x_0), \quad a_1 = \rho_1[x_0,x_1], \quad a_2 = \rho_2[x_0,x_1,x_2] - f(x_0),$$
$$a_3 = \rho_3[x_0,x_1,x_2,x_3] - \rho_1[x_0,x_1],$$

and so forth. Thus the required coefficients are formed from (but are *not* identical with) reciprocal differences appearing in the forward diagonal beginning with $f(x_0)$. Furthermore, because of the symmetry, the data from the *same* table are available for the determination of formulas in which the ordinates are introduced in other orders, by choosing "difference paths" made up of suitable contiguous diagonal segments as was done in §2.5. Each such expansion is identical with the one which would be obtained *more simply* by the use of the *inverted*-difference array corresponding to an appropriate reordering of the abscissas, but only one array of *reciprocal* differences is needed for the formation of the entire set. Thus the use of reciprocal differences, rather than inverse differences, generally is advantageous only if several such formulas are required.

However, the definition of the reciprocal difference is particularly useful in the important limiting case when the abscissas x_0, x_1, x_2, . . . all become coincident, so that the requirement that the deviation between $f(x)$ and the kth convergent of the fraction vanish at k distinct points is replaced by the requirement that the deviation and its first $k - 1$ derivatives vanish at a single point x_0. Here (9.9.9) formally tends to the form

$$f(x) = \phi_0(x_0) + \cfrac{x - x_0}{\phi_1(x_0) + \cfrac{x - x_0}{\phi_2(x_0) + \cfrac{x - x_0}{\phi_3(x_0) + \cdot \cdot}}} \qquad (9.12.6)$$

where
$$\phi_k(x) \equiv \lim_{x_0, \ldots, x_k \to x} \phi_k[x_0, \ldots, x_k], \qquad (9.12.7)$$

under the assumption that this limit exists for $k = 0, 1, \ldots$. Here, if the fraction is terminated after k divisions, it is necessary to replace $\phi_k(x_0)$ by $\phi_k(x_0) + (x - x_0)/\phi_k[x_0, \ldots, x_0, x]$ in order to restore true equality.

The consideration of this limit is complicated by the fact that the $k + 1$ arguments $x_0, \ldots, x_k$ are not symmetrically involved. Thus it is desirable to use (9.12.4) to express (9.12.7) in the form

$$\phi_k(x) = \lim_{x_0, \ldots, x_k \to x} \{\rho_k[x_0, \ldots, x_k] - \rho_{k-2}[x_0, \ldots, x_{k-2}]\}, \qquad (9.12.8)$$

so that both terms on the right are symmetrical in their arguments. Accordingly, we have also

$$\phi_k(x) = \rho_k(x) - \rho_{k-2}(x), \qquad (9.12.9)$$

with the additional abbreviation

$$\rho_k(x) \equiv \lim_{x_0, \ldots, x_k \to x} \rho_k[x_0, \ldots, x_k]. \qquad (9.12.10)$$

In addition, we have the relation

$$\phi_k(x) = \lim_{x_k \to x} \frac{x_k - x}{\rho_{k-1}[x, \ldots, x, x_k] - \rho_{k-1}[x, \ldots, x, x]}, \qquad (9.12.11)$$

from (9.12.4) and (9.12.5), and, if the limit on the right exists, it clearly is given by

$$\frac{1}{\dfrac{\partial \rho_{k-1}[x_0, \ldots, x_{k-1}]}{\partial x_{k-1}}}\Bigg|_{x_0, \ldots, x_{k-1}=x} = \frac{k}{\dfrac{d\rho_{k-1}[x, \ldots, x]}{dx}}, \quad (9.12.12)$$

in consequence of the symmetry in the arguments, so that (9.12.11) becomes

$$\phi_k(x) = \frac{k}{\rho'_{k-1}(x)}. \quad (9.12.13)$$

Thus we may evaluate the coefficients $\phi_k(x_0)$ appearing in (9.12.6) successively, by using the formulas (9.12.9) and (9.12.13) in the form

$$\rho_k(x) = \rho_{k-2}(x) + \phi_k(x), \qquad \phi_{k+1}(x) = \frac{k+1}{\rho'_k(x)}, \quad (9.12.14)$$

with the obvious starting values

$$\rho_{-2}(x) = \rho_{-1}(x) = 0, \qquad \phi_0(x) = f(x), \quad (9.12.15)$$

and evaluating the functions $\phi_k(x)$ at $x = x_0$. The function $\rho_k(x)$ is often called the kth *reciprocal derivative* of $f(x)$. In correspondence with the terminology of the preceding section, we may refer to $\phi_k(x)$ as the kth *inverse derivative* of $f(x)$.

In order to illustrate the calculation in a simple case, we consider the function $f(x) = e^x$. By using successively the first and second relations in (9.12.14) with $k = 0, 1, 2, \ldots$, we obtain the functions

$$
\begin{aligned}
&& \phi_0 &= e^x, \\
\rho_0 &= e^x, & \phi_1 &= e^{-x}, \\
\rho_1 &= e^{-x}, & \phi_2 &= -2e^x, \\
\rho_2 &= -e^x, & \phi_3 &= -3e^{-x}, \\
\rho_3 &= -2e^{-x}, & \phi_4 &= 2e^x, \\
\rho_4 &= e^x, & \phi_5 &= 5e^{-x},
\end{aligned}
$$

and so forth. If we take $x_0 = 0$ in (9.12.6), we thus obtain the coefficients in the expansion

$$e^x = 1 + \cfrac{x}{1 + \cfrac{x}{-2 + \cfrac{x}{-3 + \cfrac{x}{2 + \cdot \cdot}}}} = 1 + \cfrac{x}{1 - \cfrac{x}{2 + \cfrac{x}{3 - \cfrac{x}{2 + \cdot \cdot}}}}$$

Inspection suggests that the inverse derivatives of e^x, of even and odd orders, are given by

$$\phi_{2n}(x) = (-1)^n 2e^x \quad (n \geq 1), \qquad \phi_{2n+1}(x) = (-1)^n(2n+1)e^{-x},$$

and the truth of this conjecture is readily established by induction.

The expansion (9.12.6) is attributed to Thiele. It is related to the more general expansions considered previously as the Taylor-series expansion is related to the divided-difference polynomial interpolation formulas. Whereas the nth convergent of the "confluent" expansion (9.12.6) generally affords a better approximation to $f(x)$ in the immediate neighborhood of x_0, the corresponding convergent of a development which yields exact results at n points of an interval including x_0 is usually to be preferred for approximation over that interval.

The expansion (9.12.6) can be generalized usefully as follows. If we replace the independent variable x by $G(x)$, and write

$$f(G(x)) = F(x), \qquad \rho_k(G(x)) = P_k(x), \qquad \phi_k(G(x)) = \Phi_k(x),$$

the formulas of (9.12.14) become

$$P_k(x) = P_{k-2}(x) + \Phi_k(x), \qquad \Phi_{k+1}(x) = (k+1)\frac{G'(x)}{P_k'(x)}, \quad (9.12.16)$$

with the starting values

$$P_{-2}(x) = P_{-1}(x) = 0, \qquad \Phi_0(x) = F(x), \quad (9.12.17)$$

and (9.12.6) takes the form [compare the Bürmann-series expansion (1.7.10)]

$$F(x) = A_0 + \cfrac{G(x) - G(x_0)}{A_1 + \cfrac{G(x) - G(x_0)}{A_2 + \cfrac{G(x) - G(x_0)}{A_3 + \cdots}}} \quad (9.12.18)$$

where
$$A_k = \Phi_k(x_0). \quad (9.12.19)$$

Here, if the fraction is terminated with A_n, A_n is to be replaced by

$$A_n + \frac{G(x) - G(x_0)}{\phi_{n+1}[G(x_0), \ldots, G(x_0), G(x)]}$$

if strict equality is to be preserved.

The result of truncating (9.12.18), and neglecting the residual, is then an approximation to $F(x)$ in terms of a rational function of $G(x)$, which may be expected to be useful near x_0. It can be used, for example, to determine approximately the value of $F(x)$ when $G(x)$ takes on a prescribed value, if the corresponding value of x is unknown but is approximated by x_0. The first few Φ's are readily found to be governed by the equations

$$\Phi_0 = F, \qquad \Phi_1 = \frac{G'}{F'}, \qquad \Phi_2 = 2\frac{G'}{\Phi_1'}, \qquad \Phi_3 = 3\frac{G'}{F' + \Phi_2'}, \qquad \cdots \cdots$$
$$(9.12.20)$$

Thus, for example, if we take $F(x) = e^x$, $G(x) = \sin x$, $x_0 = 0$, we obtain the representation

$$e^x = 1 + \cfrac{\sin x}{1 + \cfrac{\sin x}{-2 + \cdot \cdot \cdot}},$$

near $x = 0$.

In particular, if we take $F(x) \equiv x$, we obtain a formula for *inverse interpolation* near $x = x_0$. For example, suppose that we require a zero $\bar{x}$ of $G(x)$ and that x_0 is a previously determined approximation to $\bar{x}$. Since then $A_0 \equiv F(x_0) = x_0$, (9.12.18) then reduces to the form

$$\bar{x} = x_0 + \cfrac{-G(x_0)}{A_1 + \cfrac{-G(x_0)}{A_2 + \cfrac{-G(x_0)}{A_3 + \cdot \cdot \cdot}}}$$

or to the more convenient equivalent form

$$\bar{x} = x_0 - \cfrac{\omega_1(x_0)}{1 - \cfrac{\omega_2(x_0)}{1 - \cfrac{\omega_3(x_0)}{1 - \cdot \cdot \cdot}}}, \qquad (9.12.21)$$

where $\qquad \omega_1(x_0) = \dfrac{G(x_0)}{A_1}, \qquad \omega_k(x_0) = \dfrac{G(x_0)}{A_k A_{k-1}} \qquad (k > 1),$ $\quad$ (9.12.22)

and where (9.12.16), (9.12.17), and (9.12.19) apply with $F(x) = x$.

Here the relations of (9.12.20) reduce to

$$\Phi_0 = x, \qquad \Phi_1 = G', \qquad \Phi_2 = 2\frac{G'}{G''}, \qquad \Phi_3 = 3\frac{G'}{1 + 2(G'/G'')'}, \qquad \cdots \cdots,$$
$$(9.12.23)$$

and there follows

$$\omega_1 = \frac{G}{G'}, \qquad \omega_2 = \frac{G}{G'}\frac{G''}{2G'}, \qquad \omega_3 = \frac{G}{G'}\left(\frac{G''}{2G'} - \frac{G'''}{3G''}\right), \qquad \cdots \cdots \quad (9.12.24)$$

The first four convergents of (9.12.21) are thus found to be

$$\bar{x}^{(1)} = x_0, \qquad \bar{x}^{(2)} = x_0 - \omega_1, \qquad \bar{x}^{(3)} = x_0 - \frac{\omega_1}{1 - \omega_2},$$

$$\bar{x}^{(4)} = x_0 - \frac{\omega_1(1 - \omega_3)}{1 - \omega_2 - \omega_3}, \qquad (9.12.25)$$

where the ω's are to be evaluated at x_0.†

In illustration, the equation $x^3 - x - 1 = 0$ is easily seen to possess one real root $\bar{x}$, which lies between $x = 1$ and $x = 2$. If we choose the crude first approximation $x_0 = 1$, and set $G(x) = x^3 - x - 1$, there follows $G_0 = -1$, $G_0' = 2$, $G_0'' = 6$, $G_0''' = 6$, and the successive convergents are found to be 1, $\frac{3}{2} = 1.5$, $\frac{9}{7} \doteq 1.29$, and $\frac{75}{56} \doteq 1.34$. If the process is iterated, starting now with $x_0 = 1.34$, the successive approximants round to 1.34, 1.3249, 1.324720, and 1.324718. The result yielded by the last approximation is in fact correct to more than the seven digits given.

Whereas expressions can be derived for the error of truncation (see Frame [87]), they are too complicated to be generally useful, and one must attempt to estimate the error in a given approximant by inspecting the behavior of the *sequence* of preceding approximants.

9.13. Supplementary References. For more elaborate techniques of discrete harmonic analysis, see Whittaker and Robinson [20], Willers [21], and Danielson and Lanczos [68]. Whittaker and Robinson also include an application of Prony's exponential approximation to the numerical solution of certain integral equations, as well as a treatment of methods for determining periodicities, with collateral references. Applications of Chebyshev approximation include those of Lanczos [129, 273], Miller [150], Gavurin [92], Grossman [98], and Sadler [201]. Other aspects of "optimum" approximation, interpolation, and integration are treated by Bernstein [35], Sard [207], Meyers and Sard [147, 148], Harrison [103], Grosch [97], and Hastings [106, 107]. See also Olds [172]. For reference texts on continued fractions, see Perron [181] and Wall [231]. The reciprocal-difference methods of Thiele [19] are treated by Nörlund [13] and Milne-Thomson [11], who also present expressions for the error relevant to truncation of a continued fraction of Thiele type. For the use of continued fractions in the solution of equations, see Frame [87].

PROBLEMS

Section 9.2

1. If $f(x) = \sin x$ when $\sin x \geq 0$ and $f(x) = 0$ when $\sin x \leq 0$, obtain the expansion

$$f(x) = \frac{1}{\pi} + \frac{1}{2} \sin x - \frac{2}{\pi} \left(\frac{\cos 2x}{2^2 - 1} + \frac{\cos 4x}{4^2 - 1} + \frac{\cos 6x}{6^2 - 1} + \cdots \right).$$

---

† The approximation $\bar{x}^{(2)}$ is that given by the classical Newton-Raphson procedure (see §10.8), the approximation $\bar{x}^{(3)}$ is attributed to Halley, and the investigation of the entire sequence appears to have been initiated by Frame.

Also compare graphically each of the three least-squares approximations corresponding to retention of harmonics through the second, fourth, and sixth with the true function over $(-\pi,\pi)$.

2. Obtain the expansion

$$x = \frac{\pi}{2} - \frac{4}{\pi}\left(\frac{\cos x}{1^2} + \frac{\cos 3x}{3^2} + \frac{\cos 5x}{5^2} + \cdots\right) \qquad (0 \leqq x \leqq \pi).$$

Assuming the validity of this expansion, show that the series represents a *triangular-wave* function of period 2π which coincides with $f(x) = |x|$ when $|x| \leqq \pi$, and sketch that function. Also compare graphically each of the first three least-squares approximations, corresponding to retention of harmonics through the first, third, and fifth, with the true function over $(0,\pi)$.

3. Obtain the expansion

$$x(\pi - x) = \frac{8}{\pi}\left(\frac{\sin x}{1^3} + \frac{\sin 3x}{3^3} + \frac{\sin 5x}{5^3} + \cdots\right) \qquad (0 \leqq x \leqq \pi)$$

and sketch the periodic function represented by the expansion. Also compare graphically each of the first three distinct least-squares approximations with the true function over $(0,\pi)$.

4. Show that the *square-wave* function $f(x)$, which is of period 2π and which is such that $f(x) = -1$ when $-\pi < x < 0$ and $f(x) = +1$ when $0 < x < \pi$, possesses the expansion

$$f(x) = \frac{4}{\pi}\left(\frac{\sin x}{1} + \frac{\sin 3x}{3} + \frac{\sin 5x}{5} + \cdots\right),$$

and verify that the expansion reduces to the average of the right- and left-hand limits of the function at its points of discontinuity. Also compare graphically the first three distinct least-squares approximations with the true function over $(-\pi,\pi)$.

5. Show that the mean integrated squared error associated with the approximation (9.2.3) over $(-\pi,\pi)$ is given by

$$\frac{1}{2\pi}\int_{-\pi}^{\pi} f^2\,dx - \left[a_0^2 + \frac{1}{2}\sum_{k=1}^{n}(a_k^2 + b_k^2)\right],$$

whereas the corresponding quantities associated with (9.2.8) and (9.2.10) over $(0,\pi)$ are given respectively by

$$\frac{1}{\pi}\int_0^{\pi} f^2\,dx - \left(a_0^2 + \frac{1}{2}\sum_{k=1}^{n} a_k^2\right)$$

and

$$\frac{1}{\pi}\int_0^{\pi} f^2\,dx - \frac{1}{2}\sum_{k=1}^{n} b_k^2.$$

Also use these results to calculate the RMS errors in each of the least-squares approximations considered in Probs. 1 to 4.

6. Suppose that $y(x)$ is to be of period 2π and is to satisfy the differential equation

$$\alpha y^{iv}(x) + \beta y''(x) + \gamma y(x) = f(x),$$

where α, β, and γ are constants and $f(x)$ is a specified function of period 2π. Show that, if an approximation to $y(x)$ is assumed in the form

$$y(x) \approx a_0 + \sum_{k=1}^{n} (a_k \cos kx + b_k \sin kx)$$

and is introduced into the differential equation, and if the coefficients are determined in such a way that the period integral of the square of the difference between the two sides of the resultant equation is as small as possible, then there follows

$$\gamma a_0 = \frac{1}{2\pi} \int_{-\pi}^{\pi} f(x)\, dx, \qquad (\alpha k^4 - \beta k^2 + \gamma)a_k = \frac{1}{\pi} \int_{-\pi}^{\pi} f(x) \cos kx\, dx \qquad (k \geqq 1),$$

$$(\alpha k^4 - \beta k^2 + \gamma)b_k = \frac{1}{\pi} \int_{-\pi}^{\pi} f(x) \sin kx\, dx.$$

Also use this result to write down a series expansion of the solution of the equation $y''(x) + \lambda y(x) = f(x)$ which is of period 2π, when $f(x)$ is the square-wave function defined in Prob. 4 and λ is a constant such that $\lambda \neq 1^2, 3^2, \ldots , (2k + 1)^2, \ldots$.

Section 9.3

7. By noticing that the relevant series is geometric, show that

$$\sum_{r=-N+1}^{N} e^{ir\alpha} = \begin{cases} e^{i\alpha/2} \dfrac{\sin N\alpha}{\sin \alpha/2} & (\alpha \neq 2\nu\pi), \\ 2N & (\alpha = 2\nu\pi), \end{cases}$$

where ν is any integer, and hence that

$$\sum_{r=-N+1}^{N} \cos r\alpha = \begin{cases} \cot \dfrac{\alpha}{2} \sin N\alpha & (\alpha \neq 2\nu\pi), \\ 2N & (\alpha = 2\nu\pi), \end{cases}$$

and

$$\sum_{r=-N+1}^{N} \sin r\alpha = \sin N\alpha.$$

8. By taking $\alpha = m\pi/N$ in the results of Prob. 7, where m is an integer, and writing $x_r = r\pi/N$, show that

$$\sum_{r=-N+1}^{N} \cos mx_r = \begin{cases} 0 & (m \neq 2\nu N), \\ 2N & (m = 2\nu N), \end{cases}$$

and

$$\sum_{r=-N+1}^{N} \sin mx_r = 0.$$

Then, by using the identity $2 \cos jx_r \cos kx_r = \cos (j - k)x_r + \cos (j + k)x_r$ and two similar identities, deduce the results of Eqs. (9.3.2) and (9.3.3).

9. Use the results of Probs. 7 and 8 to show that, if the range of summation is changed to $r = 0, 1, \ldots , N$ in (9.3.2) and (9.3.3), and if the weighting function w_r is inserted in each summand, where

$$w_r = \begin{cases} \frac{1}{2} & (r = 0), \\ 1 & (r = 1, 2, \ldots , N - 1), \\ \frac{1}{2} & (r = N), \end{cases}$$

then the right-hand members of all formulas in those equations are to be divided by the factor 2.

10. Suppose that the ordinates $f_{-N+1}, \ldots, f_{N-1}, f_N$ are empirical, with $f_{-N} \equiv f_N$, and are subject to independent normal error distributions with zero means and a common RMS value σ. Show that the corresponding RMS errors associated with the coefficients calculated from (9.3.6) are given by

$$(\delta A_0)_{\text{RMS}} = (\delta A_N)_{\text{RMS}} = \frac{\sigma}{\sqrt{2N}}, \qquad (\delta A_k)_{\text{RMS}} = (\delta B_k)_{\text{RMS}} = \frac{\sigma}{\sqrt{N}}$$

$$(k = 1, \ldots, N - 1).$$

11. Suppose that the ordinates $F_0, F_1, \ldots, F_N$ and $G_1, G_2, \ldots, G_{N-1}$ are empirical and are subject to independent normal error distributions with zero means and a common RMS value σ. Use the result of Prob. 9 to show that the corresponding RMS errors associated with the coefficients of the cosine approximation to $F(x)$ over $(0,\pi)$, calculated from (9.3.11), are given by

$$(\delta A_0)_{\text{RMS}} = (\delta A_N)_{\text{RMS}} = \sqrt{\frac{2N-1}{2N^2}}\, \sigma, \qquad (\delta A_k)_{\text{RMS}} = \sqrt{\frac{2(N-1)}{N^2}}\, \sigma$$

$$(k = 1, \ldots, N - 1),$$

whereas those associated with the coefficients of the sine approximation to $G(x)$ over $(0,\pi)$ are given by

$$(\delta B_k)_{\text{RMS}} = \sqrt{\frac{2}{N}}\, \sigma.$$

12. The following approximate values of a function $f(x)$, known to be of period 2π, are available:

x	$-\pi$	$-5\pi/6$	$-2\pi/3$	$-\pi/2$	$-\pi/3$	$-\pi/6$
$f(x)$	2.077	0.278	-1.014	-0.716	0.051	0.277

x	0	$\pi/6$	$\pi/3$	$\pi/2$	$2\pi/3$	$5\pi/6$	π
$f(x)$	1.015	3.031	4.759	4.680	3.689	3.032	2.077

Assuming first that the given values are correct to the number of places given, determine a trigonometric function of period 2π which agrees with $f(x)$, to those places, at all tabular points. If it is known that the magnitude of the errors in all given values may be as large as 0.005, and that all higher harmonics are negligible, determine how many of the calculated harmonics can be neglected if the total error is nowhere to exceed about 0.01. If, instead, it is known only that the approximate ordinates are subject to error distributions with an RMS value of about 0.0025, and if all higher harmonics are again assumed to be negligible, use the result of Prob. 10 to estimate the RMS errors in the calculated coefficients.

13. Determine a seven-term cosine-series approximation of period 2π to the function $f(x)$ of Prob. 12 over $(0,\pi)$, and analyze the results as in Prob. 12.

14. Using the following data, determine a five-term sine-series approximation of period 2π to the function $f(x)$ over $(0,\pi)$, and analyze the results as in Prob. 12:

x	0	$\pi/6$	$\pi/3$	$\pi/2$	$2\pi/3$	$5\pi/6$	π
$f(x)$	0	1.136	0.864	4.002	6.059	2.868	0

Section 9.4

15. Suppose that approximate data are available for a function known to be of the form $F(t) = Ae^{bt}$, where A and b are unknown constants. Show that the change of notation

$$\log F(t) = f(t), \qquad \log A = c$$

leads to the linear relation $f(t) = c + bt$, after which the least-squares methods of §7.3 are available for the determination of c and b, and hence of A and b.   Apply this method in the case when the following empirical values of $F(t)$ are given, and determine whether the result is consistent with the hypothetical fact that the errors in the given data do not exceed 0.0002 in magnitude:

t	9	12	15	18	21	24	27
$F(t)$	0.5820	0.4622	0.3672	0.2920	0.2320	0.1843	0.1463

16. Increase each of the given ordinates in Prob. 15 by unity, and suppose that the resultant ordinates correspond to a function $G(t)$. Show first that the assumption $G(t) \approx Ae^{bt}$ does not lead to an approximation consistent with the assumed error bounds.   Then, assuming knowledge that the true function $G(t)$ is of the form $G(t) = A_0 + A_1e^{bt}$, but without making use of any other information, use Prony's method [with $x = (t - 9)/3$] to approximate A_0, A_1, and b.

17. Given the modified data of Prob. 16, assume an approximation of the form $G(t) \approx A_0 + A_1e^{b_1t} + A_2e^{b_2t}$, and use Prony's method to determine the approximation, showing that a negative value of e^{b_2} is obtained, so that the third term is of alternating sign at successive tabular points, and hence presumably is to be interpreted as "noise" in this case.   (Take care to retain sufficiently many digits.)

Section 9.5

18. Repeat the calculations of the illustrative example, using given values of $f(x)$ rounded correctly to five decimal places.

19. The following data represent observed values of a certain physical quantity:

t	0	0.05	0.10	0.15	0.20
$F(t)$	0	0.954	1.527	1.502	0.913

t	0.25	0.30	0.35	0.40	0.45	0.50
$F(t)$	0.030	−0.752	−1.090	−0.833	−0.091	0.814

The errors in measurement are known not to exceed 0.0005.   Theory predicts that the true function $F(t)$ should satisfy the differential equation $MF''(t) + kF(t) = 0$, where $M \doteq 1.40$ and $k \doteq 248$, and hence should be of period $P \doteq 0.472$.   There is reason to believe that the difference $G(t)$ between the true function and the function actually subject to measurement satisfies an equation of the form $G''(t) + c^2G(t) = 0$ for some constant c.   Investigate the plausibility of this conjecture, and approximate the period of the perturbation $G(t)$.

Section 9.6

20. Plot the function $\pi(x) = x(x^2 - 1/4)(x^2 - 1)$ in $(-1,1)$, relevant to a five-point interpolation employing data at equally spaced points, together with the corresponding functions associated with data prescribed at the zeros of $P_5(x)$ and $T_5(x)$, on a common graph. Also determine the maximum and RMS values of these functions over $(-1,1)$.

21. Use the Lagrange interpolation formula to determine three parabolic approximations to $f(x) = e^x$ over $(-1,1)$, such that $y_1(x)$ agrees with $f(x)$ at $x = -1$, 0, and 1, $y_2(x)$ agrees with $f(x)$ at the zeros of $P_3(x)$, and $y_3(x)$ agrees with $f(x)$ at the zeros of $T_3(x)$. Show also that the errors can be expressed in the forms $x(x^2 - 1)e^{\xi_1}/6$, $x(x^2 - 3/5)e^{\xi_2}/6$, and $x(x^2 - 3/4)e^{\xi_3}/6$, respectively, where each ξ is in $(-1,1)$. Calculate the actual errors in the three approximations for $x = -1.0(0.2)1.0$, plot them on a common graph, and compare them with respect to approximate maximum and RMS values.

Section 9.7

22. Derive (9.7.8) by first obtaining the intermediate results

$$\sum_{r=0}^{n} e^{i(2r+1)\alpha} = \begin{cases} e^{i(n+1)\alpha} \dfrac{\sin (n + 1)\alpha}{\sin \alpha} & (\alpha \neq \nu\pi), \\ (-1)^{\nu}(n + 1) & (\alpha = \nu\pi) \end{cases}$$

and

$$\sum_{r=0}^{n} \cos m\theta_r = \begin{cases} 0 & [m \neq 2\nu(n + 1)], \\ (-1)^{\nu}(n + 1) & [m = 2\nu(n + 1)], \end{cases}$$

where $\alpha = m\pi/[2(n + 1)]$ and $\theta_r = (2r + 1)\pi/(2n + 2)$, and then using the identity $\cos j\theta_r \cos k\theta_r = \frac{1}{2} \cos (j - k)\theta_r + \frac{1}{2} \cos (j + k)\theta_r$.

23. Determine, to four decimal places, the coefficients in the approximation

$$e^x \approx \sum_{k=0}^{5} c_k T_k(x) \qquad (|x| \leq 1),$$

if the approximation is to be exact at the zeros of $T_6(x)$, and show that the magnitude of the error is smaller than $e/23040 \doteq 0.00012$ everywhere in $(-1,1)$. Also, recalling that $|T_k(x)| \leq 1$ in $(-1,1)$, obtain upper bounds on the errors relevant to the (weighted) least-squares approximations of degrees two, three, and four, obtained by truncation, and use Eqs. (7.8.10) to express these approximations in explicit polynomial form.

Section 9.8

24. Determine two third-degree approximations to e^x over $(-1,1)$, in addition to (9.8.17), by truncating the Maclaurin expansion of e^x instead with the x^4 term and with the x^6 term, and proceeding by the Lanczos method. Also compare the error bounds associated with these approximations with each other and with the corresponding approximation obtained in Prob. 23.

25. Obtain an approximation of the form

$$\cos x \approx A_0 + A_2 x^2 + A_4 x^4$$

with an error smaller than 5×10^{-5} over $(-1,1)$.

26. Show that the polynomials $T_k(2x - 1)$ play the same role over $(0,1)$ as do the polynomials $T_k(x)$ over $(-1,1)$ and, with the abbreviation

$$\bar{T}_k \equiv \bar{T}_k(x) \equiv T_k(2x - 1),$$

obtain the relations

$$\bar{T}_0 = 1, \qquad \bar{T}_1 = 2x - 1, \qquad \bar{T}_2 = 8x^2 - 8x + 1, \qquad \bar{T}_3 = 32x^3 - 48x^2 + 18x - 1,$$
$$\bar{T}_4 = 128x^4 - 256x^3 + 160x^2 - 32x + 1,$$
$$\bar{T}_5 = 512x^5 - 1280x^4 + 1120x^3 - 400x^2 + 50x - 1$$

and

$$1 = \bar{T}_0, \qquad 2x = \bar{T}_0 + \bar{T}_1, \qquad 8x^2 = 3\bar{T}_0 + 4\bar{T}_1 + \bar{T}_2,$$
$$32x^3 = 10\bar{T}_0 + 15\bar{T}_1 + 6\bar{T}_2 + \bar{T}_3,$$
$$128x^4 = 35\bar{T}_0 + 56\bar{T}_1 + 28\bar{T}_2 + 8\bar{T}_3 + \bar{T}_4,$$
$$512x^5 = 126\bar{T}_0 + 210\bar{T}_1 + 120\bar{T}_2 + 45\bar{T}_3 + 10\bar{T}_4 + \bar{T}_5.$$

27. Use the notation and results of Prob. 26 to obtain a third-degree polynomial approximation to e^{-x} with an error smaller than 0.001 in magnitude over (0,1).

28. After expressing a five-term (eighth-degree) truncation of the series representation

$$\frac{\sin x}{x} = 1 - \frac{x^2}{3!} + \frac{x^4}{5!} - \cdots$$

in terms of the polynomials $\bar{T}_k(x^2)$ $(0 \leq k \leq 4)$, by use of the results of Prob. 26, obtain a polynomial approximation to $\sin x$, involving as few terms as possible, with an error smaller than 10^{-5} over (0,1).

29. The modified Bessel function $K_0(x)$ possesses the asymptotic expansion

$$\sqrt{\frac{2x}{\pi}}\, e^{-x}K_0(x) = 1 - \frac{1^2}{1!8x} + \frac{(1 \cdot 3)^2}{2!(8x)^2} - \frac{(1 \cdot 3 \cdot 5)^2}{3!(8x)^3} + \cdots,$$

in which the error of truncation in the right-hand member is smaller than the first neglected term. Show that truncation with the x^{-5} term corresponds to an error smaller than 0.0008 for all $x \geq 3$. Then, after expressing the result of that truncation in terms of the functions $\bar{T}_k(3/x)$ $(0 \leq k \leq 5)$, obtain an approximation of the same type over $(3, \infty)$ involving as few terms as possible, with an error not exceeding 0.005 over that range.

Section 9.9

30. Show that an inverted difference of the sum $u(x) + v(x)$ is generally not equal to the sum of the individual inverted differences, that multiplication of $f(x)$ by a constant corresponds to multiplication of the nth inverted difference of $f(x)$ by c if n is even and by $1/c$ if n is odd, and that the addition of a constant to $f(x)$ does not affect its inverted differences.

31. Calculate the successive inverted differences $\phi_1[1,x]$, $\phi_2[1,2,x]$, $\phi_3[1,2,3,x]$, . . . for the functions x^2, x^{-2}, and $x - x^{-1}$. Then deduce the identity

$$x^2 = 1 + \cfrac{x - 1}{\cfrac{1}{3} + \cfrac{x - 2}{-12 + \cfrac{x - 3}{-\cfrac{1}{3}}}},$$

together with corresponding identities in the other two cases, and verify their correctness.

32. Form an inverted-difference array and use it to determine a function defined by a finite continued fraction which takes on the following values. Also express the result as a simple fraction.

x	0	1	2	3	4	5
$f(x)$	$\frac{3}{7}$	$\frac{7}{9}$	$\frac{13}{11}$	$\frac{21}{13}$	$\frac{31}{15}$	$\frac{43}{17}$

33. Replace the given ordinates in Prob. 32 by their three-place rounded values and repeat the determination, retaining an appropriate number of digits in the intermediate calculations and obtaining a function defined as a simple fraction whose values at the six given points round to the three-place values used. Compare the result with that of Prob. 32.

34. Proceed as in Prob. 32 with the following data:

x	0	1	2	3	4	5
$f(x)$	0	$-\frac{1}{3}$	∞	$\frac{3}{5}$	$\frac{1}{3}$	$\frac{5}{21}$

Section 9.10

35. Determine a rational function of the form (9.10.1), with $n \leq 5$, which takes on the values

x	1	2	3	4	5
$f(x)$	1	2	3	3	2

or prove that no such function exists.

36. Show that the substitution sequence

$$f(x) = w_0(x), \qquad w_{2k}(x) = w_{2k}(x_{2k}) + (x - x_{2k})w_{2k+1}(x),$$

$$w_{2k+1}(x) = w_{2k+1}(x_{2k+1}) + \frac{x - x_{2k+1}}{w_{2k+2}(x)}$$

generates the representation

$$f(x) = f(x_0) + b_1(x - x_0) + \cfrac{(x - x_0)(x - x_1)}{a_2 + b_3(x - x_2) + \cfrac{(x - x_2)(x - x_3)}{a_4 + b_5(x - x_4) + \cdots}},$$

where $a_{2k} \equiv w_{2k}(x_{2k})$ and $b_{2k+1} \equiv w_{2k+1}(x_{2k+1})$, and that the a's and b's can be determined as leading elements of columns comprising alternately first divided differences and first inverted differences relative to corresponding elements and leading elements of the preceding column. Investigate the form of the nth convergent, and illustrate the procedure by use of ordinates of

$$f(x) = \frac{6 - 6x + 3x^2}{6 - 5x + 2x^2}$$

at $x = 0, 1, 2, 3, 4$, and 5. Determine what representation would result if the definitions of $w_{2k}(x)$ and $w_{2k+1}(x)$ were interchanged. Determine what substitution sequence would generate the representation

$$f(x) = f(x_0) + b_1(x - x_0)$$
$$+ \cfrac{(x - x_0)(x - x_1)}{a_2 + b_3(x - x_2) + b_4(x - x_2)(x - x_3) + b_5(x - x_2)(x - x_3)(x - x_4) + \cdots}.$$

Section 9.11

37. Use the recurrence relations (9.11.5) and (9.11.6) to obtain the successive convergents $r_k \equiv M_k/N_k$ relevant to the illustrative example $[f(x) = \cot x, \; x_0 = 0.1,$

$x_1 = 0.2$, $x_2 = 0.3$, $x_3 = 0.4$] as follows:

$$9.967, \quad \frac{-0.29799 + x}{-0.019865}, \quad \frac{1.03656 - 0.20100x}{0.00199 + x}, \quad \frac{-2.70932 - 0.05529x + x^2}{0.00059 - 2.7199x}.$$

Also verify that the kth convergent agrees appropriately with cot x at the k appropriate points, evaluate the successive convergents at $x = 0.05, 0.15, 0.25, 0.35$, and 0.45, and compare the predicted values with the rounded true values.

38. By eliminating a_k between (9.11.5) and (9.11.6), show that

$$\frac{M_{k+1}}{N_{k+1}} - \frac{M_k}{N_k} = -(x - x_{k-1}) \frac{N_{k-1}}{N_{k+1}} \left(\frac{M_k}{N_k} - \frac{M_{k-1}}{N_{k-1}} \right)$$

and deduce the relation

$$\frac{M_{k+1}}{N_{k+1}} - \frac{M_k}{N_k} = (-1)^{k+1} \frac{(x - x_0)(x - x_1) \cdots (x - x_{k-1})}{N_k N_{k+1}}.$$

Thus, with the notation $r_k \equiv M_k/N_k$, show that the $(k + 1)$th convergent of the continued fraction (9.9.9) can be written in the form

$$r_{k+1}(x) = a_0 + \sum_{n=1}^{k} (-1)^{n+1} \frac{(x - x_0)(x - x_1) \cdots (x - x_{n-1})}{N_n(x) N_{n+1}(x)}.$$

39. Use the result of Prob. 38 to show that the kth convergent obtained in Prob. 37 can be obtained also by terminating the expansion

$$\cot x \approx 9.967 + \frac{x - 0.1}{(-0.019865)} - \frac{(x - 0.1)(x - 0.2)}{(-0.019865)(x + 0.00199)}$$
$$+ \frac{(x - 0.1)(x - 0.2)(x - 0.3)}{(x + 0.00199)(0.00059 - 2.7199x)} - \cdots$$

with the kth term.

40. Use results of Prob. 38 to show that the error expression (9.11.8) can be written in the form

$$f(x) - r_k(x) = (-1)^{k+1} \frac{\pi_k(x)/N_k(x)}{(x - x_{k-1})N_{k-1}(x) + N_k(x)\phi_k[x_0, x_1, \cdots, x_{k-1}, x]}$$

where $\pi_k(x) \equiv (x - x_0)(x - x_1) \cdots (x - x_{k-1})$.

41. Assuming knowledge of the fact that cot x becomes infinite at $x = 0$, verify that the introduction of $x = 0$ as a fifth abscissa in the text example leads to the approximate information

$$\phi_3[0.1, 0.2, 0.3, 0] \approx -3.00,$$

so that $\phi_3[0.1, 0.2, 0.3, x]$ varies from about -3.00 when $x = 0$ to about -2.70 when $x = 0.4$. Under the assumption that that function increases steadily over that interval, use the result of Prob. 40 to show that the error in the calculation of cot 0.15 from the fourth convergent would be less than about 0.0006 if no round-off errors were involved.

42. Repeat the calculations of the text example, using the following improved (four-place) approximate ordinates:

x	0.1	0.2	0.3	0.4
cot x	9.9666	4.9332	3.2327	2.3652

43. Deal as in Probs. 37, 39, and 41 with the results of Prob. 42.

44. Determine values of the first four approximate convergents to $K_1(0.3) \doteq 3.056$, where $K_1(x)$ is a modified Bessel function, introducing successively the following rounded values at $x = 0.2, 0.4, 0.6,$ and 0.8:

x	0	0.2	0.4	0.6	0.8
$K_1(x)$	∞	4.776	2.184	1.303	0.862

45. Deal as in Probs. 37, 39, and 41 with the results of Prob. 44, obtaining as much evidence as possible with regard to the accuracy afforded by the fourth convergent over the interval $(0,1)$. Also verify the conclusions deduced by comparing calculated values with the following additional rounded true values:

x	0.1	0.3	0.5	0.7	0.9	1.0
$K_1(x)$	9.854	3.056	1.656	1.050	0.7165	0.5098

Section 9.12

46. Construct the following reciprocal-difference table from the given ordinates:

x	f	ρ_1	ρ_2	ρ_3	ρ_4 .
0	2				
		-2			
1	$\frac{3}{2}$		5		
		$-\frac{10}{7}$		-2	
2	$\frac{4}{5}$		$-\frac{1}{4}$		0
		$-\frac{10}{3}$		14	
3	$\frac{1}{2}$		$-\frac{1}{13}$		0
		$-\frac{34}{5}$		66	
4	$\frac{6}{17}$		$-\frac{1}{28}$		
		$-\frac{442}{37}$			
5	$\frac{7}{26}$				

From this table, rederive (9.9.15) and also obtain the representation

$$r_5(x) = \frac{4}{5} + \cfrac{x - 2}{-\frac{10}{3} + \cfrac{x - 3}{-\frac{21}{20} + \cfrac{x - 1}{\frac{52}{3} + \cfrac{x - 4}{\frac{1}{4}}}}} = \frac{2 + x}{1 + x^2},$$

corresponding to a zigzag difference path launched from $x = 2$.

47. Obtain the formal expansion

$$\log (1 + x) = \frac{x}{1} + \frac{x}{2} + \frac{x}{3} + \frac{x}{1} + \frac{x}{5} + \cdots .$$

Also show that $\phi_{2n}(x) = 2/n$ $(n \geq 1)$ and $\phi_{2n+1}(x) = (2n + 1)(1 + x)$, so that the $(2n)$th coefficient is $2/n$ and the $(2n + 1)$th is $2n + 1$.

48. Use (9.11.5) and (9.11.6) to show that the leading convergents of the expansion obtained in Prob. 47 are given by

$$0, \ x, \ \frac{2x}{2 + x}, \ \frac{6x + x^2}{6 + 4x}, \ \frac{6x + 3x^2}{6 + 6x + x^2}, \ \frac{30x + 21x^2 + x^3}{30 + 36x + 9x^2}, \ \frac{60x + 60x^2 + 11x^3}{60 + 90x + 36x^2 + 3x^3},$$

and determine the successive approximations to $\log \frac{1}{2}$ and $\log 2$. Also use the result of Prob. 38 to show that these convergents are the partial sums of the formal expansion

$$\log(1+x) = 0 + x - \frac{x^2}{2+x} + \frac{x^3}{(2+x)(6+4x)} - \frac{x^4}{(6+4x)(6+6x+x^2)}$$
$$+ \frac{x^5}{(6+6x+x^2)(30+36x+9x^2)} - \frac{x^6}{(30+36x+9x^2)(20+30x+12x^2+x^3)} + \cdots$$

49. Obtain the formal representation

$$\tan^{-1} x = \frac{\pi}{4} + \frac{x-1}{2} + \frac{x-1}{1} + \frac{x-1}{-6} + \frac{x-1}{-\frac{1}{4}} + \cdots$$

and express the first five convergents as simple fractions. Also use the result of Prob. 38 to show that the representation can be expressed in the form

$$\tan^{-1} x = \frac{\pi}{4} + \frac{x-1}{2} - \frac{(x-1)^2}{2(1+x)} - \frac{(x-1)^3}{4(1+x)(2+x)} + \frac{(x-1)^4}{4(2+x)(1+x+x^2)} + \cdots$$

50. Obtain the formal representations

$$(x+c^2)^{\frac{1}{2}} = c + \frac{x}{2c} + \frac{x}{2c} + \frac{x}{2c} + \cdots$$

and
$$(x+c^2)^{-\frac{1}{2}} = \frac{1}{c} - \frac{x}{2c^3} + \frac{x}{\frac{2}{3c}} + \frac{x}{18c^3} + \frac{x}{\frac{2}{15c}} + \cdots,$$

where c is a positive constant.

51. With the notation

$$A_k = \frac{1}{k!} f^{(k)}(x_0),$$

use (9.12.14) to show that the first five Thiele coefficients in (9.12.6) are given by

$$a_0 = A_0, \quad a_1 = \frac{1}{A_1}, \quad a_2 = -\frac{A_1^2}{A_2}, \quad a_3 = \frac{A_2^2}{A_1(A_1A_3 - A_2^2)}, \quad a_4 = -\frac{(A_1A_3 - A_2^2)^2}{A_2(A_2A_4 - A_3^2)},$$

where $a_k \equiv \phi_k(x_0)$. Deduce also that if a function possesses the formal Taylor expansion $A_0 + A_1u + A_2u^2 + \cdots$ and the formal Thiele expansion $a_0 + \dfrac{u}{a_1} + \dfrac{u}{a_2} + \cdots$, then the leading a's can be calculated from the leading A's by use of these relations.

52. Show that the expansion (9.12.6) is nonexistent when $f(x) = \cos x$ and $x_0 = 0$, but that, when $F(x) = \cos x$, $G(x) = x^2$, and $x_0 = 0$, the leading terms of the expansion (9.12.18) are of the form

$$\cos x = 1 + \frac{x^2}{-2} + \frac{x^2}{-6} + \frac{x^2}{\frac{10}{3}} + \cdots.$$

Also obtain this form from the result of Prob. 51, with $u = x^2$.

53. Obtain the leading terms of an expansion of $\sin x$ analogous to that obtained in Prob. 52, by taking $F(x) = (\sin x)/x$, $G(x) = x^2$, and $x_0 = 0$, and also by using the result of Prob. 51.

54. The equation $x - e^{-x} = 0$ possesses a real root between $x = 0.5$ and 0.6. Making use of the fact that $e^{-0.6} \doteq 0.548812$, determine that root to five decimal places.

55. Determine the root of the equation $x^4 - 3x + 1 = 0$ between $x = 1.3$ and 1.4 to five decimal places.

CHAPTER 10

NUMERICAL SOLUTION OF EQUATIONS

10.1. Introduction. This chapter summarizes a number of methods which are available for the numerical solution of sets of linear algebraic equations (§§10.2 to 10.7), nonlinear algebraic or transcendental equations in general (§10.8), and nonlinear algebraic equations in particular (§§10.9 to 10.13). With only minor exceptions, the treatments are independent of the content of preceding chapters.

10.2. Sets of Linear Equations. A brief summary of terminologies and of certain known results, relative to solutions of sets of linear algebraic equations, is presented in this section.

We suppose first that we are concerned with a set of n equations relating n unknowns $x_1, x_2, \ldots, x_n$, and expressed in the form

$$
\begin{aligned}
a_{11}x_1 + a_{12}x_2 + \cdots + a_{1n}x_n &= c_1, \\
a_{21}x_1 + a_{22}x_2 + \cdots + a_{2n}x_n &= c_2, \\
&\cdots \cdots \cdots \cdots \cdots \cdots \cdots \\
a_{n1}x_1 + a_{n2}x_2 + \cdots + a_{nn}x_n &= c_n,
\end{aligned}
\tag{10.2.1}
$$

where the n^2 coefficients a_{ij} and the n right-hand members c_i are prescribed. Here a_{ij} represents the coefficient of x_j in the ith equation of the set.

The left-hand members may be specified by the square array of the coefficients, known as the *coefficient matrix*,

$$
\begin{array}{cccc}
a_{11} & a_{12} & \cdots & a_{1n} \\
a_{21} & a_{22} & \cdots & a_{2n} \\
\cdots & \cdots & \cdots & \cdots \\
a_{n1} & a_{n2} & \cdots & a_{nn}
\end{array}
\tag{10.2.2}
$$

whereas the complete set may be specified by the *rectangular* array,

$$
\begin{array}{ccccc}
a_{11} & a_{12} & \cdots & a_{1n} & c_1 \\
a_{21} & a_{22} & \cdots & a_{2n} & c_2 \\
\cdots & \cdots & \cdots & \cdots & \cdots \\
a_{n1} & a_{n2} & \cdots & a_{nn} & c_n
\end{array}
\tag{10.2.3}
$$

known as the *augmented matrix* and formed by adjoining the column of right-hand members to the n columns (10.2.2).

The *minor* of any element a_{ij} in the coefficient matrix is defined as the value of the *determinant*† of the square array obtained by deleting the ith row and the jth column of the coefficient array.   The *cofactor* of a_{ij}, to be denoted here by A_{ij}, is defined as the result of changing the sign of the minor $i + j$ times.   It is then true that, *if each element of any column of the coefficient matrix is multiplied by its cofactor, then the sum of these n products is the value of the determinant of that matrix.*   Furthermore, *if each element of any column is multiplied by the cofactor of the corresponding element of any other column, then the sum of these n products is zero.*   (Both statements also remain true if the word *column* is replaced by *row* throughout.)

These facts permit the direct elimination of all unknowns except an arbitrarily chosen one, say x_k, from (10.2.1).   For if we multiply each equation by the cofactor of the coefficient of x_k in that equation and add the results, they lead immediately to the consequence that the result is of the form

$$Dx_k = c_1 A_{1k} + c_2 A_{2k} + \cdots + c_n A_{nk}, \qquad (10.2.4)$$

where D represents the value of the determinant of the coefficient matrix. Thus, if $D \neq 0$, and if (10.2.1) possesses a solution, then that solution is unique, and each x_k ($k = 1, 2, \ldots, n$) is obtained from (10.2.4) by division by D.

It is then easily shown, by direct substitution, that the x's so obtained actually do satisfy (10.2.1).   For since (10.2.1) is of the form

$$\sum_{k=1}^{n} a_{ik}x_k = c_i \qquad (i = 1, 2, \ldots, n),$$

and since (10.2.4) is expressible in the form

$$Dx_k = \sum_{j=1}^{n} A_{jk}c_j \qquad (k = 1, 2, \ldots, n),$$

the result of substituting (10.2.4) into the left-hand member of the ith equation of (10.2.1) is

$$\frac{1}{D} \sum_{k=1}^{n} a_{ik} \sum_{j=1}^{n} A_{jk}c_j = \frac{1}{D} \sum_{j=1}^{n} \left(\sum_{k=1}^{n} a_{ik} A_{jk} \right) c_j.$$

Since the inner sum in the second form is the sum of the products of the elements in the ith row of the coefficient matrix and the cofactors of corresponding elements in the jth row, it is equal to D when $j = i$ and is zero when $j \neq i$, so that this quantity properly reduces to c_i.

† The definition and elementary properties of determinants are assumed.

Since the right-hand member of (10.2.4) would reduce to D if c_1, c_2, $\ldots$, c_n were replaced by a_{1k}, a_{2k}, $\ldots$, a_{nk}, it follows also that *the right-hand member of* (10.2.4) *is the value of the determinant of the matrix obtained from the coefficient matrix by replacing the column of coefficients of* x_k *by the column of right-hand members of* (10.2.1). If we denote the value of this determinant by D_k, the solution of (10.2.1) can be written in the simple form

$$x_k = \frac{D_k}{D} \qquad (k = 1, 2, \ldots, n), \tag{10.2.5}$$

if $D \neq 0$. This result is known as *Cramer's rule*.

It is convenient to write

$$\frac{A_{ij}}{D} = \tilde{A}_{ij}, \tag{10.2.6}$$

when $D \neq 0$, and to speak of this ratio as the *reduced cofactor* of a_{ij} in the matrix (10.2.2). With this notation, the result of writing out (10.2.4) for $k = 1, 2, \ldots, n$ is of the form

$$\begin{aligned}
x_1 &= \tilde{A}_{11}c_1 + \tilde{A}_{21}c_2 + \cdots + \tilde{A}_{n1}c_n, \\
x_2 &= \tilde{A}_{12}c_1 + \tilde{A}_{22}c_2 + \cdots + \tilde{A}_{n2}c_n, \\
&\;\;\cdots\cdots\cdots\cdots\cdots\cdots\cdots\cdots\cdots\cdots\cdots\cdots\cdots \\
x_n &= \tilde{A}_{1n}c_1 + \tilde{A}_{2n}c_2 + \cdots + \tilde{A}_{nn}c_n.
\end{aligned} \tag{10.2.7}$$

This set of relations is thus the result of "inverting" the relations (10.2.1), when $D \neq 0$.

The array of coefficients of the right-hand members in (10.2.7),

$$\begin{matrix}
\tilde{A}_{11} & \tilde{A}_{21} & \cdots & \tilde{A}_{n1} \\
\tilde{A}_{12} & \tilde{A}_{22} & \cdots & \tilde{A}_{n2} \\
\cdots\cdots\cdots\cdots\cdots\cdots\cdots \\
\tilde{A}_{1n} & \tilde{A}_{2n} & \cdots & \tilde{A}_{nn}
\end{matrix} \tag{10.2.8}$$

may thus be called the *inverse* of the coefficient matrix of (10.2.1) in that case, in the sense that whereas the array (10.2.2) specifies a transformation of the x's into the c's, the array (10.2.8) specifies the *inverse transformation* of the c's back into the x's.

We notice that the inverse of (10.2.2) can be obtained by first replacing each element of (10.2.2) by its reduced cofactor (cofactor divided by D), and then interchanging rows and columns.

In order to describe the situation in the case $D = 0$, as well as the case in which there are m equations relating n unknowns, where $m \neq n$, it is desirable to define the *rank* of any rectangular matrix with, say, m rows and n columns. From any such array, we may form a number of *square* subarrays, by deleting certain rows and/or columns, and compressing the remaining elements into a compact arrangement. The largest such sub-arrays would be of an order equal to the smaller of the integers m and n; the smallest would be of order one and would consist of only a single element. The rank of the given matrix is defined as the order of the *largest* such subarray *whose determinant is not zero.*

The basic theorem relevant to the *existence* of a solution of a set of m equations in n unknowns states simply that *the system is solvable if and only if the rank of the coefficient matrix is equal to the rank of the augmented matrix.*

Suppose that the ranks *are* equal, and let the common rank be r. Then r is not greater than the smaller of m and n. Now there exists at least one square $r \times r$ subarray in the coefficient matrix whose determinant is not zero. If one such subarray is found, and if $r < m$, then it can be proved that the $m - r$ equations whose coefficients are *not* involved in that subarray are implied by the other m equations and can be suppressed. If $r = n$, then n equations remain and can be solved uniquely by Cramer's rule. However, if $r < n$, then the $n - r$ unknowns in the r remaining equations whose *coefficients* are not involved in the subarray can each be assigned completely arbitrary values, after which the remaining r unknowns can be determined *in terms of them* by Cramer's rule. Thus, the general solution of the system then involves $n - r$ arbitrary constants, and the system is said to be of "defect" $n - r$, since it fails to determine a unique solution by permitting $n - r$ degrees of freedom.

The cases of most frequent practical interest are those represented by (10.2.1), in which $m = n$. In particular, if all the right-hand members c_i are *zeros*, the set is said to be *homogeneous*. In this case, the coefficient matrix and augmented matrix are automatically of the same rank, so that the set is solvable. In fact, one solution is then always the *trivial* one, for which $x_1 = x_2 = \cdots = x_n = 0$. If $D \neq 0$, this is the only possible solution. Usually this solution is of no interest, and the important homogeneous sets are those for which $D = 0$, so that the system admits nontrivial solutions. On the other hand, if at least one of the right-hand members is *not* zero, so that the trivial solution is not admissible, the interest centers mainly on the cases when a nontrivial solution *exists and is unique*, so that $D \neq 0$. Attention will be restricted principally to this last case in the following sections.

Before proceeding, it may be pointed out that, whereas the preceding results are of basic theoretical importance and are essential to an understanding of the nature of sets of linear equations, the use of Cramer's rule in actual *numerical* cases is generally highly inefficient, because of the excessive labor involved in the evaluation of $n + 1$ determinants of order n, when n is fairly large. Many other methods have been devised, certain of which are described in the following sections.

10.3. The Gauss Reduction. In principle, the simplest practical method of solving the set (10.2.1) is one due to Gauss. It consists in first dividing the first equation by a_{11} and using the result to eliminate x_1 from all succeeding equations. Next, the modified second equation is divided by the coefficient of x_2 in that equation, and the result is used to eliminate x_2 from the succeeding equations, and so forth. After this elimination has been effected n times, when $D \neq 0$, the resultant set, which is equivalent to the original one except for the effects of any round-offs committed, is of the form

$$
\begin{aligned}
x_1 + a'_{12}x_2 + a'_{13}x_3 + \cdots + a'_{1n}x_n &= c'_1, \\
x_2 + a'_{23}x_3 + \cdots + a'_{2n}x_n &= c'_2, \\
\cdots\cdots\cdots\cdots\cdots\cdots\cdots\cdots \\
x_{n-1} + a'_{n-1,n}x_n &= c'_{n-1}, \\
x_n &= c'_n,
\end{aligned}
\tag{10.3.1}
$$

where a'_{ij} and c'_i designate specific numerical values, and the solution is completed by working backward from the last equation, to obtain successively x_n, x_{n-1}, $\ldots$, x_1. It is convenient to work with the augmented *arrays* at each stage, rather than to write out each equation in full.

A renumbering of equations and/or variables will be *necessary* if, at any stage, the coefficient of x_k in the kth equation is zero, and it is *desirable* if that coefficient is small relative to other coefficients in that equation, in order that the effects of round-off errors may be minimized.

The exceptional cases in which $D = 0$ would evidence themselves through the fact that after r such eliminations, where r is the rank of the coefficient matrix, all coefficients in the $n - r$ succeeding equations would vanish (except for the errors due to round-off). Unless all right-hand members of those equations *also* were reduced to zeros at that stage, the original set would be unsolvable. If all those members were zeros, the $n - r$ equations would have been reduced to the form $0 = 0$, and hence would be ignorable. The rth equation would express x_r as the sum of a specified constant and a certain linear combination of x_{r+1}, $\ldots$, x_n, and the process of back substitution would finally express x_1, x_2, $\ldots$, x_r in similar forms.

In illustration, we consider the three equations

$$
\begin{aligned}
9.3746x_1 + 3.0416x_2 - 2.4371x_3 &= 9.2333, \\
3.0416x_1 + 6.1832x_2 + 1.2163x_3 &= 8.2049, \\
-2.4371x_1 + 1.2163x_2 + 8.4429x_3 &= 3.9339.
\end{aligned}
\tag{10.3.2}
$$

The reduced equations, corresponding to (10.3.1), are obtained in the form

$$
\begin{aligned}
x_1 + 0.32445x_2 - 0.25997x_3 &= 0.98493, \\
x_2 + 0.38624x_3 &= 1.00246, \\
x_3 &= 0.61448,
\end{aligned}
\tag{10.3.3}
$$

if five decimal places are retained, and the "back solution" yields the values

$$x_1 = 0.89643, \qquad x_2 = 0.76512, \qquad x_3 = 0.61448. \qquad (10.3.4)$$

A discussion of the reliability of these results is deferred to later sections.

This method is known as the *Gauss reduction*. A modification, known as the *Gauss-Jordan reduction*, consists in using the kth equation, at the kth stage, to eliminate x_k from the preceding equations as well as the following ones, so that the solution is obtained after n (or less) eliminations, and no back substitution is necessary.

In practice, only the coefficients are recorded at the successive stages of the reduction, the array corresponding to the first stage intermediate between (10.3.2) and (10.3.3) thus being of the form

$$
\begin{array}{cccc}
1 & 0.32445 & -0.25997 & 0.98493 \\
 & 5.19635 & 2.00702 & 5.20914 \\
 & 2.00702 & 7.80933 & 6.33427
\end{array}
$$

The necessity of recording new arrays at each of the intermediate stages is time-consuming and conducive to gross errors, particularly when many equations are involved. In the following section, a more efficient technique is described.

10.4. The Crout Reduction. A modification of the Gauss reduction, which has the advantages that it is particularly well adapted to the use of desk calculators and of large-scale computers, and that the recording (or storage) of auxiliary data (such as the repeated rewriting of modified equations or arrays) is somewhat minimized, is due to Crout.[†]

Starting with the augmented matrix **M** of the original system,

$$
\mathbf{M} =
\begin{array}{cccc:c}
a_{11} & a_{12} & \cdots & a_{1n} & c_1 \\
a_{21} & a_{22} & \cdots & a_{2n} & c_2 \\
\cdots & \cdots & \cdots & \cdots & \cdots \\
a_{n1} & a_{n2} & \cdots & a_{nn} & c_n
\end{array}
\equiv \mathbf{A} \mathbin{:} \mathbf{c}, \qquad (10.4.1)
$$

which may be considered as being partitioned into the coefficient array **A** and the **c** column, one determines next the elements of an *auxiliary matrix* **M'** of the same dimensions,

$$
\mathbf{M'} =
\begin{array}{cccc:c}
a'_{11} & a'_{12} & \cdots & a'_{1n} & c'_1 \\
a'_{21} & a'_{22} & \cdots & a'_{2n} & c'_2 \\
\cdots & \cdots & \cdots & \cdots & \cdots \\
a'_{n1} & a'_{n2} & \cdots & a'_{nn} & c'_n
\end{array}
\equiv \mathbf{A'} \mathbin{:} \mathbf{c'}, \qquad (10.4.2)
$$

† See reference [64], in which modifications which are convenient when the coefficients are *complex* are also given. Similar methods are attributed to Cholesky, Banachiewicz, Turing, and Zurmühl.

which may be considered as being partitioned, in the same way, into a square array $\mathbf{A}'$ and a $\mathbf{c}'$ column. From this matrix, one then obtains a solution column $\mathbf{x}$ whose elements are the required values of $x_1, \ldots, x_n$,

$$\mathbf{x} = \begin{matrix} x_1 \\ x_2 \\ \cdot \\ \cdot \\ \cdot \\ x_n \end{matrix} \qquad (10.4.3)$$

Each entry in (10.4.2) and (10.4.3) is obtained from previously calculated data by a continuous sequence of operations, which can be effected without the tabulation of intermediate data.

In order to describe the reduction in a simple way, it is convenient to introduce two definitions. First, the *diagonal elements* (or elements on the *principal diagonal*) of a matrix are those elements whose row and column indices are equal, and which are underlined in (10.4.1) and (10.4.2). Second, the *inner product* of a row and a column, each containing n elements, is defined as the sum of the n products of corresponding elements, the elements of a row being ordered from left to right, and the elements of a column from head to foot.

The n elements of the first column of the auxiliary matrix (10.4.2) are determined first, then the remaining n of the $n + 1$ elements of the first row. Next, the remaining $n - 1$ elements of the second column and of the second row are determined, then the remaining $n - 2$ elements of the third column and third row, and the process is continued until the array is filled.

The elements of the first column of $\mathbf{M}'$ are identical with the corresponding elements of $\mathbf{M}$; the remaining elements of the first row of $\mathbf{M}'$ (to the right of the diagonal element a_{11}') are each obtained by dividing the corresponding element of $\mathbf{M}$ by the diagonal element a_{11}'. Thus, for example, $a_{11}' = a_{11}$, $a_{21}' = a_{21}$, and $a_{12}' = a_{12}/a_{11}'$.

From this stage onward, the elements of $\mathbf{M}'$ are calculated, *in the order specified above*, according to two rules:

1. Each element on or below the principal diagonal in $\mathbf{M}'$ is obtained by subtracting from the corresponding element in $\mathbf{M}$ the inner product of its own column and its own row in the square subarray $\mathbf{A}'$, with all uncalculated elements imagined to be zeros.

2. Each element to the right of the principal diagonal in $\mathbf{M}'$ is calculated by the same procedure, followed by a division by the diagonal element in its row of $\mathbf{M}'$.

Finally, the elements of the solution column $\mathbf{x}$ are determined in the order $x_n, x_{n-1}, \ldots, x_2, x_1$, from foot to head. The element x_n is identical with c_n'.   Each succeeding element above it is obtained as the result of subtracting from the corresponding element of the $\mathbf{c}'$ column the inner product of its row in $\mathbf{A}'$ and the $\mathbf{x}$ column, with all uncalculated elements of the $\mathbf{x}$ column imagined to be zeros.

The preceding instructions are summarized by the equations

$$a_{ij}' = a_{ij} - \sum_{k=1}^{j-1} a_{ik}' a_{kj}' \qquad (i \geqq j), \qquad (10.4.4)$$

$$a_{ij}' = \frac{1}{a_{ii}'} \left[a_{ij} - \sum_{k=1}^{i-1} a_{ik}' a_{kj}' \right] \qquad (i < j), \qquad (10.4.5)$$

$$c_i' = \frac{1}{a_{ii}'} \left[c_i - \sum_{k=1}^{i-1} a_{ik}' c_k' \right], \qquad (10.4.6)$$

and $$x_i = c_i' - \sum_{k=i+1}^{n} a_{ik}' x_k, \qquad (10.4.7)$$

where i and j range from 1 to n when not otherwise restricted.† It is seen that the process defined by (10.4.7) is identical with the "back solution" of the Gauss reduction, which determines $x_1, \ldots, x_n$ from (10.3.1).

In the important cases when the coefficient array $\mathbf{A}$ is *symmetric*, so that each element a_{ij} in $\mathbf{A}$ above the principal diagonal is identical with the symmetrically placed element a_{ji} below the diagonal ($a_{ij} = a_{ji}$), as in the system (10.3.2), it can be shown that each element a_{ij}' in $\mathbf{A}'$ above the principal diagonal is given by the result of *dividing* the symmetrically placed element a_{ji}' below the diagonal by the diagonal element a_{ii}'. This fact leads to a considerable reduction in labor in such cases, particularly when n is large, since then each element below the diagonal thus can be recorded as the dividend involved in the calculation of the symmetrically placed element, before the required division by the diagonal element is effected.

It can be shown that the elements to the right of the diagonal in $\mathbf{M}'$ are identical with the elements which appear in corresponding positions in the augmented matrix of (10.3.1), obtained by the Gauss reduction. The compactness of the tabulation is a consequence of the fact that all necessary intermediate data are tabulated in the remaining spaces, which would normally be occupied by 1's and zeros.

The kth diagonal element a_{kk}' is the number by which the kth equation would be divided, in the Gauss reduction, before that equation is used to

† The mathematical derivation of these relations is included in Appendix A.

eliminate x_k from succeeding equations. In consequence of this fact, it is true that *the value of the determinant of the original coefficient matrix is the product of the diagonal elements of* **A'**.

A continuous check against calculational errors is afforded by adjoining to the columns of **M** an additional column, each of whose elements is the sum of the elements in the corresponding row of **M**. If this column is treated in the same way as the **c** column, corresponding check columns are obtained and adjoined to **M'** and **x**. The check consists in the fact that each element in the **M'** check column should *exceed by unity* the sum of the elements in its row of **M'** which lie *to the right* of the diagonal element, whereas each element in the **x** check column should exceed by unity the corresponding element in the **x** column itself. The sudden appearance of an appreciable discrepancy will generally indicate the commission of a gross calculational error.

Small discrepancies may correspond to the effects of *intermediate round-offs*, effected in the steps of the reduction, and can be removed by retaining additional significant figures in that calculation, or by an alternative procedure to be described at the end of this section. However, appreciable loss of accuracy may occur if a diagonal element which is small, relative to elements to its right, appears at an early stage of the reduction. Such a situation usually can be remedied by renumbering the equations, and it frequently may be avoided by initially ordering the equations in such a way that the coefficient of x_k in the kth equation is as large as possible relative to the other coefficients in that equation.†

For the set of Eqs. (10.3.2), the complete tabulation consists of the given matrix (and check column, if desired),

$$
\begin{array}{rrr|r|r}
9.3746 & 3.0416 & -2.4371 & 9.2333 & 19.2124 \\
3.0416 & 6.1832 & 1.2163 & 8.2049 & 18.6460 \\
-2.4371 & 1.2163 & 8.4429 & 3.9339 & 11.1560
\end{array}
\qquad (10.4.8)
$$

the auxiliary matrix (and check column),

$$
\begin{array}{rrr|r|r}
9.3746 & 0.32445 & -0.25997 & 0.98493 & 2.04941 \\
\overline{3.0416} & 5.19635 & 0.38624 & 1.00246 & 2.38870 \\
-2.4371 & \overline{2.00702} & \underline{7.03414} & 0.61448 & 1.61448
\end{array}
\qquad (10.4.9)
$$

and the solution column (and check column),

$$
\begin{array}{r|r}
0.89643 & 1.89643 \\
0.76512 & 1.76512 \\
0.61448 & 1.61448
\end{array}
\qquad (10.4.10)
$$

if five decimal places are retained in the calculations.

† It may be noticed that the set (10.3.2) is ordered in this way.

Here the computational-error check, based on the check columns, displays no discrepancies through the fifth decimal place. This fact, however, does *not* guarantee that the results are *correct* to five decimal places. Indeed, the relationship between the size of discrepancies indicated by the check column and the magnitude of the effects of inter-mediate round-offs is not a simple one. The analysis of the effects of round-off errors is complicated, when many equations are involved, and cannot be treated here (see von Neumann and Goldstine [166]).

If the calculated values are substituted into the left-hand members of the *original* equations, the presence of deviations between the resultant members and the original right-hand members serves to *indicate* the presence of errors due to intermediate round-off. But, again, the relationship between the magnitudes of these deviations and the magnitudes of the errors in the solution column is not a simple one.

However, we may notice that, if substitution of the calculated values $\bar{x}_1, \bar{x}_2, \ldots, \bar{x}_n$ yields the right-hand members $\bar{c}_1, \bar{c}_2, \ldots, \bar{c}_n$, so that

$$a_{11}\bar{x}_1 + a_{12}\bar{x}_2 + \cdots + a_{1n}\bar{x}_n = \bar{c}_1,$$
$$\ldots \ldots \ldots \ldots \ldots \ldots \ldots \ldots \ldots$$
$$a_{n1}\bar{x}_1 + a_{n2}\bar{x}_2 + \cdots + a_{nn}\bar{x}_n = \bar{c}_n,$$

whereas the true values are to satisfy the equations

$$a_{11}x_1 + a_{12}x_2 + \cdots + a_{1n}x_n = c_1,$$
$$\ldots \ldots \ldots \ldots \ldots \ldots \ldots \ldots \ldots$$
$$a_{n1}x_1 + a_{n2}x_2 + \cdots + a_{nn}x_n = c_n,$$

there follows, by subtraction,

$$a_{11}\,\delta x_1 + a_{12}\,\delta x_2 + \cdots + a_{1n}\,\delta x_n = \delta c_1,$$
$$\ldots \ldots \ldots \ldots \ldots \ldots \ldots \ldots \ldots \quad (10.4.11)$$
$$a_{n1}\,\delta x_1 + a_{n2}\,\delta x_2 + \cdots + a_{nn}\,\delta x_n = \delta c_n,$$

where
$$\delta x_k \equiv x_k - \bar{x}_k, \qquad \delta c_k \equiv c_k - \bar{c}_k. \qquad (10.4.12)$$

Thus the necessary corrections $\delta x_1, \ldots, \delta x_n$ satisfy a set of equations which differs from the original set only in that each c_k is replaced by the *residual* $c_k - \bar{c}_k$.

If this set could be solved without round-off, the corrections would thus be obtained exactly. But, since this situation generally will not exist, the corrections obtained are themselves approximate. New residuals can then be calculated, and the process can be iterated, if so desired. Each such calculation is particularly simple in the Crout procedure, since only the **c** column of **M**, the **c′** column of **M′**, and the solution column need be recalculated, all other data being unchanged.

Whereas there is no *certainty* that the iteration will converge rapidly (or at all), the method is usually an efficient one, and, by successive iteration, carrying along more and more significant figures only in the calculation of the *residuals*, it is usually possible to stabilize a large number of significant figures without undue labor.   Clearly, the same increase in accuracy could be obtained alternatively, but generally with an increase in labor, by repeating the entire calculation with retention of additional significant figures.

In the case of the preceding example, the residuals corresponding to the approximate solution (10.4.10) are found to be

$$\delta c_1 = -1.2462 \times 10^{-5}, \quad \delta c_2 = 3.6504 \times 10^{-5}, \quad \delta c_3 = -1.9095 \times 10^{-5}$$

and the approximate corrections are found to be

$$\delta x_1 = -0.59421 \times 10^{-5}, \quad \delta x_2 = 0.98893 \times 10^{-5},$$
$$\delta x_3 = -0.54016 \times 10^{-5},$$

if five significant figures are retained, yielding the improved values

$$x_1 = 0.8964240579, \quad x_2 = 0.7651298893, \quad x_3 = 0.6144745984.$$

The new residuals are found to be of the order of 10^{-10}, and another iteration would supply 14-place accuracy, the rounded 10-place values agreeing with those given above except for a one-unit change in the tenth digit of x_1.

If the coefficients and right-hand members of the original set of equations are only four-decimal-place approximations to true values, the preceding retention of 10 or more decimal places may be expected to be foolish, since it is useless to strive for a higher degree of accuracy than that which is compatible with errors *inherent* in the given system.   This problem is to be considered explicitly in §10.6.

10.5. Determination of the Inverse Matrix.   From (10.2.7) and (10.2.8), it follows that the kth column of the matrix (10.2.8), which is the *inverse* of the coefficient matrix (10.2.2), is the solution column corresponding to the result of setting $c_k = 1$ and all other c's equal to zero in (10.2.1).   Thus if, in place of the single **c** column in (10.4.1), we insert the square array

$$
\begin{array}{cccc}
1 & 0 & \cdots & 0 \\
0 & 1 & \cdots & 0 \\
\cdots & \cdots & \cdots & \cdots \\
0 & 0 & \cdots & 1
\end{array}
\qquad (10.5.1)
$$

of n columns, and treat *each* column of this array as a **c** column, we will obtain finally the array (10.2.8) in place of the single **x** column.   That is, the resultant solution array will be the inverse of the coefficient matrix of the given set of equations.   A check column can be included, if so desired, and the rules given for its use apply as stated.

The determination of this inverse matrix is particularly desirable when the set (10.2.1) is to be solved for many distinct sets of right-hand members, for (10.2.7) states that *each x_k, satisfying* (10.2.1), *is given by the inner product of the c column and the kth row of the inverse matrix* (10.2.8).

In the case of the example previously treated, the auxiliary array corresponding to the given array

$$\begin{array}{ccc} 1 & 0 & 0 \\ 0 & 1 & 0 \\ 0 & 0 & 1 \end{array}$$

is found to be

$$\begin{array}{ccc} 0.106671 & 0 & 0 \\ -0.062438 & 0.192443 & 0 \\ 0.054773 & -0.054909 & 0.142164 \end{array}$$

and the solution array is obtained in the form

$$\begin{array}{ccc} 0.148032 & -0.083594 & 0.054774 \\ -0.083594 & 0.213651 & -0.054909 \\ 0.054773 & -0.054909 & 0.142164 \end{array} \qquad (10.5.2)$$

Here six decimal places were retained, in order that five significant figures would be afforded.[†] It may be noticed that the inverse matrix possesses the same symmetry as the given matrix. (The single discrepancy of one unit is due to round-off.)

The result obtained is equivalent to the statement that, apart from the effects of round-offs, the solution of the set (10.3.2) would be of the form

$$\begin{aligned} x_1 &= 0.148032c_1 - 0.083594c_2 + 0.054774c_3, \\ x_2 &= -0.083594c_1 + 0.213651c_2 - 0.054909c_3, \qquad (10.5.3) \\ x_3 &= 0.054773c_1 - 0.054909c_2 + 0.142164c_3, \end{aligned}$$

if the right-hand members of (10.3.2) were replaced by c_1, c_2, and c_3, respectively. In particular, the substitution of the actual right-hand members into (10.5.3) again leads to (10.4.10).

The elements of (10.5.2) are the *reduced cofactors* defined in (10.2.6), in accordance with (10.2.7). Since, as was stated in §10.4, the *determinant D* of the given matrix is the product of the diagonal elements of (10.4.9),

$$D = (9.3746)(5.19635)(7.03414) \doteq 342.66,$$

the array of the cofactors themselves is obtained by multiplication by D and interchange of rows and columns.

[†] For purposes of illustrating the technique, we again ignore the fact that *inherent* errors, due to round-off in the *given* data, may adversely affect the significance of certain of the digits.

10.6. Inherent Errors. In addition to the errors due to *intermediate* round-off, which generally can be detected and removed by the methods previously described, errors due to possible inaccuracies in the coefficients and right-hand members of the given equations themselves must be taken into account.

In order to investigate these errors, we suppose that the set actually solved is

$$a_{11}x_1 + \cdots + a_{1n}x_n = c_1,$$
$$\dotfill$$
$$a_{n1}x_1 + \cdots + a_{nn}x_n = c_n, \tag{10.6.1}$$

whereas the *true* values of the coefficients are $a_{ij} + \delta a_{ij}$ and the true values of the right-hand members are $c_i + \delta c_i$. If we denote the true values of the unknowns by $x_i + \delta x_i$, there follows also

$$(a_{11} + \delta a_{11})(x_1 + \delta x_1) + \cdots + (a_{1n} + \delta a_{1n})(x_n + \delta x_n)$$
$$= c_1 + \delta c_1,$$
$$\dotfill$$
$$(a_{n1} + \delta a_{n1})(x_1 + \delta x_1) + \cdots + (a_{nn} + \delta a_{nn})(x_n + \delta x_n)$$
$$= c_n + \delta c_n, \tag{10.6.2}$$

and the result of subtracting Eqs. (10.6.1) from (10.6.2) is expressible in the form

$$a_{11}\,\delta x_1 + \cdots + a_{1n}\,\delta x_n = \delta c_1 - (x_1\,\delta a_{11} + \cdots + x_n\,\delta a_{1n}),$$
$$\dotfill$$
$$a_{n1}\,\delta x_1 + \cdots + a_{nn}\,\delta x_n = \delta c_n - (x_1\,\delta a_{n1} + \cdots + x_n\,\delta a_{nn}), \tag{10.6.3}$$

if *products* of errors, of the form $(\delta a_{ik})(\delta x_k)$, are *assumed* to be relatively negligible.

Thus, if the errors δa_{ij} and δc_i were known, the solution errors δx_i would be obtained (to a degree of accuracy consistent with this assumption) by solving a set of equations which differs from the set actually solved only in that the right-hand member c_i is to be replaced by η_i, where

$$\eta_i = \delta c_i - (x_1\,\delta a_{i1} + \cdots + x_n\,\delta a_{in}). \tag{10.6.4}$$

However, in practice, it is usually known only that the errors δa_{ij} and δc_i do not exceed a certain positive number, say ϵ, in magnitude, so that

$$-\epsilon \leqq \delta a_{ij} \leqq \epsilon, \qquad -\epsilon \leqq \delta c_i \leqq \epsilon. \tag{10.6.5}$$

Hence, in such cases, we are certain only that

$$|\eta_i| \leqq E, \tag{10.6 6}$$

where
$$E \equiv (1 + |x_1| + |x_2| + \cdots + |x_n|)\epsilon. \tag{10.6.7}$$

The solution of the set (10.6.3) can be expressed in the form

$$\delta x_k = \tilde{A}_{1k}\eta_1 + \tilde{A}_{2k}\eta_2 + \cdots + \tilde{A}_{nk}\eta_n \qquad (k = 1, 2, \ldots, n), \qquad (10.6.8)$$

with the notation of (10.2.6). Thus, if (10.6.6) is true, there follows

$$|\delta x_k| \leqq (|\tilde{A}_{1k}| + |\tilde{A}_{2k}| + \cdots + |\tilde{A}_{nk}|)E. \qquad (10.6.9)$$

The reduced cofactors involved in this expression are the elements of the kth *row* of the inverse of the coefficient matrix. Thus, if the inverse matrix is calculated, approximate upper bounds on the effects of inherent errors are obtainable from (10.6.9). They are not *strictly* upper bounds, since they were derived under the assumption that terms of the form $\delta a_{ik} \, \delta x_k$ are small in magnitude relative to E, as defined in (10.6.7). However, unless the upper bounds predicted under this assumption are such that the truth of the assumption is contradicted, they may be accepted as close approximations to the true upper bounds (which could be attained, in any case, only when *all* the errors combined in the most unfavorable way).

In the case of the preceding numerical example, if it is supposed that the coefficients and right-hand members are merely rounded approximations to true values, there follows $E \approx 3.28\epsilon = 1.64 \times 10^{-4}$, and reference to (10.5.2) yields the estimates

$$|\delta x_1|_{\max} \approx 0.29E = 0.48 \times 10^{-4}, \qquad |\delta x_2|_{\max} \approx 0.35E = 0.57 \times 10^{-4},$$
$$|\delta x_3|_{\max} \approx 0.25E = 0.41 \times 10^{-4}.$$

Thus, we could be confident only that the solution of the *true* equations is such that

$$0.89637 < x_1 < 0.89648, \qquad 0.76507 < x_2 < 0.76519,$$
$$0.61443 < x_3 < 0.61452, \qquad (10.6.10)$$

so that we could write $x_1 = 0.8964$, $x_2 = 0.7651$, and $x_3 = 0.6145$, with the last digit in doubt by one unit in each case.

Unless the given system of equations is to be solved for various sets of right-hand members, so that the determination of the inverse matrix is advisable in any case, an error estimate which does not involve the calculation of the elements of that matrix is desirable. It is clear that the upper bound (10.6.9) would correspond to the value of δx_k which satisfies a set of equations of the form

$$a_{11} \, \delta x_1 + \cdots + a_{1n} \, \delta x_n = \pm E,$$
$$\cdots \cdots \cdots \cdots \cdots \cdots \cdots \cdots \cdots \qquad (10.6.11)$$
$$a_{n1} \, \delta x_1 + \cdots + a_{nn} \, \delta x_n = \pm E,$$

for *some* choice of the ambiguous signs of each of the n right-hand members. However, the manner in which the signs are to be associated with successive equations cannot be determined unless the signs of the relevant cofactors of the coefficients of δx_k in these equations are known. Furthermore, a different combination of signs may be needed to maximize each of the δx's.

Reference to the Crout reduction shows that each of the elements in the solution column is obtained as a linear combination of the elements of the c' column of the auxiliary matrix, each of which is, in turn, a linear combination of the elements of the c column (that is, of the original right-hand members). Thus, if each entry in the c column were $+E$, and if, in the calculation of each element of the c' and x columns, we were to replace all subtractions by additions, it follows that no element of the resultant x column could be exceeded in magnitude by a corresponding element obtained by solving (10.6.11) with *any* prescribed combination of signs.

Hence, if an additional column with *unity* as *each* element is adjoined to the matrix M and is transformed just as the c column except for the fact that all subtractions are replaced by additions, the result of multiplying by E the elements of the final corresponding column, adjoined to the solution column, gives (approximate) upper bounds on the possible errors in the corresponding elements of the solution column, due to possible errors in the coefficients and right-hand members of the given equations (this procedure appears to be due to Milne [10]). The bounds obtained in this way usually exceed the more precise bounds afforded by (10.6.9), but are obtained much more simply.

In the case of the illustrative example, the inherent-error check columns adjoined to the given, auxiliary, and final arrays are found to be

$$
\begin{array}{ccc}
1 & 0.10667 & 0.28640 \\
1 & 0.25488 & 0.35215 \\
1 & 0.25185 & 0.25185
\end{array}
$$

Here it happens that the upper bounds, obtained by multiplying the successive elements of the last column by E, are identical with those afforded by the preceding analysis.

The fact that this situation is not a general one may be illustrated, for example, by the case when only two equations are involved. Here, the estimates afforded by (10.6.9) are

$$
|\delta x_1|_{\max} \approx \frac{|a_{12}| + |a_{22}|}{|D|} E, \qquad |\delta x_2|_{\max} \approx \frac{|a_{11}| + |a_{21}|}{|D|} E,
$$

whereas it is readily verified that the estimates afforded by the simpler procedure are

$$
|\delta x_1|_{\max} \approx \frac{|a_{11}a_{22} - a_{12}a_{21}| + |a_{12}a_{21}| + |a_{11}a_{12}|}{|a_{11}| \, |D|} E,
$$

$$
|\delta x_2|_{\max} \approx \frac{|a_{11}| + |a_{21}|}{|D|} E.
$$

Whereas the estimates for $|\delta x_2|_{max}$ are identical, it is seen that the latter estimate for $|\delta x_1|_{max}$ exceeds the former estimate except in special cases, such as that in which $a_{11}a_{22} > a_{12}a_{21} > 0$.

Systems in which small errors in the coefficients or right-hand members may correspond to large errors in the solution are often said to be *ill-conditioned* systems and are essentially characterized by the fact that the *determinant* of the coefficient matrix is small, in magnitude, relative to certain of the cofactors of elements of that matrix.† When such a system is encountered, one must either make the inherent errors small by retaining a large number of significant figures in the given data, when this is possible, or merely accept the fact that inaccuracies in the given data then permit the solution to be determined only within relatively wide error limits.

10.7. Gauss-Seidel Iteration and Relaxation. In many sets of linear equations which arise in practice, the equations can be ordered in such a way that the coefficient of x_k in the kth equation is large in magnitude relative to all other coefficients in that equation. Such sets are often amenable to an iterative process in which the set is first rewritten in the form

$$x_1 = \frac{1}{a_{11}}(c_1 - a_{12}x_2 - a_{13}x_3 - \cdots - a_{1n}x_n),$$

$$x_2 = \frac{1}{a_{22}}(c_2 - a_{21}x_1 - a_{23}x_3 - \cdots - a_{2n}x_n), \qquad (10.7.1)$$

$$\cdots \cdots \cdots \cdots \cdots \cdots \cdots \cdots \cdots \cdots$$

$$x_n = \frac{1}{a_{nn}}(c_n - a_{n1}x_1 - a_{n2}x_2 - \cdots - a_{n,n-1}x_{n-1}).$$

The initial approximation is taken to be

$$x_1^{(0)} = \frac{c_1}{a_{11}}, \qquad x_2^{(0)} = \frac{c_2}{a_{22}}, \qquad \cdots, \qquad x_n^{(0)} = \frac{c_n}{a_{nn}}. \qquad (10.7.2)$$

The next approximation is obtained by replacing the unknowns *in the right-hand members* of (10.7.1) by these initial approximations, and the feed-back process is to be repeated until the input and output of a cycle agree within the specified tolerance. The iteration may or may not converge.

In the case of the system (10.3.2), about 10 such iterations are required for three-place accuracy. If the iteration is modified in such a way that each unknown in each right-hand member is replaced by its most recently

† More specific measures of the "condition" of a matrix have been proposed by von Neumann and Goldstine [166], Turing [227], and others. Whereas these measures are of marked theoretical importance, their usefulness in explicit practical cases is limited by the amount of computation involved in their evaluation.

calculated approximation, rather than by the approximation afforded by the preceding cycle, the rate of convergence depends upon the order in which the x's are modified. In particular, if they are modified in their natural order, the number of cycles required to afford three-place accuracy is reduced to about six. The latter procedure is often called *Gauss-Seidel iteration*, although its attribution to either Gauss or Seidel appears to be improper.

In the frequently occurring cases when the coefficient matrix is symmetric, so that $a_{ji} = a_{ij}$, the iteration will converge if and only if all the n quantities

$$a_{11}, \quad \begin{vmatrix} a_{11} & a_{12} \\ a_{12} & a_{22} \end{vmatrix}, \quad \begin{vmatrix} a_{11} & a_{12} & a_{13} \\ a_{12} & a_{22} & a_{23} \\ a_{13} & a_{23} & a_{33} \end{vmatrix}, \quad \cdots, \quad \begin{vmatrix} a_{11} & \cdots & a_{1n} \\ \cdots & \cdots & \cdots \\ a_{1n} & \cdots & a_{nn} \end{vmatrix}$$

are positive (or become positive when the signs of all a's are changed) (see Reich [191]).

There exist many other numerical techniques for solving sets of linear equations, some of which are reductions which would yield the exact solution of a set of n equations in n unknowns after a finite number of steps if no round-offs were effected (as is true for the Gauss, Gauss-Jordan, and Crout reductions), and others which are basically iterative, in the sense that generally an infinite number of steps would be required to afford exactness in the absence of round-off (as in the Gauss-Seidel process).

Particular mention should be made of the *method of conjugate gradients*, due to Hestenes and Stiefel, which would terminate in the absence of round-off, and of a rather extensive class of other "gradient methods" and related methods.

On the other extreme, there exist the so-called "relaxation methods," apparently invented by Gauss, and revived and popularized by Southwell, in which the rapidity (or existence) of convergence depends upon the ingenuity of the computer. Because of their flexibility, they are processes which do not lend themselves to mechanization, but which are useful for hand computation in many situations.

In applying the relaxation procedure to the solution of a set of equations of the form

$$a_{11}x_1 + a_{12}x_2 + \cdots + a_{1n}x_n = c_1,$$
$$\cdots \cdots \cdots \cdots \cdots \cdots \cdots \cdots \cdots \qquad (10.7.3)$$
$$a_{n1}x_1 + a_{n2}x_2 + \cdots + a_{nn}x_n = c_n,$$

we first define *residuals* $R_1, R_2, \ldots, R_n$ by the equations

$$c_1 - a_{11}x_1 - a_{12}x_2 - \cdots - a_{1n}x_n = R_1,$$
$$\cdots \cdots \cdots \cdots \cdots \cdots \cdots \cdots \cdots \qquad (10.7.4)$$
$$c_n - a_{n1}x_1 - a_{n2}x_2 - \cdots - a_{nn}x_n = R_n,$$

The unknowns x_1, x_2, . . . , x_n are then *estimated*, and the corresponding residuals are calculated, after which the estimated values of the unknowns are to be successively modified (one or more at a time) in such a way that the magnitudes of all residuals are eventually reduced effectively to zero.

Reference to (10.7.4) shows that when x_i is *increased by unity*, and all other x's are held fixed, R_j decreases by a_{ji}. Thus the *transpose* of the coefficient matrix,

$$
\begin{matrix}
a_{11} & a_{21} & a_{31} & \cdots & a_{n1} \\
a_{12} & a_{22} & a_{32} & \cdots & a_{n2} \\
\cdot & \cdot & \cdot & \cdots & \cdot \\
a_{1n} & a_{2n} & a_{3n} & \cdots & a_{nn}
\end{matrix}
\tag{10.7.5}
$$

in which the rows and columns of the original matrix are interchanged, serves as a *relaxation table*, in the sense that *the successive entries in the kth row of* (10.7.5) *represent the decreases in the successive residuals which correspond to a unit increase in* x_k. If the original coefficient matrix is symmetrical, the matrix (10.7.5) is then identical with it.

The situations which generally are most favorable to this process are those in which each of the diagonal elements a_{11}, a_{22}, . . . , a_{nn} is large in magnitude relative to the other elements in its row and column. For, in such cases, an increase in x_k of about R_k/a_{kk} will nearly reduce R_k to zero, but will affect the other residuals by relatively small amounts, and subsequent modifications of other x's generally will not seriously nullify the effect of this reduction.

It may be seen that the so-called Gauss-Seidel iteration consists in determining successive corrections in exactly this way, since it defines the modified x_k, say x_k^*, by the equation

$$
x_k^* = \frac{1}{a_{kk}} (c_k - a_{k1}x_1 - \cdots - a_{k,k-1}x_{k-1} - a_{k,k+1}x_{k+1} - \cdots - a_{kn}x_n)
$$
$$
= \frac{1}{a_{kk}} (R_k + a_{kk}x_k) = x_k + \frac{R_k}{a_{kk}}.
$$

The advantages associated with the relaxation process follow from the fact that the values of the residuals are known at each stage. Thus it is possible to focus attention at each stage on the residual of *largest* magnitude and either to reduce its magnitude effectively to zero or proceed otherwise if an alternative procedure appears to be desirable, rather than to modify the x's successively in a preassigned cyclic order as in the Gauss-Seidel iteration. At the same time, the fact that an efficient use of the process requires a *decision* after each step not only places a premium on the ingenuity of the computer, but also makes the procedure poorly suited to large-scale programed calculators.

A typical sequence of relaxations, as applied to the result of first rounding all numerical coefficients in (10.3.2) to three digits, is included for purposes of illustration.

			9.37	3.04	−2.44
			3.04	6.18	1.22
			−2.44	1.22	8.44

Δx_1	Δx_2	Δx_3	R_1 ⑨	R_2 ⑥	R_3 ⑧
0	0	0	9.23	8.20	3.93
1			−0.14	5.16	6.37
		1	2.30	3.94	−2.07
	1		−0.74	−2.24	−3.29
			−7.40	−22.40	−32.90 × 10⁻¹
		−4	−17.16	−17.52	0.86
	−3		−8.04	1.02	4.52
−1			1.33	4.06	2.08
	1		−1.71	−2.12	0.86
			−17.10	−21.20	8.60 × 10⁻²
	−4		−4.94	3.52	13.48
		2	−0.06	1.08	−3.40
			−0.60	10.80	−34.00 × 10⁻³
		−4	−10.36	15.68	−0.24
	3		−19.48	−2.86	−3.90
−2			−0.74	3.22	−8.78
		−1	−3.18	4.44	−0.34
	1		−6.22	−1.74	−1.56
−1			3.15	1.30	−4.00

The residual table is written down immediately, and columns are provided for successive *changes* in the estimated unknowns and for the successive values of the three residuals. Values of the *diagonal* elements, rounded to the nearest integer, are encircled above the corresponding residuals, for convenience in estimating appropriate changes in the x's.

Starting arbitrarily with the crude approximation $x_1 = x_2 = x_3 = 0$, the *initial* residuals are then merely the right-hand members of the given equations and are listed in the first row of the calculation. Since the largest residual at this stage is $R_1 = 9.23$, we increase x_1 by the integer nearest $R_1/a_{11} \approx R_1/9$, and so enter a unit in the Δx_1 column and subtract unity times the first row of the relaxation table from the row of residuals. At this stage R_3 is largest in magnitude, and x_3 is increased by $1 \approx 6.37/8$, after which a unit increase in x_2 is called for. At this stage, each residual is less than one-half the corresponding rounded diagonal coefficient, and it is convenient to multiply the residuals by a factor of 10. The corresponding changes in the x's accordingly are then to be divided by 10 when all these changes are eventually accumulated.

The approximate solution at the last stage of the tabulation given is $x_1 = 0.897$, $x_2 = 0.764$, and $x_3 = 0.615$. It may be noticed that, with this arrangement of the calculations, the entries in the relaxation table need only be multiplied by *integers*. Also, it is possible to avoid all intermediate round-off without carrying more decimal places than are involved in the given data. In particular, the residuals corresponding to the three-place approximations obtained at the last stage given would be *exactly* 0.00315, 0.00130, and -0.00400 if the *given* three-digit data were exact.

However, it is desirable to accumulate the increments in the x's, from time to time, and to calculate the corresponding residuals directly, in order to avoid the propagation of the effects of *gross* errors.

Relaxation methods are particularly useful when a fairly large number of equations is involved and when only the diagonal elements and their neighbors in the coefficient matrix differ from zero, that is, when the kth equation involves, say, only x_{k-1}, x_k, and x_{k+1}, as in Eqs. (6.17.17).

10.8. Iterative Methods for Solving Nonlinear Equations. Most of the useful methods for obtaining an approximate real solution of a real equation, of the form

$$f(x) = 0, \tag{10.8.1}$$

involve iterative processes in which an initial approximation z_0 to a desired real root $x = \alpha$ is obtained, by rough graphical methods or otherwise, and a certain recurrence relation is used to generate a sequence of successive approximations $z_1, z_2, \ldots, z_n, \ldots$ which converges (in a certain associated class of cases) to the limit α.

One such method is that of *successive substitutions*, in which (10.8.1) is first rewritten in an equivalent form

$$x = F(x), \tag{10.8.2}$$

and the recurrence relation is of the simple form

$$z_{k+1} = F(z_k). \tag{10.8.3}$$

Generally there are many convenient ways of rewriting (10.8.1) in the form (10.8.2), and the convergence or divergence of the sequence of approximations may depend upon the particular form chosen.

In order to see why this is so, we may notice first that, since $F(\alpha) = \alpha$, (10.8.3) implies the relation

$$\alpha - z_{k+1} = F(\alpha) - F(z_k) = (\alpha - z_k)F'(\xi_k), \tag{10.8.4}$$

where ξ_k lies between z_k and α, under the assumption that $F(x)$ possesses a continuous derivative over that range. If the iteration converges, so that $z_k \to \alpha$ as $k \to \infty$, then, for sufficiently large k, we must have $F'(\xi_k) \approx F'(\alpha)$, and hence

$$\alpha - z_k \approx A[F'(\alpha)]^k, \tag{10.8.5}$$

where A is a constant, and this deviation tends to zero as k increases only if $|F'(\alpha)| < 1$. Thus it appears that, in order that the iteration converge to $x = \alpha$, it is *necessary* that $|F'(x)| < 1$ in the neighborhood of $x = \alpha$.

If we here define the *convergence factor* ρ_k as the ratio of the error in z_{k+1} to the error in z_k, it follows that if z_k is near α, then $\rho_k \approx F'(\alpha)$. Unless $|F'(\alpha)| \leqq 1$, a small error in z_k is *increased* in magnitude by the iteration, and we say that the iteration is then *asymptotically unstable* at α. The number $F'(\alpha)$ may be called the *asymptotic convergence factor*.

If the initial approximation is sufficiently near α, and if the iteration is asymptotically stable at α [so that $|F'(\alpha)| < 1$], the sequence of iterates will indeed converge to α, in such a way that ultimately the successive approximations tend toward α from one direction if $0 < F'(\alpha) < 1$, and oscillate about α with decreasing amplitude if $-1 < F'(\alpha) < 0$.

In the special cases when $F'(\alpha) = 0$, the nature of the convergence depends upon the behavior of the higher derivatives of $F(x)$ near $x = \alpha$.

In illustration, a rough plot of the function $y = x^3 - x - 1$ shows that the real root of the equation

$$x^3 - x - 1 = 0 \tag{10.8.6}$$

is between $x = 1$ and $x = 2$, and is near $x = 1.3$. This equation can be conveniently written in the form (10.8.2) in various ways, such as $x = x^3 - 1$, $x = 1/(x^2 - 1)$, and $x = (x + 1)^{\frac{1}{3}}$. However, only the third (and least convenient) of these particular forms is such that the derivative of the right-hand member is smaller than unity in absolute value near $x = 1.3$. Hence, we may use the recurrence formula

$$z_{k+1} = (z_k + 1)^{\frac{1}{3}} \tag{10.8.7}$$

and, with $z_0 = 1.3$, obtain the sequence $z_1 \doteq 1.3200$, $z_2 \doteq 1.3238$, $z_3 \doteq 1.3245$, $z_4 \doteq z_5 \doteq 1.3247$, when four decimal places are retained. The true value is 1.3247179573, to 10 places.

In view of (10.8.5), we may notice that, if the iteration converges, and if $F'(\alpha) \neq 0$, the approximation

$$\alpha \approx z_k + A\beta^k$$

will be valid for *some* constants A and β, independent of k, when k is sufficiently large. If we rewrite this relation with k replaced by $k + 1$ and by $k + 2$, and eliminate the unknown A and β from the resultant three relations, we may deduce the approximation

$$\frac{\alpha - z_{k+2}}{\alpha - z_{k+1}} \approx \frac{\alpha - z_{k+1}}{\alpha - z_k},$$

which yields the estimate

$$\alpha \approx \frac{z_k z_{k+2} - z_{k+1}^2}{z_{k+2} - 2z_{k+1} + z_k}$$

or, equivalently,

$$\alpha \approx z_{k+2} - \frac{(z_{k+2} - z_{k+1})^2}{z_{k+2} - 2z_{k+1} + z_k} \equiv z_{k+2} - \frac{(\Delta z_{k+1})^2}{\Delta^2 z_k}, \qquad (10.8.8)$$

where

$$\Delta z_k \equiv z_{k+1} - z_k, \qquad \Delta^2 z_k \equiv \Delta z_{k+1} - \Delta z_k = z_{k+2} - 2z_{k+1} + z_k.$$

Thus, if three successive iterates z_k, z_{k+1}, and z_{k+2} are known, this relation affords an *extrapolation* which may be expected to provide an improved estimate of α, when the iteration converges. This procedure is often called *Aitken's δ^2 process*. In the preceding example, with $z_3 = 1.3245$, $\Delta z_2 = 0.0007$, and $\Delta^2 z_1 = -0.0031$, to four places, (10.8.8) yields the extrapolation $\alpha \approx 1.3245 + 0.0002 = 1.3247$, which happens to agree with z_4 to four places and is correct to those four places. If additional digits had been retained in the calculation of the iterates z_1, z_2, and z_3, even though those digits were not of apparent importance to the iterates themselves, the approximate value of α obtained from them by an extrapolation based on (10.8.8) would have been found to be correct to additional places.

In a wide class of related methods for dealing with (10.8.1), a recurrence formula of the type

$$z_{k+1} = z_k - \frac{f(z_k)}{\gamma_k} \qquad (10.8.9)$$

is used, with a suitable definition of the auxiliary sequence γ_0, γ_1, . . . , γ_k, ... The relation (10.8.3) can be specialized to (10.8.9) by writing $F(x) = x - \phi(x)f(x)$, where $\phi(x)$ is a function such that $\phi(z_k) = 1/\gamma_k$. It should be noticed, however, that the function $F(x) - x$ relevant to the method of successive substitutions is not necessarily proportional to $f(x)$, but is required only to be a function which vanishes at the required point α for which f vanishes. Conversely, the explicit definition of a function $\phi(x)$ which takes on the chosen value $1/\gamma_k$ when $x = z_k$ obviously is not necessary in the present case.

It is clear that if the z sequence converges, so that $z_{k+1} - z_k \to 0$, and if γ_k remains finite, there then follows $f(z_k) \to 0$, so that z_k tends to a solution of (10.8.1). In particular, the requirement $z_{k+1} = \alpha$, where $f(\alpha) = 0$, would imply that

$$\gamma_k = \frac{0 - f(z_k)}{\alpha - z_k}, \qquad (10.8.10)$$

so that γ_k would then represent the slope of the secant line joining the points $P_k(z_k,f_k)$ and $P(\alpha,0)$ in Fig. 10.1. Thus it is desirable to define the γ sequence in such a way that this situation is *approximated* at each stage of the calculation.

In the method of "false position" (*regula falsi*), the iteration is initiated

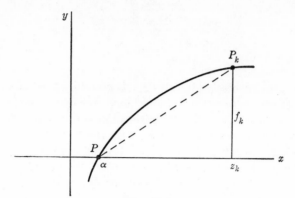

FIG. 10.1

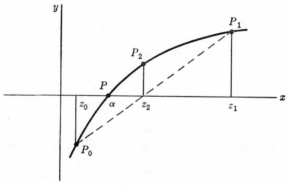

FIG. 10.2

by finding z_0 and z_1 such that f_0 and f_1 are of opposite signs and by defining γ_1 as the slope of the secant P_0P_1 (Fig. 10.2), so that

$$z_2 = z_1 - \frac{z_1 - z_0}{f_1 - f_0} f_1 = \frac{f_1 z_0 - f_0 z_1}{f_1 - f_0}. \tag{10.8.11}$$

In each following iteration, γ_k is taken as the slope of the line joining P_k and the most recently determined point at which the ordinate differs in sign from that at P_k. The procedure is seen to be merely iterated linear inverse interpolation and is clearly certain to converge, although the *rate* of convergence may be slow. In the case of (10.8.6), with

$z_0 = 1.3$ and $z_1 = 1.4$, the next three iterates may be found as follows:

z_k	f_k	$1/\gamma_k$	$-f_k/\gamma_k$
1.3	-0.103	—	—
1.4	0.344	0.224	-0.077
1.323	-0.00731	0.219	0.0016
1.3246	-0.000503	0.219	0.000110
1.324710			

As this example illustrates, the factor γ_k often changes slowly after the first few steps, and the rate of convergence then is only slightly reduced if, from such a stage onward, γ_k is assigned a constant value.

In this illustration, the approximation z_4 was obtained by *interpolation* based on z_3 and z_1, in accordance with the preceding description of the procedure. If, instead, the *last two* abscissas available are used, so that here z_4 is obtained by *extrapolation* based on z_3 and z_2, with $1/\gamma_3 \doteq 0.235$, a better approximation (1.324718) is obtained. More generally, whereas the systematic use of the slope of the secant $P_{k-1}P_k$ cannot be guaranteed to yield a convergent sequence when it requires extrapolation, this modified procedure is usually advantageous when it does converge, and its use near the end of the calculation is often desirable.

It is of importance to notice that, since $f(\alpha) = 0$, the general recurrence relation (10.8.9) implies the relation

$$\alpha - z_{k+1} = \alpha - z_k - \frac{f(\alpha) - f(z_k)}{\gamma_k}$$

$$= (\alpha - z_k)\left[1 - \frac{1}{\gamma_k}f'(\xi_k)\right], \quad (10.8.12)$$

where ξ_k is between z_k and α. Thus the *convergence factor* ρ_k at the kth stage is given, to a first approximation, by $1 - [f'(\alpha)/\gamma_k]$ when z_k is near α, and, unless this factor is smaller than unity in magnitude, so that

$$0 < \frac{f'(\alpha)}{\gamma_k} < 2 \quad (10.8.13)$$

when k is large, convergence of z_k to α generally cannot be obtained.

An important method, known as the *Newton-Raphson method*, consists in taking γ_k in (10.8.9) as the slope of the curve $y = f(x)$ at the point z_k (Fig. 10.3), so that (10.8.9) becomes

$$z_{k+1} = z_k - \frac{f(z_k)}{f'(z_k)}. \quad (10.8.14)$$

This iteration is seen to be the special case of (10.8.3) in which

$$F(x) = x - \frac{f(x)}{f'(x)},$$

and hence $F'(x) = f(x)f''(x)/[f'(x)]^2$. Thus, if $f'(\alpha) \neq 0$ and $f''(\alpha)$ is finite, there follows $F'(\alpha) = 0$, so that the convergence factor tends to zero when and if $z_k \to \alpha$.

In order to examine the behavior of the error $\alpha - z_k$, we rewrite

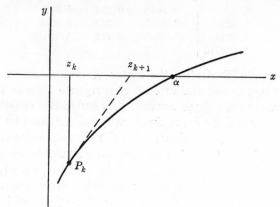

FIG. 10.3

(10.8.14) in the equivalent form

$$\alpha - z_{k+1} = \alpha - z_k - \frac{f(\alpha) - f(z_k)}{f'(z_k)} \tag{10.8.15}$$

and recall that

$$f(\alpha) - f(z_k) = (\alpha - z_k)f'(z_k) + \tfrac{1}{2}(\alpha - z_k)^2 f''(\xi_k),$$

where ξ_k lies between z_k and α, if $f''(x)$ is continuous in that interval, so that (10.8.15) becomes

$$\alpha - z_{k+1} = -\tfrac{1}{2}(\alpha - z_k)^2 \frac{f''(\xi_k)}{f'(z_k)}. \tag{10.8.16}$$

Thus, if the iteration converges to α, there follows

$$\alpha - z_{k+1} \approx -\frac{1}{2} \frac{f''(\alpha)}{f'(\alpha)} (\alpha - z_k)^2, \tag{10.8.17}$$

when k is sufficiently large.

It is important to notice that here the error in z_{k+1} tends to be proportional to the *square* of the error in z_k, as $k \to \infty$, whereas in the other methods so far considered the two successive errors generally tend to be in a constant ratio, if the iteration converges. We say that such an iteration is a *second-order* process, whereas the preceding methods generally are *first-order* processes.

If this method is applied to (10.8.6), the recurrence formula (10.8.14) becomes

$$z_{k+1} = z_k - \frac{z_k^3 - z_k - 1}{3z_k^2 - 1} = \frac{2z_k^3 + 1}{3z_k^2 - 1}$$

and, with $z_0 = 1.3$, the results of the first two iterations are $z_1 = 1.325$ and $z_2 = 1.324718$, when rounded to the places given.

Use can be made of (10.8.16) to predict in advance the probable number of correct digits in each iterate. For, since here f''/f' has a value of about 2 when $x = z_0 = 1.3$, it may be expected that the coefficient of $(\alpha - z_k)^2$ in (10.8.17) will have a value *approximating* -1, so that the error ϵ_k in the kth iterate will be approximately the *square* of that in the preceding iterate, and will be of negative sign. If, initially, it is known that the true value lies between 1.3 and 1.4, and hence that z_0 is in error by less than 0.1, it can be predicted that z_1 will be in error by less than about 0.01, so that three places would be retained. With ϵ_0 reestimated

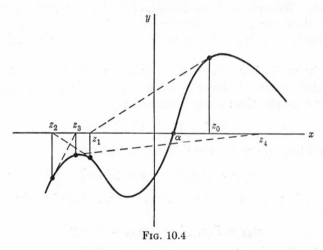

FIG. 10.4

as $z_1 - z_0 \doteq 0.03$, there follows $|\epsilon_1| \approx 10^{-3}$. Hence ϵ_2 may be expected to be less than about 10^{-6}, so that six places would be retained at that stage. A comparison of z_1 and z_2 confirms the earlier prediction (although this method of error estimation may be undependable in early stages, in other cases) and suggests that the error in the next iterate z_3 will be in about the *twelfth* decimal place.

If the curve representing $y = f(x)$ possesses turning points or inflections in the interval between the initial estimate $x = z_0$ and the true root $x = \alpha$, or between z_0 and z_1, the iteration may not converge to α, as is illustrated in Fig. 10.4, although it may well converge to some *other* root. However, if $f'(x)$ and $f''(x)$ do not change sign in the interval (z_0, α), and if $f(z_0)$ and $f''(z_0)$ have the same sign, so that the iteration is initiated at a point at which the curve representing $y = f(x)$ is concave *away* from the x axis (as, for example, in Fig. 10.3), it is easily seen, by geometrical considerations, that successive iterates must tend to $x = \alpha$ and that they all lie between z_0 and α. If $f(z_0)$ and $f''(z_0)$ have opposite signs, the first iterate

z_1 is on the opposite side of α and convergence is uncertain unless $f'(x)$ and $f''(x)$ also do not change sign at $x = \alpha$ or in the interval (z_1, α), in which case convergence then follows as before.

The methods outlined in this section can be combined and modified in various ways. In particular, if $f'(z_k)$ begins to change slowly with k after (say) r iterations, the Newton-Raphson procedure may be modified by taking $\gamma_k = f'(z_r)$ for all $k \geq r$. The method of false position may be modified, for example, by taking γ_k as the slope of the secant $P_0 P_1$ for *all* k, where P_0 and P_1 are two fixed points on the curve $y = f(x)$, near to and separated by the point P at which $x = \alpha$, or by taking γ_k as the slope of the secant $P_0 P_k$, where P_0 is an appropriately chosen fixed point on the curve. Whereas such modifications lead to appreciable reductions in labor, their use clearly may also reduce the rate of convergence, or may instigate divergence, if the condition (10.8.13) is violated when k is large.

Also, the methods are readily generalized to the treatment of two or more *simultaneous* nonlinear equations (algebraic or transcendental). Thus, for example, the two simultaneous equations

$$f(x,y) = 0, \qquad g(x,y) = 0 \tag{10.8.18}$$

can be written (in various ways) in equivalent forms

$$x = F(x,y), \qquad y = G(x,y), \tag{10.8.19}$$

and the method of *successive substitutions* can be based on the recurrence formulas

$$x_{k+1} = F(x_k, y_k), \qquad y_{k+1} = G(x_k, y_k). \tag{10.8.20}$$

When the iteration converges to the true solution pair, say $x = \alpha$ and $y = \beta$, it can be shown that the errors in the kth iterates tend to be described by the relations

$$\alpha - x_k \approx A_1 \lambda_1^k + B_1 \lambda_2^k, \qquad \beta - y_k \approx A_2 \lambda_1^k + B_2 \lambda_2^k$$

where A_1, A_2, B_1, and B_2 are constants, independent of k, and where λ_1 and λ_2 are the roots of the equation

$$\begin{vmatrix} \lambda - F_x & -F_y \\ -G_x & \lambda - G_y \end{vmatrix} = 0$$

or
$$\lambda^2 - (F_x + G_y)\lambda + (F_x G_y - F_y G_x) = 0, \tag{10.8.21}$$

with the partial derivatives evaluated at (α, β), if $F_x G_y \neq F_y G_x$ at that point. The constants A_1, B_1, and A_2, B_2 will be conjugate complex if the same is true of λ_1, λ_2. Thus the iteration will be asymptotically stable at (α, β) if and only if the roots λ_1 and λ_2 are smaller than unity in absolute value, the necessary and sufficient conditions for which are

$$|F_x + G_y| \leq F_x G_y - F_y G_x + 1 < 2. \tag{10.8.22}$$

A more stringent pair of conditions, which is *sufficient* (but generally not necessary) for asymptotic stability, is of the form

$$|F_x| + |F_y| < 1, \qquad |G_x| + |G_y| < 1. \tag{10.8.23}$$

As before, these conditions are not sufficient for *convergence*, in that the iteration may fail to converge even though they are satisfied, unless the iteration is started with (x_0, y_0) sufficiently near (α, β).

The *Newton-Raphson iteration*, as applied to the solution of (10.8.18), is based on the result of replacing (α, β) by (x_{k+1}, y_{k+1}) in the right-hand members of the Taylor expansions

$$0 = f(\alpha, \beta) = f(x_k, y_k) + (\alpha - x_k)f_x(x_k, y_k) + (\beta - y_k)f_y(x_k, y_k) + \cdots, \tag{10.8.24}$$

$$0 = g(\alpha, \beta) = g(x_k, y_k) + (\alpha - x_k)g_x(x_k, y_k) + (\beta - y_k)g_y(x_k, y_k) + \cdots,$$

and neglecting nonlinear terms in $x_{k+1} - x_k$ and $y_{k+1} - y_k$, so that the recurrence formulas are of the form

$$\begin{aligned}(x_{k+1} - x_k)f_x(x_k, y_k) + (y_{k+1} - y_k)f_y(x_k, y_k) &= -f(x_k, y_k), \\ (x_{k+1} - x_k)g_x(x_k, y_k) + (y_{k+1} - y_k)g_y(x_k, y_k) &= -g(x_k, y_k).\end{aligned} \tag{10.8.25}$$

Rather than resolve these equations for x_{k+1} and y_{k+1}, it is usually convenient to solve them, as written, for the *corrections* $\Delta x_k \equiv x_{k+1} - x_k$ and $\Delta y_k \equiv y_{k+1} - y_k$, which are to be added to x_k and y_k to yield the following iterates. When the iteration converges, the errors in the $(k + 1)$th iterates generally tend to become linear combinations of the *squares* of the errors in the kth iterates (that is, the iteration is a *second-order* process), whereas, in the method of successive substitutions, based on (10.8.20), the new errors generally tend to become linear combinations of the preceding errors themselves.

When the so-called *Jacobian determinant* of f and g,

$$J \equiv \begin{vmatrix} \dfrac{\partial f}{\partial x} & \dfrac{\partial f}{\partial y} \\[2ex] \dfrac{\partial g}{\partial x} & \dfrac{\partial g}{\partial y} \end{vmatrix}, \tag{10.8.26}$$

vanishes at the point (x_k, y_k), the equations (10.8.25) do not possess a unique solution. More generally, if J vanishes at or near the point (α, β), slow convergence or divergence of the iteration may be anticipated, and modified procedures are generally needed (see Milne [10]).

10.9. Iterated Synthetic Division. When $f(x)$ is a polynomial, of degree n, so that the equation to be solved is an *algebraic* one, methods such as those of the preceding section can be systematized by the use of *synthetic division.*

For this purpose, suppose that

$$f(x) = x^n + a_1 x^{n-1} + \cdots + a_{n-1} x + a_n, \qquad (10.9.1)$$

and, first, let $f(x)$ be divided by the linear expression $x - z$, so that

$$\begin{aligned} f(x) &= x^n + a_1 x^{n-1} + \cdots + a_{n-1} x + a_n \\ &= (x - z)(x^{n-1} + b_1 x^{n-2} + \cdots + b_{n-2} x + b_{n-1}) + R, \end{aligned} \qquad (10.9.2)$$

where $x^{n-1} + \cdots + b_{n-1}$ represents the quotient, and R is the constant remainder. Here the coefficients $b_1, \ldots, b_{n-1}$ and the remainder R depend upon z. By setting $x = z$ in (10.9.2), it follows, in particular, that

$$R = f(z). \qquad (10.9.3)$$

If now the quotient in (10.9.2) is again divided by $x - z$, so that

$$\begin{aligned} x^{n-1} &+ b_1 x^{n-2} + \cdots + b_{n-2} x + b_{n-1} \\ &= (x - z)(x^{n-2} + c_1 x^{n-3} + \cdots + c_{n-3} x + c_{n-2}) + R', \end{aligned} \qquad (10.9.4)$$

and hence

$$f(x) = (x - z)^2(x^{n-2} + c_1 x^{n-3} + \cdots + c_{n-2}) + (x - z)R' + R,$$

there follows also

$$R' = f'(z), \qquad (10.9.5)$$

and, indeed, if the process is repeated k times, it is easily seen that the remainder $R^{(k)}$ is then $f^{(k)}(z)/k!$.

The method of synthetic division is based on the fact that, by equating coefficients of $x^{n-1}, x^{n-2}, \ldots, x$, and 1 in the two members of (10.9.2), we obtain the relations

$$a_1 = b_1 - z, \qquad a_2 = b_2 - zb_1, \qquad \cdots,$$
$$a_{n-1} = b_{n-1} - zb_{n-2}, \qquad a_n = R - zb_{n-1}.$$

Thus, if we introduce the recurrence formula

$$b_k = a_k + zb_{k-1} \qquad (k = 1, 2, \ldots, n) \qquad (10.9.6)$$

with

$$b_0 = 1, \qquad (10.9.7)$$

it follows that this formula will generate the coefficients of the quotient of (10.9.2) with $k = 1, 2, \ldots, n - 1$, and also that

$$R = f(z) = b_n = a_n + zb_{n-1}. \qquad (10.9.8)$$

Further, the c's in (10.9.4) are related, for $k = 1, 2, \ldots, n - 2$, to the b's as the b's are related to the a's, and there follows also

$$R' = f'(z) = c_{n-1} = b_{n-1} + zc_{n-2}. \qquad (10.9.9)$$

For actual calculation, it is convenient to arrange the entries in parallel columns (or rows), in the form

1	1	1
a_1	b_1	c_1
a_2	b_2	c_2
.	.	.
.	.	.
.	.	.
a_{n-2}	b_{n-2}	c_{n-2}
a_{n-1}	b_{n-1}	R'
a_n	R	

so that each element is obtained by adding to its left-hand neighbor z times its upward neighbor.

Thus, if the roots of the algebraic equation $f(x) = 0$ are $x = \alpha_1, \alpha_2,$ . . . . , α_n, and if the Newton-Raphson procedure were to be used to approximate α_1, starting with an initial approximation z, the next approximation, say z^*, would be given simply by

$$z^* = z - \frac{R}{R'}, \tag{10.9.10}$$

and the process would then be repeated with z replaced by z^*. This method of tabulation avoids much of the labor involved in evaluating the polynomials $f(z)$ and $f'(z)$ by calculating powers of z and forming linear combinations of them.†

In the simple case of the cubic equation (10.8.6), for which

$$f(x) = x^3 - x - 1,$$

the first two iterations (starting with $z = 1.3$) would be tabulated as follows:

$z =$	1.3		1.325	
1	1	1	1	1
0	1.3	2.6	1.325	2.65
-1	0.69	4.07	0.755625	4.267
-1	-0.103		0.001203	
$\Delta z =$	0.025		-0.000282	

The approximation obtained at this stage is thus 1.324718, in accordance with the results obtained in the preceding section.

Once the iteration is terminated, so that one zero of $f(x)$ is approximated and the last entry in the b column is effectively reduced to zero, the remaining entries in the b column are (approximately) the coefficients of the reduced polynomial, of degree $n - 1$, whose zeros are the remaining zeros of $f(x)$.

† This procedure for applying the Newton-Raphson iteration to the solution of algebraic equations is sometimes known as the Birge-Vieta method.

A simpler procedure, due to S. N. Lin (see [135] and [136]), is based on the fact that, in virtue of (10.9.8), the condition $f(z) = 0$ is equivalent to the condition $a_n + zb_{n-1} = 0$. That is, if and only if the assumed value of z were a root of $f(x) = 0$, then the corresponding value of b_{n-1} (which depends upon z) would be such that $z = -a_n/b_{n-1}(z)$. *Lin's iteration* is the result of applying the method of successive substitutions to the equation written in this form, so that the revised estimate z^* is defined by the formula

$$z^* = -\frac{a_n}{b_{n-1}} \tag{10.9.11}$$

and hence
$$z^* - z = -\frac{a_n + zb_{n-1}}{b_{n-1}}$$

or, equivalently, in virtue of (10.9.8),

$$z^* = z - \frac{R}{b_{n-1}}. \tag{10.9.12}$$

In this method, the formation of the c column is avoided, so that the labor per iteration is reduced by nearly one-half. However, if this method is applied to the example treated above, the first three iterations may be obtained as follows:

$z =$	1.3	1.45	0.91	-5.8
1	1	1	1	
0	1.3	1.45	0.91	
-1	0.69	1.102	-0.172	
-1	-0.103	0.598	-1.157	
$\Delta z =$	0.15	-0.54	-6.7	

Clearly, the iteration is not convergent in this case.

In order to investigate the Lin procedure more closely, we may notice that, since (10.9.8) gives

$$b_{n-1}(z) = \frac{f(z) - a_n}{z},$$

the recurrence relation written in the form (10.9.11) can also be put in the form

$$z^* = -\frac{a_n z}{f(z) - a_n}.$$

Thus Lin's method is equivalent to applying the method of successive substitutions to the result of writing $f(x) = 0$ in the form

$$x = -\frac{a_n x}{f(x) - a_n} \equiv F(x). \tag{10.9.13}$$

In the example just considered, (10.9.13) becomes $x = 1/(x^2 - 1)$, which, as was seen in §10.8, is not suitable for successive substitutions since the convergence factor $F'(x)$ has a value of about -5 near the real root, whereas, for convergence, its absolute value should be smaller than unity. In confirmation, we may notice that the error in $z^* \doteq 1.45$ is indeed about five times the error in $z = 1.3$ and is of opposite sign.

More generally, we find from (10.9.13) that

$$F'(x) = a_n \frac{xf'(x) - f(x) + a_n}{[f(x) - a_n]^2},$$

and hence, at a zero α_r of $f(x)$, Lin's method possesses the asymptotic convergence factor

$$\rho = F'(\alpha_r) = 1 + \frac{\alpha_r}{a_n} f'(\alpha_r) \equiv 1 + \alpha_r \frac{f'(\alpha_r)}{f(0)}. \tag{10.9.14}$$

Thus the result of applying Lin's iteration to a good approximation to α_r will lead to a *poorer* one unless $|\rho| \leq 1$. That is, a *necessary* condition for convergence to α_r is that

$$|\rho| = \left| 1 + \frac{\alpha_r}{a_n} f'(\alpha_r) \right| < 1. \tag{10.9.15}$$

This criterion is a useful one if a rough approximation to α_r is known initially, unless $f'(x)$ varies rapidly near $x = \alpha_r$. If we recall that $a_n = (-1)^n \alpha_1 \alpha_2 \cdots \alpha_n$ and that $f'(\alpha_r) = (\alpha_r - \alpha_1) \cdots (\alpha_r - \alpha_n)$, where the factor $(\alpha_r - \alpha_r)$ is to be omitted, we may deduce that (10.9.15) can also be expressed in the form

$$|\rho| = \left| 1 - \left[\left(1 - \frac{\alpha_r}{\alpha_1} \right) \left(1 - \frac{\alpha_r}{\alpha_2} \right) \cdots \left(1 - \frac{\alpha_r}{\alpha_n} \right) \right] \right| < 1, \tag{10.9.16}$$

in terms of the *remaining* roots of $f(x) = 0$.

It is of interest to notice that, since

$$b_{n-1} = \frac{R - a_n}{z} = \frac{f(z) - f(0)}{z},$$

it follows that b_{n-1} is the slope of the secant joining the ordinate at $x = 0$ and the ordinate at $x = z$. Thus, (10.9.12) is equivalent to the result of taking γ as the slope of that secant in the more general recurrence relation (10.8.9), and the Lin iteration therefore amounts to determining z^* by linear interpolation (or extrapolation) based on the *fixed* ordinate $f(0)$ and the most recently calculated ordinate $f(z)$ (see Fig. 10.5). Also the requirement (10.9.15) is easily interpreted as demanding that the ratio of the slope of the curve at P to the slope of the secant P_0P be *positive and less than two*.

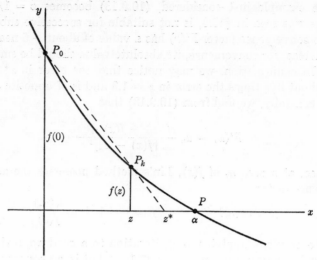

FIG. 10.5

In the case of the equation

$$x^4 - 8x^3 + 23x^2 + 16x - 50 = 0, \qquad (10.9.17)$$

a real root is easily seen to lie between $x = 1$ and $x = 2$. If Lin's iteration is used, starting with $z = 1.5$, the results of the first three iterations are as follows:

$z =$	1.5	1.39	1.421	1.4125
1	1	1	1	
-8	-6.5	-6.61	-6.579	
23	13.25	13.8121	13.6512	
16	35.875	35.1988	35.3984	
-50	3.8125	-1.0737	0.3011	
$\Delta z =$	-0.11	0.031	-0.0085	

The true roots of (10.9.17) are $\pm \sqrt{2}$ and $4 \pm 3i$. The rate of convergence of the Lin iteration, in this case, might have been predicted in advance by approximating α_r by 1.5 in (10.9.14) to obtain $\rho \approx -\frac{1}{3}$. The *asymptotic* convergence factor is -0.25, to two places.†

When the Lin iteration is unstable in the neighborhood of a zero α_r of a polynomial $f(x)$, stability can be attained by translating the origin to a new point $x = c$, if that point is sufficiently near to α_r. For, if we make

† When the ratio of successive values of Δz_k becomes nearly constant, that ratio serves as an estimate of ρ, and a generally improved value of Δz_k then is given by $(\Delta z_k)(1 + \rho + \rho^2 + \cdots) = (\Delta z_k)/(1 - \rho)$.

the change of variables $x = t + c$, and apply the Lin iteration to the new polynomial

$$\bar{f}(t) \equiv f(t + c) \equiv t^n + \bar{a}_1 t^{n-1} + \cdots + \bar{a}_{n-1} t + \bar{a}_n,$$

reference to (10.9.13) shows that this process is equivalent to the application of the method of successive substitutions to the result of writing $\bar{f}(t) = 0$ in the form

$$t = -\frac{\bar{a}_n t}{f(t + c) - \bar{a}_n} = -\frac{t f(c)}{f(t + c) - f(c)} \equiv \bar{F}(t).$$

Thus, at a zero $t = \alpha_r - c$ of $f(t + c)$, we may obtain the expression

$$\rho = \bar{F}'(\alpha_r - c) = 1 - (c - \alpha_r)\frac{f'(\alpha_r)}{f(c)}$$

for the asymptotic convergence factor. Since $f(\alpha_r) = 0$, we have also $f(c)/(c - \alpha_r) \equiv [f(c) - f(\alpha_r)]/(c - \alpha_r) = f'(\xi_r)$, where ξ_r lies between α_r and c. Thus there follows

$$\rho = 1 - \frac{f'(\alpha_r)}{f'(\xi_r)} \qquad (\xi_r \text{ between } \alpha_r \text{ and } c),$$

and this factor is near zero when c is sufficiently near α_r.

Hence, if c is a fair approximation to α_r, and if $f'(x)/f'(\alpha_r)$ is not small between $x = c$ and $x = \alpha_r$, asymptotic stability generally will be introduced by translating the origin to $x = c$. Clearly, this process amounts to using $f(c)$ as the fixed ordinate, in place of $f(0)$, in Fig. 10.5.

In those cases when the coefficients $a_1, \ldots, a_n$ of $f(x)$ are inexact, it is desirable to have upper bounds on the corresponding inherent possible errors relevant to the roots of $f(x) = 0$. If α_r is obtained as a root of the equation

$$f(\alpha_r) = \alpha_r^n + a_1\alpha_r^{n-1} + \cdots + a_{n-1}\alpha_r + a_n = 0,$$

whereas the *true* coefficients are $a_1 + \delta a_1, \ldots, a_n + \delta a_n$, then the corresponding true root $\alpha_r + \delta\alpha_r$ must satisfy the equation

$$(\alpha_r + \delta\alpha_r)^n + (a_1 + \delta a_1)(\alpha_r + \delta\alpha_r)^{n-1} + \cdots$$
$$+ (a_{n-1} + \delta a_{n-1})(\alpha_r + \delta\alpha_r) + (a_n + \delta a_n) = 0.$$

If the first equation is subtracted from the second, and if it is assumed that the relative errors are sufficiently small to permit neglect of second-order terms, it follows that, to a first approximation, $\delta\alpha_r$ must satisfy the equation

$$[n\alpha_r^{n-1} + (n - 1)a_1\alpha_r^{n-2} + \cdots + a_{n-1}]\,\delta\alpha_r$$
$$+ \alpha_r^{n-1}\,\delta a_1 + \alpha_r^{n-2}\,\delta a_2 + \cdots + \delta a_n = 0,$$

and hence

$$\delta\alpha_r \approx \frac{\alpha_r^{n-1}\,\delta a_1 + \alpha_r^{n-2}\,\delta a_2 + \cdots + \delta a_n}{-f'(\alpha_r)}. \qquad (10.9.18)$$

In particular, if each coefficient is known to be in error by less than ϵ,

$$|\delta a_i| < \epsilon \qquad (i = 1, 2, \ldots, n), \qquad (10.9.19)$$

there follows, within the same degree of approximation,

$$|\delta \alpha_r|_{\max} \approx \frac{1 + |\alpha_r| + |\alpha_r|^2 + \cdots + |\alpha_r|^{n-1}}{|f'(\alpha_r)|} \epsilon$$

or
$$|\delta \alpha_r|_{\max} \approx \frac{|\alpha_r|^n - 1}{(|\alpha_r| - 1)|f'(\alpha_r)|} \epsilon. \qquad (10.9.20)$$

Thus, in the case of the real root of (10.8.6), it is found that errors of magnitude ϵ in the coefficients would correspond to a maximum error of very nearly the same magnitude in the root, if the errors are small. In the case of the root $x = \sqrt{2}$ of (10.9.17), the maximum error in the root is found to be about one-sixth of the maximum error in the coefficients.

The preceding methods are valid, in principle, for the determination of *complex* roots as well as real ones. However, since a real initial approximation leads necessarily to real iterates, when the coefficients are real, the process then must be initiated with a complex initial estimate, and operations with complex numbers are involved in each step of the process. When the coefficients are real, the complex roots occur in conjugate pairs, and it is generally preferable to exploit this fact by seeking *quadratic real factors*, rather than linear complex ones, by a generalized method of synthetic division.

Before treating such processes, we present two additional general methods which each possess certain favorable properties.

10.10. Bernoulli's Iteration. A method, originally due to Daniel Bernoulli, for obtaining roots of the algebraic equation

$$x^n + a_1 x^{n-1} + \cdots + a_{n-1} x + a_n = 0, \qquad (10.10.1)$$

is based on the related recurrence formula

$$\mu_k + a_1 \mu_{k-1} + \cdots + a_{n-1} \mu_{k-n+1} + a_n \mu_{k-n} = 0, \qquad (10.10.2)$$

having the *same coefficients* as (10.10.1).

If the roots of (10.10.1) are $\alpha_1, \alpha_2, \ldots, \alpha_n$, and if (10.10.2) is considered as a *difference equation*, its general solution is found to be†

$$\mu_k = C_1 \alpha_1^k + C_2 \alpha_2^k + C_3 \alpha_3^k + \cdots + C_n \alpha_n^k, \qquad (10.10.3)$$

† If a solution of (10.10.2) is assumed in the form $\mu_k = \alpha^k$, it is found that the characteristic equation determining admissible values of α is of the same form as (10.10.1). Thus $\alpha_1^k, \alpha_2^k, \ldots, \alpha_n^k$ are all solutions, and superposition leads to (10.10.3), which can be shown to represent the *most general* solution, if no roots are repeated, when only integral values of k are considered.

where the n C's are constants, independent of k, which are determined by the values of μ_0, μ_1, . . . , and μ_{n-1}, if no roots are repeated. Under this assumption, let the roots be numbered in *decreasing* order of magnitude, so that α_1 here denotes the *largest* root of (10.10.1). Then since (10.10.3) can be written in the form

$$\mu_k = C_1\alpha_1^k \left[1 + \frac{C_2}{C_1}\left(\frac{\alpha_2}{\alpha_1}\right)^k + \frac{C_3}{C_1}\left(\frac{\alpha_3}{\alpha_1}\right)^k + \cdots + \frac{C_n}{C_1}\left(\frac{\alpha_n}{\alpha_1}\right)^k \right], \quad (10.10.4)$$

if $C_1 \neq 0$, it follows that, in any sequence generated by (10.10.2), the kth term is approximated by $C_1\alpha_1^k$ as $k \to \infty$ and, indeed, that the ratio

$$r_k = \frac{\mu_k}{\mu_{k-1}} \quad (10.10.5)$$

tends to α_1 as $k \to \infty$, if the largest root α_1 is real and unrepeated and if no other root has equal magnitude, unless μ_0, μ_1, . . . , μ_{n-1} are so chosen that the coefficient C_1 of α_1^k in (10.10.3) is zero.

If the largest root α_1 is *complex*, and the coefficients of (10.10.1) are real, then α_2 is the complex conjugate of α_1 and is of equal magnitude. If we write

$$\alpha_1 = \xi_1 + i\eta_1 = \beta_1 e^{i\phi_1}, \qquad \alpha_2 = \xi_1 - i\eta_1 = \beta_1 e^{-i\phi_1}, \quad (10.10.6)$$

where $\beta_1 > 0$ and ξ_1, η_1, β_1, and ϕ_1 are *real*, the terms corresponding to α_1 and α_2 in (10.10.3) can be expressed in the real form

$$\beta_1^k(C_1 \cos k\phi_1 + C_2 \sin k\phi_1),$$

if C_1 and C_2 are replaced by $(C_1 - iC_2)/2$ and $(C_1 + iC_2)/2$, respectively, in (10.10.3).

Thus, if α_1 and $\bar{\alpha}_1$ are not repeated and if all other roots are smaller in magnitude than β_1, it follows that

$$\mu_k \approx \beta_1^k(C_1 \cos k\phi_1 + C_2 \sin k\phi_1) \qquad (k \to \infty). \quad (10.10.7)$$

But, if μ_k were given exactly by the right-hand member of (10.10.7), it would satisfy the recurrence relation

$$\mu_{k+1} - 2\mu_k\beta_1 \cos \phi_1 + \beta_1^2\mu_{k-1} = 0, \quad (10.10.8)$$

and conversely, as is easily verified. A second relation, involving the two real unknown quantities β_1 and ϕ_1, would then be obtained, by replacing k by $k - 1$, in the form

$$\mu_k - 2\mu_{k-1}\beta_1 \cos \phi_1 + \beta_1^2\mu_{k-2} = 0. \quad (10.10.9)$$

The result of eliminating $\cos \phi_1$ from these two relations is

$$(\mu_{k-1}^2 - \mu_k\mu_{k-2})\beta_1^2 = \mu_k^2 - \mu_{k+1}\mu_{k-1}, \quad (10.10.10)$$

whereas the result of eliminating β_1^2 is

$$2(\mu_{k-1}^2 - \mu_k\mu_{k-2})\beta_1 \cos \phi_1 = \mu_k\mu_{k-1} - \mu_{k+1}\mu_{k-2}. \qquad (10.10.11)$$

Thus, if we introduce the definitions

$$s_k = \mu_k^2 - \mu_{k+1}\mu_{k-1}, \qquad t_k = \mu_k\mu_{k-1} - \mu_{k+1}\mu_{k-2}, \qquad (10.10.12)$$

these relations become

$$\beta_1^2 \equiv \xi_1^2 + \eta_1^2 = \frac{s_k}{s_{k-1}}, \qquad 2\beta_1 \cos \phi_1 \equiv 2\xi_1 = \frac{t_k}{s_{k-1}}. \qquad (10.10.13)$$

It follows that, unless it happens that $C_1 = C_2 = 0$ in (10.10.3), because of a very special choice of $\mu_0, \mu_1, \ldots, \mu_{n-1}$, the ratios s_k/s_{k-1} and t_k/s_{k-1} will *tend* to β_1^2 and $2\beta_1 \cos \phi_1$ as $k \to \infty$, from which limits the constants β_1 and ϕ_1, or ξ_1 and η_1, specifying the desired dominant complex root pair in (10.10.6), can be calculated.

If α_1 is a *repeated* real root, of multiplicity two, so that $\alpha_2 = \alpha_1$, and all other roots are of smaller magnitude, then the combination of terms corresponding to α_1 and α_2 in (10.10.3) is of the form $\alpha_1^k(c_1 + c_2k)$. Since μ_k must then tend to such a form as $k \to \infty$, it follows that μ_k must tend to satisfy the relation

$$\mu_{k+1} - 2\mu_k\alpha_1 + \mu_{k-1}\alpha_1^2 = 0, \qquad (10.10.14)$$

as $k \to \infty$. Whereas an approximation to α_1, which tends to α_1 as $k \to \infty$, could be obtained as the appropriate one of the two roots of this equation, the solution of a quadratic equation can be avoided by rewriting (10.10.14) with k replaced by $k - 1$, and eliminating α_1^2 from the two relations, to give

$$2\alpha_1 = \frac{t_k}{s_{k-1}}, \qquad (10.10.15)$$

with the notation of (10.10.12).

Other exceptional cases, in which several roots have the same maximum absolute value, can be treated in a similar way.

When the largest root α_1 is real and unrepeated, and there are no other roots with the same absolute value, the ratio r_k tends to α_1, the rapidity of the convergence depending upon the magnitude of the ratio α_2/α_1 of the *two* largest roots. If α_1 and α_2 are conjugate complex, (10.10.7) shows that r_k will tend to oscillate about the value zero (although the period of the oscillation may comprise several iterations), whereas, if $\alpha_2 = \alpha_1$ [or $\alpha_2 \approx \alpha_1$], the convergence of the ratio r_k to α_1 will be slow; here the ratio t_k/s_{k-1} converges more rapidly to $2\alpha_1$ [or to $\alpha_1 + \alpha_2$]. In this manner, after several iterations, the behavior of the sequence of r's generally will indicate the true situation, and recourse can be had to the appropriate one of (10.10.13) and (10.10.15) when that sequence is not convergent. The more complicated situations seldom occur in practice.

If α_1 is real and unrepeated, the *ideal* situation would be that in which $\mu_0, \mu_1, \ldots, \mu_{n-1}$ were so chosen that $C_2 = \cdots = C_n = 0$ in (10.10.3), so that $\mu_0, \mu_1, \ldots, \mu_{n-1}$ would be respectively proportional to 1, α_1, $\ldots, \alpha_1^{n-1}$. The first calculated value of r, $r_n = \mu_n/\mu_{n-1}$, then clearly would be identical with α_1. In such cases, the starting values could be taken efficiently as successive powers of a previously determined *approximation* to α_1. If no information is easily available with regard to the nature of the largest root or roots, the starting values

$$\mu_0 = \mu_1 = \cdots = \mu_{n-2} = 0, \qquad \mu_{n-1} = 1$$

are often convenient. For this set of values it is easily seen that the undesirable case $C_1 = 0$ cannot occur.

A particularly notable set of n starting values, having the same property, is that determined by use of the formula

$$\mu_r = -(a_1\mu_{r-1} + a_2\mu_{r-2} + \cdots + a_{r-1}\mu_1 + ra_r)$$
$$(r = 1, 2, \ldots, n), \quad (10.10.16)$$

with $\mu_0 = \mu_{-1} = \cdots = 0$. For this set of starting values it can be shown† that all the C's in (10.10.3) are *unity*, and hence that μ_k is then identified with the sum $\alpha_1^k + \alpha_2^k + \cdots + \alpha_n^k$ for all $k \geqq 1$. Thus, in particular, if $|\alpha_1| \gg |\alpha_2|, \ldots, |\alpha_n|$, there then follow both $\alpha_1 \approx \mu_k/\mu_{k-1}$ and $\alpha_1 \approx \mu_k^{1/k}$ when k is sufficiently large. With the convention that $a_r = 0$ when $r > n$, it is seen that the recurrence formula (10.10.16) reduces to (10.10.2) when $r > n$. This special procedure is closely related to the Graeffe procedure described in the following section.

In the case of the example (10.8.6), the Bernoulli recurrence relation is merely $\mu_k = \mu_{k-2} + \mu_{k-3}$. If the iteration is begun with the starting values 1.30, 1.69, and 2.20, about 16 iterations are needed to establish the real root 1.3247 . . . to five significant figures, although each iteration requires very little labor. The remaining roots are complex, with an absolute value of about 0.9, so that the ratio of the magnitude of the dominant root to that of the subdominant root pair is about 1.5. The relative slowness of the convergence is due to the relative nearness of this ratio to unity. The fact that the subdominant roots are complex causes the sequence of iterates to tend to its limit in an oscillatory manner.

In the case of the example (10.9.17), the recurrence relation is

$$\mu_k = 8\mu_{k-1} - 23\mu_{k-2} - 16\mu_{k-3} + 50\mu_{k-4}$$

† The proof depends upon certain properties of *symmetric functions* [see equation (8.14.28)].

and, with the arbitrarily chosen starting values 0, 0, 0, 1, the ensuing calculation is as follows:

μ_k	r_k	s_k	t_k	s_k/s_{k-1}	t_k/s_{k-1}
8	8	23	8	—	—
41	5.12	657	200	28.565	8.696
128	3.12	16261	5224	24.750	7.951
3	0.02	406537	130600	25.001	8.031
−3176	−1059	10163401	3251272	25.000	7.997
−25475	8.02				

From the irregular behavior of the r sequence, it may be deduced that *either* the process has not yet begun to converge satisfactorily *or* there is a pair of dominant complex roots.   To test the second hypothesis, the s and t sequences are constructed, and the convergence of the sequences of ratios in the last two columns is evident.   The true dominant roots are $\xi_1 \pm i\eta_1 = 4 \pm 3i$, so that $\beta_1^2 \equiv \xi_1^2 + \eta_1^2 = 25$ and $2\xi_1 = 8$.   The approximations afforded by the four successive pairs of ratios are $4.348 \pm 3.108i$, $3.976 \pm 2.990i$, $4.016 \pm 2.979i$, and $3.998 \pm 3.002i$.

The Bernoulli iteration has the useful property that it yields the dominant root (or roots) regardless of the starting values [except in the unlikely case when (10.10.16) is satisfied, in which case another root or root pair will result].   That is, it is not necessary to initiate the iteration with a *sufficiently accurate* approximation, as is the case for many other iterative methods.   This fact is of particular importance in those cases when *only* complex roots are present, since even rough approximations then are not readily obtained.   The calculation is remarkably simple (and readily mechanized) when the dominant root is real and unequaled in absolute value, and is not unduly complicated otherwise.

10.11 Graeffe's Root-squaring Technique.   Graeffe's iterative method for determining roots of the algebraic equation

$$f(x) \equiv x^n + a_1 x^{n-1} + a_2 x^{n-2} + \cdots + a_{n-1}x + a_n = 0 \quad (10.11.1)$$

consists in forming a sequence of *equations*, such that the roots of each equation are the *squares* of the roots of the preceding equation in the sequence, for the purpose of ultimately obtaining an equation whose roots are so widely separated in magnitude that they can be read approximately from the equation, by inspection.

The principle of the method can be illustrated by a consideration of the general equation of fourth degree, which can be written in the form

$$\begin{aligned} f(x) &= x^4 + a_1 x^3 + a_2 x^2 + a_3 x + a_4 \\ &= (x - \alpha_1)(x - \alpha_2)(x - \alpha_3)(x - \alpha_4) = 0 \end{aligned} \quad (10.11.2)$$

or, equivalently,

$$f(x) = x^4 - (\alpha_1 + \alpha_2 + \alpha_3 + \alpha_4)x^3$$
$$+ (\alpha_1\alpha_2 + \alpha_1\alpha_3 + \alpha_1\alpha_4 + \alpha_2\alpha_3 + \alpha_2\alpha_4 + \alpha_3\alpha_4)x^2$$
$$- (\alpha_1\alpha_2\alpha_3 + \alpha_1\alpha_2\alpha_4 + \alpha_1\alpha_3\alpha_4 + \alpha_2\alpha_3\alpha_4)x + \alpha_1\alpha_2\alpha_3\alpha_4 = 0, \quad (10.11.3)$$

where α_1, α_2, α_3, and α_4 are the roots.

If the roots are all real and are widely separated in magnitude, so that $|\alpha_1| \gg |\alpha_2| \gg |\alpha_3| \gg |\alpha_4|$, the result of retaining only the dominant part of each coefficient in (10.11.3) is

$$x^4 - \alpha_1 x^3 + \alpha_1\alpha_2 x^2 - \alpha_1\alpha_2\alpha_3 x + \alpha_1\alpha_2\alpha_3\alpha_4 \approx 0. \quad (10.11.4)$$

Thus the four roots are given approximately, in this case, by equating to zero the four linear expressions $x + a_1$, $a_1 x + a_2$, $a_2 x + a_3$, and $a_3 x + a_4$.

If, say, α_1 and α_2 are conjugate complex, so that $\alpha_1 = \beta_1 e^{i\phi_1}$ and $\alpha_2 = \beta_1 e^{-i\phi_1}$, and also $|\alpha_1| = |\alpha_2| \gg |\alpha_3| \gg |\alpha_4|$, the approximation replacing (10.11.4) is then

$$x^4 - 2\beta_1 x^3 \cos \phi_1 + \beta_1^2 x^2 - \beta_1^2\alpha_3 x + \beta_1^2\alpha_3\alpha_4 \approx 0. \quad (10.11.5a)$$

The complex roots are then approximated by the zeros of the quadratic $x^2 + a_1 x + a_2$, and the remaining roots are found by equating $a_2 x + a_3$ and $a_3 x + a_4$ to zero.

If, say, $\alpha_1 = \alpha_2$ and $|\alpha_1| = |\alpha_2| \gg |\alpha_3| \gg |\alpha_4|$, the approximate relation is

$$x^4 - 2\alpha_1 x^3 + \alpha_1^2 x^2 - \alpha_1^2\alpha_3 x + \alpha_1^2\alpha_3\alpha_4 \approx 0, \quad (10.11.5b)$$

and the approximate roots are obtained in the same way. Other, more unusual situations can be analyzed similarly.

The root-squaring process itself is based on the fact that the product

$$(-1)^n f(-x) f(x) = (x^2 - \alpha_1^2)(x^2 - \alpha_2^2) \cdots (x^2 - \alpha_n^2) \quad (10.11.6)$$

is a polynomial of degree n in x^2, whose zeros are the squares of the zeros of $f(x)$. Thus, if $f(x) = x^n + a_1 x^{n-1} + a_2 x^{n-2} + \cdots + a_{n-1} x + a_n$ is multiplied, term by term, by

$$(-1)^n f(-x) = x^n - a_1 x^{n-1} + a_2 x^{n-2} - \cdots$$
$$+ (-1)^{n-1} a_{n-1} x + (-1)^n a_n,$$

and x^2 is then replaced by x, the result $f_2(x)$ is a polynomial of degree n with zeros $\alpha_1^2, \ldots, \alpha_n^2$. By repeating the process, a polynomial $f_4(x)$ with zeros $\alpha_1^4, \ldots, \alpha_n^4$ is obtained, then $f_8(x)$ with zeros α_k^8, and so forth.

If all roots are real, unrepeated, and of distinct magnitudes, the iteration is concluded when the magnitude of each coefficient in an equation is the square of the magnitude of the corresponding coefficient in the preceding equation, within the tolerance adopted. Suppose that the *original* roots are $\alpha_1, \ldots, \alpha_n$, and that k root squarings are needed, so that the roots of the final equation are $\alpha_1^m, \ldots, \alpha_n^m$, where $m = 2^k$. If the final equation is of the form

$$f_m(x) = x^n - A_1 x^{n-1} + A_2 x^{n-2} - \cdots$$
$$+ (-1)^{n-1} A_{n-1} x + (-1)^n A_n = 0, \quad (10.11.7)$$

there then follows

$$\alpha_1^m \approx A_1, \qquad \alpha_2^m \approx \frac{A_2}{A_1}, \qquad \alpha_3^m \approx \frac{A_3}{A_2}, \qquad \cdots, \qquad \alpha_n^m \approx \frac{A_n}{A_{n-1}}.$$
$$(10.11.8)$$

Each of the right-hand members will be positive, and the proper sign must be chosen for the real mth root of each of these expressions, by substitution of the two possibilities into the original equation or otherwise.

A *double* original root α_1 would evidence itself by the fact that, after k root squarings, the equation would be approximately of the form

$$f_m(x) \approx x^n - 2\alpha_1^m x^{n-1} + \alpha_1^{2m} x^{n-2} - (\alpha_1^2 \alpha_3)^m x^{n-3} + \cdots = 0, \quad (10.11.9)$$

where again $m = 2^k$, so that the magnitude of the coefficient of x^{n-1} would tend to be *half* the square of the magnitude of the corresponding coefficient in the preceding equation. Similarly, if α_r were a double real root, the coefficient of x^{n-r} would have this property. Thus α_r would then satisfy both of the relations

$$\alpha_r^{2m} \approx \frac{A_{r+1}}{A_{r-1}}, \qquad \alpha_r^m \approx \frac{A_r}{2A_{r-1}}, \qquad (10.11.10)$$

and would be determined as the real root, with appropriate sign, of either equation.

A conjugate complex root pair $\alpha_{1,2} = \beta_1 e^{\pm i\phi_1}$ would cause the kth equation to be approximately of the form

$$f_m(x) \approx x^n - 2\beta_1^m x^{n-1} \cos m\phi_1 + \beta_1^{2m} x^{n-2} - (\beta_1^2 \alpha_3)^m x^{n-3} + \cdots = 0,$$
$$(10.11.11)$$

where $m = 2^k$, so that the coefficient of x^{n-1} in the kth equation would tend to fluctuate in magnitude and sign in the same way as $-2\beta_1^m \cos m\phi_1$, as k and $m = 2^k$ increased, and hence again would not tend to be the square of the corresponding coefficient in the $(k-1)$th equation. The same sort of oscillation would occur in the coefficient of x^{n-r} if α_r and α_{r+1} were a complex root pair, and, for k sufficiently large, β_r and ϕ_r could be determined from the relations

$$\beta_r^{2m} \approx \frac{A_{r+1}}{A_{r-1}}, \qquad 2\beta_r^m \cos m\phi_r \approx \frac{A_r}{A_{r-1}}. \qquad (10.11.12)$$

The magnitude β_r would thus be the positive real $(2m)$th root of A_{r+1}/A_{r-1}, whereas the appropriate one of the values of ϕ_r obtained from the second relation would have to be selected, by trial and error or otherwise.

When only one pair of complex roots is present, say

$$\beta_r e^{\pm i\phi_r} \equiv \xi_r \pm i\eta_r,$$

the selection of the appropriate value of ϕ_r satisfying this relation can be avoided by noticing that, since the sum of all roots of (10.11.1) is given by $-a_1$, there follows

$$\alpha_1 + \alpha_2 + \cdots + \alpha_{r-1} + 2\xi_r + \alpha_{r+2} + \cdots + \alpha_n = -a_1. \quad (10.11.13)$$

Hence ξ_r is given immediately when the remaining $n-2$ roots are known, after which η_r is given by $\sqrt{\beta_r^2 - \xi_r^2}$.

If *two* pairs of complex roots are present, say

$$\beta_r e^{\pm i\phi_r} \equiv \xi_r \pm i\eta_r \qquad \text{and} \qquad \beta_s e^{\pm i\phi_s} \equiv \xi_s \pm i\eta_s,$$

the corresponding relation is

$$2(\xi_r + \xi_s) = -(a_1 + \alpha_1 + \cdots + \alpha_{r-1} + \alpha_{r+2} + \cdots \\ + \alpha_{s-1} + \alpha_{s+2} + \cdots + \alpha_n). \quad (10.11.14)$$

A second linear relation between ξ_1 and ξ_2 is then obtained by recalling that the sum of the *reciprocals* of the roots is $-a_{n-1}/a_n$, so that

$$\frac{1}{\alpha_1} + \cdots + \frac{1}{\xi_r + i\eta_r} + \frac{1}{\xi_r - i\eta_r} + \cdots + \frac{1}{\xi_s + i\eta_s} + \frac{1}{\xi_s - i\eta_s} \\ + \cdots + \frac{1}{\alpha_n} = -\frac{a_{n-1}}{a_n}$$

or, after rationalizing the reciprocals of the complex numbers and transposing terms,

$$2\left(\frac{\xi_r}{\beta_r^2} + \frac{\xi_s}{\beta_s^2}\right) = -\left(\frac{a_{n-1}}{a_n} + \frac{1}{\alpha_1} + \cdots + \frac{1}{\alpha_n}\right), \quad (10.11.15)$$

where the reciprocals of the four complex roots are to be omitted in the right-hand member. Since the magnitudes β_r and β_s are known, the relations (10.11.14) and (10.11.15) comprise two linear equations for the determination of ξ_r and ξ_s, after which $\eta_r = \sqrt{\beta_r^2 - \xi_r^2}$ and $\eta_s = \sqrt{\beta_s^2 - \xi_s^2}$.

Rather than actually multiplying together the polynomials $f(x)$ and $(-1)^n f(-x)$, in order to obtain the coefficients of the function $f_2(x)$, it is desirable to work with detached coefficients, and to obtain formulas relating the new coefficients to the original ones. For this purpose, it is convenient to write

$$f(x) = A_0 x^n - A_1 x^{n-1} + A_2 x^{n-2} - \cdots = \sum_{i=0}^{\infty} (-1)^i A_i x^{n-i}, \quad (10.11.16)$$

with the convention that $A_i = 0$ when $i > n$. If we use this convention, there follows

$$(-1)^n f(x) f(-x) = \sum_{i=0}^{\infty} (-1)^i A_i x^{n-i} \sum_{j=0}^{\infty} A_j x^{n-j}$$

$$= \sum_{i=0}^{\infty} \sum_{j=0}^{\infty} (-1)^i A_i A_j x^{2n-(i+j)}.$$

Since clearly only the even powers of x will remain, we may write $i + j = 2k$ and, after changing the limits appropriately, we have

$$(-1)^n f(x) f(-x) = f_2(x^2) = \sum_{k=0}^{\infty} (-1)^k A_k^*(x^2)^{n-k},$$

where
$$A_k^* = \sum_{i=0}^{2k} (-1)^{i+k} A_i A_{2k-i}.$$

Thus $f_2(x)$ is given by

$$f_2(x) = \sum_{k=0}^{\infty} (-1)^k A_k^* x^{n-k} \qquad (10.11.17)$$

where

$$A_k^* = A_k^2 - 2A_{k-1}A_{k+1} + 2A_{k-2}A_{k+2} - 2A_{k-3}A_{k+3} + \cdots, \qquad (10.11.18)$$

and where the series of products terminates when either the first subscript reduces to zero or the second increases to n. This formula is convenient because of the fact that the coefficients A_{k-r} and A_{k+r} involved in each product are symmetrically placed about A_k.

The procedure may be illustrated by the simple case of the cubic $f(x) = x^3 - x - 1$ considered in (10.8.6), for which $A_0 = 1$, $A_1 = 0$, $A_2 = -1$, and $A_3 = +1$, in accordance with (10.11.16). By making use of (10.11.18), the coefficients of the successive equations, again written in the form $x^3 - A_1 x^2 + A_2 x - A_3 = 0$, are obtained as follows in the first six iterations:

	1	A_1	A_2	A_3
f	1	0	-1	1
f_2	1	2	1	1
f_4	1	2	-3	1
f_8	1	10	5	1
f_{16}	1	90	5	1
f_{32}	1	8090	-155	1
f_{64}	1	65448410	7845	1

The coefficient A_3 here remains fixed, whereas the coefficient A_1 in f_{64} is the square of that in f_{32} to five significant figures. The persistent fluctuation of A_2 indicates that the roots α_2 and α_3 are conjugate complex.

Thus the sequence of approximations to α_1 is 0, $\sqrt{2}$, $\sqrt[4]{2}$, $\sqrt[8]{10}$, $\sqrt[16]{90}$, $\sqrt[32]{8090}$, $\sqrt[64]{6544\,8410}$, . . . , or 0, 1.4, 1.2, 1.33, 1.3248, 1.3247, ...
The fact that the *positive* sign is correct would be determined most easily by noticing that $f(x)$ changes sign between $x = 1$ and $x = 2$. Reference to the first equation of (10.11.12), taking into account the fact that here $A_3 \equiv 1$, shows that the corresponding sequence of values of the magnitude β_2 of the complex root pair consists of the reciprocal square roots of these numbers, so that the best available approximation is $\beta_2 \approx 0.86884$, to five places. Rather than use the second relation of (10.11.12), which would involve choosing the appropriate value of cos ϕ_2 for which cos $64\phi_2 = 0.68263$ from among 64 possibilities, we use (10.11.13) to obtain $2\xi_2 = -\alpha_1$, and hence $\xi_2 \approx -0.6624$. Finally, there follows $\eta_2 = \sqrt{\beta_2^2 - \xi_2^2} \approx 0.5622$, so that the approximate roots are 1.3247 and $-0.6624 \pm 0.5622i$.

In order to illustrate the calculation involved in less simple cases, we display the results of five iterations as applied to the equation $x^4 - 10x^3 + 35x^2 - 50x + 24 = 0$, when only three digits are retained.

	A_0	A_1	A_2	A_3	A_4
f	1.00	1.00(1)	3.50(1)	5.00(1)	2.40(1)
f_2	1.00	3.00(1)	2.73(2)	8.20(2)	5.76(2)
f_4	1.00	3.54(2)	2.65(4)	3.58(5)	3.32(5)
f_8	1.00	7.23(4)	4.49(8)	1.11(11)	1.10(11)
f_{16}	1.00	4.33(9)	1.86(17)	1.22(22)	1.21(22)
f_{32}	1.00	1.84(19)	3.45(34)	1.49(44)	1.46(44)

Here an integer in parentheses following a number represents the power of 10 by which that number is to be multiplied to give the desired coefficient. The entries are obtained simply by use of (10.11.18). For example, the coefficients in f_{16} may be calculated as follows:

$$A_1 = 10^8[(7.23)^2 - 2(1.00)(4.49)],$$
$$A_2 = 10^{16}[(4.49)^2 - 2(7.23)(1.11)(10^{-1}) + 2(1.00)(1.10)(10^{-5})],$$
$$A_3 = 10^{22}[(1.11)^2 - 2(4.49)(1.10)(10^{-3})],$$
$$A_4 = 10^{22}(1.10)^2.$$

In a sixth iteration, the squared term in (10.11.18) obviously would not be modified to three digits by the product terms in any case, so that the iteration is terminated. Here all roots are clearly real, and the application of (10.11.8) to f_{32} yields the approximations $\alpha_1 \approx 4.000$, $\alpha_2 \approx 3.001$, $\alpha_3 \approx 2.000$, $\alpha_1 \approx 0.999$. The correctness of the positive signs is assured here by the fact that the expression for $f(-x)$ involves only positive coefficients, so that no negative real roots can be present.

It is of some interest to notice that the use of (10.11.8) at earlier stages of the iteration would yield the following sequences of approximate roots:

	1	2	3	4
f	10.000	3.500	1.429	0.480
f_2	5.477	3.017	1.733	0.838
f_4	4.338	2.941	1.917	0.981
f_8	4.049	2.979	1.991	0.999
f_{16}	4.002	3.000	2.000	1.000
f_{32}	4.000	3.001	2.000	0.999

The Graeffe method possesses the theoretical advantages that the iteration leads to *all* zeros of $f(x)$ at the same time, and that (as in the Bernoulli iteration) there is no question of the existence of ultimate convergence, if appropriate attention is paid to the control of round-off errors. However, it is often rather laborious, and the extraction of algebraic roots of high order, which is involved in the process, is conveniently effected in machine calculation only by an iterative process (see Prob. 36).

A serious disadvantage follows from the fact that a gross error committed at any stage of the calculation invalidates all subsequent calculations, whereas the other iterative methods considered would suffer only a reduction in the rate of convergence.

Rather than use this method for the complete determination of the roots, it is often convenient merely to iterate sufficiently to obtain crude approximations, when such approximations are not easily obtained by other methods, and then to improve these approximations by simpler or more rapidly convergent methods.

The root-squaring process is also useful in connection with the Bernoulli iteration, in cases when that iteration appears to converge slowly, since the rate of convergence increases with increasing values of the ratio of the magnitudes of the dominant and subdominant roots. Thus the convergence will be improved if the original equation is replaced by one whose roots are, say, the squares or fourth powers of the original roots.

10.12. Iterated Synthetic Division with Quadratic Factors. Lin Iteration. Among the most troublesome algebraic equations, in practice, are those which possess two or more pairs of complex roots. Whereas the methods of §§10.10 and 10.11 can be used in such cases, and will always generate convergent sequences of approximations, the convergence is often slow and the labor involved may be excessive. We next treat two methods which are similar to those considered in §10.9, but in which successive approximations to a *quadratic* factor are generated. Both methods have the property that the iteration may not converge unless the initial approximation is sufficiently good and, in fact, one of them may not yield a convergent sequence even in that case. Thus, in troublesome cases, the use of the Bernoulli or Graeffe iteration may be desirable in order to afford a reasonably good initial estimate.

If the polynomial

$$f(x) = x^n + a_1 x^{n-1} + \cdots + a_{n-1} x + a_n \qquad (10.12.1)$$

is divided by the quadratic expression $x^2 + px + q$, so that

$$\begin{aligned} f(x) &= x^n + a_1 x^{n-1} + \cdots + a_{n-1} x + a_n \\ &= (x^2 + px + q)(x^{n-2} + b_1 x^{n-3} + \cdots + b_{n-3} x + b_{n-2}) + Rx + S, \end{aligned}$$
$$(10.12.2)$$

the requirement that this expression be a factor of $f(x)$ imposes the two conditions

$$R = 0, \qquad S = 0, \qquad (10.12.3)$$

where R and S are the coefficients of the linear remainder and are certain functions of the parameters p and q.

In order to obtain a simple method for obtaining R and S without actually effecting the long division, we equate coefficients of like powers of x in the two members of (10.12.2) and thus obtain the relations

$$\begin{aligned} a_1 &= b_1 + p, \qquad a_2 = b_2 + p b_1 + q, \qquad a_3 = b_3 + p b_2 + q b_1, \\ & \cdots, \qquad a_k = b_k + p b_{k-1} + q b_{k-2}, \qquad \cdots, \\ a_{n-2} &= b_{n-2} + p b_{n-3} + q b_{n-4}, \qquad a_{n-1} = R + p b_{n-2} + q b_{n-3}, \\ a_n &= S + q b_{n-2}. \end{aligned} \qquad (10.12.4)$$

Thus, if we introduce the recurrence formula

$$b_k = a_k - p b_{k-1} - q b_{k-2} \qquad (k = 1, 2, \ldots, n) \qquad (10.12.5)$$

with

$$b_{-1} = 0, \qquad b_0 = 1, \qquad (10.12.6)$$

it follows that this formula will generate the coefficients of the quotient in (10.12.2) with $k = 1, 2, \ldots, n - 2$, and also that

$$R = b_{n-1} = a_{n-1} - p b_{n-2} - q b_{n-3}, \qquad (10.12.7)$$
$$S = b_n + p b_{n-1} = a_n - q b_{n-2}. \qquad (10.12.8)$$

Hence the expression $x^2 + px + q$ will factor $f(x)$ if and only if

$$R \equiv a_{n-1} - p b_{n-2} - q b_{n-3} = 0 \qquad (10.12.9)$$

and

$$S \equiv a_n - q b_{n-2} = 0.$$

Lin's iteration consists in applying the method of successive substitutions to the result of rewriting (10.12.9) in the form

$$p = \frac{a_{n-1} - q b_{n-3}}{b_{n-2}}, \qquad q = \frac{a_n}{b_{n-2}},$$

so that "improved" values of p and q are defined by the formulas

$$p^* = \frac{a_{n-1} - qb_{n-3}}{b_{n-2}}, \qquad q^* = \frac{a_n}{b_{n-2}}, \tag{10.12.10}$$

and hence

$$p^* - p = \frac{a_{n-1} - pb_{n-2} - qb_{n-3}}{b_{n-2}}, \qquad q^* - q = \frac{a_n - qb_{n-2}}{b_{n-2}},$$

or, equivalently, in virtue of (10.12.7) and (10.12.8),

$$p^* = p + \frac{R}{b_{n-2}}, \qquad q^* = q + \frac{S}{b_{n-2}}. \tag{10.12.11}$$

In analogy to (10.9.14), it is known that, if p and q are to be such that the zeros of $x^2 + px + q$ approximate the true zeros α_1 and α_2 of $f(x)$, then the two relevant asymptotic convergence factors are (see Prob. 75)

$$\rho_1 = 1 + \frac{\alpha_1 \alpha_2}{\alpha_2 - \alpha_1} \frac{f'(\alpha_1)}{a_n}, \qquad \rho_2 = 1 - \frac{\alpha_1 \alpha_2}{\alpha_2 - \alpha_1} \frac{f'(\alpha_2)}{a_n}. \tag{10.12.12}$$

That is, if either or both of these factors exceeds unity in absolute value, then one or both of the zeros of the modified expression $x^2 + p^*x + q^*$ generally will afford *poorer* approximations to α_1 and α_2 than the zeros of the expression $x^2 + px + q$. Thus, if $x^2 + px + q$ is to converge to $(x - \alpha_1)(x - \alpha_2)$, it is generally necessary that

$$|\rho_1| < 1, \qquad |\rho_2| < 1. \tag{10.12.13}$$

In addition, it is necessary that the *initial* estimates of p and q not differ excessively from $-(\alpha_1 + \alpha_2)$ and $\alpha_1 \alpha_2$, respectively.

The result (10.12.12) is useful only if fair approximations to a pair of roots can be obtained in advance. In analogy to (10.9.16), the conditions (10.12.13) can also be expressed in the form

$$\left| 1 - \left[\left(1 - \frac{\alpha_k}{\alpha_3} \right) \left(1 - \frac{\alpha_k}{\alpha_4} \right) \cdots \left(1 - \frac{\alpha_k}{\alpha_n} \right) \right] \right| < 1 \qquad (k = 1, 2). \tag{10.12.14}$$

In the absence of preliminary information, the iteration may be started with arbitrarily chosen values of p and q, in the hope that convergence to *some* root pair (real or complex) will ensue. With the convenient initial choice $p = 0$, $q = 0$, the *first* iteration always yields the quadratic

$$x^2 + \frac{a_{n-1}}{a_{n-2}} x + \frac{a_n}{a_{n-2}},$$

whose zeros will approximate the two *smallest* roots of $f(x) = 0$ if those roots are sufficiently small relative to the others. It is seen that the initial choice $p = a_1$, $q = a_2$, corresponding to the quadratic $x^2 + a_1 x + a_2$, whose zeros would approximate the two *largest* roots of $f(x) = 0$ if those roots were sufficiently separated in magnitude from the others, leads always to $b_{n-2} = 0$ in the first iteration, so that the following iteration then is undefined. This fact indicates that convergence of the Lin iteration to the *largest* root pair generally cannot be obtained *when that pair is widely separated in magnitude from the others*, as can be seen also by noticing that (10.12.14) then will tend to be violated.

In the more general case, however, (10.12.14) shows that the possibility of convergence to the largest root pair, or to any other chosen root pair, depends in a fairly complicated way upon the configuration of all the roots.

The calculation can be arranged in parallel columns, as follows:

1	1
a_1	b_1
.	.
.	.
.	.
a_{n-2}	b_{n-2}
a_{n-1}	R
a_n	S

Here each entry in the b column *except the last* is obtained by subtracting from its left-hand neighbor p times its first upward neighbor and q times its second upward neighbor. (In calculating b_0 and b_1, the missing entries are taken to be zero.) The last element (S) is calculated in the same way except that its *first upward neighbor* is imagined to be replaced by zero. Finally,

$$\Delta p \equiv p^* - p = \frac{R}{b_{n-2}} \quad \text{and} \quad \Delta q \equiv q^* - q = \frac{S}{b_{n-2}}.$$

In illustration, the quartic equation

$$f(x) \equiv x^4 - 8x^3 + 39x^2 - 62x + 50 = 0 \qquad (10.12.15)$$

possesses the complex roots $1 \pm i$ and $3 \pm 4i$, and $f(x)$ is factorable in the form $f(x) = (x^2 - 2x + 2)(x^2 - 6x + 25)$. The first steps in a Lin iteration, assuming ignorance of this information, and starting with $p = q = 0$, may be tabulated as follows:

$p =$	0	-1.6	-1.95	-2.009	-2.008	-2.003	-2.0007
$q =$	0	1.3	1.82	1.970	2.001	2.003	2.0012
1	1	1	1	1	1	1	
-8	-8	-6.4	-6.05	-5.991	-5.992	-5.997	
39	39	27.5	25.38	24.994	24.967	24.985	
-62	-62	-9.7	-1.50	0.015	0.124	0.057	
50	50	14.2	3.81	0.762	0.041	-0.045	
$\Delta p =$	-1.6	-0.35	-0.059	0.001	0.005	0.0023	
$\Delta q =$	1.3	0.52	0.150	0.031	0.002	-0.0018	

Thus, at this stage, the approximate factorization is

$$f(x) \approx (x^2 - 2.001x + 2.001)(x^2 - 5.997x + 24.985).$$

The Lin iteration technique is perhaps the simplest known method for the numerical solution of algebraic equations, when two or more pairs of complex roots are present. However, it possesses the disadvantage that convergence is not certain, even though the starting values are good approximations to true values, and that the rate of convergence, when present, is often rather slow. The following section describes a somewhat more elaborate method, which usually has better convergence properties.

Use of (10.12.11) shows that the relation (10.12.2) is equivalent to the relation

$$f(x) = (x^2 + px + q)(x^{n-2} + b_1 x^{n-3} + \cdots + b_{n-3} x)$$
$$+ b_{n-2}(x^2 + p^* x + q^*). \quad (10.12.16)$$

Thus it follows that if, in dividing $f(x)$ by the trial factor $x^2 + px + q$, the steps in the division are terminated when the remainder is *quadratic*, the new Lin trial factor $x^2 + p^* x + q^*$ can be obtained by dividing that remainder by its leading coefficient. For this reason, Aitken [27] refers to the new Lin trial factor as the *reduced penultimate remainder*.

It may be mentioned that Lin also suggested a modification of his technique, in which the new value q^* is calculated *first*, from the second relation of (10.12.10), after which q^* is used in place of q, in the first relation of (10.12.10), for the calculation of an "improved" value of p. An equivalent procedure consists in first calculating Δp and Δq by the preceding method, and then calculating a modified Δp from the formula

$$(\Delta p)_{mod} = \Delta p - \frac{b_{n-3}}{b_{n-2}} \Delta q. \quad (10.12.17)$$

In some cases this modification affords improved convergence; in others (including the present example) the reverse is true.

10.13. Bairstow Iteration. Another iterative method for solving algebraic equations, apparently first devised by Bairstow, but rediscovered by Hitchcock and others, differs from the Lin method in that the equations

$$R(p,q) = 0, \quad S(p,q) = 0 \quad (10.13.1)$$

are solved by Newton-Raphson iteration, rather than by the method of successive substitutions used by Lin, so that it is a *second-order* process.

In virtue of the relations (10.12.7) and (10.12.8), we have

$$R = b_{n-1} \quad S = b_n + p b_{n-1}, \quad (10.13.2)$$

and hence the Newton-Raphson recurrence relations (10.8.25) become

$$\frac{\partial b_{n-1}}{\partial p} \Delta p + \frac{\partial b_{n-1}}{\partial q} \Delta q + b_{n-1} = 0$$

and

$$\left(\frac{\partial b_n}{\partial p} + p\frac{\partial b_{n-1}}{\partial p} + b_{n-1}\right) \Delta p + \left(\frac{\partial b_n}{\partial q} + p\frac{\partial b_{n-1}}{\partial q}\right) \Delta q + b_n + pb_{n-1} = 0,$$

where $\Delta p \equiv p^* - p$ and $\Delta q \equiv q^* - q$. If the second relation is simplified, by subtracting from it p times the first equation, the two relations become

$$\frac{\partial b_{n-1}}{\partial p} \Delta p + \frac{\partial b_{n-1}}{\partial q} \Delta q + b_{n-1} = 0,$$

$$\left(\frac{\partial b_n}{\partial p} + b_{n-1}\right) \Delta p + \frac{\partial b_n}{\partial q} \Delta q + b_n = 0. \qquad (10.13.3)$$

If we recall that the b's are defined in terms of the coefficients of $f(x)$ by the recurrence formula (10.12.5),

$$b_k = a_k - pb_{k-1} - qb_{k-2} \qquad (k = 1, 2, \ldots, n)$$
$$b_{-1} = 0, \qquad b_0 = 1, \qquad (10.13.4)$$

it remains only to determine the partial derivatives involved in (10.13.3). For this purpose, we obtain from the relation (10.13.4) the additional relations

$$-\frac{\partial b_k}{\partial p} = b_{k-1} + p\frac{\partial b_{k-1}}{\partial p} + q\frac{\partial b_{k-2}}{\partial p} \qquad (k = 1, 2, \ldots, n)$$

$$\frac{\partial b_{-1}}{\partial p} = 0, \qquad \frac{\partial b_0}{\partial p} = 0 \qquad (10.13.5)$$

and $\quad -\frac{\partial b_k}{\partial q} = b_{k-2} + p\frac{\partial b_{k-1}}{\partial q} + q\frac{\partial b_{k-2}}{\partial q} \qquad (k = 1, 2, \ldots, n)$

$$\frac{\partial b_{-1}}{\partial q} = 0, \qquad \frac{\partial b_0}{\partial q} = 0. \qquad (10.13.6)$$

Hence, if we introduce a new recurrence formula

$$c_k = b_k - pc_{k-1} - qc_{k-2} \qquad (k = 1, 2, \ldots, n-1) \qquad (10.13.7)$$
$$c_{-1} = 0, \qquad c_0 = 1,$$

it follows, from (10.13.5), that

$$\frac{\partial b_k}{\partial p} = -c_{k-1} \qquad (k = 1, 2, \ldots, n) \qquad (10.13.8)$$

and, from (10.13.6), that

$$\frac{\partial b_k}{\partial q} = -c_{k-2} \qquad (k = 1, 2, \ldots, n), \qquad (10.13.9)$$

where the c's are obtained from the b's just as the b's are obtained from the a's.

Thus the first $n - 4$ of the c's are the coefficients in the relation

$$x^{n-2} + b_1 x^{n-3} + \cdots + b_{n-3}x + b_{n-2}$$
$$= (x^2 + px + q)(x^{n-4} + c_1 x^{n-5} + \cdots + c_{n-5}x + c_{n-4}) + R'x + S'$$

$$(10.13.10)$$

and also
$$R' = c_{n-3}, \qquad S' = c_{n-2} + pc_{n-3}. \qquad (10.13.11)$$

In particular, we have

$$\frac{\partial b_{n-1}}{\partial p} = -c_{n-2}, \qquad \frac{\partial b_{n-1}}{\partial q} = -c_{n-3}, \qquad \frac{\partial b_n}{\partial q} = -c_{n-2}, \qquad (10.13.12)$$

so that three of the four desired coefficients in (10.13.3) are now identified, and are calculable from (10.13.7). When $k = n$, Eq. (10.13.8) gives

$$\frac{\partial b_n}{\partial p} = -c_{n-1}, \qquad (10.13.13)$$

and hence the remaining coefficient in (10.13.3) is given by

$$\frac{\partial b_n}{\partial p} + b_{n-1} = -\bar{c}_{n-1}, \qquad (10.13.14)$$

where, in accordance with (10.13.7),

$$\bar{c}_{n-1} = c_{n-1} - b_{n-1} = -pc_{n-2} - qc_{n-3}. \qquad (10.13.15)$$

The basic equations of the Bairstow iteration then take the simple form

$$c_{n-2}\, \Delta p + c_{n-3}\, \Delta q = b_{n-1},$$
$$\bar{c}_{n-1}\, \Delta p + c_{n-2}\, \Delta q = b_n, \qquad (10.13.16)$$

and the principal calculation involved in an iteration can be arranged as follows:

1	1	1
a_1	b_1	c_1
.	.	.
.	.	.
.	.	.
a_{n-4}	b_{n-4}	c_{n-4}
a_{n-3}	b_{n-3}	c_{n-3}
a_{n-2}	b_{n-2}	c_{n-2}
a_{n-1}	b_{n-1}	$\bar{c}_{n-1}$
a_n	b_n	

Here each element in the b column (*including* b_n), and each element of the c column *except the last one* ($\bar{c}_{n-1}$), is calculated as in the Lin iteration, as the result of subtracting from the element to its left p times the last calculated element above it and q times the next-to-last element above it.

The element $\bar{c}_{n-1}$ is calculated in the same way except that the element to its *left* is imagined to be replaced by zero.

In addition, it is necessary to solve the simultaneous linear equations (10.13.16) for the corrections to be added to p and q to give p^* and q^*. For this purpose, the quantities

$$D = c_{n-2}^2 - \bar{c}_{n-1}c_{n-3} \qquad (10.13.17)$$

and $\quad D_p = b_{n-1}c_{n-2} - b_n c_{n-3}, \qquad D_q = -b_{n-1}\bar{c}_{n-1} + b_n c_{n-2} \qquad (10.13.18)$

may be tabulated, after which there follows

$$\Delta p = \frac{D_p}{D}, \qquad \Delta q = \frac{D_q}{D}. \qquad (10.13.19)$$

The first three stages of the result of applying the Bairstow iteration to the equation (10.12.15), again starting with $p = q = 0$, appear as follows:

$p, q =$	0,	0	−1.3,	1.3	−1.9,	1.9	−1.998, 1.998
1	1	1	1	1	1	1	
−8	−8	−8	−6.7	−5.4	−6.10	−4.20	
39	39	39	29.0	20.7	25.51	15.63	
−62	−62	0	−15.6	33.9	−1.94	37.7	
50	50		−8.0		−2.16		
$D =$	1521		612		403		
$D_p, D_q =$	−2018, 1950		−366, 363		−39.4, 39.4		
$\Delta p, \Delta q =$	−1.3, 1.3		−0.6, 0.6		−0.098, 0.098		

The next (fourth) iteration gives $p \approx -1.9999992$ and $q \approx 1.9999992$, if sufficiently many digits are retained in the calculation.

A comparison of these results with those obtained in the preceding section illustrates the fact that, whereas the Bairstow iteration may converge more slowly than the Lin iteration in the *early* stages, when both iterations converge, its *ultimate* rate of convergence in such cases is far superior. This is due to the fact that it is a second-order process, whereas the Lin iteration is a first-order process.

Furthermore, the Bairstow iteration *will* converge if the starting values of p and q are sufficiently close to true values, whereas in the Lin iteration this is not always the case. On the other hand, the Bairstow iteration appears to be somewhat more sensitive to the choice of starting values than does the Lin iteration, in the sense that, if the Lin iteration *is* asymptotically stable at (α_1, α_2), it may converge with starting values which correspond to cruder approximations to (α_1, α_2) than are required for convergence of the Bairstow iteration.

Various modifications of both the Lin and Bairstow procedures are possible. A somewhat similar method, due to Friedman [89], involves two separate synthetic divisions per iteration, so that the labor involved is comparable with that of the Bairstow procedure. However, it is *not* a second-order process, so that its convergence properties are more nearly comparable to those of the Lin procedure.

It is possible to show that, when the Friedman iteration is used for extraction of a *linear* factor, the first step in an iteration is identical with the *Lin* iteration which determines z^* from the starting value z by use of (10.9.12). In place of then recalculating *all* the b's and R, with z replaced by z^*, the Friedman procedure next *retains* the values of b_0, b_1, . . . , b_{n-2}, and recalculates only b_{n-1} and R in this way. If these new values are designated by b_{n-1}^* and R^*, the cycle is concluded by again using the Lin formula (10.9.12) to calculate $z^{**} = z^* - (R^*/b_{n-1}^*)$, to serve as the starting value in the next two-step cycle.

In the case of a *quadratic* factor, the two steps in a Friedman iteration are equivalent to first calculating p^* and q^* from the starting values p and q by the *modified* Lin procedure, based on the use of (10.12.17), and then *retaining* the values of b_0, b_1, . . . , b_{n-3}, recalculating only b_{n-2}, R, and S with p and q replaced by p^* and q^*, and applying the *unmodified* Lin formulas to them.

In some cases, the Friedman procedure is superior to the Lin method, in others inferior. Either may converge when the other does not.

10.14. Supplementary References. A comprehensive bibliography of known methods for solving sets of linear algebraic equations has been compiled by Forsythe [80] and is included in [176]. See also Taussky [221], Bodewig [48], and Forsythe [81]. A few papers treating special methods are listed in the present bibliography. Householder [3] gives concise treatments of several of the modern methods. Error analyses are included in Hotelling [115, 116], Bargmann, Montgomery, and von Neumann [30], von Neumann and Goldstine [166], Lonseth [138], Redheffer [190], Fadeeva [74], Dwyer [72], Goldstine and von Neumann [95], and de la Garza [91]. Certain problems in linear programming, and in other fields, involve the treatment of sets of simultaneous linear *inequalities*. Some available methods are outlined in Charnes, Cooper, and Henderson [53]. Turing [227] discusses measures of the "condition" of a matrix. Schröder [210] appears to have initiated the classification with respect to "order" of iterative methods for solving nonlinear equations. More recent studies of general properties of such methods include those of Hamilton [101] and Bodewig [49]. The Graeffe procedure is analyzed by Bodewig [47], Hoel and Wall [114], and Ostrowski [174]; the Bernoulli iteration by Aitken [23]. The method of Lin [135, 136] is studied by Aitken [26] and is generalized by Luke and Ufford [142] to the extraction of factors of degree greater than two. See also Aitken [27]. For the application of Newton-Raphson iteration to the determination of quadratic factors of polynomials, see Bairstow [28] and Hitchcock [112].

PROBLEMS

Section 10.2

1. Solve the following set of equations by use of determinants, without introducing round-offs:

$$1.4x_1 + 2.3x_2 + 3.7x_3 = 6.5,$$
$$3.3x_1 + 1.6x_2 + 4.3x_3 = 10.3,$$
$$2.5x_1 + 1.9x_2 + 4.1x_3 = 8.8.$$

2. Determine D times the inverse of the coefficient matrix in Prob. 1 without introducing round-offs, where $D = -0.249$ is the determinant of that matrix. Then use this matrix to obtain explicit expressions for Dx_1, Dx_2, and Dx_3 when the respective right-hand members are replaced by c_1, c_2, and c_3, and check the results when the c's are assigned the values given. Also use this result to investigate the significance of the solution if it is supposed that the given coefficients are exact, but that the given right-hand members are only rounded numbers.

3. Show that the equations

$$\omega x_1 + 3x_2 + x_3 = 5,$$
$$2x_1 - x_2 + 2\omega x_3 = 3,$$
$$x_1 + 4x_2 + \omega x_3 = 6$$

possess a unique solution when $\omega \neq \pm 1$, that no solution exists when $\omega = -1$, and that infinitely many solutions exist when $\omega = 1$. Also, investigate the corresponding situation when the right-hand members are replaced by zeros.

Section 10.3

4. By considering the result of increasing each x by unity in each equation of (10.2.1), establish the validity of the following *error check:*

If to each equation is adjoined an entry representing the sum of the coefficients and the right-hand member of that equation, and if the column of those entries is transformed under the Gauss (or Gauss-Jordan) reduction in the same way as the column of right-hand members, then, at each succeeding step, the transformed entry associated with any transformed equation will equal the sum of the coefficients and the right-hand member of that equation, except for the effects of intermediate round-offs or gross errors.

5. Solve the set of equations in Prob. 1 by the Gauss reduction, retaining only five decimal places in the intermediate calculation, and using the error check of Prob. 4.

6. Proceed as in Prob. 5 with the following set of equations:

$$8.467x_1 + 5.137x_2 + 3.141x_3 + 2.063x_4 = 29.912,$$
$$5.137x_1 + 6.421x_2 + 2.617x_3 + 2.003x_4 = 25.058,$$
$$3.141x_1 + 2.617x_2 + 4.128x_3 + 1.628x_4 = 16.557,$$
$$2.063x_1 + 2.003x_2 + 1.628x_3 + 3.446x_4 = 12.690.$$

7. Repeat the calculation of Prob. 6, using the Gauss-Jordan reduction.

Section 10.4

8, 9. Proceed as in Probs. 5 and 6, using the Crout reduction.

10, 11. Assuming the given data to be exact, and starting with the approximate solutions of Probs. 8 and 9, obtain the solutions of those problems with 10-place accuracy by use of the Crout reduction.

12. Solve the following set of equations, as it stands, by the Crout reduction, retaining only five decimal places in the intermediate calculation. Then repeat the calculation after an appropriate reordering of equations and renumbering of variables, using the computational-error check in both cases:

$$1.423x_1 + 2.316x_2 + 3.218x_3 = 8.553,$$
$$2.316x_1 + 3.751x_2 + 1.244x_3 = 7.342,$$
$$3.218x_1 + 1.244x_2 + 6.173x_3 = 13.349.$$

Section 10.5

13, 14. Determine the inverse of the coefficient matrix in Probs. 8 and 9 by the Crout reduction, retaining five decimal places. Also evaluate the determinant of the coefficient matrix in each case.

Section 10.6

15, 16. Use the results of Probs. 13 and 14 to obtain approximate upper bounds on the inherent errors relevant to the solutions of Probs. 8 and 9, assuming (a) that the coefficients are exact and the errors in the right-hand members cannot exceed ϵ in magnitude and (b) that the coefficients as well as the right-hand members may be in error by as much as $\pm\epsilon$. In each case, determine what can be said about the solution if the errors in the given data are due to round-off.

17, 18. Reestimate the error bounds considered in Probs. 15 and 16 by use of the inherent-error check column.

19. If $x_1, \ldots, x_n$ satisfy the equations

$$\sum_{k=1}^{n} a_{ik}x_k = c_i \qquad (i = 1, 2, \ldots, n),$$

show that there follows

$$\sum_{k=1}^{n} a_{ik} \frac{\partial x_k}{\partial c_r} = \begin{cases} 0 & (i \neq r), \\ 1 & (i = r). \end{cases}$$

and

$$\sum_{k=1}^{n} a_{ik} \frac{\partial x_k}{\partial a_{rs}} = \begin{cases} 0 & (i \neq r), \\ -x_s & (i = r), \end{cases}$$

and deduce the relations

$$\frac{\partial x_k}{\partial c_r} = \tilde{A}_{rk}, \qquad \frac{\partial x_k}{\partial a_{rs}} = -\tilde{A}_{rk}x_s.$$

20. Use the results of Prob. 19, and the data of Prob. 13, to obtain approximations to the changes in the values of x_1, x_2, and x_3 in Prob. 1 corresponding (a) to an increase of 0.05 in $c_3 \equiv 8.8$ and (b) to a decrease of 0.05 in $a_{23} \equiv 4.3$.

21. Use the results of Prob. 19, and the data of Prob. 14, to obtain approximations to the changes in the values of x_1, x_2, x_3, and x_4 in Prob. 6, corresponding (a) to an increase of 0.001 in $c_3 \equiv 16.557$ and (b) to a decrease of 0.001 in $a_{23} \equiv 2.617$.

Section 10.7

22. Determine the solution of the following set of equations, to four decimal places, by use of the Gauss-Seidel iteration:

$$3.955x_1 - 1.013x_2 = 0.3068,$$
$$-1.007x_1 + 3.926x_2 - 1.023x_3 = 0.8669,$$
$$-1.013x_2 + 3.887x_3 - 1.038x_4 = 1.3168,$$
$$-1.021x_3 + 3.841x_4 = 2.7997.$$

23. Investigate (empirically) the efficiency of the Gauss-Seidel iteration in the case of the equations in Prob. 1.

24. Determine the solution of the equations in Prob. 22, to four places, by use of a relaxation procedure.

25. Experiment with the application of relaxation methods to the equations in Prob. 1.

Section 10.8

26. Suppose that the equation $x^2 + a_1x + a_2 = 0$ possesses real roots α and β. Show that the iteration $z_{k+1} = -(a_1z_k + a_2)/z_k$ is stable near $x = \alpha$ if $|\alpha| > |\beta|$, the iteration $z_{k+1} = -a_2/(z_k + a_1)$ is stable near $x = \alpha$ if $|\alpha| < |\beta|$, and the iteration $z_{k+1} = -(z_k^2 + a_2)/a_1$ is stable near $x = \alpha$ if $2|\alpha| < |\alpha + \beta|$.

27. With the notation of Prob. 26, show that the iteration

$$z_{k+1} = z_k - (z_k^2 + a_1z_k + a_2)\phi(z_k)$$

is stable near $x = \alpha$ if $0 < (\alpha - \beta)\phi(\alpha) < 2$, that the asymptotic convergence factor is $\rho = 1 - (\alpha - \beta)\phi(\alpha)$, and that the three iterations of Prob. 26 are the special cases in which $\phi(x) = 1/x$, $1/(x + a_1)$, and $1/a_1$.

28. If $x = \alpha$ is a root of $f(x) = 0$, if successive approximations to α are generated by the iteration $z_{k+1} = F(z_k)$, and if $F(x)$ possesses $r + 1$ continuous derivatives and is such that

$$F(\alpha) = \alpha, \qquad F'(\alpha) = F''(\alpha) = \cdots = F^{(r)}(\alpha) = 0,$$

for some $r \geq 1$, show that

$$\alpha - z_{k+1} = (-1)^r \frac{(\alpha - z_k)^{r+1}}{(r + 1)!} F^{(r+1)}(\xi_k),$$

where ξ_k lies between z_k and α, so that the iteration is a process of order $r + 1$ or greater.

29. With the notation of Prob. 28, show that the iteration corresponding to the definition

$$F(x) = x - \phi_1(x)f(x) - \phi_2(x)[f(x)]^2 - \phi_3(x)[f(x)]^3 - \cdots$$

is at least of second order if $1 - \phi_1 f' = 0$, at least of third order if also

$$2\phi_1' f' + \phi_1 f'' + 2\phi_2 f'^2 = 0,$$

and at least of fourth order if further

$$3\phi_1'' f' + 3\phi_1' f'' + \phi_1 f''' + 6\phi_2' f'^2 + 6\phi_2 f'f'' + 6\phi_3 f'^3 = 0,$$

under the assumption that the ϕ's and an appropriate number of their derivatives are finite at $x = \alpha$. Thus deduce that the formula

$$z_{k+1} = z_k - \frac{f_k}{f_k'} - \frac{f_k''}{2f_k'} \left(\frac{f_k}{f_k'}\right)^2 - \left(\frac{f_k''^2}{2f_k'^2} - \frac{f_k'''}{6f_k'}\right) \left(\frac{f_k}{f_k'}\right)^3 - \cdots,$$

with $f_k^{(n)} \equiv f^{(n)}(z_k)$, yields a process of order equal to the number of terms retained in the right-hand member.

30. Rederive the formula of Prob. 29 by writing $z_{k+1} - z_k = h$ and

$$f(z_k + h) = f_k + hf_k' + \frac{h^2}{2} f_k'' + \frac{h^3}{6} f_k''' + \cdots ,$$

assuming an expansion of the form $h = -(\phi_1 f_k + \phi_2 f_k^2 + \phi_3 f_k^3 + \cdots)$, requiring that the coefficients of successive powers of f_k vanish in the result of substituting the second expansion into the first, and so obtaining the conditions $1 - \phi_1 f_k' = 0$, $2\phi_2 f_k' - \phi_1^2 f_k'' = 0$, $6\phi_3 f_k' - 6\phi_1 \phi_2 f_k'' + \phi_1^3 f_k''' = 0$, $\cdots$.

31. Use the formula of Prob. 29 to approximate the real root of $x^3 - x - 1 = 0$, taking $z_0 = 1.3$ and calculating separately the approximations to z_1 afforded by retention of one, two, and three correction terms. Also investigate the approximations corresponding to the choice $z_0 = 1$.

32. The real root α of the equation $x + \log x = 0$ lies between 0.56 and 0.57. Show that the iteration $z_{k+1} = -\log z_k$ is unstable near $x = \alpha$, and verify this fact by calculation. Then show that the iteration $z_{k+1} = e^{-z_k}$ is stable near $x = \alpha$, and determine α to five places.

33. Suppose that the solution of Prob. 32 is required, but that only values of $\log_{10} x$ are to be used. Determine a convenient value of the constant c for which the iteration

$$z_{k+1} = z_k - c(z_k + \log z_k) \equiv (1 - c)z_k - c(\log 10) \log_{10} z_k$$

is stable near $x = \alpha$, and use the result to determine α to five places.

34, 35. Repeat the determination of Probs. 32 and 33, using the Newton-Raphson iteration with $f(x) = x + \log x$ and with $f(x) = x - e^{-x}$, respectively.

36. Show that the Newton-Raphson iterations, as applied to $f(x) = x^n - a$ and to $f(x) = 1 - (a/x^n)$, for the determination of $\alpha \equiv a^{1/n}$, are of the respective forms

$$z_{k+1} = \frac{1}{n} \left[(n - 1)z_k + \frac{a}{z_k^{n-1}} \right]$$

and

$$z_{k+1} = \frac{1}{n} \left[(n + 1)z_k - \frac{z_k^{n+1}}{a} \right],$$

and that, if $\epsilon_k \equiv \alpha - z_k$, there follows approximately

$$\epsilon_{k+1} \approx -\frac{n - 1}{2\alpha} \epsilon_k^2$$

and

$$\epsilon_{k+} \approx \frac{n + 1}{2\alpha} \epsilon_k^2,$$

respectively, when $z_k \approx \alpha$. (Notice that the second iteration formula possesses a constant denominator and that the two sequences approach α from above and from below, respectively, when $\alpha > 0$.) Also use both iterations to determine $(3.4765)^{\frac{1}{2}}$ and $(0.049672)^{\frac{1}{2}}$ to five places.

37. Use the results of Prob. 29, with $f(x) = x^2 - a$ and with $f(x) = 1 - (a/x^2)$, to obtain third-order iterations leading to $\alpha \equiv a^{\frac{1}{2}}$ in the forms

$$z_{k+1} = \frac{1}{2} \left(z_k + \frac{a}{z_k} \right) - \frac{1}{8z_k} \left(z_k - \frac{a}{z_k} \right)^2$$

and

$$z_{k+1} = \frac{1}{2} z_k \left(3 - \frac{z_k^2}{a} \right) + \frac{3}{8} z_k \left(1 - \frac{z_k^2}{a} \right)^2,$$

and use them to determine $(16.324)^{\frac{1}{2}}$ and $(0.049672)^{\frac{1}{2}}$ to four places.

38. By applying the Newton-Raphson procedure to $f(x) = 1 - 1/(ax)$, obtain the recurrence formula

$$z_{k+1} = z_k(2 - az_k),$$

for the iterative determination of the reciprocal of a without effecting division, and show that, if ϵ_k denotes the error in z_k, there follows $\epsilon_{k+1} = a\epsilon_k^2$ in this case. Also obtain the third-order iteration $z_{k+1} = z_k(3 - 3az_k + a^2z_k^2)$, and show that the error in the calculation of z_{k+1} due to the first neglected term in the formula of Prob. 29 is then approximated by $a^2\epsilon_k^3$ when $z_k \approx 1/a$.

39. Suppose that $f(x)$ possesses two zeros α_1 and α_2 which are nearly coincident, so that $f'(x)$ vanishes at a point β between α_1 and α_2. Show that, if β is calculated first, then initial approximations to the zeros of $f(x)$ are given by

$$\alpha_{1,2} \approx \beta \pm \left[-\frac{2f(\beta)}{f''(\beta)} \right]^{\frac{1}{2}},$$

if $f(\beta)$ and $f''(\beta)$ are of opposite sign, after which improved values may be obtained by usual methods. Also, use this procedure to determine to four places the two real roots of the equation

$$3x^4 + 8x^3 - 6x^2 - 25x + 19 = 0.$$

40. Determine the smallest root of the equation $\tan x = cx$ to five places, with $c = 1.01$, $c = 2$, and $c = 30$.

Determine all real roots of the following equations to five places:

41. $x^3 - 2x - 5 = 0.$†

42. $x^3 - 9x^2 + 18x - 6 = 0.$

43. $x^4 - 16x^3 + 72x^2 - 96x + 24 = 0.$

44. $x^4 - 3x + 1 = 0.$

45. $x^2 - 3x - 4\sin^2 x = 0.$

46. Determine $F(x,y)$ and $G(x,y)$ such that the Newton-Raphson iteration for a solution (α,β) of the equations $f(x,y) = 0$ and $g(x,y) = 0$ is expressed in the form

$$x_{k+1} = F(x_k,y_k), \qquad y_{k+1} = G(x_k,y_k),$$

and show that F_x, F_y, G_x, and G_y vanish when $(x,y) = (\alpha,\beta)$ in nonexceptional cases.

47. Determine to five places the real solution of the equations

$$x = \sin(x + y), \qquad y = \cos(x - y).$$

48. Determine to five places the real solution of the equations

$$4x^3 - 27xy^2 + 25 = 0, \qquad 4x^2y - 3y^3 - 1 = 0$$

which lies in the first quadrant.

49. Determine to five places the real solution of the equations

$$\sin x \sinh y = 0.2, \qquad \cos x \cosh y = 1.2$$

which lies nearest the origin.

† This equation was used by Wallis in 1685 to illustrate the Newton-Raphson method and has been included as an example in most subsequent works dealing with the numerical solution of equations.

Section 10.9

50. If α_r is a root of the equation $f(x) \equiv x^n + a_1 x^{n-1} + \cdots + a_{n-1} x + a_n = 0$, and if the coefficients are inexact, such that the *relative* error in each coefficient does not exceed η in magnitude, show that the corresponding maximum error in α_r is given approximately by

$$|\delta\alpha_r|_{\max} \approx \frac{|a_1\alpha_r^{n-1}| + |a_2\alpha_r^{n-2}| + \cdots + |a_{n-1}\alpha_r| + |a_n|}{|f'(\alpha_r)|} \eta,$$

if η is small.

51. If $\bar{\alpha}$ is an approximation to a root α of the equation $f(x) = 0$, and if $f(\bar{\alpha}) = \epsilon$, show that $\alpha - \bar{\alpha} = -\epsilon/f'(\xi)$, where ξ is between $\bar{\alpha}$ and α, if $f'(x)$ is continuous.

52. Show that the result of replacing x by $t + c$ in

$$f(x) \equiv x^n + a_1 x^{n-1} + \cdots + a_{n-1} x + a_n$$

is of the form $\bar{f}(t) \equiv t^n + R^{(n-1)} t^{n-1} + R^{(n-2)} t^{n-2} + \cdots + R' t + R$, where the coefficients can be determined by continuing the process leading to (10.9.5) until it terminates, with α replaced by c. Also illustrate this procedure in the case when

$$f(x) = x^3 - x - 1$$

and $c = 1.3$, showing that the calculations may be arranged as follows:

1	1	1	1	1
0	1.3	2.6	3.9	
−1	0.69	4.07		
−1	−0.103			

53. Apply the Lin iteration to the equation

$$t^3 + 3.9t^2 + 4.07t - 0.103,$$

obtained in Prob. 52, starting with $t_0 = 0$. Thus obtain the real root of the equation $x^3 - x - 1 = 0$ to five places.

54. The equation of Prob. 43, $x^4 - 16x^3 + 72x^2 - 96x + 24 = 0$, possesses roots approximated by 0.3, 1.7, 4.5, and 9.4. Use (10.9.15) or (10.9.16) to predict that the Lin iteration will be stable only for the smallest root, with a convergence factor of about $\frac{1}{3}$, and determine that root to five places by Lin iteration.

55. Use the result of Prob. 29 to devise a third-order iteration process extending (10.9.10), of the form

$$z^* = z - \frac{R}{R'} - \frac{R''}{R'} \left(\frac{R}{R'}\right)^2,$$

where $R'' = d_{n-2}$ and $d_k = c_k + z d_{k-1}$. Also determine the real zero of (10.8.6) to six decimal places by this method, starting with $z = 1.3$.

56 to 58. Determine the real roots of the equations in Probs. 41, 42, and 44 to five places, by either of the methods of §10.9.

59 to 61. Determine approximately the maximum inherent error in each root obtained in Probs. 56 to 58, assuming (a) that each coefficient in the given equation (except the leading one) may be in error by ± 0.1 and (b) that each such coefficient is correct within 1 per cent (see Prob. 50).

62. With the notation of §10.9, show that

$$f(z) = b_n(z) = z^n + a_1 z^{n-1} + \cdots + a_{n-1}z + a_n,$$
$$f'(z) = c_{n-1}(z) = z^{n-1} + b_1(z)z^{n-2} + \cdots + b_{n-2}(z)z + b_{n-1}(z),$$

and

$$\frac{1}{2!}f''(z) = z^{n-2} + c_1(z)z^{n-3} + \cdots + c_{n-3}(z)z + c_{n-2}(z).$$

Also deduce, in particular, that the iteration

$$z^* = z - \frac{R}{b_{n-1} + zb_{n-2}}$$

may be expected to yield results intermediate between those given by the Lin and Newton-Raphson iterations, on the average, when the desired root is small in magnitude, and show that its asymptotic convergence factor, near a root α_r, is given by

$$1 + \frac{\alpha_r f'(\alpha_r)}{2f(0) + \alpha_r f'(0)}.$$

Section 10.10

63. Determine the largest root in Prob. 42 to four places by Bernoulli iteration.

64. Determine the largest root in Prob. 43 to four places by Bernoulli iteration. Also, after replacing x by $1/x$, determine the smallest root in a similar way. Then determine all roots to four places.

65. Show that the Bernoulli iteration converges very slowly when applied to Prob. 41, and account for this fact. Then translate the origin to a convenient point near the root, replace x by $1/x$, and apply the iteration to determine the reciprocal of the real root to six places.

66. Show that the μ, s, and t sequences all behave unsatisfactorily when the Bernoulli iteration is applied to Prob. 44. Then replace x by $1/x$, use the iteration to determine the smallest root to four places, and determine the other real root after translating the origin to a nearby point and replacing x by $1/x$. Finally, determine the remaining roots and account for the original difficulty.

67. Apply the Bernoulli iteration to the equation

$$x^4 - 8x^3 + 39x^2 - 62x + 50 = 0,$$

determining the larger pair of complex roots to three significant figures.

Section 10.11

68 to 71. Determine all roots of the equations in Probs. 41 to 44, to three decimal places, by the Graeffe procedure.

72. Use the Graeffe procedure to determine all roots of the equation of Prob. 67 to three significant figures.

Section 10.12

73. Show that the equation

$$x^4 - 9.00x^3 + 29.08x^2 - 39.52x + 18.82 = 0$$

has roots near $x = 1$ and $x = 2$ and two roots near $x = 3$, and determine the roots to four decimal places by extracting an approximate quadratic factor by Lin iteration, starting with $(x - 3)^2$.

74. Determine all roots of the equation

$$x^4 + 9x^3 + 36x^2 + 51x + 27 = 0$$

to four decimal places by iterative Lin extraction of a quadratic factor.

75. With the notation of §10.12, show that the Lin iteration (10.12.11) can be written in the form

$$p^* - p = \frac{qR}{a_n - S}, \qquad q^* - q = \frac{qS}{a_n - S}$$

and that

$$Rx_1 + S = f(x_1), \qquad Rx_2 + S = f(x_2),$$

where x_1 and x_2 are the zeros of $x^2 + px + q$, and hence deduce the relations

$$x_1(p^* - p) + (q^* - q) = \frac{qf(x_1)}{a_n - S}, \qquad x_2(p^* - p) + (q^* - q) = \frac{qf(x_2)}{a_n - S}.$$

Then show that these relations can be written in the forms

$$(x_2 - x_1)(x_1^* - x_1) = \frac{qf(x_1)}{a_n - S} - (x_1^* - x_1)(x_2^* - x_2),$$

$$(x_2 - x_1)(x_2^* - x_2) = -\frac{qf(x_2)}{a_n - S} + (x_1^* - x_1)(x_2^* - x_2),$$

where x_1^* and x_2^* are the zeros of $x^2 + p^*x + q^*$, and deduce that, when (x_1, x_2) and (x_1^*, x_2^*) are near (α_1, α_2), there follows

$$\alpha_1 - x_1^* \approx \left[1 + \frac{\alpha_1\alpha_2}{\alpha_2 - \alpha_1}\frac{f'(\alpha_1)}{a_n}\right](\alpha_1 - x_1) \equiv \rho_1(\alpha_1 - x_1),$$

$$\alpha_2 - x_2^* \approx \left[1 - \frac{\alpha_1\alpha_2}{\alpha_2 - \alpha_1}\frac{f'(\alpha_2)}{a_n}\right](\alpha_2 - x_2) \equiv \rho_2(\alpha_2 - x_2),$$

where ρ_1 and ρ_2 are the convergence factors listed in (10.12.12). Thus show that, if the zeros x_1 and x_2 of $x^2 + px + q$ approximate two zeros α_1 and α_2 of $f(x)$, and if x_1^* and x_2^* are the zeros of $x^2 + p^*x + q^*$, then x_1^* is generally a poorer approximation to α_1 than x_1 unless $|\rho_1| < 1$ and x_2^* a poorer approximation to α_2 than x_2 unless $|\rho_2| < 1$.

76. In the case of a quartic equation, show that the asymptotic convergence factors relevant to the root pair α_1, α_2 are

$$\rho_1 = \frac{\alpha_1}{\alpha_3\alpha_4}(\alpha_3 + \alpha_4 - \alpha_1), \qquad \rho_2 = \frac{\alpha_2}{\alpha_3\alpha_4}(\alpha_3 + \alpha_4 - \alpha_2),$$

where α_3 and α_4 are the remaining roots. Show, in particular, that the Lin iteration should converge rapidly to the root pair near $x = 3$ in Prob. 73, but that convergence to the pair near $x = 1$ and $x = 2$ should be very slow, and verify the last fact by direct calculation.

77. Determine the first five quadratics yielded by the Lin iteration as applied to the equation $x^4 - 4x^3 + 7x^2 - 16x + 12 = 0$, starting with $p = q = 0$, and show that one of the zeros of the sequence of quadratics tends to approximate the smallest zero $(x = 1)$ of the given equation. Also, use the fact that the four zeros are $x = 1, 3,$ and $\pm 2i$ to show that this situation is in accordance with the results of Prob. 75.

Section 10.13

78, 79. Repeat the determinations of Probs. 73 and 74, using the Bairstow iteration.

80. Show that, if the Newton-Raphson iteration is applied to the equations $b_{n-1} = 0$ and $b_n = 0$, rather than to the equivalent equations $b_{n-1} = 0$ and $b_n + pb_{n-1} = 0$, then the Bairstow procedure is modified only to the extent that $\bar{c}_{n-1}$ is replaced by c_{n-1} in (10.13.16), so that *all* elements in the c column then are to be calculated from elements in the b column by the same rule. Also, apply this procedure to the example in the text, showing that the modification leads to somewhat slower convergence in that case.

81. With the notation of (10.12.2) and (10.13.11), show that the Bairstow iteration can be described by the equations

$$(S' - pR')\,\Delta p + R'\,\Delta q = R,$$
$$-qR'\,\Delta p + S'\,\Delta q = S.$$

(These are the forms originally given by Bairstow.)

APPENDIX A

JUSTIFICATION OF THE CROUT REDUCTION

The Gauss reduction of §10.3 reduces the set of equations

$$
\begin{aligned}
a_{11}x_1 + a_{12}x_2 + a_{13}x_3 + \cdots + a_{1n}x_n &= c_1, \\
a_{21}x_1 + a_{22}x_2 + a_{23}x_3 + \cdots + a_{2n}x_n &= c_2, \\
&\cdots \\
a_{n1}x_1 + a_{n2}x_2 + a_{n3}x_3 + \cdots + a_{nn}x_n &= c_n
\end{aligned}
\tag{A1}
$$

to an equivalent set of the form

$$
\begin{aligned}
x_1 + a'_{12}x_2 + a'_{13}x_3 + \cdots + a'_{1n}x_n &= c'_1, \\
x_2 + a'_{23}x_3 + \cdots + a'_{2n}x_n &= c'_2, \\
&\cdots \\
x_n &= c'_n,
\end{aligned}
\tag{A2}
$$

after which the required values of $x_n, x_{n-1}, \ldots, x_1$ are obtained simply by solving the equations (A2) successively, in reverse order.

Since, in the Gauss reduction, the kth equation of (A2) is obtained by a sequence of operations which involve the subtraction of multiples of the first $k-1$ equations of (A2) from the kth equation of (A1) and the division of the result by a constant, it follows also that the kth equation of (A1) can be expressed as a linear combination of the first k equations of (A2), so that a set of constants a'_{ij} exists, with $i \geq j$, such that

$$
\begin{aligned}
a'_{11}c'_1 &= c_1, \\
a'_{21}c'_1 + a'_{22}c'_2 &= c_2, \\
&\cdots \\
a'_{n1}c'_1 + a'_{n2}c'_2 + a'_{n3}c'_3 + \cdots + a'_{nn}c'_n &= c_n.
\end{aligned}
\tag{A3}
$$

The Crout reduction amounts to first determining the coefficients a'_{ij} in such a way that the elimination of $c'_1, \ldots, c'_n$ between (A2) and (A3) leads to (A1), then determining $c'_1, \ldots, c'_n$ from (A3), and finally resolving (A2) for $x_1, \ldots, x_n$ by the "back solution" of the Gauss procedure.

In order to simplify the derivation of formulas for the determination of the coefficients a'_{ij} involved in both (A2) and (A3), it is convenient to

486

introduce the temporary notations

$$\alpha_{ij} = \begin{cases} a'_{ij} & (i \geq j), \\ 0 & (i < j), \end{cases} \qquad \beta_{ij} = \begin{cases} 0 & (i \geq j), \\ a'_{ij} & (i < j). \end{cases} \tag{A4}$$

The three sets (A1) to (A3) can then be specified by the equations

$$\sum_{j=1}^{n} a_{ij}x_j = c_i, \tag{A1'}$$

$$x_k + \sum_{j=1}^{n} \beta_{kj}x_j = c'_k, \tag{A2'}$$

and

$$\sum_{k=1}^{n} \alpha_{ik}c'_k = c_i, \tag{A3'}$$

where all indices range from 1 to n.

The introduction of (A2') into (A3') then gives

$$\sum_{k=1}^{n} \alpha_{ik}x_k + \sum_{j=1}^{n} \left(\sum_{k=1}^{n} \alpha_{ik}\beta_{kj} \right) x_j = c_i,$$

and this relation is equivalent to (A1') if

$$\alpha_{ij} + \sum_{k=1}^{n} \alpha_{ik}\beta_{kj} = a_{ij}. \tag{A5}$$

In virtue of (A4), the first term α_{ij} is zero unless $i \geq j$ and the summand in the second term vanishes unless both $k \leq i$ and $k < j$. Thus, when $i \geq j$, (A5) becomes

$$a'_{ij} + \sum_{k=1}^{j-1} a'_{ik}a'_{kj} = a_{ij} \qquad (i \geq j), \tag{A6}$$

whereas, when $i < j$, it can be written in the form

$$a'_{ii}a'_{ij} + \sum_{k=1}^{i-1} a'_{ik}a'_{kj} = a_{ij} \qquad (i < j). \tag{A7}$$

These relations, together with the relations

$$a'_{ii}c'_i + \sum_{k=1}^{i-1} a'_{ik}c'_k = c_i \tag{A8}$$

and

$$x_i + \sum_{k=i+1}^{n} a'_{ik}x_k = c'_i, \tag{A9}$$

which are equivalent to (A3′) and (A1′), respectively, are identical with the relations (10.4.4) to (10.4.7) of §10.4, establishing the validity of the Crout reduction as described in that section.

Clearly, the compactness of the relevant tabulation follows from the fact that, after suppressing the diagonal 1's in the coefficient matrix of (A2) and the right-hand members of (A3), which are also contained in the matrix of (A1), the remaining elements of the *two* matrices associated with (A2) and (A3) can be recorded in a *single* auxiliary matrix.

In order to establish the relation

$$a'_{ii}a'_{ij} = a'_{ji} \qquad (i < j) \tag{A10}$$

in the special cases when the given coefficient array is *symmetric*, so that

$$a_{ji} = a_{ij}, \tag{A11}$$

we may verify that (A6) and (A7) imply the relation

$$a'_{ii}a'_{ij} - a'_{ji} = a_{ij} - a_{ji} + \sum_{k=1}^{i-1} (a'_{ik}a'_{kj} - a'_{jk}a'_{ki}) \qquad (i < j)$$

which can be written in the form

$$a'_{ii}a'_{ij} - a'_{ji} = \sum_{k=1}^{i-1} [a'_{ki}(a'_{kk}a'_{kj} - a'_{jk}) - a'_{kj}(a'_{kk}a'_{ki} - a'_{ik})] \qquad (i < j), \tag{A12}$$

if (A11) is true. When $i = 1$, the sum on the right is absent, so that (A10) is established in that case. When $i > 1$, (A12) expresses $a'_{ii}a'_{ij} - a'_{ji}$ as a linear combination of terms of the form $a'_{rr}a'_{rs} - a'_{sr}$, where $r < i$ and $r < s$, so that (A10) is established by induction on i.

The validity of the *calculational-error check* described in §10.4 follows from the fact that an increase of each solution element x_i by *unity* would correspond to an increase of c_i by $\sum_{k=1}^{n} a_{ik}$, according to (A1′), and to an increase of c'_i by $1 + \sum_{k=i+1}^{n} a'_{ik}$, according to (A2′).

Since the kth equation of (A2) can be obtained by subtracting from the kth equation of (A1) a certain linear combination of the first $k - 1$ equations of (A1), and dividing the result by a'_{kk}, it follows, from the elementary properties of determinants, that the determinant of any square array of order k formed from elements in the first k rows of the augmented matrix of (A1) is given by the result of multiplying the determinant of the corresponding array in (A2) by $a'_{11}a'_{22} \cdots a'_{kk}$. In particular, we thus obtain the useful results

$$a_{11} = c'_{11}, \qquad \begin{vmatrix} a_{11} & a_{12} \\ c_{21} & a_{22} \end{vmatrix} = a'_{11}a'_{22}, \qquad \begin{vmatrix} a_{11} & a_{12} & a_{13} \\ a_{21} & a_{22} & a_{23} \\ a_{31} & a_{32} & a_{33} \end{vmatrix} = a'_{11}a'_{22}a'_{33},$$

$$\cdots, \qquad \begin{vmatrix} a_{11} & \cdots & a_{1n} \\ \cdots & \cdots & \cdots \\ a_{n1} & \cdots & a_{nn} \end{vmatrix} = a'_{11}a'_{22} \cdots a'_{nn}. \quad (A13)$$

When the matrix composed of the coefficients in (A1) is *symmetric*, it is said to be also *positive definite* if and only if each of the *n principal minors* indicated in (A13) is positive. It follows that this matrix is positive definite if and only if all the diagonal elements of the associated Crout auxiliary matrix are positive.

BIBLIOGRAPHY

GENERAL REFERENCES

1. Bruins, E. M.: "Numerieke wiskunde" [Numerical Mathematics], Servire, den Haag (1951).
2. Hartree, D. R.: "Numerical Analysis," Clarendon Press, Oxford (1952).
3. Householder, Alton S.: "Principles of Numerical Analysis," McGraw-Hill Book Company, Inc., New York (1953).
4. Jordan, Charles: "Calculus of Finite Differences," 2d ed., Chelsea Publishing Company, New York (1947).
5. Kantorovich, L. V., and V. I. Krylov: "Approximate Methods of Higher Analysis" (Russian), 3d ed., Moscow-Leningrad (1950).
6. Kowalewski, Gerhard: "Interpolation und genäherte Quadratur," B. G. Teubner, Leipzig (1932).
7. Krylov, A. N.: "Lectures on Approximate Computations" (Russian), 5th ed., Moscow-Leningrad (1950).
8. Lipka, Joseph: "Graphical and Mechanical Computation," John Wiley & Sons, Inc., New York (1918).
9. Markoff, A. A.: "Differenzenrechnung" (German translation), B. G. Teubner, Leipzig (1896).
10. Milne, William Edmund: "Numerical Calculus," Princeton University Press, Princeton, N. J. (1949).
11. Milne-Thomson, L. M.: "Calculus of Finite Differences," Macmillan & Co., Ltd., London (1933).
12. Mineur, Henri: "Techniques de calcul numérique," Librairie Polytechnique Ch. Béranger, Paris (1952).
13. Nörlund, Niels E.: "Vorlesungen über Differenzenrechnung," Springer-Verlag OHG, Berlin (1924).
14. Runge, Carl, and H. König: "Vorlesungen über numerisches Rechnen," Springer-Verlag OHG, Berlin (1924).
15. Salvadori, Mario G., and Melvin L. Baron: "Numerical Methods in Engineering," Prentice-Hall, Inc., New York (1952).
16. von Sanden, Horst: "Practical Mathematical Analysis," Methuen & Co., Ltd., London (1923).
17. Scarborough, James B.: "Numerical Mathematical Analysis," 2d ed., Johns Hopkins Press, Baltimore (1950).
18. Steffensen, J. F.: "Interpolation," The Williams & Wilkins Company, Baltimore (1927).
19. Thiele, T. N.: "Interpolationsrechnung," B. G. Teubner, Leipzig (1909).
20. Whittaker, E. T., and G. Robinson: "The Calculus of Observations," 3d ed., Blackie & Son, Ltd., Glasgow (1940).

21. Willers, Fr. A.: "Methoden der praktischen Analysis," 2d ed., Walter De Gruyter & Company, Berlin (1950). ["Practical Analysis" (translated by Robert T. Beyer), Dover Publications, New York (1948).]

22. Zurmühl, R.: "Praktische Mathematik für Ingenieure und Physiker," Springer-Verlag OHG, Berlin-Gottingen-Heidelberg (1953).

COLLATERAL TEXTS AND JOURNAL REFERENCES

23. Aitken, A. C.: On Bernoulli's Numerical Solution of Algebraic Equations, *Proc. Roy. Soc. Edinburgh*, **46**:289–305 (1926).

24. ———: On the Graduation of Data by the Orthogonal Polynomials of Least Squares, *Proc. Roy. Soc. Edinburgh*, **53**:54–78 (1932).

25. ———: On Interpolation by Iteration of Proportional Parts, without the Use of Differences, *Proc. Edinburgh Math. Soc.*, **3**(2):56–76 (1932).

26. ———: Studies in Practical Mathematics, VI, On the Factorization of Polynomials by Iterative Methods, *Proc. Roy. Soc. Edinburgh*, **63**:174–191 (1951).

27. ———: Studies in Practical Mathematics, VII, On the Theory of Methods of Factoring Polynomials by Iterated Division, *Proc. Roy. Soc. Edinburgh*, **64**:326–335 (1952).

28. Bairstow, L.: "Investigations Relating to the Stability of the Aeroplane," Reports and Memoranda No. 154 of Advisory Committee for Aeronautics (1914).

29. Banachiewicz, T.: Zur Berechnung der Determinanten, wie auch der Inversen, und zur darauf basierten Auflösung der Systeme linearen Gleichungen, *Acta Astron.*, **3**:41–72 (1937).

30. Bargmann, V., D. Montgomery, and J. von Neumann: "Solution of Linear Systems of High Order," Princeton, N. J., Institute for Advanced Study Report, BuOrd, Navy Dept. (1946).

31. Bashforth, F., and J. C. Adams: "An Attempt to Test the Theories of Capillary Action . . . with an Explanation of the Method of Integration Employed," Cambridge University Press, Cambridge (1883), pp. 15–62.

32. Bateman, H.: "Differential Equations," Longmans, Green & Co., Ltd., London (1918).

33. Beard, R. E.: Some Notes on Approximate Product-Integration, *J. Inst. Actuar.*, **73**:356–416 (1947).

34. Bennett, A. A., W. E. Milne, and H. Bateman: Numerical Integration of Differential Equations, *Bull. Natl. Research Council No. 92*, Natl. Acad. Sci., Washington, D.C. (1933).

35. Bernstein, Serge: "Leçons sur les propriétés extrémales et la meilleure approximation des fonctions analytiques d'une variable réele," Gauthier-Villars & Cie, Paris (1926).

36. ———: Sur les formules de quadrature de Cotes et Tchebycheff, *C. R. Acad. Sci. URSS*, new series, **14**:323–326 (1937).

37. Bickley, W. G.: A Simple Method for the Numerical Solution of Differential Equations, *Phil. Mag.*, **13**(7):1006–1114 (1932).

38. ———: Formulae for Numerical Differentiation, *Math. Gaz.*, **25**:19–27 (1941).

39. ———: Difference and Associated Operators, with Some Applications, *J. Math. and Phys.*, **27**:183–192 (1948).

40. ——— and J. C. P. Miller: The Numerical Summation of Slowly Convergent Series of Positive Terms, *Phil. Mag.*, **22**(7):754–767 (1936).

41. Bieberbach, Ludwig: On the Remainder of the Runge-Kutta Formula in the Theory of Ordinary Differential Equations, *Z. angew. Math. u. Phys.*, **2**:233–248 (1951).

42. Birge, Raymond T., and J. W. Weinberg: Least Squares Fitting of Data by Means of Polynomials, *Revs. Mod. Phys.*, **19**:298–360 (1947).

43. Birkhoff, G. D.: General Mean Value and Remainder Theorems with Applications to Mechanical Differentiation and Quadrature, *Trans. Am. Math. Soc.*, **7**:107–136 (1906).

44. Birkhoff, Garrett, and D. M. Young: Numerical Quadrature of Analytic and Harmonic Functions, *J. Math. and Phys.*, **29**:217–221 (1950).

45. Blanch, Gertrude: On Modified Divided Differences, *MTAC*, **8**:1—11 (1954).

46. ——— and I. Rhodes: Seven Point Lagrangian Integration Formulas, *J. Math. and Phys.*, **22**:204–207 (1943).

47. Bodewig, E.: On Graeffe's Method of Solving Algebraic Equations, *Quart. Appl. Math.*, **4**:177–190 (1946).

48. ———: Bericht über die verschiedenen Methoden zur Lösung eines Systems linearer Gleichungen mit reellen Koeffizienten, *Nederl. Akad. Wetensc. Proc.*, **50**:930–941, 1104–1166, 1285–1295 (1947); **51**:53–64, 211–219 (1948).

49. ———: On Types of Convergence and on the Behavior of Approximations in the Neighborhood of a Multiple Root of an Equation, *Quart. Appl. Math.*, **7**:325–333 (1949).

50. Boole, George: "Finite Differences," 3d ed., G. E. Stechert & Company, New York (1931). [First edition Cambridge (1860).]

51. Brouwer, Dirk: On the Accumulation of Errors in Numerical Integration, *Astron. J.*, **46**:149–153 (1937).

52. Burnett, D.: The Numerical Calculation of $\int_0^\infty x^m e^{-x} f(x)\, dx$, *Proc. Cambridge Phil. Soc.*, **33**:359–362 (1937).

53. Charnes, A., W. W. Cooper, and A. Henderson: "An Introduction to Linear Programming," John Wiley & Sons, Inc., New York (1953).

54. Chebyshev [Tchebicheff], P. L.: Sur les Quadratures, *J. Math. Pures Appl.*, **19**(2):19–34 (1874).

55. Cherry, P. M.: Summation of Slowly Convergent Series, *Proc. Cambridge Phil. Soc.*, **46**:436–449 (1950).

56. Collatz, L.: "Eigenwertaufgaben mit technischen Anwendungen," Akademische Verlagsgesellschaft m.b.H., Leipzig (1949).

57. ———: Iterationsverfahren für komplex Nullstellen algebraisher Gleichungen, *Z. angew. Math. Mech.*, **30**:97–101 (1950).

58. ———: "Numerische Behandlung von Differentialgleichungen," Springer-Verlag OHG, Berlin-Göttingen-Heidelberg (1951).

59. ———: Über die Instabilität beim Verfahren der zentralen Differenzen für Differentialgleichungen zweiter Ordnung, *Z. angew. Math. u. Phys.*, **4**:153–154 (1953).

60. Computation Laboratory: "A Manual of Operation for the Automatic Sequence Controlled Calculator," Harvard University Press, Cambridge, Mass. (1946).

61. Comrie, L. J. (editor): "Interpolation and Allied Tables," Second revised reprint from Nautical Almanac for 1937, H. M. Stationary Office, London (1948).

62. Cornock, A. F., and J. M. Hughes: The Evaluation of the Complex Roots of Algebraic Equations, *Phil. Mag.*, **34**(7):314–320 (1943).

63. Cramér, Harald: "Mathematical Methods of Statistics," Princeton University Press, Princeton, N.J. (1946).

64. Crout, Prescott D.: A Short Method for Evaluating Determinants and Solving Systems of Linear Equations with Real or Complex Coefficients, *Trans. AIEE*, **60**:1235–1240 (1941).

65. Curry, Haskell B.: Note on Iterations with Convergence of Higher Degree, *Quart. Appl. Math.*, **9**:204–205 (1951).

66. Curtiss, J. H.: Sampling Methods for Differential and Difference Equations, *Proc. Seminar on Scientific Computation*, Nov., 1949, pp. 87–109, IBM Corp., New York (1950).

67. Daniell, P. J.: Remainders in Interpolation and Quadrature Formulae, *Math. Gaz.*, **24**:238–244 (1940).

68. Danielson, G. C., and C. Lanczos: Some Improvements in Practical Fourier Analysis, *J. Franklin Inst.*, **233**:365–380, 435–452 (1942).

69. Domb, C.: On Iterative Solutions of Algebraic Equations, *Proc. Cambridge Phil. Soc.*, **45**:237–240 (1949).

70. Doodson, A. T.: A Method for the Smoothing of Numerical Tables, *Quart. J. Mech. Appl. Math.*, **3**:217–224 (1950).

71. Duncan, W. J.: Assessment of Error in Approximate Solution of Differential Equations, *Quart. J. Mech. Appl. Math.*, **1**:470–476 (1948).

72. Dwyer, Paul S.: "Linear Computations," John Wiley & Sons, Inc., New York (1951).

73. Engineering Research Associates, Inc.: "High-Speed Computing Devices," McGraw-Hill Book Company, Inc., New York (1950).

74. Fadeeva, V. N.: "Computational Methods of Linear Algebra" (Russian), Moscow-Leningrad (1950). [Chap. 1, Basic Material from Linear Algebra, translated by Curtis D. Benster, *Natl. Bur. Standards Rept.* 1644.]

75. Feldheim, Ervin: Théorie de la convergence des procédés d'interpolation et de quadrature mécanique, *Mém. sci. math. acad. sci. Paris* No. 95 (1939).

76. Feller, William: "An Introduction to Probability Theory and Its Applications," John Wiley & Sons, Inc., New York (1950).

77. Filon, L. N. G.: On a Quadrature Formula for Trigonometric Integrals, *Proc. Roy. Soc. Edinburgh*, **49**:38–47 (1928).

78. Fisher, R. A.: "Statistical Methods for Research Workers," 10th ed., Oliver & Boyd, Ltd., Edinburgh (1945).

79. Forsythe, George E.: Round-off Errors in Numerical Integration on Automatic Machinery, *Bull. Am. Math. Soc.*, **56**:61–62 (1950).

80. ———: Tentative Classification of Methods and Bibliography on Solving Systems of Linear Equations, *Natl. Bur. Standards INA Rept.* 52-7 (1951). (Reprinted in [176].)

81. ———: Solving Algebraic Equations Can Be Interesting, *Bull. Am. Math. Soc.*, **59**:299–329 (1953).

82. Fort, Tomlinson: "Finite Differences and Difference Equations in the Real Domain," Oxford University Press, New York (1948).

83. Fox, L.: The Solution by Relaxation Methods of Ordinary Differential Equations, *Proc. Cambridge Phil. Soc.*, **45**:50–68 (1949).

84. ———: Practical Methods for the Solution of Linear Equations and the Inversion of Matrices, *J. Roy. Statist. Soc.*, **12B**:120–136 (1950).

85. ——— and E. T. Goodwin: Some New Methods for the Numerical Integration of Ordinary Differential Equations, *Proc. Cambridge Phil. Soc.*, **45**:373–388 (1949).

86. ———, H. D. Huskey, and J. H. Wilkinson: Notes on the Solution of Algebraic Linear Simultaneous Equations, *Quart. J. Mech. Appl. Math.*, **1**:149–173 (1948).

87. Frame, J. S.: The Solution of Equations by Continued Fractions, *Am. Math. Monthly*, **60**:293–305 (1953).

88. Frazer, R. A., W. J. Duncan, and A. R. Collar: "Elementary Matrices and Some Applications to Dynamics and Differential Equations," The Macmillan Company, New York (1946).

89. Friedman, B.: Note on Approximating Complex Zeros of a Polynomial, *Comm. Pure Appl. Math.*, **2**:195–208 (1949).

90. Fry, Thornton C.: Some Numerical Methods for Locating Roots of Polynomials, *Quart. Appl. Math.*, **3**:89–105 (1945).

91. de la Garza, A.: Error Bounds on Approximate Solutions to Systems of Linear Algebraic Equations, *MTAC*, **7**:81–84 (1953).

92. Gavurin, N. K.: Application of Polynomials of Best Approximation to Optimal Convergence of Iterative Processes (Russian), *Uspekhi Matem. Nauk* 5, **3**(37): 156–160 (1950).

93. Geiringer, Hilda: "On the Solution of Systems of Linear Equations by Certain Iterative Methods," Reissner Anniversary Volume Contributions to Applied Mechanics, J. W. Edwards, Publisher, Inc., Ann Arbor, Mich. (1948), pp. 365–393.

94. Gill, S.: A Process for the Step-by-Step Integration of Differential Equations in an Automatic Digital Computing Machine, *Proc. Cambridge Phil. Soc.*, **47**:96–108 (1951).

95. Goldstine, Herman H., and John von Neumann: Numerical Inverting of Matrices of High Order II, *Proc. Am. Math. Soc.*, **2**:188–202 (1951).

96. Greenwood, Robert E., and Basil B. Danford: Numerical Integration with a Weight Function x, *J. Math. and Phys.*, **28**:99–106 (1949).

97. Grosch, H. R. J.: The Use of Optimum Interval Mathematical Tables, *Proc. Sci. Comp. Forum, 1948*, pp. 23–27, IBM Corp., New York, 1950.

98. Grossman, D. P.: On the Problem of the Numerical Solution of Systems of Simultaneous Linear Algebraic Equations (Russian), *Uspekhi Matem. Nauk* 5, **3**(37):87–105 (1950).

99. Guest, P. G.: Orthogonal Polynomials in the Least Squares Fitting of Observations, *Phil. Mag.*, **41**(7):124–137 (1950).

100. ———: Estimation of the Errors of the Least-squares Polynomial Coefficients, *Australian J. Sci. Research*, **3**A:364–375 (1950).

101. Hamilton, Hugh J.: Roots of Equations by Functional Iteration, *Duke Math. J.*, **13**:113–121 (1946).

102. Hardy, G. H.: "Divergent Series," Clarendon Press, Oxford (1949).

103. Harrison, Joseph O., Jr.: Piecewise Polynomial Approximation for Large-scale Digital Calculators, *MTAC*, **3**:400–407 (1948).

104. Hartree, Douglas R.: "Calculating Instruments and Machines," University of Illinois Press, Urbana, Ill. (1949).

105. ———: Notes on Iterative Processes, *Proc. Cambridge Phil. Soc.*, **45**:230–236 (1949).

106. Hastings, Cecil, Jr.: Rational Approximations in High-speed Computing, *Proc. Comp. Seminar, December, 1949*, pp. 57–61, IBM Corp., New York (1951).

107. ———, Mrs. David K. Hayward, and James P. Wong, Jr.: Approximations in Numerical Analysis—A Report on a Study, in J. H. Curtis, Jr. (editor), "Numerical Analysis," Proceedings of Symposia in Applied Mathematics, vol. VI, McGraw-Hill Book Company, Inc., New York (1955).

108. Hayes, J. G., and T. Vickers: The Fitting of Polynomials to Unequally-spaced Data, *Phil. Mag.*, **42**(7):1387–1400 (1951).

109. Hestenes, Magnus R., and Marvin L. Stein: The Solution of Linear Equations by Minimization, *Natl. Bur. Standards NAML Rept.* 52–45 (1951).

110. Hestenes, Magnus R., and Eduard Stiefel: Method of Conjugate Gradients for Solving Linear Systems, *Natl. Bur. Standards Rept.* 1659 (1952).

111. Heun, K.: Neue Methode zur approximativen Integration der Differentialgleichungen einer unabhängigen Variable, *Z. angew. Math. u. Phys.*, **45**:23–38 (1900).

112. Hitchcock, Frank L.: An Improvement on the G. C. D. Method for Complex Roots, *J. Math. and Phys.*, **23**:69–74 (1944).

113. Hoel, Paul G.: "Introduction to Mathematical Statistics," John Wiley & Sons, Inc., New York (1947).

114. ———— and D. D. Wall: The Accuracy of the Root-squaring Method for Solving Equations, *J. Math. and Phys.*, **26**:156–164 (1947).

115. Hotelling, Harold: Some New Methods in Matrix Calculation, *Ann. Math. Statistics*, **14**:1–34 (1943).

116. ————: Further Points on Matrix Calculation and Simultaneous Equations, *Ann. Math. Statistics*, **14**:440–441 (1943).

117. ————: Practical Problems of Matrix Calculation, *Proc. Symposium Math. Stat. Prob. Berkeley*, pp. 275–294 (1949).

118. Householder, A. S., G. E. Forsythe, and H. H. Germond (editors): "Monte Carlo Method," Nat. Bur. Standards Applied Mathematics Series, vol. 12, U. S. Govt. Printing Office, Washington, D.C. (1951).

119. Huskey, Harry D., and Douglas R. Hartree: On the Precision of a Certain Procedure of Numerical Integration, *J. Research Natl. Bur. Standards*, **42**:57–62 (1949).

120. Ince, E. L.: "Ordinary Differential Equations," Longmans, Green & Co., Ltd., London (1927).

121. Irwin, J. O.: "On Quadrature and Cubature, Tracts for Computers, X," Cambridge University Press, London (1923).

122. Jackson, D.: "The Method of Numerical Integration in Exterior Ballistics," War Dept. Document 984, U. S. Govt. Printing Office, Washington, D.C. (1921).

123. ————: "The Theory of Approximation," vol. 11, Am. Math. Soc. Coll. Pub., New York (1930).

124. ————: "Fourier Series and Orthogonal Polynomials," Carus Mathematical Monographs, Math. Assoc. of America, Oberlin, Ohio (1941).

125. Jolley, L. B. W.: "Summation of Series," Chapman & Hall, Ltd., London (1925).

126. Kantorovich, L. V.: On the Method of Steepest Descent (Russian), *Doklady Akad. Nauk SSSR*, **56**:233–236 (1947).

127. Kaplan, E. L.: Numerical Integration near a Singularity, *J. Math. and Phys.*, **31**:1–28 (1952).

128. Kutta, W.: Beitrag zur näherungsweisen Integration totaler Differentialgleichungen, *Z. angew. Math. u. Phys.*, **46**:435–453 (1901).

129. Lanczos, Cornelius: Trigonometric Interpolation of Empirical and Analytic Functions, *J. Math. and Phys.*, **17**:123–199 (1938).

130. ————: Solution of Systems of Linear Equations by Minimized Iterations, *Natl. Bur. Standards NAML Rept.* 52–13 (1951).

131. ————: Analytical and Practical Curve Fitting of Equidistant Data, *Natl. Bur. Standards Rept.* 1591 (1952).

132. Levy, H., and E. A. Baggot: "Numerical Studies in Differential Equations," C. A. Watts & Co., Ltd., London (1934).

133. Lewis, D. C.: Polynomial Least Square Approximations, *Am. J. Math.*, **69**:273–278 (1947).

134. Lidstone, G. J.: Notes on Interpolation, *J. Inst. Actuar.*, **71**(II):68–95 (1943).

135. Lin, Shih-nge: A Method of Successive Approximations of Evaluating the Real and Complex Roots of Cubic and Higher-order Equations, *J. Math. and Phys.*, **20**:231–242 (1941).

136. ————: A Method for Finding Roots of Algebraic Equations, *J. Math. and Phys.*, **22**:60–77 (1943).

137. Lindelöf, E.: Remarques sur l'intégration numérique des équations différentielles ordinaires, *Acta Soc. Sci. Fennicae* (*Phys. Mat.*), **2A**(13) (1938).

138. Lonseth, A. T.: The Propagation of Error in Linear Problems, *Trans. Am. Math. Soc.*, **62**(2):193–212 (1947).

139. Lotkin, M.: On the Accuracy of Runge-Kutta's Method, *MTAC*, **5**:128–133 (1951).

140. ———: A New Integrating Procedure of High Accuracy, *J. Math and Phys.*, **31**:29–34 (1952).

141. ———: A New Integration Procedure, *J. Math. and Phys.*, **32**:171–179 (1953).

142. Luke, Y. L., and Dolores Ufford: On the Roots of Algebraic Equations, *J. Math. and Phys.*, **30**:94–101 (1951).

143. Madelung, E.: Über eine Methode zur schnellen numerischen Lösung von Differentialgleichungen zweiter Ordnung, *Z. Physik*, **67**:516–518 (1931).

144. Matthieu, P.: Über die Fehlerabschätzung beim Extrapolationsverfahren von Adams, *Z. angew. Math. Mech.*, **31**:356–370 (1951).

145. McClintock, Emory: An Essay on the Calculus of Enlargement, *Am. J. Math.*, **2**:101–161 (1879).

146. Mehler, F. G.: Bemerkungen zur Theorie der mechanischen Quadraturen, *J. Reine angew. Math.*, **63**:152–157 (1864).

147. Meyers, Leroy F., and Arthur Sard: Best Approximate Integration Formulas, *J. Math. and Phys.*, **29**:118–123 (1950).

148. ——— and ———: Best Interpolation Formulas, *J. Math. and Phys.*, **29**:198–206 (1950).

149. Michel, J. G. L.: Central Difference Formulae Obtained by Means of Operator Expansions, *J. Inst. Actuar.*, **72**:470–480 (1946).

150. Miller, J. C. P.: Two Numerical Applications of Chebyshev Polynomials, *Proc. Roy. Soc. Edinburgh*, **62**:204–210 (1946)

151. ———: Checking by Differences, *MTAC*, **4**:3–11 (1950).

152. Miller, K. S., and F. J. Murray: A Mathematical Basis for an Error Analysis of Differential Analyzers, *J. Math. and Phys.*, **32**:136–161 (1953).

153. Milne, William Edmund: The Remainder in Linear Methods of Approximation, *J. Research Natl. Bur. Standards*, **43**:501–511 (1949).

154. ———: Note on the Runge-Kutta Method, *J. Research Natl. Bur. Standards*, **44**:549–550 (1950).

155. ———: "Numerical Solution of Differential Equations," John Wiley & Sons, Inc., New York (1953).

156. von Mises, R.: Zur numerischen Integration von Differentialgleichungen, *Z. angew. Math. Mech.*, **10**:81–92 (1930).

157. ———: Über allgemeine Quadraturformeln, *J. Reine angew. Math.*, **174**:56–67 (1936).

158. ——— and H. Pollaczek-Geiringer: Praktische Verfahren der Gleichungauflösung, *Z. angew. Math. Mech.*, **9**(I):58–77 (1929).

159. Mitchell, A. R., and Craggs, J. W.: Stability of Difference Relations in the Solution of Ordinary Differential Equations, *MTAC*, **7**:127–129 (1953).

160. Mitchell, A. R., and D. E. Rutherford: On the Theory of Relaxation, *Proc. Glasgow Math. Assoc.*, **1**:101–110 (1952).

161. Mohr, Ernst: Über das Verfahren von Adams zur Integration gewöhnlicher Differentialgleichungen, *Math. Nachr.*, **5**:209–218 (1951).

162. Mood, Alexander M.: "Introduction to the Theory of Statistics," McGraw-Hill Book Company, Inc., New York (1950).

163. Moors, B. P.: "Valeur approximative d'une intégrale définie," Gauthier-Villars & Cie, Paris, 1905.

164. Morris, Joseph: An Escalator Process for the Solution of Linear Simultaneous Equations, *Phil. Mag.*, **37**(7):106–120 (1946).
165. Moulton, F. R.: "New Methods in Exterior Ballistics," University of Chicago Press, Chicago (1926).
166. von Neumann, John, and H. H. Goldstine: Numerical Inverting of Matrices of High Order, *Bull. Am. Math. Soc.*, **53**:1021–1099 (1947).
167. Neville, E. H.: Iterative Interpolation, *J. Indian Math. Soc.*, **20**:87–120 (1934).
168. Nörlund, N. E.: "Leçons sur les séries d'interpolation," Gauthier-Villars & Cie, Paris (1926).
169. Nyström, E. J.: Zur Praktischen Integration von linearen Differentialgleichungen, *Soc. Sci. Fennica Commentationes Phys.-Math.*, **14**(XI) (1943).
170. ————: Zur numerischen Lösung von Randwertaufgaben bei gewöhnlichen Differentialgleichungen, *Acta Math.*, **76**:158–184 (1945).
171. Obrechkoff, N.: Sur les quadratures méchaniques (Bulgarian, French summary), *Spisanie Bulgar. Akad. Nauk.*, **65**:191–289 (1942).
172. Olds, C. D.: The Best Polynomial Approximation of Functions, *Am. Math. Monthly*, **57**:617–621 (1950).
173. Olver, F. W. J.: The Evaluation of Zeros of High-degree Polynomials, *Trans. Roy. Soc. (London)*, **244A**:385–415 (1952).
174. Ostrowski, Alexander: Recherches sur la méthode de Graeffe et les zéros des polynomes et des series de Laurent, *Acta Math.*, **72**:99–155 (1940).
175. ————: On the Rounding Off of Difference Tables for Linear Interpolation, *MTAC*, **6**:212–214 (1952).
176. Paige, L. J., and Olga Taussky (editors): "Simultaneous Linear Equations and the Determination of Eigenvalues," Natl. Bur. Standards Applied Mathematics Series, vol. 29, U. S. Govt. Printing Office, Washington, D.C. (1953).
177. Peano, G.: Resto nelle formule di quadratura expresso con un integrale definito, *Atti accad. nazl. Lincei Rend.*, **22**(5):562–569 (1913).
178. ————: Residuo in formulas de quadratura, *Mathesis*, **34**:5–10 (1914).
179. Pearson, Karl: "On the Construction of Tables and on Interpolation, I, Univariate Tables, Tracts for Computers, II," Cambridge University Press, London (1920).
180. ————: "On the Construction of Tables and on Interpolation, II, Bi-variate Interpolation, Tracts for Computers, III," Cambridge University Press, London (1920).
181. Perron, O.: "Die Lehre von Kettenbrüchen," B. G. Teubner, Leipzig (1929).
182. Polachek, H.: On the Solution of Systems of Linear Equations of High Order, *Naval Ordnance Lab. Rept.* NOLM-9522, White Oaks, Md. (1948).
183. de Prony, R.: Essai expérimentale et analytique, *J. école polytech. (Paris)*, **1**(2):24–76 (1795).
184. Radau, R.: Sur les formules de quadrature à coefficients égaux, *C. R. Acad. Sci. Paris*, **90**:520–529 (1880).
185. ————: Étude sur les formules d'approximation qui servent à calculer la valeur d'une intégrale définie, *J. Math. Pures Appl.*, **6**(3):283–336 (1880).
186. ————: Remarque sur le calcul d'une intégrale définie, *C. R. Acad. Sci. Paris*, **97**:157–158 (1883).
187. Rademacher, Hans: On the Accumulation of Errors in Processes of Integration on High-Speed Calculating Machines, *Proc. Symposium Large-scale Digital Calculating Machinery*, pp. 176–185, Harvard University Press, Cambridge, Mass. (1948).
188. Radon, Johann: Restausdrücke bei Interpolations- und Quadraturformeln durch bestimmte Integrale, *Monatsh. Math.*, **42**:389–396 (1935).

189. ———: Zur mechanischen Kubatur, *Monatsh. Math.*, **52**:286–300 (1948).
190. Redheffer, Raymond: Errors in Simultaneous Linear Equations, *Quart. Appl. Math.*, **6**:342–343 (1948).
191. Reich, Edgar: On the Convergence of the Classical Iterative Method of Solving Linear Simultaneous Equations, *Ann. Math. Statistics*, **20**:448–451 (1949).
192. Reiz, Anders: On the Numerical Solution of Certain Types of Integral Equations, *Ark. Mat.*, **29A**(29) (1943).
193. Rémès, E. J.: Sur les termes complémentaires de certaines formules d'analyse approximative, *C. R. Acad. Sci. URSS*, **26**:129–133 (1940).
194. Rhodes, E. C.: "Smoothing, Tracts for Computers, VI," Cambridge University Press, London (1921).
195. Richardson, Lewis F., and J. Arthur Gaunt: The Deferred Approach to the Limit, *Trans. Roy. Soc. (London)*, **226A**:299–361 (1927).
196. Richter, Willy: Sur l'erreur commise dans la méthode d'intégration de Milne, *C. R. Acad. Sci. Paris*, **233**:1342–1344 (1951).
197. Rosser, J. B.: Note on Zeros of the Hermite Polynomials and Weights for Gauss' Mechanical Quadrature Formula, *Proc. Am. Math. Soc.*, **1**:388–389 (1950).
198. ———: Transformations to Speed the Convergence of Series, *J. Research Natl. Bur. Standards*, **46**:56–64 (1951).
199. Runge, C.: Über die numerische Auflösung von Differentialgleichungen, *Math. Ann.*, **46**:167–178 (1895).
200. Rutishauser, Heinz: Über die Instabilität von Methoden zur Integration gewöhnlicher Differentialgleichungen, *Z. angew. Math. u. Phys.*, **3**:65–74 (1952).
201. Sadler, D. H.: Maximum-interval Tables, *MTAC*, **4**:129–132 (1950).
202. Salzer, H. E.: Formulas for Finding the Argument for which a Function has a Given Derivative, *MTAC*, **5**:213–215 (1951).
203. ———: Equally Weighted Quadrature Formulas Over Semi-infinite and Infinite Intervals, *J. Math. and Phys.*, **34**:54–63 (1955).
204. Samuelson, Paul A.: Iterative Computation of Complex Roots, *J. Math. and Phys.*, **28**:259–267 (1949).
205. Sard, Arthur: Integral Representations of Remainders, *Duke Math. J.*, **15**:333–345 (1948).
206. ———: The Remainder in Approximations by Moving Averages, *Bull. Am. Math. Soc.*, **54**:788–792 (1948).
207. ———: Best Approximate Integration Formulas; Best Approximation Formulas, *Am. J. Math.*, **71**:80–91 (1949).
208. Sasuly, Max: "Trend Analysis of Statistics," Brookings Institution, Washington, D.C. (1934).
209. Schoenberg, I. J.: On Smoothing Operations and their Generating Functions, *Natl. Bur. Standards Rept.* 1734 (1952).
210. Schröder, Ernst: Über unendliche viele Algorithmen zur Auflösung der Gleichungen, *Math. Ann.*, **2**:317–365 (1870).
211. Shohat, J. A., and C. Winston: On Mechanical Quadratures, *Rend. Circ. Mat. Palermo*, **58**:153–165 (1934).
212. Shohat, J. A., E. Hille, and J. L. Walsh: A Bibliography on Orthogonal Polynomials, *Bull. Natl. Research Council No.* 103, Natl. Acad. Sci., Washington, D.C. (1940).
213. Southwell, R. V.: "Relaxation Methods in Engineering Science," Oxford University Press, New York (1940).
214. ———: "Relaxation Methods in Theoretical Physics," Oxford University Press, New York (1946).

215. Spencer, J.: On the Graduation of the Rate of Sickness and Mortality Presented by the Experience of the Manchester Unity of Oddfellows During the Period 1893–97, *J. Inst. Actuar.*, **38**:334–343 (1904).

216. Stein, Marvin L.: Gradient Methods in the Solution of Systems of Linear Equations, *J. Research Natl. Bur. Standards*, **48**:407–413 (1952).

217. Sterne, Theodore E.: The Accuracy of Numerical Solutions of Ordinary Differential Equations, *MTAC*, **7**:159–164 (1953).

218. Störmer, C.: Méthode d'intégration numérique des équations différentielles ordinaires, *C. R. Congr. Intern. Math. Strasbourg 1920*, Toulouse, Privat, pp. 243–257 (1921).

219. Szasz, O.: Summation of Slowly Convergent Series, *J. Math. and Phys.*, **28**:272–279 (1950).

220. Szego, G.: "Orthogonal Polynomials," Am. Math. Soc. Coll. Pub., vol. 23, New York (1939).

221. Taussky, Olga (editor): "Contributions to the Solution of Systems of Linear Equations and the Determination of Eigenvalues," Natl. Bur. Standards Applied Mathematics Series, vol. 39, U. S. Govt. Printing Office, Washington, D.C. (1954).

222. Temple, G.: The General Theory of Relaxation Methods Applied to Linear Systems, *Proc. Roy. Soc. (London)*, **169A**:476–500 (1938).

223. ———— and W. G. Bickley: "Rayleigh's Principle," Oxford University Press, New York (1933).

224. Todd, John: Notes on Modern Numerical Analysis, I, Solution of Differential Equations by Recurrence Relations, *MTAC*, **4**:39–44 (1950).

225. Tollmien, W.: Über die Fehlerabschätzung beim Adamsschen Verfahren zur Integration gewöhnlicher Differentialgleichungen, *Z. angew. Math. Mech.*, **18**:83–90 (1938).

226. ————: Bemerkung zur Fehlerabschätzung beim Adamsschen Interpolationsverfahren, *Z. angew. Math. Mech.*, **33**:151–155 (1953).

227. Turing, A. M.: Rounding-off Errors in Matrix Processes, *Quart. J. Mech. Appl. Math.*, **1**:287–308 (1948).

228. Turton, F. J.: The Errors in the Numerical Solution of Differential Equations, *Phil. Mag.*, **28**(7):359–363 (1939).

229. de la Vallée Poussin, C.: "Leçons sur l'approximation des fonctions d'une variable réelle," Gauthier-Villars & Cie, Paris (1952).

230. Wall, H. S.: Note on the Expansion of a Power Series into a Continued Fraction, *Bull. Am. Math. Soc.*, **51**:97–105 (1945).

231. ————: "Continued Fractions," D. Van Nostrand Company, Inc., New York (1948).

232. Walsh, J. L.: "Interpolation and Approximation by Rational Functions in the Complex Plane," Am. Math. Soc. Coll. Pub., vol. 20, New York (1934).

233. Weissinger, Johannes : Eine verschärfte Fehlerabschätzung zum Extrapolationsverfahren von Adams, *Z. angew. Math. Mech.*, **30**:356–363 (1950).

234. ————: Eine Fehlerabschätzung für die Verfahren von Adams und Störmer, *Z. angew. Math. Mech.*, **32**:62–67 (1952).

235. Whittaker, E. T., and G. N. Watson: "Modern Analysis," 4th ed., Cambridge University Press, Cambridge (1927).

236. Wiener, Norbert: "Extrapolation, Interpolation, and Smoothing of Stationary Time Series," Technology Press, M.I.T., Cambridge, Mass. (1949).

237. Wilson, E. M.: A Note on the Numerical Integration of Differential Equations, *Quart. J. Mech. Appl. Math.*, **2**:208–211 (1949).

238. Winston, C.: On Mechanical Quadratures Involving the Classical Orthogonal Polynomials, *Ann. Math.*, **35**:658–677 (1934).
239. Wolfenden, Hugh H.: "The Fundamental Principles of Mathematical Statistics," The Macmillan Co. of Canada, Ltd., Toronto (1942).
240. Zurmühl, Rudolf: Runge-Kutta Verfahren zur numerischen Integration von Differentialgleichungen n-ter Ordnung, *Z. angew. Math. Mech.*, **28**:173–182 (1948).
241. ――――: "Matrizen," Springer-Verlag OHG, Berlin (1950).

MATHEMATICAL TABLES

The following references provide tabulations of functions, zeros of functions, and coefficients of formulas which are directly relevant to techniques of numerical analysis. For additional sources, and for more general tables of mathematical functions, reference should be made to the *Index of Mathematical Tables* [242] and to periodic listings in *Mathematical Tables and Other Aids to Computation* (*MTAC*).

242. Fletcher, A., J. C. P. Miller, and L. Rosenhead: "Index of Mathematical Tables," McGraw-Hill Book Company, Inc., New York (1946).
243. Anderson, R. L., and E. E. Houseman: Tables of Orthogonal Polynomial Values Extended to $N = 104$, *Iowa State Coll. Agr. Exp. Sta. Research Bull. No.* 297, pp. 595–672 (1942).
244. Comrie, L. J. (editor): "Chambers's Six-figure Mathematical Tables," W. & R. Chambers, Ltd., London (1949).
245. ――――: "Interpolation and Allied Tables," Second revised reprint from Nautical Almanac for 1937, H. M. Stationary Office, London (1948).
246. Davis, H. T.: "Tables of the Higher Mathematical Functions, I," Principia Press, Bloomington, Ind. (1933).
247. ――――: "Tables of the Higher Mathematical Functions, II," Principia Press, Bloomington, Ind. (1935).
248. De Lury, Daniel B.: "Values and Integrals of the Orthogonal Polynomials up to $n = 26$," University of Toronto Press, Toronto (1950).
249. Glover, James W.: "Tables of Applied Mathematics in Finance, Insurance, and Statistics," George Wahr Publishing Co., Ann Arbor, Mich. (1930).
250. Greenwood, R. E., and J. J. Miller: Zeros of the Hermite Polynomials and Weights for Gauss' Mechanical Quadrature Formula, *Bull. Am. Math. Soc.*, **54**:765–769 (1948).
251. Kopal, Zdenek: A Table of the Coefficients of the Hermite Quadrature Formula, *J. Math. and Phys.*, **27**:259–261 (1949).
252. Lowan, Arnold N., Norman Davids, and Arthur Levenson: Tables of the Zeros of the Legendre Polynomials of Order 1–16 and the Weight Coefficients for Gauss's Mechanical Quadrature Formula, *Bull. Am. Math. Soc.*, **48**:739–743 (1942).
253. ―――― and Herbert Salzer: Table of Coefficients in Numerical Integration Formulae, *J. Math. and Phys.*, **22**:49–50 (1943).
254. ―――― and ――――: Table of Coefficients for Numerical Integration without Differences, *J. Math. and Phys.*, **24**:1–21 (1945).
255. ――――, ――――, and Abraham Hillman: A Table of Coefficients for Numerical Differentiation, *Bull. Am. Math. Soc.*, **48**:920–924 (1942).
256. Luke, Yudell L.: Coefficients to Facilitate Interpolation and Integration of Linear Sums of Exponential Functions, *J. Math. and Phys.*, **31**:267–275 (1953).

257. Salzer, H. E.: Coefficients for Numerical Differentiation with Central Differences, *J. Math. and Phys.*, **22**:115–135 (1943).

258. ———: Table of Coefficients for Inverse Interpolation with Central Differences, *J. Math. and Phys.*, **22**:210–224 (1943).

259. ———: Coefficients for Numerical Integration with Central Differences, *Phil. Mag.*, **35**:262–264 (1944).

260. ———: Table of Coefficients for Inverse Interpolation with Advancing Differences, *J. Math. and Phys.*, **23**:75–102 (1944).

261. ———: Table of Coefficients for Differences in Terms of the Derivatives, *J. Math. and Phys.*, **23**:210–212 (1944).

262. ———: A New Formula for Inverse Interpolation, *Bull. Am. Math. Soc.*, **50**:513–516 (1944).

263. ———: Inverse Interpolation for Eight-, Nine-, Ten-, and Eleven-point Direct Interpolation, *J. Math. and Phys.*, **24**:106–108 (1945).

264. ———: Table of Coefficients for Double Quadrature without Differences, for Integrating Second Order Differential Equations, *J. Math. and Phys.*, **24**:135–140 (1945).

265. ———: Coefficients for Mid-interval Numerical Integration with Central Differences, *Phil. Mag.*, **36**:216–218 (1945).

266. ———: Coefficients for Facilitating the Use of the Gaussian Quadrature Formula, *J. Math. and Phys.*, **25**:244–246 (1946).

267. ———: Tables for Facilitating the Use of Chebyshev's Quadrature Formula, *J. Math. and Phys.*, **26**:191–194 (1947).

268. ———: "Table of Coefficients for Obtaining the First Derivative without Differences," Natl. Bur. Standards Applied Mathematics Series, vol. 2, U. S. Govt. Printing Office, Washington, D.C. (1948).

269. ———: Coefficients for Facilitating Trigonometric Interpolation, *J. Math. and Phys.*, **27**:274–278 (1949).

270. ———: "Tables of Coefficients for the Numerical Calculation of Laplace Transforms," Natl. Bur. Standards Applied Mathematics Series, vol. 30, U. S. Govt. Printing Office, Washington, D.C. (1953).

271. ———: New Formulas for Facilitating Osculatory Interpolation, *J. Research Natl. Bur. Standards*, **52**:211–216 (1954).

272. ———, Ruth Zucker, and Ruth Capuano: Table of the Zeros and Weight Factors of the First Twenty Hermite Polynomials, *J. Research Natl. Bur. Standards*, **48**:111–116 (1952).

273. "Tables of Chebyshev Polynomials $S_n(x)$ and $C_n(x)$," Natl. Bur. Standards Applied Mathematics Series, vol. 9, U. S. Govt. Printing Office, Washington, D.C. (1952). (Introduction by C. Lanczos.)

274. "Tables of Functions and Zeros of Functions," Natl. Bur. Standards Applied Mathematics Series, vol. 37, U. S. Govt. Printing Office, Washington, D.C. (1954).

275. "Tables of Lagrangian Coefficients for Sexagesimal Interpolation," Natl. Bur. Standards Applied Mathematics Series, vol. 35, U. S. Govt. Printing Office, Washington, D.C. (1954).

276. "Tables of Lagrangian Interpolation Coefficients," Natl. Bur. Standards Columbia Press Series, vol. 4, Columbia University Press, New York (1944).

DIRECTORY OF METHODS

A. Interpolation
  1. Based on polynomials
     a. Using an arbitrary set of ordinates, without differences
        (1) Noniterative: §3.2
        (2) Iterative: §2.7
     b. Using differences formed from ordinates at equally spaced points
        (1) Near beginning or end of tabulation: §4.3
        (2) Inside tabular range
           (*a*) Using both odd and even differences: §§4.5, 4.6
           (*b*) Using only even differences or only odd differences: §4.7
        (3) With throwback: §4.10
     c. Using divided differences formed from an arbitrary set of ordinates: §2.5
     d. Using ordinates and slopes: §8.2
     e. Using ordinates at appropriately selected points: §§9.6, 9.7
     f. In two-way tables: Probs. 55 to 57 of Chap. 5
     g. Inverse: §2.8
  2. Based on ratios of polynomials: §§9.9 to 9.12
  3. Based on sines and/or cosines: Prob. 7 of Chap. 3; see also B.4†
  4. Based on exponential functions: see B.5†
B. Approximation
  1. By polynomials
     a. Determined as truncated Taylor expansions: §§1.3, 1.7
     b. Determined by exact fit over a discrete set of points: see A.1
     c. Determined by least-squares methods
        (1) Using an arbitrary finite set of ordinates: §7.3
        (2) Using ordinates at equally spaced points: §7.11

---

† The approximating functions obtained by least squares incorporating a number of ordinates equal to the number of independent coordinate functions fit the data exactly at those points, and thus are strictly interpolative functions.

(3) Using a continuous range of ordinates
    (a) Over a finite interval: §§7.5, 7.8; Prob. 31 of Chap. 7
    (b) Over a semi-infinite interval: §7.6
    (c) Over an infinite interval: §7.7
  d. Economized by use of Chebyshev polynomials: §9.8
2. By products of exponential functions and polynomials: §§7.6, 7.7
3. By ratios of polynomials: see A.2
4. By sines and/or cosines
  a. With prescribed periods
    (1) Using a finite set of ordinates: §§9.3, 9.7; Prob. 31 of Chap. 7
    (2) Using a continuous range of ordinates: §9.2
  b. With periods to be determined: §9.5
5. By exponential functions: §9.4

C. *Numerical Differentiation*
  1. Using ordinates without differences: §§3.3, 3.8
  2. Using differences formed from ordinates at equally spaced points
    a. Near beginning or end of tabulation: §5.3; Prob. 5 of Chap. 4
    b. Inside tabular range
      (1) Near tabular point: §5.3; Prob. 11 of Chap. 4
      (2) Near mid-point between tabular entries: §5.3; Prob. 13 of Chap. 4

D. *Numerical Integration*
  1. Using ordinates at equally spaced points, without differences: §§3.5, 5.10
  2. Using differences based on ordinates at equally spaced points
    a. Over range near beginning or end of tabulation: §5.4; Prob. 5 of Chap. 4
    b. Over range centered at interior tabular point: §5.6; Prob. 11 of Chap. 4
    c. Over range centered midway between interior tabular points: Prob. 13 of Chap. 4
  3. Using calculated ordinates at appropriately selected points
    a. Integrals of the form $\int_a^b f(x)\ dx$: §8.5
    b. Integrals of the form $\int_a^\infty e^{-\alpha x}f(x)\ dx$: §8.6
    c. Integrals of the form $\int_a^\infty (x-a)^\beta e^{-\alpha x}f(x)\ dx$: §8.6
    d. Integrals of the form $\int_{-\infty}^\infty e^{-\alpha^2 x^2}f(x)\ dx$: §8.7
    e. Integrals of the form $\int_{-a}^a f(x)\ dx/\sqrt{a^2-x^2}$: §8.8; Prob. 37 of Chap. 8
    f. Integrals of the form $\int_{-a}^a f(x)\ \sqrt{a^2-x^2}\ dx$: Prob. 24 of Chap. 8

3. Checking tables by use of differences: §4.9
4. Expression of differences in terms of derivatives: §5.3
5. Subtabulation: §5.7; Probs. 16 and 17 of Chap. 5
6. Calculation of mean values over given intervals from mean values over other intervals: Prob. 18 of Chap. 5
7. Determination of unknown periodicities from empirical data: §9.5
8. Continued-fraction expansions: §§9.9 to 9.12
9. Evaluation of determinants: §10.4
10. Inversion of matrices: §10.5

INDEX

Boldface figures in parentheses refer to problem numbers